Supplemental Material

W0019677

Download Included

The ARRL Handbook for Radio Communications 2020 Edition

You may download supplemental material that includes the fully searchable digital edition of this printed book, as well as expanded content, software, PC board templates, and other support files.

System Requirements: The digital edition and expanded content (PDF files) are viewed using Adobe *Acrobat Reader* software and are compatible with any Windows or Macintosh system with that software installed. *Acrobat Reader* is a free download at **www.adobe.com**. PDF files are *Linux* readable and can also be viewed on iOS and Android devices. Other included software is Windows compatible, only.

How to Redeem Your Coupon and Download the Supplemental Material:

1. Go to the following ARRL e-store link:
   www.arrl.org/shop/ARRL-Handbook-2020-eBook

2. Click the "Add to Cart" button.

3. Enter the Coupon Code found below, and click the "Submit Coupon Code" button. **This code will discount the full purchase price of the download.** The code may only be used one time.

4. Follow the on-screen instructions to Checkout. Upon completing your order, you will receive instructions to download and save the installation file. We recommend saving the file to a new folder on your computer. Double-click the installation file to begin the software installation, and follow the instructions.

The Coupon Code included with your book is not for resale, has no cash value, and will not be replaced if lost or stolen. Content subject to availability.

Code expires December 31, 2021.

Coupon Code:

H20V812132

2020

The ARRL HANDBOOK FOR RADIO COMMUNICATIONS

NINETY-SEVENTH EDITION

Editor

H. Ward Silver, NØAX

Contributing Editors

Steven R. Ford, WB8IMY
Mark J. Wilson, K1RO

Editorial Assistant

Maty Weinberg, KB1EIB

Technical Consultants

Bob Allison, WB1GCM
Edward F. Hare, Jr., W1RFI
Zachary H.J. Lau, W1VT

Cover Design

Sue Fagan, KB1OKW
Bob Inderbitzen, NQ1R

Production

Michelle Bloom, WB1ENT
Jodi Morin, KA1JPA
David F. Pingree, N1NAS

Additional Contributors to the 2020 Edition

John Brooks, N9ZL
Jim Brown, K9YC
Glen Brown, W6GJB
Ralph Crumrine, NØKC
Don Daso, K4ZA
Joel Hallas, W1ZR
Bill Koch, W2RMA
Rick Lindquist, WW1ME
Glenn Loake, GØGBI
Helmut Berka, DL2MAJ
Oliver Micic, DG7XO
Carl Luetzelschwab, K9LA
Phil Salas, AD5X
Rob Sherwood, NCØB
Cory Sickles, WA3UVV
George Steber, WB9LVI
Jim Tonne, W4ENE
Paul Wade, W1GHZ

Published by:

ARRL The national association for AMATEUR RADIO®

225 Main Street, Newington, CT 06111-1400 USA

www.arrl.org

Printed in the USA

ISBN: 978-1-62595-107-6 Softcover
ISBN: 978-1-62595-113-7 Six-Volume Set

Kindle eBook Editions
ISBN: 978-1-62595-091-8 — Volume 1
ISBN: 978-1-62595-092-5 — Volume 2
ISBN: 978-1-62595-093-2 — Volume 3
ISBN: 978-1-62595-094-9 — Volume 4
ISBN: 978-1-62595-095-6 — Volume 5
ISBN: 978-1-62595-096-3 — Volume 6

Ninety-Seventh Edition

About the cover:
The collection of components comprises the HF Packer miniHFPA2 amplifier kit. Although the kit is not featured in this 2020 edition of the ARRL Handbook, its components represent the spirit of project design and craftsmanship that has been part of Amateur Radio from the beginning.

Contents

A more detailed Table of Contents is included at the beginning of each chapter.

VOLUME 2

PRACTICAL DESIGN AND PRINCIPLES — PART 1

VOLUME 5

EQUIPMENT CONSTRUCTION AND STATION ACCESSORIES

VOLUME 6

TEST EQUIPMENT, TROUBLESHOOTING, RFI, AND INDEX

DOWNLOADABLE CONTENT AND TOOLS

Foreword

Welcome to the 97th edition of the *ARRL Handbook for Radio Communications*. First published in 1929, "the Handbook" has guided and supported generations of amateurs. Like Amateur Radio itself, the *ARRL Handbook* is continually being updated and renewed by the community of knowledgeable amateurs who realize the value of a resource like the *Handbook*.

What's new in the 97th edition? There are quite a few new and interesting elements inside:

- Solar Cycle 24 at the sunspot minimum by K9LA
- An RF choke for ac generator outputs by W6GJB and K9YC
- A brand-new section on Rotators, long-needed in the **Antennas** chapter
- Updated material on Yaesu's System Fusion platform by WA3UUV
- Updates to the annual transceiver survey with the latest radios

Test equipment and measurements are an important part of building and maintaining an up-to-date amateur station in the face of rapidly changing technology. Rob Sherwood, NCØB, has worked with the ARRL Lab on receiver testing and contributed four papers on the subject dealing with test procedures and noise. Paul Wade, W1GHZ, another frequent *Handbook* contributor, provided a collection of ways better use an antenna analyzer, an increasingly can't-do-without instrument in the ham station.

Another set of changes began with the 2018 edition as the CD-ROM sent with every book was dropped in favor of a downloadable set of supplemental material. This eliminated many problems associated with supporting multiple operating systems. Please do look for the "download code" sent with your copy of the book and use it to transfer the material to your computer's hard drive. There's a lot of great material waiting for you!

The supplemental information in the 97th edition includes three new projects from our DX friends around the world, starting with a pair of articles from the DARC *CQ DL*:

- A Bi-stable Transfer Relay by DG7XO
- 10-Watt Audio Amp by DL2MAJ

To go with that audio amplifier, there is:

- An Audio Splitter by GØGBI, from the RSGB's *Radcom*

There are also a number of new items from right here in North America:

- Amplifier Overshoot — Drive Protection by AD5X
- 2304 MHz 70 W Rover Amplifier by W2RMA and N9ZL
- A Small Lightweight Switch-Mode High Voltage Power Supply by NØKC
- Universal MMIC Preamp by W1GHZ
- A Tunable RF Preamplifier Using a Variable Capacitance Diode by WB9LVI

Once again this year, we are pleased and grateful to include the latest versions of Jim Tonne's *ELSIE* filter design software and several other design and layout utilities. Jim also contributed the new supplemental item that extends his recent contributions to the **Transmitting** chapter:

- Speech Processing: Some New Ideas by Jim Tonne, W4ENE

I hope you enjoy the *ARRL Handbook* and find it useful whether you're a new ham just learning the ropes, an experienced ham enhancing a station or skill — or even if you're not a ham at all (yet)! Our goal is to provide you with a solid, trustworthy source of information to help you make the most of your Amateur Radio interests, whether that is public service, experimentation, radiosport, or making friends around the world as hams have done for a century. Thanks for being a *Handbook* reader!

73, Howard Michel, WB2ITX
ARRL Chief Executive Officer
September 2019

ARRL Handbook Downloadable Supplemental Content (print edition only)

A wealth of additional material for this *Handbook* is available with the downloadable supplemental content. As a purchaser of the print edition, you are entitled to download this material — see the instructions for doing so on the insert at the front of the printed book.

Searchable Edition of The Handbook

The downloadable content includes a PDF version of this edition of *The Handbook*, including text, drawings, tables, illustrations and photographs. Using *Adobe Reader*, you can view, print or search the entire book.

Supplemental Files for Each Chapter

The downloadable content contains supplemental information for most chapters of this book. This includes articles from *QST, QEX* and other sources, material from previous editions of *The ARRL Handbook*, tables and figures in support of the chapter material, and files that contain information to build and test the projects provided in the chapters. The supplemental information is arranged in folders for each chapter.

Companion Software

The following software is also included with the downloadable supplemental content:

TubeCalculator, a *Windows* application by Bentley Chan and John Stanley, K4ERO, accompanies the tube type RF power amplifier discussion in the **RF Power Amplifiers** chapter.

The following *Windows* programs by Tonne Software (**www.tonnesoftware.com**) are provided by Jim Tonne, W4ENE.

ClassE — Designs single-ended Class E RF amplifiers.

Diplexer — Designs both high-pass/low-pass and band-pass/band-stop types of diplexer circuits.

Helical Filter — Designs and analyzes helical-resonator bandpass filters for the VHF and UHF frequency ranges.

JJSmith — A graphics-intensive transmission-line calculator based on the Smith chart.

Elsie — The free student edition of Elsie, a lumped-element filter design and analysis program.

MeterBasic — Designs and prints professional-quality analog meter scales on your printer. The full featured version of *Meter* is available from Tonne Software.

OptLowpass — Designs and analyzes very efficient transmitter output low-pass filters.

Pi-El — Designs and analyzes pi-L networks for transmitter output.

PIZZA — A mapping program that generates printable azimuth-equidistant or rectangular maps showing the great-circle path and the sunrise-sunset terminator between your location and selectable locations.

Quad Net — Designs and analyzes active quadrature ("90-degree") networks for use in SSB transmitters and receivers.

SVC Filter — Standard-value component routine to design low-pass and high-pass filters and delivers exact-values as well as nearest-5% values.

Tower — Analyzes vertical antennas. Plots resistance, reactance, and impedance at the base as a function of frequency.

The Amateur's Code

The Radio Amateur is:

CONSIDERATE...never knowingly operates in such a way as to lessen the pleasure of others.

LOYAL...offers loyalty, encouragement and support to other amateurs, local clubs, and the American Radio Relay League, through which Amateur Radio in the United States is represented nationally and internationally.

PROGRESSIVE...with knowledge abreast of science, a well-built and efficient station and operation above reproach.

FRIENDLY...slow and patient operating when requested; friendly advice and counsel to the beginner; kindly assistance, cooperation and consideration for the interests of others. These are the hallmarks of the amateur spirit.

BALANCED...radio is an avocation, never interfering with duties owed to family, job, school or community.

PATRIOTIC...station and skill always ready for service to country and community.

—The original Amateur's Code was written by Paul M. Segal, W9EEA, in 1928.

Common Schematic Symbols Used in Circuit Diagrams

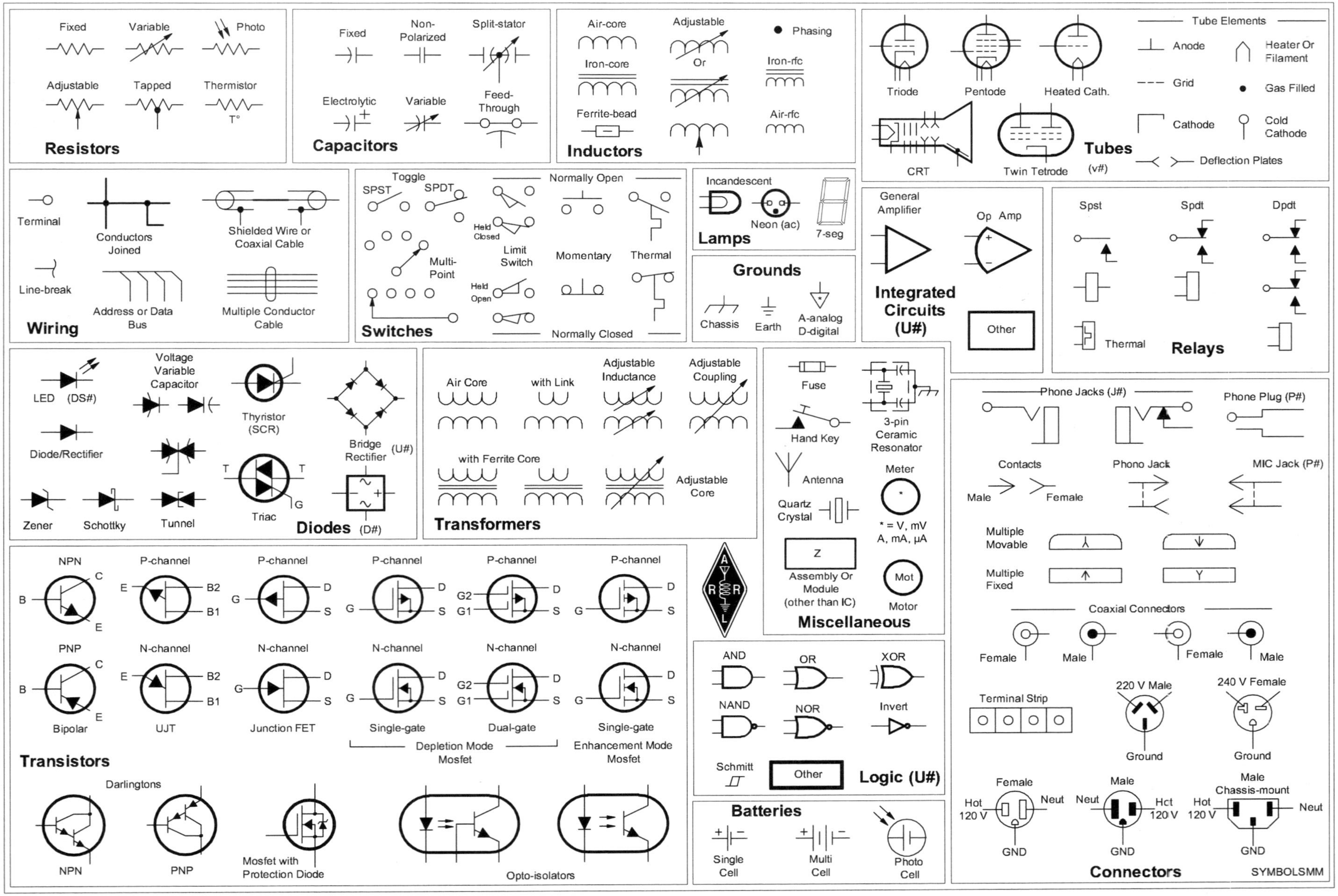

ARRL Membership Benefits and Services

ARRL membership includes *QST* magazine, plus dozens of other services and resources to help you get involved and enjoy Amateur Radio to the fullest. Here are just a few…

Find...

...a License Exam Session
www.arrl.org/exam

...a Licensing Class
www.arrl.org/class

...a Radio Club (ARRL-affiliated)
www.arrl.org/clubs

...a Hamfest or Convention
www.arrl.org/hamfests

Members-Only Web Services

Enjoy exclusive access to members-only benefits on the ARRL website.

QST Digital Edition

In addition to the printed copy of *QST*, all members have access to the online, monthly digital version at no additional cost. *QST* apps are also available.

Archives

ARRL members can browse ARRL's extensive online *QST* archive, including downloading and viewing *QST* product reviews. *QST* Product Reviews help our members make smarter, more informed purchasing decisions for Amateur Radio equipment.

E-Mail Forwarding Service

E-mail sent to your arrl.net address will be forwarded to any e-mail account you specify.

E-Newsletters

Subscribe to the weekly **ARRL Letter** and a variety of other e-newsletters and announcements: ham radio news, radio clubs, public service, contesting and more!

ARRL as Advocate

ARRL supports legislation and regulatory measures that preserve and protect meaningful access to the radio spectrum. Our **Regulatory Information Branch** answers member questions concerning FCC rules and operating practices. ARRL's **Volunteer Counsel** and **Volunteer Consulting Engineer** programs open the door to assistance with antenna regulation and zoning issues.

Technical Information Service

Call or e-mail our expert ARRL Technical Information Service specialists for answers to all your technical and operating questions. This service is FREE to ARRL members.

Public Service

ARRL works closely with FEMA, Red Cross, and other agencies to keep Amateur Radio's emergency communications capabilities in disaster response plans. Public service and emergency communication volunteers enjoy support and training from ARRL.

Group Benefits*

- ARRL Ham Radio Equipment Insurance
- Liberty Mutual Auto and Home Insurance (*US Only)

About the ARRL

The seed for Amateur Radio was planted in the 1890s, when Guglielmo Marconi began his experiments in wireless telegraphy. Soon he was joined by dozens, then hundreds, of others who were enthusiastic about sending and receiving messages through the air — some with a commercial interest, but others solely out of a love for this new communications medium. The United States government began licensing Amateur Radio operators in 1912.

By 1914, there were thousands of Amateur Radio operators — hams — in the United States. Hiram Percy Maxim, a leading Hartford, Connecticut inventor and industrialist, saw the need for an organization to unify this fledgling group of radio experimenters. In May 1914 he founded the American Radio Relay League (ARRL) to meet that need.

ARRL is the national association for Amateur Radio in the US. ARRL numbers within its ranks the vast majority of active radio amateurs in the nation and has a proud history of achievement as the standard-bearer in amateur affairs. ARRL's underpinnings as Amateur Radio's witness, partner, and forum are defined by five pillars: Public Service, Advocacy, Education, Technology, and Membership. ARRL is also International Secretariat for the International Amateur Radio Union, which is made up of similar societies in 150 countries around the world.

ARRL's Mission Statement: To advance the art, science, and enjoyment of Amateur Radio.
ARRL's Vision Statement: As the national association for Amateur Radio in the United States, ARRL:

- Supports the awareness and growth of Amateur Radio worldwide;
- Advocates for meaningful access to radio spectrum;
- Strives for every member to get involved, get active, and get on the air;
- Encourages radio experimentation and, through its members, advances radio technology and education; and
- Organizes and trains volunteers to serve their communities by providing public service and emergency communications.

At ARRL headquarters in the Hartford, Connecticut suburb of Newington, the staff helps serve the needs of members. ARRL publishes the monthly journal *QST* and an interactive digital version of *QST*, as well as newsletters and many publications covering all aspects of Amateur Radio. Its headquarters station, W1AW, transmits bulletins of interest to radio amateurs and Morse code practice sessions. ARRL also coordinates an extensive field organization, which includes volunteers who provide technical information and other support services for radio amateurs as well as communications for public service activities. In addition, ARRL represents US radio amateurs to the Federal Communications Commission and other government agencies in the US and abroad.

Membership in ARRL means much more than receiving *QST* each month. In addition to the services already described, ARRL offers membership services on a personal level, such as the Technical Information Service, where members can get answers — by phone, e-mail, or the ARRL website — to all their technical and operating questions.

A bona fide interest in Amateur Radio is the only essential qualification of membership; an Amateur Radio license is not a prerequisite, although full voting membership is granted only to licensed radio amateurs in the US. Full ARRL membership gives you a voice in how the affairs of the organization are governed. ARRL policy is set by a Board of Directors (one from each of 15 Divisions). Each year, one-third of the ARRL Board of Directors stands for election by the full members they represent. The day-to-day operation of ARRL HQ is managed by a Chief Executive Officer and his/her staff.

Join ARRL Today! No matter what aspect of Amateur Radio attracts you, ARRL membership is relevant and important. There would be no Amateur Radio as we know it today were it not for ARRL. We would be happy to welcome you as a member! Join online at **www.arrl.org/join**. For more information about ARRL and answers to any questions you may have about Amateur Radio, write or call:

ARRL — The national association for Amateur Radio®
225 Main Street
Newington CT 06111-1400 USA
Tel: 860-594-0200
FAX: 860-594-0259
e-mail: **hq@arrl.org**
www.arrl.org

Prospective new radio amateurs call (toll-free):
800-32-NEW HAM (800-326-3942)
You can also contact ARRL via e-mail at **newham@arrl.org**
or check out the ARRL website at **www.arrl.org**

US Amateur Radio Bands

US AMATEUR POWER LIMITS

FCC 97.313 An amateur station must use the minimum transmitter power necessary to carry out the desired communications.
(b) No station may transmit with a transmitter power exceeding 1.5 kW PEP.

Amateurs wishing to operate on either 2,200 or 630 meters must first register with the Utilities Technology Council online at **https://utc.org/plc-database-amateur-notification-process/.** You need only register once for each band.

2,200 Meters (135 kHz)

630 Meters (472 kHz)

5 W EIRP maximum, except in Alaska within 496 miles of Russia where the power limit is 1 W EIRP.

160 Meters (1.8 MHz)

Avoid interference to radiolocation operations from 1.900 to 2.000 MHz

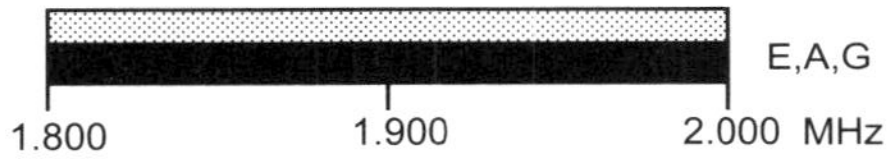

80 Meters (3.5 MHz)

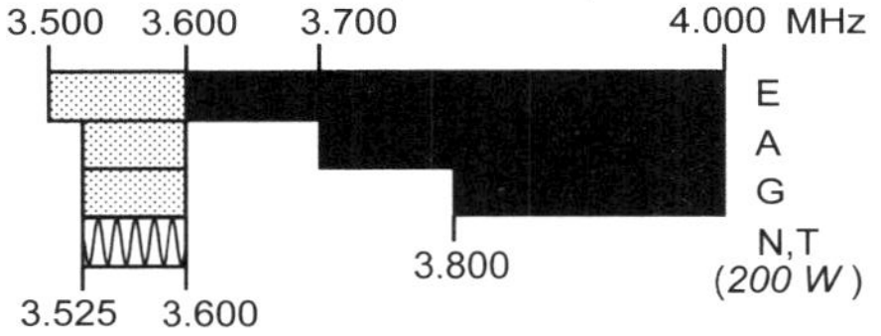

60 Meters (5.3 MHz)

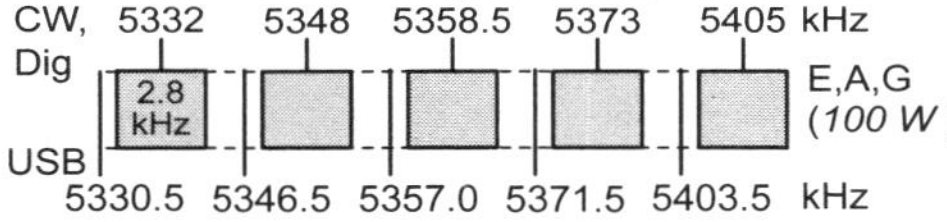

General, Advanced, and Amateur Extra licensees may operate on these five channels on a secondary basis with a maximum effective radiated power (ERP) of 100 W PEP relative to a half-wave dipole. Permitted operating modes include upper sideband voice (USB), CW, RTTY, PSK31 and other digital modes such as PACTOR III. Only one signal at a time is permitted on any channel.

40 Meters (7 MHz)

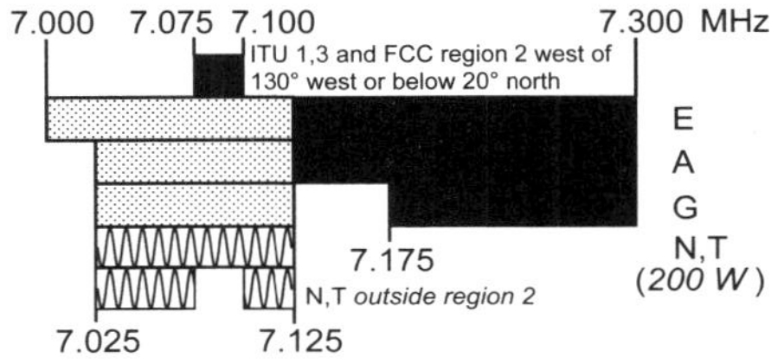

See Sections 97.305(c), 97.307(f)(11) and 97.301(e). These exemptions do not apply to stations in the continental US.

30 Meters (10.1 MHz)

Avoid interference to fixed services outside the US.

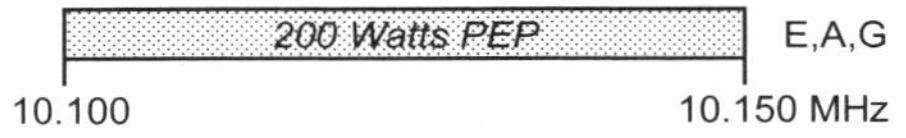

20 Meters (14 MHz)

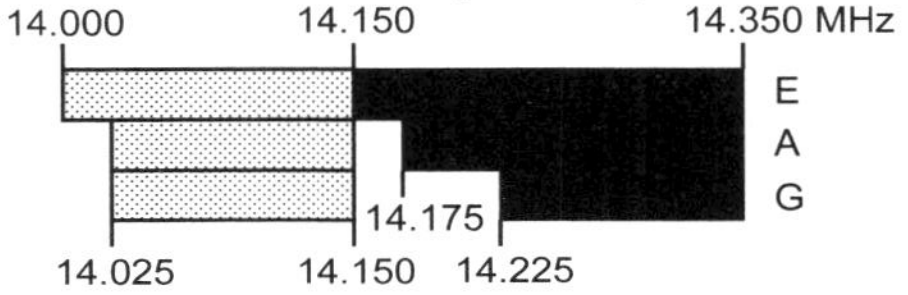

17 Meters (18 MHz)

15 Meters (21 MHz)

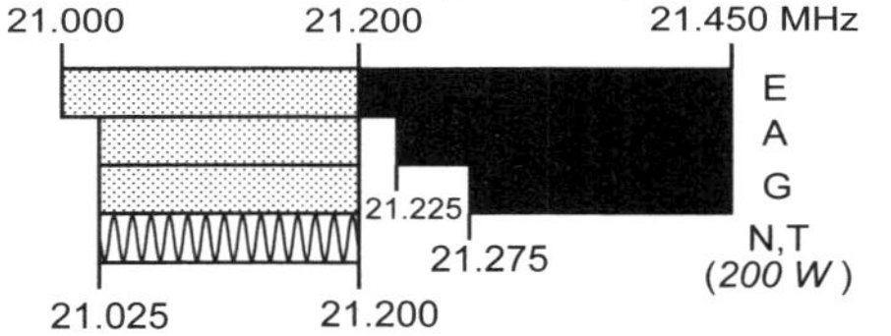

12 Meters (24 MHz)

10 Meters (28 MHz)

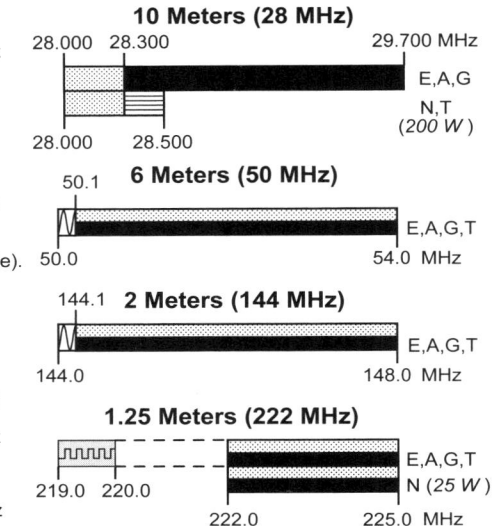

6 Meters (50 MHz)

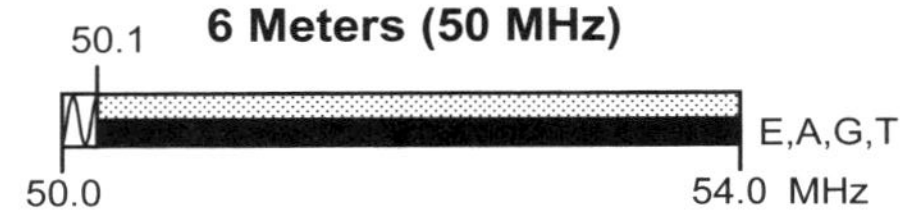

2 Meters (144 MHz)

1.25 Meters (222 MHz)

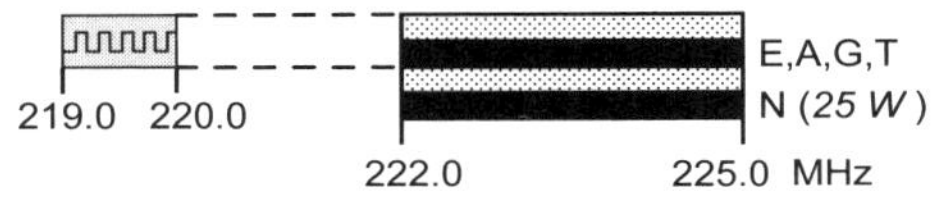

*Geographical and power restrictions may apply to all bands above 420 MHz. See *The ARRL Operating Manual* for information about your area.

70 cm (420 MHz)*

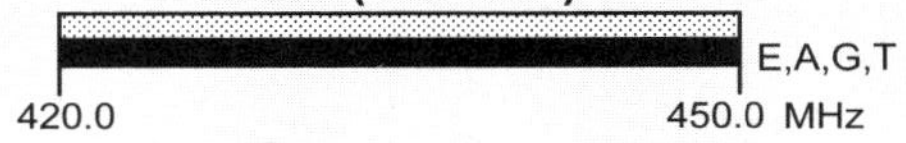

33 cm (902 MHz)*

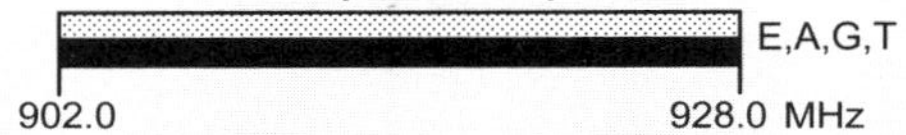

23 cm (1240 MHz)*

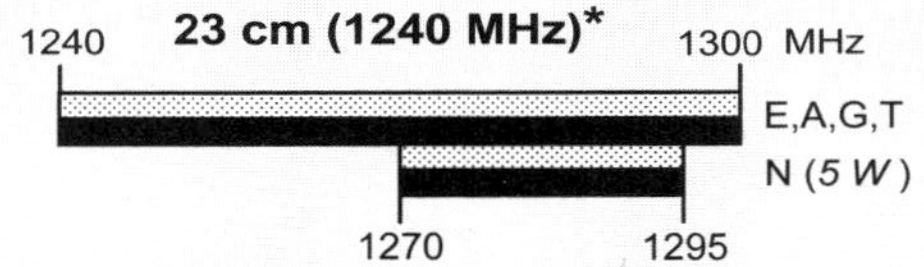

All licensees except Novices are authorized all modes on the following frequencies:

2300-2310 MHz	10.0-10.5 GHz ‡	122.25-123.0 GHz
2390-2450 MHz	24.0-24.25 GHz	134-141 GHz
3300-3500 MHz	47.0-47.2 GHz	241-250 GHz
5650-5925 MHz	76.0-81.0 GHz	All above 275 GHz

‡ No pulse emissions

KEY

Note:
CW operation is permitted throughout all amateur bands.

MCW is authorized above 50.1 MHz, except for 144.0-144.1 and 219-220 MHz.

Test transmissions are authorized above 51 MHz, except for 219-220 MHz

= RTTY and data
= phone and image
= CW *only*
= SSB phone
= USB phone, CW, RTTY, and data.
= Fixed digital message forwarding systems *only*

E = Amateur Extra
A = Advanced
G = General
T = Technician
N = Novice

See *ARRLWeb at www.arrl.org* for detailed band plans.

ARRL
We're At Your Service

ARRL Headquarters:
860-594-0200 (Fax 860-594-0259)
email: hq@arrl.org

Publication Orders:
www.arrl.org/shop
Toll-Free 1-888-277-5289 (860-594-0355)
email: orders@arrl.org

Membership/Circulation Desk:
www.arrl.org/membership
Toll-Free 1-888-277-5289 (860-594-0338)
email: membership@arrl.org

Getting Started in Amateur Radio:
Toll-Free 1-800-326-3942 (860-594-0355)
email: newham@arrl.org

Exams: 860-594-0300 email: vec@arrl.org

 rev. 9/22/2017

Contents

Chapter 1

What is Amateur (Ham) Radio?

Amateur Radio enthusiasts — "hams" — often have been at the forefront of the incredible blaze of progress over the past century in wireless and electronics, leading to technology that has broadened our horizons and touched virtually all of our lives. In the days before the telephone and household electricity were commonplace and the Internet not yet conceived, hams *pioneered* personal communication. It was the first wireless social medium.

From sophisticated smartphones, tablets, devices worn on your wrist, and diminutive laptop PCs that go anywhere, we enjoy wireless technology that's changing so rapidly, it's literally difficult to keep current. People-to-people communication is the goal, whether by voice, text, or image. But Amateur Radio remains vital and active today. In this chapter, Rick Lindquist, WW1ME provides an overview of Amateur Radio activities and licensing requirements.

1.1 Do-It-Yourself Wireless

Amateur Radio, better known as "ham radio," is many things to many people — more than 700,000 of them in the US alone. Ham radio hobbyists have at their fingertips the ability to directly contact fascinating people they may never meet who live in distant places they'll never visit. They do this without any external infrastructure, such as a cell network or the Internet, sometimes using simple, inexpensive — often homemade — equipment and antennas. Since the early days of wireless, these experimenters, who had to learn by trial and error, because little information was available at the time, developed and refined the means to contact one another without wires. They do this because it's fun and offers a sense of accomplishment — "*I* made this happen!" — that you can't get on a smartphone.

As a radio amateur, you can meet new friends, win awards, exchange "QSLs" (the ham's calling card), challenge yourself and others in on-the-air competitions ("radiosport"), educate yourself about radio science and technology, contribute to your community, travel, promote international goodwill, and continue the century-old wireless communication tradition. Your station is yours and yours alone, and it's independent of any other communication network — no contract, no bill to pay each month.

Let's take a closer look.

THE SECOND CENTURY OF HAM RADIO

We may think of "wireless" as a relatively modern term that applies to a wide variety of electronic devices, but it's been around for more than a century. At some point along the way, "radio" (and later "television") took over as the preferred term. Being able to communicate from one place to another without any connecting wires was a goal of late 19th and early 20th century experimenters. Equipment and methods for early wireless often were rudimentary — a simple crystal radio to listen, and a "spark gap" transmitter (it *actually* threw sparks) to send Morse code, coupled with what was then called an "aerial" — we'd call it an antenna today. Little to no ready-made equipment was available, and parts for these early radio do-it-yourselfers were expensive and hard to obtain. On a good night, their transmissions might even span 50 miles! In the early 20th century, when not everyone had a telephone and calling long-distance was pricey, ham radio was, in more contemporary terms, "really cool technology."

In 1914, just two years after these early hams were required to hold licenses from the federal government, inventor and industrialist Hiram Percy Maxim, 1AW, and radio enthusiast Clarence Tuska, 1WD, established the American Radio Relay League (ARRL) to bring these US radio hobbyists under one tent to serve their common interests. These two founding fathers of ham radio and their peers would be awestruck to see how the world of Amateur Radio and wireless technology has expanded and evolved in the intervening years.

Figure 1.1 — The ink barely dry on her Technician class license, 12-year-old Melina Rights, KM6ARN, of San Diego, got on the air from her dad's station during the ARRL International DX Contest. Her friend Elle Davis looks on.

Figure 1.2 — NASA Astronaut Tim Kopra, KE5UDN, at NA1SS aboard the International Space Station. [NASA Photo]

Figure 1.4 — Electrical engineering student Matthew Stevens, NJ4Y, of Auburndale, Florida, operates during ARRL's National Parks on the Air event from Gulf Islands National Seashore. [Matthew Stevens, NJ4Y, photo]

Figure 1.3 — TV Personality Ariel Tweto took the helm at the Pilot Station School Radio Club's WL7CXM in Alaska during the School Club Roundup. She gave a motivational speech to the students during her visit. [Donn Gallon, KL7DG, photo]

Figure 1.5 — Radio amateurs travel to all parts of the world to operate from rare places. Bob Schmieder, KK6EK, was co-leader of a "DXpedition" to remote Heard Island, a spot that's inhospitable to humans but quite comfortable for the native penguin population.

Hams on the Front Lines

Over the years, the military and the electronics industry have often drawn on the ingenuity of radio amateurs to improve designs or solve problems. Hams provided the keystone for the development of modern military communication equipment, for example. In the 1950s, the Air Force needed to convert its long-range communication from Morse code to voice, and jet bombers had no room for skilled radio operators. At the time, hams already were experimenting with and discovering the advantages of single sideband (SSB) voice equipment. With SSB, hams were greatly extending the distances they could transmit.

Air Force Generals Curtis LeMay and Francis "Butch" Griswold, both radio amateurs, hatched an experiment that used ham radio equipment at the Strategic Air Command headquarters. Using an SSB station in an aircraft flying around the world, LeMay and Griswold were able to stay in touch with Offutt Air Force Base in Nebraska from anywhere. The easy modification of this ham radio equipment to meet military requirements saved the government millions of dollars in research costs.

More recent technological experimentation has focused on such techniques as software defined radio (SDR). This amazing approach enables electronic circuit designers to employ *software* to replace more costly — and bulkier — hardware components. It's no coincidence or surprise that radio amateurs have been among those investigators doing the ground-level research and experimentation to bring this technology from the laboratory to the marketplace. Transceivers built on the SDR model continue to become more commonplace within the Amateur Radio community and represent the future of equipment design.

Affirming the relationship between Amateur Radio and cutting-edge technology, the late Howard Schmidt, W7HAS, was White House Cybersecurity Coordinator from 2009 to 2012. An ARRL member, Schmidt, who died in 2017, was one of the world's leading authorities on computer security, with some 40 years of experience in government, business and law enforcement. Schmidt credits ham radio with helping to launch his career. "Building ... computers to support my ham radio hobby gave me the technical skills that I needed to ... start doing computer crime investigations and work on the early stages of computer forensics, in turn enabling me to start working on cybersecurity issues," he once said. Hams are often found in industry and the military as technology presses ahead.

While Maxim and Tuska were not the first hams, the organization they founded, now known as ARRL — the national association for Amateur Radio, has championed and sustained these radio pioneers and their successors. Now more than a century down the road — light years in terms of radio science and technology — Amateur Radio continues to adapt to the times. While many traditions continue, today's ham radio is *not* the ham radio of yesteryear.

THE ORIGINAL SOCIAL MEDIUM

In this age of multiple sophisticated communication platforms, it's not uncommon for people to ask, "Ham radio? Do they still *do* that?" Yes, "they" do. But, given the proliferation of communication alternatives, the larger question may be, *Why*?

Ham radio is a hands-on technological and social medium — *personal* communication with no bills, minutes, or data plans. It's personal communication that's "off the grid," a wireless service you can rely on when other serves become unavailable.

It doesn't cost a lot to get into Amateur Radio, and participation is open and accessible to everyone. Hams are mothers, fathers, and children of all ages, ethnic backgrounds, physical abilities, and walks of life who belong to a unique worldwide community of licensed radio hobbyists. Some are even well-known celebrities. All find joy and excitement by experiencing radio communication and electronics on a very personal level across a spectrum of activities.

In the United States, the Federal Communications Commission (FCC) grants licenses in the Amateur Radio Service. With an emphasis on "service," the FCC has laid down five essential principles underlying Amateur Radio's fundamental purpose (see sidebar "Ham Radio's Rules of the Airwaves"). These recognize ham radio's value to the public as a "voluntary noncommercial communication service, particularly with respect to providing emergency communications." The service also exists to continue and expand Amateur Radio's "proven ability" to advance the state of the radio art, as well as both technical and communication skills. Further, the FCC says, the Amateur Radio Service should help to expand the "existing reservoir of trained operators, technicians, and electronics experts," and continue and extend the radio amateur's "unique ability to enhance international goodwill."

HAMS ARE EVERYWHERE

The driver of that car sporting an odd-looking antenna may be a ham equipped to

Ham Radio's Rules of the Airwaves

International and national radio regulations govern the operational and technical standards of all radio stations. The International Telecommunication Union (ITU) governs telecommunication on the international level and broadly defines radio services through the international *Radio Regulations*. In the US, the Federal Communication Commission (FCC) is the agency that administers and oversees the operation of nongovernmental and nonmilitary stations — including Amateur Radio. Title 47 of the *US Code of Federal Regulations* governs telecommunication, and Part 97 of the Code spells out the Amateur Radio Service rules.

Experimentation has always been the backbone of Amateur Radio, and the Amateur Service rules provide a framework within which hams enjoy wide latitude to experiment in accordance with the "basis and purpose" of the service. The rules should be viewed as vehicles to promote healthy activity and growth, rather than as constraints leading to stagnation. The FCC's rules governing Amateur Radio recognize five aspects, paraphrased below, in the Basis and Purpose of the Amateur Service.

- Amateur Radio's value to the public, particularly with respect to providing emergency communication support
- Amateur Radio's proven ability to contribute to the advancement of the radio art
- Encouraging and improving the Amateur Service through rules that help advance communication and technical skills
- Maintaining and expanding the Amateur Service as a source of trained operators, technicians and electronics experts
- Continuing and extending the radio amateur's unique ability to enhance international goodwill

The Amateur Radio Service rules, Part 97, are in six sections: General Provisions, Station Operation Standards, Special Operations, Technical Standards, Providing Emergency Communication and Qualifying Examination Systems. Part 97 is available in its entirety on the ARRL and FCC websites (see the Resources section at the end of this chapter for further information).

enjoy his or her hobby while on the road — called mobile operation. Your neighbor on the next block with the wires strung between trees or, perhaps, a tower supporting what looks like a very large old-fashion television antenna probably is one too.

Modern technology continues to make ham radio more accessible to all, including those living on tight budgets or facing physical challenges. People lacking mobility may find the world of Amateur Radio a rewarding place to find lasting friendships — on the next block, in the next state, or around the world.

Figure 1.6 — Brian Mileshosky, N5ZGT, logs contacts during the 2017 NM5FD Field Day operation, while his son, Landon, and Daughter, Audrey, look on. [Rick Naething, AE5JI, Photo.]

Hams are ambassadors. For many radio amateurs, a relaxing evening at home is talking on the radio with a friend in Frankfort, Kentucky or Frankfurt, Germany. Unlike any other hobby, Amateur Radio recognizes no international or political boundaries, and it brings the world together in friendship.

1.1.1 Making It Happen

A major feature of Amateur Radio's more than 100-year heritage has been the ham's ability to make do with what's at hand to get on the air. It is in the pursuit of such hands-on, do-it-yourself activities that this *Handbook* often comes into play, especially as electronic components remain plentiful today and circuit designs are increasingly complex and creative.

Amateur Radio has always been about what its participants bring *to* it and what they make *of* it. Hams communicate with one another using equipment they've bought or built, or a combination of the two, over a wide range of the radio frequency spectrum. The methods hams use to keep in touch range from the venerable Morse code — no longer a licensing requirement, by the way — to voice, modern digital (ie, computer-coded) modes, and even television.

The hybridization of Amateur Radio, computer technology, and the Internet has become a fact of life, as hams invent ever more creative ways to exploit technology. For many, if not most, hams, a computer and Internet access are essential station components. Today it's possible for a ham to control a transmitting and receiving station via the Internet using nothing more than a laptop or smartphone — even if that station is thousands of miles distant. The wonder of software defined radio (SDR) techniques has even made it possible to create *virtual* radio communication gear. SDRs require a minimum of physical components; sophisticated computer software does the heavy lifting!

1.1.2 Your Ham Radio Comfort Zone

Amateur Radio offers such a wide range of activities that everyone can find a comfortable niche. As one of the few truly *international* hobbies, ham radio makes it possible to communicate with other similarly licensed aficionados all over the world. On-the-air competition called contesting or "radiosport" — just to pick one activity many hams enjoy —harnesses those competitive instincts and helps participants to improve their skills and stations. Further, and perhaps more important, Amateur Radio serves the public by supporting communication in disasters and emergencies, while also serving as a platform for sometimes cutting-edge scientific experimentation. Many of those who got into ham radio as youngsters — such as Nobel Laureate Joe Taylor, K1JT — credit that involvement with their later success in technology careers.

Ham radio's horizon extends into space. The International Space Station boasts more than one ham radio station, and most ISS crew members are Amateur Radio licensees. Thanks to the Amateur Radio on the International Space Station (ARISS) program, suitably equipped hams can talk directly with NASA astronauts in space — it doesn't take a lot of gear. Hams also contact each other through Earth-orbiting satellites designed and built by the non-profit Radio Amateur Satellite Corporation (AMSAT) and by educational entities here in the US and abroad. Some radio amateurs even bounce radio signals off the Moon and back to other hams on Earth.

Hams talk with one another from vehicles, while hiking or biking in the mountains, from remote camp sites, or while boating. Some hams enjoy sharing photos over the air too, using one of the television modes available to radio amateurs. Through these activities and others, hams establish lifelong friendships, learn a lot and, perhaps most important, have a *lot* of fun. Along the way, radio amateurs often contribute a genius that propels technological innovation.

Most likely you're already a ham, have experimented with radio and electronics, or are part of the Maker movement, and you're thinking about getting your ham license. This *Handbook* is an invaluable resource that reveals and explains the "mysteries" governing electronics in general and in radio — or wireless — communication in particular, especially as it pertains to Amateur Radio.

1.1.3 What's in it for Me?

As a community *of* communities, Amateur Radio can be whatever *you* want it to be. Whether you are looking for relaxation, excitement, enjoyment or a way to stretch your mental (and physical) horizons, Amateur Radio can provide it — even if time and money are tight. However it happens, communication between individuals is at the core of nearly all ham radio activities. In its most basic form, ham radio is two people saying "Hello!" to each other over the air, perhaps using inexpensive handheld transceivers (a combination transmitter-receiver) or even homemade gear. In "Hamspeak," a two-way, on-the-air communication is known as a "QSO" — an old radiotelegraph, or Morse code, abbreviation often pronounced "CUE-so."

Ham radio can also be a group activity. Hams with common interests often gather on the airwaves to share their thoughts and even pictures. These get-togethers are called "nets" or "roundtables," depending on their formality. When hams meet on the air for an extended on-the-air conversation, they sometimes call it "ragchewing."

Nets form when like-minded hams gather on the air on a regular schedule. Nets often provide an on-the-air venue to find other hams with similar interests both inside and outside of Amateur Radio. Topics may be as diverse as vintage radio, chess, gardening, rock climbing, railroads, computer programming, teaching, or an interest in certain types of radio equipment. Faith-based groups and scattered friends and families may also organize nets. You can find your special interest in *The ARRL Net Directory* on the ARRL website (**www.arrl.org/arrl-net-directory**).

1.2 Joining the Ham Radio Community

Morse code has been a major player in Amateur Radio's legacy, although as a licensing requirement some prospective hams found it a roadblock. Today it's no longer necessary to learn Morse code to become an Amateur Radio licensee. You still must hold a license granted by the Federal Communications Commission (FCC) to operate an Amateur Radio station in the United States, in any of its territories and possessions or from any vessel or aircraft registered in the US. There are no age or citizenship requirements to obtain a US Amateur Radio license, and the cost is minimal, sometimes free. Young people not yet in their teens regularly pass ham radio exams!

The FCC offers three classes — or levels — of Amateur Radio license. From the easiest to the most difficult, they are Technician, General and Amateur Extra Class. Applicants must take and pass a multiple-choice written examination for each license as they move up the licensing ladder. Official question pools for all ham radio license classes are publically available. The higher you climb the ladder, the more challenging the test and the more generous the operating privileges. To reach the top — Amateur Extra — you must pass the examinations for all three license classes.

1.2.1 Moving Through the Ranks

Most people start out in Amateur Radio by getting a Technician Class license or "ticket," as a ham license is sometimes called. Obtaining a Technician license requires passing a 35 question multiple-choice exam. The test covers FCC rules and regulations governing the airwaves, courteous operating procedures and techniques, and some basic electronics. The privileges earned give Technicians plenty of room to explore and activities to try. For some, the Technician license is the only one they'll ever want or need.

Technicians enjoy a wide, but somewhat limited, range of voice and digital radio operating privileges. These include access to some "high frequency" (HF or short-wave) frequency "bands" or segments of the radio spectrum. Depending upon license class, hams have access to up to 10 distinct HF bands in the range from 1.8 to 29.7 MHz, where most direct international communication happens. (Frequency and wavelength terms are explained in the **Electrical Fundamentals** chapter.) Technicians also have all amateur privileges in the VHF-UHF and microwave spectrum, though, which allow operation on widely available FM voice repeaters. A repeater greatly extends the communication range of low-power, handheld radios or mobile stations too far apart to communicate with each other directly. The "Tech ticket" is a great introduction to the fun and excitement of ham radio and to the ways of the hobby.

By upgrading to General Class, a Technician licensee earns additional operating privileges, such as access to all Amateur Radio HF bands. Upgrading to General entails passing another 35 question multiple-choice exam. In addition to Technician privileges, Generals enjoy worldwide communication using voice, digital, image, and television techniques.

Reaching the pinnacle of the Amateur Radio license structure — Amateur Extra class — means passing a more demanding 50-question examination. Amateur Extra licensees enjoy privileges on all frequency bands and communication modes available to hams. The exam may be challenging, but many hams consider it well worth the effort!

1.2.2 Study Aids

You can prepare for the exam on your own, with a group of friends or by taking a class sponsored by a ham radio club in your area. The ARRL offers materials and lesson plans for hams wishing to teach Amateur Radio licensing classes. Anyone can set up license-study classes. Many Amateur Radio clubs hold periodic classes, usually for the Technician license. The ARRL supports Registered Amateur Radio Instructors, but registration is not necessary to conduct a class. The ARRL website, **www.arrl.org**, offers information on classes, clubs or volunteer examiners (VEs) in your area (more on VEs below).

Help is available at every step. The ARRL publishes study materials for all license classes. Visit the ARRL website or contact the ARRL's New Ham Desk for more information on how to get started. The Resources section at the end of this chapter includes an address and telephone number. The ARRL can help you find ham radio clubs in your area as well as ARRL-registered instructors and local Volunteer Examiner teams. Additional information on the ARRL website includes frequencies hams can use, popular operating activities, and how to order the latest ARRL study guide.

For newcomers seeking to obtain a Technician license, *The ARRL Ham Radio License Manual* includes the complete, up-to-date

Figure 1.7 — Parachute Mobile! "Jumper 1," Mark Meltzer, AF6IM, gives new meaning to mobile operation as he enjoys making contacts and enjoying the view, combining his enthusiasm for skydiving and Amateur Radio. [Captain Jim Wilson, RCAF, photo]

question pool, with the correct answers and clear explanations. The manual assumes no prior electronics background. It delves into the details behind the questions and answers, so you will *understand* the material, rather than simply memorize the correct answers.

If you already have some electronics background or just want brief explanations of the material, you might find *ARRL's Tech Q&A* manual a more appropriate choice. It also includes the entire Technician question pool to help you prepare.

When you are ready to upgrade to a General Class license, *The ARRL General Class License Manual* or *ARRL's General Q&A* can help you prepare. In like fashion, *The ARRL Extra Class License Manual* and *ARRL's Extra Q&A* will guide your study efforts for the Amateur Extra Class license. Check the ARRL website for detailed information on these and other license study options.

Figure 1.8 — The ARRL Field Day "Get on the Air" (GOTA) at the Huntsville Amateur Radio Club's K4BFT setup in Alabama attracted a group of teachers from the nearby US Space and Rocket Center Space Camp. Todd Cline, K7KDT, demonstrates a digital "waterfall" as club members John Boyette, KK5KKT (leaning at left), and Geoff Suiter, KK4IV (at keyboard), operate the station. [William Martin, KK4FDF, photo]

1.2.3 Taking the Test

While the FCC grants US Amateur Radio licenses, volunteer examiners (VEs) now administer all Amateur Radio testing. Other countries have adopted similar systems. Ham radio clubs schedule regular exam sessions, so you shouldn't have to wait long or travel far once you're ready. Exam sessions often are available on weekends (frequently at ham radio gatherings called "hamfests") or evenings. Most volunteer examiner teams charge a small fee to recover the cost of administering the test and handling the FCC paperwork.

The ARRL is a Volunteer Examiner Coordinator (VEC) and supports the largest VE program in the nation. More information about the VE program is available on the ARRL website.

The questions for each 35- or 50-question test come from a large "question pool" that's specific to each license class. All three question pools — Technician, General and Amateur Extra — are available to the public in study guides and on the Internet. If you're studying, make sure you're working with the latest version, since question pools are updated on a set schedule. The Resources section at the end of this chapter has more information on where to find the question pools.

1.2.4 Your Ham Radio Mentor

The learning doesn't stop after you pass the exam and earn your Amateur Radio ticket. New hams often learn the ropes from a mentor. In ham radio parlance, such an experienced ham willing to help newcomers is called an "Elmer." This individual teaches newcomers about Amateur Radio operating, often on a one-to-one basis. Your local ham radio club may be able to pair you up with an Elmer who will be there for you as you

ARRL — the national association for Amateur Radio®

The American Radio Relay League (ARRL) is the internationally recognized society representing Amateur Radio in the US. Since its founding in 1914, the ARRL — the national association for Amateur Radio — has grown and evolved along with Amateur Radio. ARRL Headquarters and the Maxim Memorial Station W1AW are in Newington, Connecticut, near Hartford. Through its dedicated volunteers and a professional staff, the ARRL promotes the advancement of the Amateur Service in the US and around the world.

The ARRL is a nonprofit, educational and scientific organization dedicated to the promotion and protection of the many privileges that ham radio operators enjoy. Of, by and for the radio amateur, ARRL numbers some 160,000 members — the vast majority of active amateurs in North America. Licensees can become Full Members, while unlicensed persons are eligible to become Associate Members with all membership privileges except for voting in ARRL elections. Anyone with a genuine interest in Amateur Radio belongs in the ARRL.

The ARRL volunteer corps is called the Field Organization. Working at the state and local level, these individuals tackle ARRL's goals to further Amateur Radio. They organize emergency communication in times of disaster and work with agencies such as American Red Cross and Citizen Corps. Other volunteers keep state and local government officials abreast of the good that hams do at the state and local level.

When you join ARRL, you add your voice to those who are most involved with ham radio. The most prominent benefit of ARRL membership is its monthly journal *QST*, the premiere Amateur Radio magazine issued monthly in print and digital form. *QST* contains stories you'll want to read, articles on projects to build, announcements of upcoming contests and activities, reviews of new equipment, reports on the role hams play in emergencies and much more.

Being an ARRL member is far more than a subscription to *QST*. The ARRL represents your interests before the FCC and Congress, sponsors operating events throughout the year and offers membership services at a personal level. These include:

- low-cost ham equipment insurance
- the Volunteer Examiner program
- the Technical Information Service (which answers your questions about Amateur Radio technical topics)
- the QSL Service (which lets you exchange postcards with hams in other countries to confirm your contacts with them)

For answers to any questions about Amateur Radio, e-mail, call or write ARRL Headquarters. See the Resources section at the end of this chapter for contact information.

Figure 1.9 — This iconic brick building houses W1AW, the station operated by the ARRL in Newington, Connecticut, and known around the world. W1AW memorializes Hiram Percy Maxim, one of the founders of the ARRL. Visitors are welcome and often operate the station. [Rick Lindquist, WW1ME, photo]

Figure 1.10 — Voice modes are the most popular way hams use to communicate with each other. Ruth Willet, KM4LAO, makes a few contacts using single-sideband (SSB) mode for a National Parks on the Air activation. A mechanical engineering and engineering physics student at Kettering University, Ruth is from Lawrenceville, Georgia. [Sharon Willet, KM4TVU, photo]

study, buy your first radio and set up your station — which many hams call their "radio shack" or "ham shack," a term held over from the days when ham stations often were in small buildings separate from the owner's residence. Elmers also are pleased and proud to help you with your first on-the-air contacts.

Elmers who belong to the international Courage Kenny Handiham Program (**handiham.org/wordpress1/**) focus on making study materials and ham radio station operation accessible to those with physical disabilities. Local Handi-Hams assist such prospective radio amateurs in getting licensed, and the Handi-Ham System may lend basic radio gear to get the new ham on the air.

1.2.5 Your Ham Radio Identity

Ham radio operators know and recognize each other by a unique call sign (some hams shorten this to simply "call") that the FCC issues when you get your license. Your call sign not only identifies your station on the air, it's an individual ham radio identity, and many hams become better known by their call signs than by their names! Once your license and call sign grant appear online in the FCC's active Amateur Radio Service database, you have permission to operate. The FCC went "paperless" in 2015 and no longer routinely prints or mails license documents. Licensees can print their own "official copy" from the FCC Universal Licensing System (ULS) site, however.

A call sign also identifies the issuing country. US call signs, for example, begin with W, K, N or A followed by some combination of letters and one numeral. Each combination is different. One well-known ham radio call sign is W1AW, assigned to the Hiram Percy Maxim Memorial Station at ARRL Headquarters in Newington, Connecticut.

FCC-assigned call signs come in several flavors, with the shortest — and typically most desirable — combinations available only to Amateur Extra Class licensees. The FCC routinely assigns initial call signs to new Technician licensees in the longest format. These call signs start with two letters, a numeral from 0 to 9, and three more letters. The first part of a call sign including the numeral is called a *prefix*. The part following the numeral is called a *suffix* and is unique to a specific licensee. Typical prefixes in Canada are VE and VA, while the common prefix in Mexico is XE.

At one time, the numeral indicated a US station's geographical region — 1 for New England, 6 for California and 9 or Ø (zero) for the Midwest. The FCC has made ham radio call signs portable, however — just like telephone numbers. So a call sign with "1" following the prefix may belong to a ham located in Florida.

You don't have to keep the call sign the FCC assigns. The FCC's *vanity call sign* program permits a ham to select a new personalized call sign from among the database of certain unassigned call signs, based on the applicant's license class, and file an application for it — free of charge!

1.3 Your Ham Radio Station

Amateur Radio costs as much or as little as your budget and enthusiasm dictate. Most hams set up home-based stations. By tradition the room or place where a station is located is your "ham shack," but many lower-profile hams carry their stations with them in the form of relatively inexpensive handheld transceivers, some quite compact and inexpensive. Without requiring any antenna beyond the one attached to the radio itself, such radios can accompany you when you're out and about or traveling.

On the other end of the scale, radio amateurs serious about radio contesting or DXing (contacting distant stations in other countries) often invest in the latest equipment and extensive antenna systems. Most hams fall somewhere between these extremes. They have a modest equipment complement, simple wire antennas suspended between two trees and maybe a small "beam" (directional antenna) on a backyard tower or mast. Whatever your investment level, you'll be able to talk around the world.

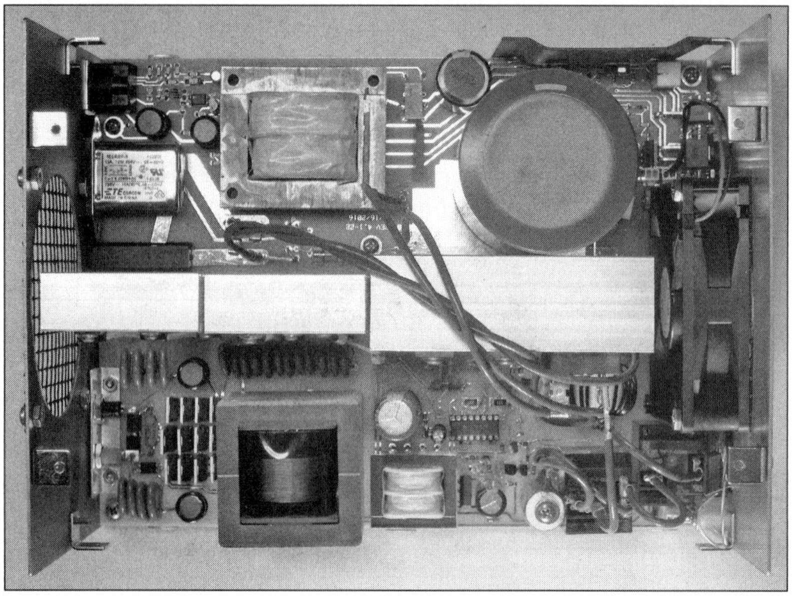

Figure 1.11 — Radio amateurs have long been known for experimenting with electronics and building their own radio equipment, such as this professionally constructed lightweight, high-voltage switching mode power supply, which was the focus of a *QST* article by Ralph Crumrine, NØKC, its builder.

Hamfests

Amateur Radio's broader social world extends beyond making on-the-air acquaintances. Regular ham radio gatherings, usually called "hamfests," offer opportunities to meet other hams in person — called "an eyeball contact" in ham parlance. Hams also enjoy buying, selling and trading ham radio equipment and accessories in the hamfest "flea market." *Every* ham loves a bargain. Other hamfest visitors take advantage of classroom sessions or forums to learn more about particular aspects of the hobby.

Hamfests are great places to get good deals on gear — some vendors offer substantial hamfest discounts — and to expand your knowledge. Thousands of radio amateurs from the US and around the world gather each spring at Hamvention® in Xenia, Ohio. This truly international event epitomizes the goodwill that exists among the world's Amateur Radio enthusiasts.

Hamvention® every May near Dayton, Ohio, attracts upward of 25,000 radio amateurs from all over the world. [Bob Inderbitzen, NQ1R, photo]

1.3.1 How Much Does It Cost?

Early radio amateurs generally built their own gear, mainly out of necessity; there were no well-stocked radio emporiums in the early 20th century. Constructing ham radio equipment from kits became popular in the mid-20th century, and several manufacturers still provide parts kits and circuit boards to make it even easier to build equipment yourself. A lot of hams still like to design and build their own equipment (called "homebrewing"), saving money in the bargain. Many of these amateurs proudly stand at the forefront of technology and keep up with advances that may be applied within or even outside the hobby. Indeed, the projects you'll find in this *Handbook* provide a wide variety of equipment and accessories that make ham radio more convenient and enjoyable.

Today's radio amateurs most often start out using off-the-shelf commercially-made transceivers purchased new or on the used market, perhaps at a ham radio flea market or hamfest or through an Internet auction or classified ad site. An abundance of ham gear is readily available, and there's something out there within your budget to meet your needs. Used higher-end VHF or VHF-UHF (or "dual-band") handheld transceivers often are available for $100 to $200 or so. The entrance of Chinese manufacturers into the ham radio market has dramatically driven down the cost of a compact VHF-UHF handheld, with some models selling for as little as $25!

Those interested in HF work can get in on the ground floor with a used, but serviceable, transceiver in the $200 to $500 range, and an excellent selection of new transceivers is available in the $500 to $1500 range. "Flea-power" CW (Morse code) transceivers covering single bands sell new for less than $100 in kit form; a new low-power four-band CW transceiver manufactured in China and marketed by a US ham radio dealer is available for less than $300. An HF antenna such as a simple backyard dipole suspended from available trees is both inexpensive and effective. You'll find some great equipment choices advertised in ARRL's monthly journal, *QST*. In addition to advertising new ham gear, *QST* includes comprehensive equipment reviews.

More elaborate antennas and various accessories can add appreciably to the cost of your

Figure 1.12 — Steve Galchutt, WGØAT, gets on the air from Knights Peak, a 10,459-foot mountain near Manitou Springs, Colorado. With him are Peanut (standing guard on the left), and Boo, his pack goat companions. This way, Steve can enjoy both mountain climbing and ham radio, as a Summits on the Air (SOTA) program enthusiast.

Keeping a Log

Keeping a log — on paper or on your computer — of your on-air activity is optional, but there are some important reasons for doing so. These include:

Awards tracking — A log lets you track contacts required for DXCC, WAS and other awards. Some computer logging programs do this automatically, so you can see how well you are progressing toward your goal.

An operating diary — A log book is a good place to record general information about your station. For example, you may want to note comparisons between different antennas or pieces of equipment based on reports from other stations. Your log is also a logical place to record new acquisitions (complete with serial numbers in case your gear is ever stolen). You can track other events as well, including the names and call signs of visiting operators, license upgrades, contests, propagation and so forth.

Legal protection — Good record keeping can help you protect yourself if you are ever accused of intentional interference or ever have a problem with unauthorized use of your call sign.

Paper or Computer?

Many hams, even some with computers, still keep "hard copy" log books. A paper log is low tech; it doesn't consume power, it's flexible and can never suffer a hard-drive crash! Preprinted log sheets are available, or you can create your own customized log sheets in no time using word processing or publishing software.

On the other hand, computer logging offers many advantages, especially for contesters, DXers and those chasing awards. For example, a computerized log can instantly indicate whether you need a particular station for DXCC or WAS. Contesters use computer logs to manage contact data during a contest and to weed out duplicate contacts in advance. Major contest sponsors prefer to receive computer log files, and some do not accept paper logs at all. Computer logs can also tell you at a glance how far along you are toward certain awards and even print QSL labels. And of course computer logs make it easy to submit your contacts to ARRL's online Logbook of The World (LoTW).

Several of the most popular computer logging programs (and regular updates) are available at no cost, while others are available for a small fee. You also can purchase logging software from commercial vendors. Some are general-purpose programs, while others are optimized for contesting, DXing or other activities. Check the ads in *QST* and compare capabilities and requirements before you choose.

station, but less-expensive alternatives are available, including building your own.

1.3.2 Computers and Ham Radio

Amateur Radio and computers have been best friends for years. Radio amateurs discovered decades ago that interconnecting their PCs with their ham stations not only makes operating more convenient but can open the door to additional activities on the ham bands. Most radio amateurs now have a computer in the shack, often one that's dedicated to ham radio tasks. Software is available for many ham radio applications, from record keeping to antenna and circuit design.

Figure 1.13 — Ella Dietzel, KM4QJM, runs a string of single-sideband (SSB) voice contacts at Schofield Middle School Radio Club (N4SMS) in Aiken, South Carolina, while a classmate looks on. [Kent Hufford, KQ4KK, photo.]

Probably the most common use for a computer in the ham shack is logging your contacts — keeping a record of the stations you have communicated with on the air. This is especially true for contesters, where speed and accuracy are paramount. While there's no longer a legal requirement to maintain a detailed logbook of your on-the-air activities, many hams still keep one, even for casual operating, and computer logging can make the task less tedious (see sidebar "Keeping a Log").

Many computer logging applications let you also control many or most of your radio's functions, such as frequency or band selection, without having to leave your logging program. It's also possible to control various accessories, such as antenna rotators or selection switches, by computer.

Via your computer's soundcard, you can enjoy *digital modes* with nothing more than a couple of simple connections, operating software (often free) and an interface. RTTY (radioteletype) and PSK31 are two of the most popular HF "keyboard-to-keyboard" digital modes. PSK31 lets you communicate over great distances with a very modest ham station, typically at extremely low power levels.

Computers also can alert you to DX activity on the bands, help you practice taking Amateur Radio license examinations or improve your Morse code skill. Many ham radio organizations, interest groups, individuals maintain and, of course, equipment retailers maintain websites too.

1.4 Getting on the Air

Amateur Radio is a *social* activity as well as a technical pursuit. It's a way to make new friends and acquaintances on the air that you may later meet in person. Some ham radio relationships last a lifetime, even though the individuals sometimes never meet face to face. Ham radio can be the glue that keeps high school and college friends in touch through the years.

Amateur Radio also can cement relationships between radio amateurs of different nationalities and cultures, leading to greater international goodwill and understanding — something that's especially beneficial in this era of heightened cultural tensions and misperceptions. When you become an Amateur Radio operator, you become a "world citizen." In return you can learn about the lives of the radio amateurs you contact in other countries.

Figure 1.14 — Young Hope Lea, KM4IPF, contacted other stations via an Amateur Radio satellite during an operation from the Wright Brothers National Memorial in Kitty Hawk, North Carolina. [James Lea, WX4TV, photo]

"*What do hams say to each other?*" you might wonder. When they meet for the first time on the air, hams typically exchange pleasantries in the form of signal reports as well as names and locations (abbreviated "QTH" by hams). Radio signal reports indicating how well the operators are hearing (or "copying") each other over the air. This name/location/signal report pattern is typical, regardless of radio mode. With these preliminaries out of the way, ham radio conversations often turn to equipment or may extend to other interests.

Although English is arguably the most common language on the ham bands (even spoken by hams whose first language may be something other than English), English speakers sometimes can make a favorable impression on hams in other countries if they can speak a little of the other person's language — even if it's as simple as *danke, gracias,* or *arigato.*

1.4.1 Voice Modes

We've mentioned the use of voice (or "phone," short for "radiotelephone") and Morse code (or CW) on the amateur bands.

Figure 1.15 — Adam Nathanson, N4EKV, of Lafayette, California, turned his ham radio shack over to daughters Amber (front) and Audrey (rear) for Kids Day. [Adam Nathanson, N4EKV, photo]

Although more hams are embracing digital modes every day, phone and CW by far remain the most popular Amateur Radio communication modes. Ham voice modes are amplitude modulation (AM), which includes the narrower-bandwidth single sideband (SSB), and frequency modulation (FM). For the most part, SSB is heard on HF, while FM is the typical voice mode employed on VHF, UHF, and microwave bands.

The great majority of ham radio HF phone operators use SSB (subdivided further into upper sideband and lower sideband), but a few still enjoy and experiment with the heritage "full-carrier AM." Once the primary ham radio voice mode, this type of AM still is heard on the standard broadcast band (530 to 1710 kHz). Today's AM buffs appreciate its warm, rich audio quality, and the simplicity of circuit design encourages restoring or modifying vintage radios that use vacuum tubes or even building from scratch. For more information about AM operation, visit **www.arrl.org/am-phone-operating-and-activities**.

Figure 1.16 — An Amateur Radio balloon project by Bill Brown, WB8ELK; Paul Verhage, KD4STH, and Ann Boes, KDØQCA, carries a 4-H Lab Revolution student experiment at 53,000 feet. [Jeff Ducklow, NØNQN, photo]

1.4.2 Morse Code

Morse code was the very first radio transmission mode, although it wasn't long before early experimenters figured out how to transmit the human voice and even music over the airwaves. Morse is also the original digital mode; the message is transmitted by turning a radio signal on and off (a "1" and a "0" in digital terms) in a prescribed pattern to represent individual letters, numerals and characters. This pattern is the International Morse Code, sometimes called the "radio code," which varies in many respects from the original Morse-Vail Code (or "American Morse") used by 19th century railroad telegraphers. Leaning on longstanding tradition, hams often refer to Morse transmissions as "CW," after an archaic definition for "continuous wave" which described the type of radio wave involved.

Federal regulations once required that prospective radio amateurs be proficient in sending and receiving Morse code in order to operate on "worldwide" (ie, shortwave or HF) ham bands. Although this is no longer the case for any class of Amateur Radio license in the US, many hams still embrace CW as a favorite mode and use it routinely. Hams typically send Morse code signals by manipulating a manual telegraph key, a "semi-automatic" key (called a "bug") or a CW "paddle" and an electronic keyer that forms the dots and dashes. Most hams decipher Morse code "by ear," either writing down the letters, numerals and characters as they come through the receiver's headphones or speaker or simply reading it in their heads. Some use one of the available computer-based or standalone accessories that can translate CW into plain text without the need to learn the code.

Hams who enjoy CW cite its narrow bandwidth — a CW signal takes up very little of the radio spectrum — simpler equipment and the ability of a CW signal to "get through" noise and interference with minimal transmitting power. CW is a common low-power (QRP) mode.

1.4.3 FM Repeaters

Hams often make their first contacts on local voice repeaters, although in recent years the nearly ubiquitous cell phone has reduced the popularity of — and even the need for — repeaters for everyday ham communication. Repeaters still have a definite role in supporting communication during disasters and emergencies, however. Repeaters can greatly extend the useful range of a typical handheld FM transceiver much in the same way a cell tower retransmits your voice or text messages, and they carry the vast majority of VHF/UHF traffic, making local and even regional mobile communication possible for many hams. Located on hilltops, tall buildings or other high structures, repeaters strengthen signals and retransmit them. This provides communication over much farther distances than would be possible when operating point to point or "direct." The wider coverage can be especially important if the repeater is ever pressed into service during an emergency.

Typically, hams use repeaters for brief contacts, although socializing and "ragchewing" are routine on some "machines," as repeaters are often called. All repeater users give priority to emergency communications. Most repeaters are maintained by clubs or groups of hams. If you use a particular repeater frequently, you should join and support the repeater organization. Some hams set up their own repeaters as a service to the community.

The best way to learn the customs of a particular repeater is to listen for a while before transmitting. Most repeaters are *open*, meaning that any amateur may use the repeater, although repeaters typically require users to transmit an access tone (which you can select on any modern FM transceiver). A few repeaters are *closed*, meaning that usage is restricted to members of the club or group that owns and operates the repeater. Some repeaters still have autopatch capability that allows amateurs to make telephone calls through the repeater. The *ARRL Repeater Directory* shows repeater locations, frequencies, capabilities, and whether the repeater is open or closed.

1.4.4 Digital Modes

Digital modes are used to exchange information between computers as individual characters — either in complete files or one character at a time in "keyboard-to-keyboard" contacts. Amateurs use modes originally invented for commercial or military applications and also invent their own! Innovation in digital communications is one of Amateur Radio's most important and active contributions.

The two most popular digital modes today are FT8, one of several modes in the *WSJT-X* software package (**physics.princeton.edu/pulsar/k1jt/wsjtx.html**), and either PACTOR or WINMOR which are used to exchange email and other types of information as part of the Winlink system (**winlink.org**). Both FT8 and WINMOR use your PC with its sound card interfaced to a transceiver. The later versions of PACTOR that are most widely used require a special modem between the PC and radio. These modes are described in the **Digital Protocols and Modes** chapter. You'll also find many helpful articles about using them in the *ARRL Operating Manual* and on the ARRL website.

The free package of *WSJT-X* software includes a number of specialized digital modes developed by a team led by Joe Taylor, K1JT, that are optimized for different applications: JT65 for EME, MSK144 for meteor scatter, FT8 for HF operation, WSPR for very low-power beacons, and more. FT8, released in 2017, quickly became extremely popular due to its ability to exchange data with signals many times weaker than the noise. FT8 is a great mode for hams in noisy neighborhoods or who can't put up big antennas.

Hams interested in public service, especially emergency communications, make use of the Winlink system (**www.winlink.org**) to maintain contact while camping, boating, or just traveling. Along with PACTOR or WINMOR, which actually transfer data over the air, an email "client" program such as *Winlink Express* is required to manage the information. Many public service teams include Winlink as part of their training and operation programs. The system acts as a worldwide gateway between Amateur Radio and the Internet although the restrictions on commercial content must be strictly followed.

Two other keyboard-to-keyboard modes used by hams to "talk by typing" include radioteletype or RTTY and PSK31. Often pronounced "ritty," radioteletype was originally developed for point-to-point communications. Hams replaced the original electromechanical teleprinters with PCs, sound cards, and software such as *fldigi* which is free and supports many different modes (see **www.w1hkj.com**). RTTY's distinctive two-tone FSK (frequency-shift keying) signals are common on the HF bands.

Somewhat lower in frequency than the RTTY signals, you'll hear single tones with a buzzing modulation. This is PSK31 which stands for "Phase-shift Keying, 31 baud." 31 baud may not sound very fast but it is an average typing speed — perfect for hams to chat back and forth. PSK31 is very effective at low power levels and is one of the many modes in the *fldigi* package.

Another amateur innovation is the *Automatic Packet Reporting System* or APRS which combines position information (such as from GPS) with text messages and packet radio. This worldwide system (**www.aprs.org**) uses continuously monitoring "gateway" receivers to listen for the low-power APRS signals, relaying the information to Internet servers where the information is viewed. Hams use APRS in their vehicles, while biking or boating, for weather reporting, and even to track high-altitude balloons during experiments.

FT8, PACTOR/WINMOR, RTTY, PSK31, and APRS are just a small fraction of the many different digital modes used in Amateur Radio. New variations and innovations are being released all the time as experimenters try a new modulation or encoding scheme. This is a great example of the Amateur Service fulfilling its Basis and Purpose by "contribut(ing) to the advancement of the radio art."

1.4.5 Image Communication

Users of current technology often enjoy sharing photos or even talking face-to-face. While not as sophisticated, several ham radio communication modes allow the exchange of still or moving images over the air, and without any data charges. Advances in technology have brought the price of image transmission equipment within reach of the average ham's budget. This has caused a surge of interest in image communication.

Amateur TV (ATV) is full-motion video over the air, sometimes called "fast-scan TV." An even more advanced form of this is digital Amateur Radio TV (DATV), which is used to transmit images and voice to Earth via the ham radio stations on the International Space Station (ISS). Amateur Radio communication takes on an exciting, new dimension when you can actually *see* the person you're communicating with. In addition, (D)ATV has proved to be very useful in emergency and disaster communication situations and can transmit a high-definition image. Amateur groups in some areas have set up ATV repeaters, allowing lower-power stations to communicate over a fairly wide area. Since this is a wide-bandwidth mode, operation is limited to the UHF bands (70 centimeters and higher).

DATV folds nicely into a newer Amateur Radio technological initiative called high-speed multimedia (HSMM), which supports networks such as Broadband-Hamnet and AREDN. The ham bands above 50 MHz can support computer-to-computer communication at speeds high enough to support multimedia applications — voice, data and image. One approach adapts IEEE 802 technologies, particularly 802.11b, operating on specific

Figure 1.17 — European Space Agency Astronaut Tim Peake, KG5BVI/GB1SS, was the first International Space Station crew member to take advantage of the recently commissioned Ham TV digital Amateur Radio television (DATV) system on the space station while answering questions from students in England during a scheduled contact. [Sian Cleaver photo]

Amateur Radio frequencies in the 2400 to 2450 MHz band.

SSTV or "slow-scan TV" is an older, narrow-bandwidth image mode that remains popular in Amateur Radio. Instead of full-motion video, SSTV enthusiasts exchange photographs and other static images. Individual SSTV pictures take anywhere from 8 seconds to about 2 minutes to send, depending on the transmission method. These days most SSTV operation is done in color, using computers and soundcards in conjunction with software that's often free. Images are converted into a series of audio tones representing brightness level and colors. Since SSTV is a narrow-band mode, it is popular on HF on the same frequencies used for voice operation.

1.5 Your Ham Radio "Lifestyle"

After getting some on-the-air experience, many Amateur Radio enthusiasts focus on a particular mode or operating style and may identify themselves primarily as contesters, DXers, CW operators, or VHF-UHFers. Other radio amateurs center their operating on such activities as specialized or experimental modes, operating in the microwave bands, mobile ham radio, very low-power operating (known as "QRP") and radio direction finding (RDF).

1.5.1 Ham Radio Contesting — Radiosport

Ham radio contesting, often called "radiosport," continues to grow in worldwide popularity. Hardly a weekend goes by when there isn't a ham radio contest of some sort. These on-the-air competitions range from regional operating events with a few hundred participants to national and worldwide competitions with thousands of stations on the air at the same time, attempting to communicate with one another for points — and bragging rights.

Objectives vary from one event to another, but ham radio contests typically involve trying to contact — or "work" — as many other contest participants on the air as possible within a specified period. In each contact, participants exchange certain information, often a signal report and a location, as the contest's rules dictate. A lot of contest scoring schemes place a premium on two-way contacts with stations in certain countries, states, or zones. Top scorers in the various entry categories usually get certificates, but a few events offer sponsored plaques and trophies. Competition can be fierce among individual contesters and among contest clubs.

Contests embrace nearly every mode and operating preference available to Amateur Radio — voice, Morse code, and digital modes. Some members of the contesting community are earnest competitors who constantly tweak their stations and skills to better their scores. Others take a more casual approach. All have lots of fun.

In the ARRL International DX Contest, for example, participants try to contact as many DX (foreign) stations as possible over the course of a weekend. Experienced hams with top-notch stations easily contact 1000 or more stations in more than 100 different countries in a single weekend, but even operators with more modest stations can make lots of contacts too.

Other popular contests include state QSO parties, where the goal is to contact stations in as many of the sponsoring state's counties. ARRL November Sweepstakes (SS) is a high-energy US-and-Canadian contest that attracts thousands of operators each fall. One weekend is dedicated to CW, another to voice. VHF, UHF, and microwave contests focus on making contacts using our highest-frequency bands. Digital-mode contests have gained in popularity in recent years, thanks to computer soundcards, radios that offer digital-mode capabilities, and software that is often free.

You can find information on contests each month in ARRL's monthly membership journal *QST;* the contest calendar on the ARRL website also provides up-to-date information on upcoming operating events. The ARRL's bimonthly publication *National Contest Journal* (*NCJ*) focuses on topics of particular interest to contesting novices and veterans alike. For timely contest news and information, check "The ARRL Contest Update" e-newsletter at **www.arrl.org/contest-update-issues**, available to ARRL members every other week via e-mail and on the ARRL website.

Figure 1.18 — Sean Kutzko, KX9X, uses a handheld antenna to make contacts through an Amateur Radio satellite. [Ward Silver, NØAX, photo]

ARRL FIELD DAY

An emergency communication training exercise with some elements of a contest, ARRL Field Day (FD) prompts thousands of participants outdoors the field on the fourth full weekend of June. Portable gear in tow, hams take to the hills, forests, campsites, parking lots and even emergency operations centers or vans to take part. Tracing its origins to the 1930s, Field Day started out as a way to publicly demonstrate ham radio's ability to operate "in the field" and "off the grid." The goal is not only to make lots of contacts but to operate successfully under the sorts of conditions that could prevail in the aftermath of a disaster or emergency.

Most stations are set up outdoors and use emergency power sources, such as generators, solar panels, wind turbines, and batteries. Creativity reigns when it comes to power sources! Over the years, Field Day's contest-like nature has led to plenty of good-natured competition among clubs and groups. Field Day stations range from simple to elaborate. If a real disaster were to strike, stations such as these could be set up quickly wherever needed, without having to rely on commercial power.

1.5.2 Chasing DX

People unfamiliar with ham radio often ask, "How far can you talk?" Well, "talking far" is what chasing "DX" is all about. DX stations are those in distant places around the world. Chasing DX is a time-honored ham radio tradition. Hams who focus on contacting stations in far-flung and rare locations are called "DXers." Ham radio pioneers a century ago often competed in terms of how far *they* could talk; spanning the Atlantic via ham radio in the early 1920s was a stupendous accomplishment in its day.

Figure 1.19 — ARRL Field Day is the largest Amateur Radio event on the planet, with tens of thousands of hams participating in the 24-hour event each June. These members of the Cheshire County DX Club of Keene, New Hampshire, are enjoying the fun and camaraderie that this popular operating event evokes. [Heather Goodell, photo]

DXers often have as a goal attaining DX Century Club (DXCC) membership, earning a place on the vaunted DXCC "Honor Roll" or entering the ARRL DX Challenge.

Working DX does not necessarily require an expensive radio and huge antenna system. It's possible to work DX all over the world with very low power and/or with modest antennas, including wires hung from trees or mobile (ie, vehicle-mounted) antennas.

Some hams specialize in certain ham bands to work DX, such as 160 meters, where DXing can be challenging due to the low operating frequency involved, not to mention frequent noise and infrequent DX propagation. Others prefer "the high bands," such as 20, 15 and 10 meters, where DX typically is more common and, in fact, typically abounds in times of favorable propagation.

DXPEDITIONS

DXers who have run out of new countries to work sometimes couple a love of ham radio and travel to *become* the DX! "DXpeditions" are journeys by hams to "rare" countries having few or no hams, where they set up a station (or stations), often making thousands of contacts in the space of a few days. They not only have a great time but can promote international goodwill.

Some DXpeditions are huge productions. In early 2016, a 14-member team of radio amateurs traveled to the South Sandwich Islands near Antarctica and then to South Georgia Island. South Sandwich and South Georgia each count as a separate country (or "entity") for the DXCC award. In less than one month, the team completed more than 100,000 two-way contacts with other hams around the world from their remote encampment. Another team of operators in early 2016 traveled to remote Heard Island, in the Indian Ocean north of Antarctica, to brave the elements, logging some 75,000 contacts. Members of the worldwide Amateur Radio community dig deep into their pockets to fund DXpeditions such as this one, which cost upward of $450,000.

Most DXpeditions are smaller affairs in which one or two operators may combine a vacation with some on-air fun — sometimes called "holiday style" operating. Activity often peaks in conjunction with major DX contests. If you don't want to drag your radio and antennas along, fully equipped DX stations sometimes are available to rent in more-frequented locations, such as Hawaii and the Caribbean islands.

DX SPOTS AND NETS

The beginning DXer can get a good jump on DXCC by frequenting the DX spotting sites on the Internet. A DX spotting website is essentially an Internet clearing house of reports — or "spots" — posted by other DXers of stations actually heard or worked. The DX Summit website, **www.dxsummit.fi**, hosted in Finland is a popular one. Users around the world post spots in real time. Each lists the call sign and frequency of the DX station as well as the call sign of the station that posted the spot. Knowing where the DX station is being heard can tell you if you're likely to hear the DX station at *your* location.

Figure 1.20 — Polish radio amateurs Pawel Piotrowski, SP7AH (left), and Dariusz Karcz, SQ7FPD, operate from the SNØHQ Polish Amateur Radio Union headquarters station during the IARU HF World Championship. [Henryk Kotowski, SMØJHF, photo]

Figure 1.21 — Pete Kobak, KØBAK, gets on the air next to the Statue of Liberty using a highly portable station. [Pete Kobak, KØBAK, photo]

A newer wrinkle in identifying the presence of DX stations is something called the Reverse Beacon Network (RBN). An informal, growing volunteer network, the RBN consists of wideband receivers installed at scattered locations across the US and around the world that can "skim" the call signs of CW and certain digital-mode signals from a band or bands and display them on a website. DX spotting sites or programs also can import these data to offer a clue as to which stations are on the air at the time. Operators also can use the RBN to see where their own signals are being heard and how well, which can be very useful information when running antenna and equipment tests.

DX nets offer another DX gateway. On DX nets, a net control station tracks which DX stations have checked into the net, then allows individual operators on frequency to try working one of the DX stations. This permits weaker stations to be heard instead of their signals being covered up by stations calling in a "pileup."

1.5.3 Operating Awards

Earning awards that reflect Amateur Radio operating accomplishments is a time-honored tradition. Literally hundreds of operating awards are available to suit your level of activity and sense of accomplishment. Here are a few popular ones.

WORKED ALL CONTINENTS

The Worked All Continents (WAC) certificate is a good starting point for newcomers. Sponsored by the International Amateur Radio Union (IARU), earning WAC requires working and confirming contacts with one station on each of six continents (excluding Antarctica).

WORKED ALL STATES

Hams who can confirm two-way ham radio contacts with stations in each of the 50 United States can apply for the popular ARRL's Worked All States (WAS) award. Those who enjoy operating different bands and a seek a greater challenge may attempt the ARRL's 5-Band WAS (5BWAS) award by confirming contacts with all 50 US states on each of the 80, 40, 20, 15 and 10 meter bands.

A twist on the WAS award is the ARRL's Triple Play Award. Introduced in 2009, it was an instant hit. To earn the Triple Play Award, an amateur must contact other amateurs in each of the 50 US states using voice, Morse code and a digital mode, such as RTTY or PSK31. All qualifying contacts must be confirmed via the ARRL's Logbook of the World (LoTW — see sidebar, "Logbook of The World). The Triple Play Award is available to hams worldwide.

QSL Cards

Long before the Internet and e-mail, hams began the custom of exchanging postcards that became known as QSL cards or simply QSLs. "QSL" is another radiotelegraph, or Morse code, abbreviation that means "I confirm receipt of your transmission." A QSL card contains information to verify that a two-way contact took place. Exchanging QSL cards can enhance your ham radio enjoyment and even lead to a regular correspondence.

Hams still take great pride in having distinctive QSL cards to exchange following a contact, although today, thanks to the Internet, electronic means exist, such as ARRL's Logbook of The World (see sidebar, "Logbook of The World") to confirm contacts.

DX stations, especially those in very rare places, are often inundated with QSL cards and requests from US hams. To ease the cost and administrative burden, most DX QSLs travel via QSL bureaus, which ship cards in bulk, then sort and distribute them on the receiving end. The Outgoing QSL Service is available to ARRL members at nominal cost. The incoming QSL bureaus are available to all amateurs. Bureau instructions and addresses are on the ARRL website.

Logbook of The World

Instead of exchanging and collecting QSL cards, more and more radio amateurs are taking advantage of the ARRL's Logbook of The World to confirm contacts for award credit. LoTW is a world repository of individual radio contact records submitted by users. When both participants in a radio contact submit matching QSO records to LoTW, the result is a virtual QSL that each ham can apply toward ARRL award credit. Uploading contact data costs nothing; users only pay to "redeem" their contact credits for an award, such as ARRL's DXCC, VUCC, WAS and the WPX and WAZ Awards sponsored by CQ Communications.

Once signed up as an LoTW user, you can submit new contact records whenever you wish. Your submissions are matched against those of other Logbook users. Whenever a match occurs, you receive instant credit for the contact.

To minimize the chance of fraudulent submissions, all LoTW QSO records are digitally "signed" by the licensee, who must hold an LoTW certificate. Visit the Logbook of The World website, **www.arrl.org/logbook-of-the-world**, to learn more.

Figure 1.22 — These youthful operators put ET3AA — the station of the Ethiopian Amateur Radio Society (EARS) — on the air during the ARRL 10 Meter Contest. [Ken Claerbout, K4ZW, photo]

DX CENTURY CLUB

The most prestigious and popular DX award is the DX Century Club (DXCC), sponsored by the ARRL. Earning DXCC is quite a challenge. You must confirm two-way contact with stations in 100 countries (or "entities," as they're known in the DXCC program). Hams with very simple stations have earned DXCC. Operating in various DX contests when stations all over the world are looking for contact is a good way to combine DXing and contesting and to get a leg up on earning DXCC. There's also a 5-Band DXCC (5BDXCC) for earning DXCC on each of five bands, 80, 40, 20, 15 and 10 meters.

Top-rung DX enthusiasts have been challenging themselves and each other through the ARRL DXCC Challenge. This ongoing activity involves confirming contacts with DXCC entities on all bands from 160 through 6 meters.

VHF/UHF CENTURY CLUB

Hams who operate on the VHF and UHF bands have a "century club" of their own, the VHF/UHF Century Club. Instead of working 100 DXCC entities, participants earn awards for making two-way contacts with a specified number of Maidenhead 2° × 1° grid locators or "grid squares," as they're more commonly known. Grid squares are designated by a combination of two letters and two numbers and represent a specific area on the globe. For operations on 6 meters, 2 meters, and satellite, operators must contact 100 individual grid squares. More information is on the ARRL website, **www.arrl.org/awards/vucc**.

1.5.4 Satellite Communication

Amateur Radio established its initial foothold in space in 1961, with the launch of the OSCAR 1 satellite (OSCAR is an acronym for Orbiting Satellite Carrying Amateur Radio). Since then, amateurs have launched dozens of satellites, most of the low-Earth orbit (LEO) variety and a small number in the high-Earth orbit category. The history of Amateur Radio satellites and information on which ones are in operation is available on the AMSAT website, **www.amsat.org**.

Amateurs have pioneered several developments in the satellite industry, including low-Earth orbit communication "birds" and PACSATs — orbiting packet-radio bulletin board systems — and CubeSats which are standard-sized miniature satellites constructed by student teams around the world. Operating awards are available from ARRL and other organizations specifically for satellite operation.

Satellite operation is neither complex nor difficult; it's possible to work through some satellites with nothing more than a dual-band (VHF/UHF) handheld radio and perhaps a small portable antenna. More serious satellite work requires some specialized equipment. You may be able to work several Amateur Radio satellites (OSCARs) with the equipment that's now in your shack!

Figure 1.23 — Island County Amateur Radio Club members Jon Edwards, AE7TE (right), and Wayne Jeffers, WJ7H, use hand-held antennas and radios to successfully contact NA1SS on the International Space Station from the club's ARRL Field Day site on Washington's Whidbey Island. Hams can use the same sort of basic equipment to operate through Amateur Radio satellites. [Vince Bond, K7NA, photo]

AMATEUR RADIO IN SPACE

The Amateur Radio on the International Space Station (ARISS) program, **www.ariss.org**, is the international consortium for ham radio in space. It's a cooperative venture of ARRL, the Radio Amateur Satellite Corporation (AMSAT), and NASA in the US, and other international space agencies and Amateur Radio organizations around the world.

An all-volunteer program, ARISS seeks to inspire students worldwide to pursue careers in science, technology, engineering, and math (STEM) by making available opportunities to speak — interview, actually — via ham radio with on-orbit ISS crew members. ARISS-International includes representatives of nine countries, including the US, several European nations and Japan, Russia and Canada. ARISS-provided ham gear in three ISS modules makes possible analog voice and digital communication — including digital Amateur Radio television (DATV) between earthbound hams and ISS crew members as well as via the onboard ISS digipeater packet radio mailbox and APRS digipeater.

ARISS arranges and schedules contacts with schools, institutions, and events around the globe in advance. Then, a demonstration station is set up at the school or other location, and students can ask an ISS crew member — most hold ham radio licenses — about their time in space and life aboard the space station. These voice contacts typically take place using VHF FM (2 meter) equipment.

A more-recent role involving the ISS is the deployment of Amateur Radio satellites into orbit from the station, after they are transported to the station as cargo.

1.5.5 QRP: Low-Power Operating

A very active segment of the Amateur Radio community enjoys operating with minimal transmitting power. They call themselves "QRP operators" or "QRPers" after the Morse code abbreviation for "I shall decrease transmitter power." According to the FCC Amateur Radio rules, "An amateur station must use the minimum transmitter power necessary to carry out the desired communications." The FCC allows most hams to transmit or "run" up to 1500 W (watts), and many hams run 100 W. QRPers, however, typically use 5 W or less — sometimes *far* less (one ham achieved WAS while running 2 milliwatts — that's two-thousandths of a watt!).

Operating QRP can be challenging. Other stations may need to dig deep for your often weak signal, so patience becomes a real virtue, both for the low-power enthusiast and the station on the other end of the contact. What their stations lack in transmitting power QRPers make up for with effective antennas and skillful operating, and they make contacts around the world. This operating style has become so popular that many Amateur Radio competitions (this is called "radiosport") now include an entry category for stations running 5 W or less output power.

One of the best reasons to operate QRP is that low-power equipment typically is lightweight and less expensive. Many QRP operators enjoy designing and building their own "flea-power" transceivers, and various organizations support low-power operating by offering kits, circuits, and advice. A few commercial manufacturers also market QRP equipment and kits. The QRP Amateur Radio Club International (**www.qrparci.org**) is perhaps the oldest organization to advance and promote QRP as a ham radio way of life. In addition to sponsoring various operating events throughout the year, QRP ARCI publishes *QRP Quarterly*, which includes articles of interest to both QRP operators and the broader ham radio community.

1.5.6 Operating Mobile

Many hams enjoy operating on the fly — usually from a car or truck but sometimes from a boat, a motorcycle, a bicycle and even while on foot (sometimes called "pedestrian mobile" or "manpack radio")! Operating radio gear installed in a motor vehicle is the most common form of "mobile," and manufacturers today offer a wide range of ham radio gear, including antennas, designed for such work. A mobile station can be as simple as a basic VHF or dual-band VHF/UHF radio and a little antenna attached magnetically to the roof, or as complex as an HF station and a more substantial antenna system. Some mobile stations are very sophisticated, with capabilities that rival those of fixed stations.

While most hams who operate mobile use FM or SSB, a significant number enjoy the challenge of using CW while on the road. It takes a bit of practice, in part because the operator must learn to understand (or "copy") Morse code without having to write it down — and because a vehicle is not always a very steady platform for sending Morse code.

Hams on bicycle treks or hikes carry along lightweight radio gear. A lot of cyclists or hikers pack a small ham radio transceiver and wire antenna along with their sleeping bag, food, and water.

Figure 1.24 — Marc Franco, N2UO, uses this 20-foot diameter parabolic dish for Earth-Moon-Earth communication.

1.5.7 VHF, UHF, and Microwave Operating

Hams use many modes and techniques to extend the range of their line-of-sight VHF, UHF, and microwave signals. Those who explore the potential of VHF/UHF communication often are called "weak-signal" operators to differentiate them from FM operators who communicate locally — although the signals involved often are not really *weak*.

These enthusiasts and experimenters probe the limits of propagation in the upper reaches of the Amateur Radio spectrum, often with the goal of discovering just how far they can communicate. They use directional antennas (beams or parabolic dishes) and very sensitive receivers. In some instances, they also employ considerable transmitter output power. As a result of their efforts, distance records are broken almost yearly. On 2 meters, for example, conversations between stations hundreds and even thousands of miles apart are not uncommon even though the stations are far beyond "line of sight" separation. Maximum distances decrease as frequencies increase, but communication regularly can span several hundred miles, even at microwave frequencies.

Weak-signal operators for many years depended on SSB and CW, but computer/sound card-based digital modes are now part of their arsenal. These modes use state-of-the-art digital signal processing (DSP) software for transmitting and receiving very weak signals that can be well below levels that the human ear can detect.

MOONBOUNCE (EME)

EME (Earth-Moon-Earth) communication, commonly called "moonbounce," fascinates many amateurs. The concept is simple: Use the Moon as a passive reflector of VHF and UHF signals. Considering the total path of some 500,000 miles, EME is the ultimate DX — at least to date. The first two-way amateur EME contacts took place in 1952.

In its earliest days EME was a CW mode activity requiring large antennas and high power. Advances in technology, such as low-noise receivers and digital signal processing (DSP) tools, have made EME contacts possible for more and more amateurs with modest stations.

METEOR SCATTER

Years ago hams discovered they could bounce signals off the ionized trails of vaporized matter that follow meteors entering Earth's atmosphere. Such trails often can reflect VHF radio signals for several seconds, during which stations can exchange extremely brief reports. During meteor showers, the ionized region becomes large enough — and lasts long enough — to sustain short contacts. It's exciting to hear a signal from hundreds of miles away pop out of the noise just for an instant!

Amateurs experimenting with meteor-scatter propagation use transmitter powers of 100 W or more and beam antennas. Most contacts are made using SSB, CW or digital modes. Although most SSB and CW QSOs are made during annual meteor showers, digital mode contacts are possible any day of the year.

1.5.8 Vintage Radio

Many, if not most, veteran radio amateurs have a nostalgic streak, and this extends toward vintage radio gear. Present-day commercial Amateur Radio equipment has reached a level of complexity that often requires specialized test and troubleshooting equipment to repair or align. Modern component manufacturing technology such as surface-mount devices (SMDs) has become so commonplace that a modular approach to equipment repair is commonplace; rather than troubleshoot and replace a defective

Figure 1.25 — Restoring and using vintage Amateur Radio gear is one interest of Dennis Lazar, W4DNN. Hams often call older, tube-type equipment "boatanchors," because of its weight, compared to today's far-lighter solid-state gear. [Dennis Lazar, W4DNN, photo]

component, many manufacturers now prefer to swap out an entire module.

Yet many amateurs still would rather repair and adjust their own equipment and covet the days when this was simpler and easier. This is but one reason behind the surge in vintage radio collecting and operating. Others enjoy vintage gear for its lower cost and wider availability, the novelty of operating older gear on today's ham bands, and for its rarity and antique value. Many of these radios are affectionately called "boat anchors" by vintage radio aficionados, since early radio gear tends to be relatively large and heavy.

Some enthusiasts enjoy the challenge of collecting and restoring older radios, sometimes striving to bring the equipment back to its original factory condition. Other vintage radio enthusiasts may have a parallel interest in conventional AM voice transmission. These activities take vintage radio fans back to an era when it was much more common for amateurs to build their own station equipment.

Figure 1.26 — Amateur Radio Direction Finding (ARDF) equipment need not be expensive. Yagis made from measuring tapes and PVC pipe are very popular for direction finding on 2 meters with a handheld transceiver. Here, Dan Slater, AG6HF (left), tests an antenna he built. [Joe Moell, KØOV, photo]

1.5.9 Radio Direction Finding (DF)

Radio direction finding, or DFing, is the art of locating a signal or noise source by tracking it with portable receivers and directional antennas. Direction finding is not only fun, it has a practical side as well. Hams who are proficient at DFing have been instrumental in hunting down signals from illegal jammers and malfunctioning transmitters, tracking down sources of interference on the ham bands — intentional or inadvertent — or pinning down the location of a suspected "pirate" (unlicensed ham station) in the area. Because DFing only involves receiving, it does not require a ham ticket.

"Fox hunting" — also called "T-hunting," "radio-orienteering" or "bunny hunting" — is ham radio's answer to hide-and-seek. One player is designated the fox; he or she hides a transmitter, and the other players attempt to find it. Rules vary, but the fox must generally place the transmitter within certain boundaries and transmit at specific intervals.

Fox hunts differ from place to place. American fox hunts often employ teams of fox hunters cruising in vehicles over a wide area. European and other fox hunters restrict their events to smaller areas and conduct fox hunts on foot. Competitions held on the national and international levels attract hundreds of participants and follow the European model.

1.6 Public Service

Volunteering to provide communication as a public service is a key facet of the Basis and Purpose of the Amateur Radio Service and has been a traditional responsibility of Amateur Radio from the start. Today, this most often involves ham radio's volunteer efforts during disasters and emergencies.

When Hurricane Sandy struck New York City and the Middle Atlantic States in the fall of 2012, the Amateur Radio community from Maine to the Carolinas responded to requests for assistance, activated local nets and supported the operations of the Hurricane Watch Net and the VoIP Hurricane Net. Hams volunteered around the clock to bridge the gap in the wake of downed utility lines to provide communication for evacuation efforts, as well as to link hospitals experiencing communications breakdowns, shelters, emergency operations centers and non-government relief agencies, such as The American Red Cross and The Salvation Army, which has its own Amateur Radio contingent, The Salvation

Figure 1.27 — Dragan Tuip, KG7OQT, an 11-year-old ARRL member from Snoqualmie, Washington, took first place in his grade and division for a portable *WinLink* (e-mail via ham radio) "go box" for emergency communication. The IEEE also named him a "rising star." [Martin Tuip, KG7HAX, photo]

Figure 1.28 — After hurricanes devastated Puerto Rico in 2017, Amateur Radio operators Val Hotzfeld, NV9L (left), and ARRL Emergency Preparedness Manager Mike Corey, KI1U, were among those who volunteered to travel to the island to support communications on behalf of the American Red Cross.

Figure 1.29 — Carol Wilson, KCØMOM (left), and her daughter Kristi Lundy, KCØINX, had a great time operating in the 2016 ARRL November Sweepstakes (phone weekend). [Mike Wilson, K2KR, photo]

Army Team Emergency Radio Network (SATERN). Radio amateurs also assisted after the storm by helping officials to assess damage. Many hams also are part of SKYWARN, which helps to identify and track severe weather activity via ham radio and coordinates its efforts with the National Weather Service.

Public service can take less dramatic forms: Hams also step forward to provide communication for walkathons, marathons, bike races, parades and other community events. The Boston and New York City marathons are two major events that welcome Amateur Radio assistance.

1.6.1 Public Service Communication

The ability to provide communication during disasters is a major justification for Amateur Radio's existence. Government officials on all levels and the general public have come to recognize that Amateur Radio works when other communications networks are unavailable. Despite the proliferation of cell phones and other personal communication devices, Amateur Radio continues to prove its value, since it can operate without an existing man-made infrastructure. Ham radio doesn't need the mobile telephone network or the Internet.

Battery-powered equipment allows hams to provide essential communication even when power is knocked out. If need be, hams can make and install antennas on the spot from available materials. In the wake of hurricanes, forest fires, earthquakes and other natural disasters that cripple or compromise normal communications, hams may be called upon to handle thousands of messages in and out of the stricken region. The work that hams do during crisis situations cultivates good relations with neighbors and with local governments.

Amateur Radio operators have a long tradition of operating "off the grid" from backup power sources. Through events such as Field Day, hams cultivate the ability to set up communication posts wherever they are needed. Moreover, Amateur Radio can provide computer networks (with over-the-air links as needed) and other services, such as video, that no other service can deploy on the fly, even on a wide scale.

1.6.2 Public Service Communication Organizations

Should a disaster or emergency arise, volunteer teams of amateurs may be invited by emergency managers to work with first responders, the Red Cross, and medical personnel to provide or supplement communication. Hams sometimes are called upon to fill the communication gap between agencies whose radio systems are incompatible with one another.

ARES AND RACES

Ham radio disaster response activities typically take place under the umbrella of the Amateur Radio Emergency Service (ARES®), sponsored by the ARRL, and the Radio Amateur Civil Emergency Service (RACES), administered by the Federal Emergency Management Agency (FEMA). RACES works with government agencies to maintain civil preparedness and provide communication in times of civil emergency. RACES is activated at the request of a local, state or federal official. To maintain their edge and readiness, hams affiliated with emergency communication teams assess their systems and themselves through regularly scheduled nets and simulated emergency tests (SETS).

ARES and RACES organizations frequently work hand-in-hand. Amateurs serious about disaster response communication typically are active in both groups or may carry dual ARES/RACES membership. FCC rules make it possible for ARES and RACES to use many of the same frequencies, so an ARES group also enrolled in RACES can work within either organization as circumstances dictate.

MILITARY AUXILIARY RADIO SYSTEM (MARS)

Begun in 1925, MARS is authorized by the US Department of Defense (DOD) and administered by the US Army and Air Force. The primary mission of MARS is to provide contingency HF radio communication support to the DOD and the military. MARS relies on volunteers from within the Amateur Radio ranks, who receive specialized training in military messaging formats and military standard digital messaging protocols. MARS also supports US combat commands by providing humanitarian assistance and disaster relief. It also offers contingency communication for Defense Support to Civil Authorities (DSCA) when authorized, and provides "morale and welfare communications" in support of the DOD. MARS members serve as the liaison between the DOD and the larger Amateur Radio community during times of disaster.

Figure 1.30 — The Wilson High School Amateur Radio Emergency Communications team in Long Beach, California, is made up of young women. Here, team members practice passing and copying message traffic. [Devon Day, KF6KEE, photo]

MARS volunteers joined Amateur Radio organizations to assist with medical and humanitarian relief efforts in the wake of the devastating 2010 earthquake in Haiti. In 2016, MARS partnered with the Hurricane Watch Net to provide updated disaster information to the hospital ship USS *Comfort* deploying to Haiti after Hurricane Matthew struck Haiti.

Amateur Radio licensees interested in joining either MARS branch must be at least 18 years old (in some cases, amateurs who are 17 may join with the signature of a parent or legal guardian). Volunteers and must have access to an Amateur Radio HF rig. MARS operations take place on DOD-authorized frequencies outside of the Amateur Radio bands and consist of regularly scheduled training nets to practice military message formatting using military standard digital protocols.

1.6.3 Public Service and Traffic Nets

The ARRL came into existence to coordinate and promote the formation of message-handling nets, so public service and traffic nets are part of a tradition that dates back almost to the dawn of Amateur Radio. In those early days, nets were needed to communicate over distances greater than a few miles. From their origination point, messages (also called "traffic") leapfrogged from amateur station to amateur station to their destination — thus the word "relay" in American Radio Relay League. It still works that way today, although individual stations typically have a much greater range.

Some nets and stations are typically only active in emergencies. These include Amateur Radio station WX4NHC at the National Hurricane Center, the Hurricane Watch Net, SKYWARN (weather observers), The Salvation Army Team Emergency Radio Network (SATERN), The Waterway Net and the VoIP (voice over Internet protocol) SKYWARN/Hurricane Net.

THE NATIONAL TRAFFIC SYSTEM (NTS)

The National Traffic System™ (NTS™) exists to pass formal written messages from any point in the US to any other point. Messages, which follow a standard format called a "Radiogram," are relayed from one ham to another, using a variety of modes, including voice, Morse code, RTTY, or packet. An NTS operator who lives near the recipient typically delivers the message by telephone.

During disasters or emergencies, radiograms communicate information critical to saving lives or property or to inquire about the health or welfare of disaster victims. At such times, the NTS works in concert with the Amateur Radio Emergency Service (ARES) and other emergency and disaster-relief organizations, such as the American Red Cross and The Salvation Army.

The NTS oversees many existing traffic nets, which meet daily. Most nets are local or regional. Handling routine message traffic such as birthday and holiday greetings keeps NTS participants prepared for emergencies.

1.7 Ham Radio in the Classroom

Amateur Radio is a terrific teaching tool! Many individuals began their path towards careers in electronics and wireless communication thanks to their experiences with Amateur Radio as children and teenagers.

Amateur Radio complements any school curriculum and gives students a chance to make a direct and immediate connection with their studies. For example, the math and science used in Amateur Radio apply equally in the classroom. Even geography takes on a new meaning when students are able to contact other countries around the globe and even to speak with the people who live in them!

Local volunteers are important to establishing an active Amateur Radio presence in schools. An HF or satellite station or even a VHF or UHF handheld transceiver tuned to the local repeater can prove an exciting and educational experience for pupils and volunteers alike.

Thanks to the Amateur Radio on the International Space Station (ARISS) program,

Figure 1.31 — The Amateur Radio on the International Space Station (ARISS) program celebrating a milestone — its 1000th school radio contact — in 2016. Astronaut Tim Kopra, KE5UDN, on the ISS answered questions from students gathered at the University of North Dakota in Grand Forks, organized by the North Dakota Space Grant Consortium (NDSGC).

Ham Radio
Saves Lives

Figure 1.32 — At Eisenhower Middle School in Lawton, Oklahoma, Jada, KF5TAT (left) and Kerson, KF5TAQ sit at the Viking Radio Club station in the classroom of teacher Clifton Harper, KE5YZB. The school received a ham radio equipment grant through the ARRL Foundation. Harper also attended an ARRL Education & Technology Program Teacher's Institute on Wireless Technology at ARRL Headquarters. [Pamely Harper, KF5JXO, photo]

Figure 1.33 — Bil Paul, KD6JUI, gets on the air from his kayak, using a multiband antenna of his own design and construction. [Jeff Brook, photo]

amateurs all over the nation have made it possible for students to speak directly with astronauts in space via ham radio.

1.7.1 ARRL Amateur Radio Education & Technology Program

Through the ARRL Amateur Radio Education & Technology Program (ETP), Amateur Radio can become a valuable resource for the classroom teacher. The goal of the ETP is "to build a foundation of wireless technology literacy to US teachers and students." Launched in 2000 the program continues to offer resources to schools, including ham radio equipment, at no cost, thanks to the support of donors in the Amateur Radio community. The ETP emphasizes the integration of technology, math, science, geography, writing, speaking and social responsibility within a global society. Applying Amateur Radio as part of the class curriculum offers students a new dimension to learning. Each summer the ETP sponsors Teachers Institute on Wireless Technology sessions for educators, to enable them to make the most effective use of the ETP in their schools.

Amateur Radio emphasizes self-challenge, the value of lifelong learning and the importance of public service. From a more practical standpoint, future employers will be looking for candidates who are familiar not only with computers but with the sorts of wireless communication concepts used in Amateur Radio.

The ETP offers a range of resources to encourage educators. These include publications related to the use of technology in wireless communications; workshops, tips and ideas for teaching wireless technology in schools, community groups and clubs; and lesson plans and projects to help provide authentic, hands-on technological experiences for students.

Schools interested in incorporating Amateur Radio into their curricula, using it as an enrichment program or as a club activity may apply to become Project schools. See **www.arrl.org/education-technology-program** for more information on the ARRL Education & Technology Program.

1.8 Resources

ARRL—the National Association for Amateur Radio
225 Main St
Newington, CT 06111-1494
860-594-0200
Fax: 860-594-0259
e-mail: **hq@arrl.org**
Prospective hams call 1-800-32 NEW HAM (1-800-326-3942)
www.arrl.org
Membership organization of US ham radio operators and those interested in ham radio. Publishes study guides for all Amateur Radio license classes, a monthly journal, *QST*, and many books on Amateur Radio and electronics.

Amateur Radio Service Rules & Regulations — FCC Part 97
Available on the ARRL website:
www.arrl.org/part-97-amateur-radio

AMSAT NA (The Radio Amateur Satellite Corporation)
10605 Concord St #304
Kensington, MD 20895
888-322-6728 or 301-822-4376
www.amsat.org
Membership organization for those interested in Amateur Radio satellites.

Courage Kenny Handiham Program
3915 Golden Valley Rd
MR #78446
Golden Valley, MN 55422
612-775-2291 or 866-426-3442
handiham.org/wordpress1/
Provides assistance to persons with disabilities who want to earn a ham radio license or set up a station.

OMIK Amateur Radio Association
www.omikradio.org
OMIK, an ARRL affiliated club, is the largest predominately African-American Amateur Radio organization in the US. It promotes fellowship and Amateur Radio advancement and offers scholarships and other financial assistance for college-bound youth.

The ARRL Ham Radio License Manual
www.arrl.org/ham-radio-license-manual
Complete introduction to ham radio, including the exam question pool, complete explanations of the subjects on the exams. Tips on buying equipment, setting up a station and more.

The ARRL's Tech Q&A
www.arrl.org/shop/
Contains all of the questions in the Technician class question pool, with correct answers highlighted and explained in plain English. Includes many helpful diagrams.

General Information and Other Study Material
The ARRL website (**www.arrl.org**) carries a wealth of information for anyone interested in getting started in Amateur Radio. For complete information on all options available for study material, check out the "Welcome to the World of Ham Radio" page, **www.arrl.org/what-is-ham-radio** and its associated links. You can also use the ARRL website to search for clubs, classes and Amateur Radio exam sessions near you.

1.9 Glossary

AM (Amplitude modulation) — The oldest voice operating mode still found on the amateur bands. The most common HF voice mode, SSB, is actually a narrower-bandwidth variation of AM.

Amateur Radio — A radiocommunication service for the purpose of self-training, intercommunication and technical investigation carried out by licensed individuals interested in radio technique solely with a personal aim and without pecuniary interest. (*Pecuniary* means payment of any type, whether money or goods.) Also called "ham radio."

Amateur Radio operator — A person holding an FCC license to operate a radio station in the Amateur Radio Service.

Amateur Radio station — A station licensed by the FCC in the Amateur Radio Service, including necessary equipment.

Amateur (Radio) Service — A radiocommunication service for the purpose of self-training, intercommunication and technical investigations carried out by licensed individuals interested in radio technique solely with a personal aim and without pecuniary interest.

AMSAT (Radio Amateur Satellite Corporation) — An international membership organization that designs, builds and promotes the use of Amateur Radio satellites, which are called "OSCARs."

APRS—Automatic Packet/Position Reporting System, a marriage of an application of the Global Positioning System and Amateur Radio to relay position and tracking information.

ARES (Amateur Radio Emergency Service) — An ARRL program for radio amateurs who participate in emergency communication.

ARISS — An acronym for Amateur Radio on the International Space Station. NASA, ARRL, AMSAT, and others cooperate in managing the ARISS program on a national and international level.

ARRL — The national association for Amateur Radio in the US; the US member-society in the ***IARU*** (International Amateur Radio Union).

ATV (Amateur television) — An Amateur Radio operating mode for sharing real-time video. ATV may be analog or digital.

Band — A range of frequencies in the radio spectrum, usually designated by approximate wavelength in meters. For example, 7.0 to 7.3 MHz (megahertz) is the 40 meter amateur band. Hams are authorized to transmit on many different bands.

Bandwidth — In general, the width of a transmitted signal in terms of occupied spectrum. FCC definition: "The width of a frequency band outside of which the mean power of the transmitted signal is attenuated at least 26 dB below the mean power of the transmitted signal within the band."

Beacon — An amateur station transmitting communication for the purposes of observation of propagation and reception or other related experimental activities.

Beam antenna — A ham radio antenna having directional characteristics to enhance the transmitted signal in one direction at the expense of others. A "rotary beam" can be pointed in any direction.

Broadcasting — Transmissions intended for reception by the general public, either direct or relayed. Amateur Radio licensees are not permitted to engage in broadcasting.

Call sign — A series of unique letters and numerals that the FCC assigns to an individual who has earned an Amateur Radio license.

Contact — A two-way communication between Amateur Radio operators.

Contest — A competitive Amateur Radio operating activity in which hams use their stations to contact the most stations within a designated time period.

Courage Kenny Handiham Program — Membership organization for ham radio enthusiasts with various physical disabilities and abilities.

CW — A synonym for radiotelegraphy (ie, Morse code by radio). CW is an abbreviation for "continuous wave," a term used in the early years of wireless.

Digital communication — Computer-based communication modes such as RTTY, PSK31, packet and other radio transmissions that employ an accepted digital code to convey intelligence or data.

Dipole antenna — Typically, a wire antenna with a feed line connected to its center and having two legs. Dipoles most often are used on the high-frequency (HF) amateur bands.

DSP (digital signal processing) — Technology that allows software to replace electronic circuitry.

DX — A ham radio abbreviation that refers to distant stations, typically those in other countries.

DXCC — DX Century Club, a popular ARRL award earned for contacting Amateur Radio operators in 100 different countries or "entities."

DXpedition — A trip to a location — perhaps an uninhabited island or other geographical or political entity — which has few, if any, Amateur Radio operators, thus making a contact rare.

Elmer — A traditional term for a person who enjoys helping newcomers get started in ham radio; a mentor.

Emergency communication — Amateur Radio communication during a disaster or emergency that support or supplants traditional means of telecommunication.

FCC (Federal Communications Commission) — The government agency that regulates Amateur Radio in the US.

Field Day — A popular, annual Amateur Radio activity sponsored by ARRL, during which hams set up radio stations, often outdoors, using emergency power sources to simulate an emergency situation.

Field Organization — A cadre of ARRL volunteers who perform various services for the Amateur Radio community at the state and local level.

FM (Frequency modulation) — A method of transmitting voice and the mode commonly used on ham radio repeaters.

Fox hunt — A competitive radio direction-finding activity in which participants track down the one or more hidden transmitters.

Fast-scan television — A mode of operation that Amateur Radio operators can use to exchange live TV images from their stations. Also called *ATV (Amateur Television)*.

Ham band — A range of frequencies in the radio spectrum on which ham radio communication is authorized.

Ham radio — Another name for Amateur Radio.

Ham radio operator — A radio operator holding a license granted by the FCC to operate on Amateur Radio frequencies.

HF (high frequency) — The radio frequencies from 3 to 30 MHz.

HSMM (high-speed multimedia) — A digital radio communication technique using spread spectrum modes primarily on UHF to simultaneously send and receive video, voice, text, and data.

IARU (International Amateur Radio Union) — The international organization made up of national Amateur Radio organizations or societies such as the ARRL.

Image — Facsimile and television signals.

International Morse Code — A digital code in which alphanumeric characters are represented by a defined set of short and long transmission elements — called "dots and dashes" or "dits and dahs" — that many Amateur Radio operators use to communicate.

ITU (International Telecommunication Union) — An agency of the United Nations that allocates the radio spectrum among the various radio services.

MARS — Military Auxiliary Radio System, a volunteer adjunct communication program that supports the mission of the US Department of Defense. Most MARS operators are Amateur Radio operators.

Mode — A type of ham radio communication, such as frequency modulation (FM voice), slow-scan television (SSTV), SSB (single sideband voice), CW (Morse code), or digital (eg, PSK-31 or JT65).

Morse code — A communication mode characterized by on/off keying of a radio signal to convey intelligence. Hams use the International Morse Code.

Net — An on-the-air meeting of hams at a set time, day and radio frequency, usually for a specific purpose.

Packet radio — A computer-to-computer radio communication mode in which information is encapsulated in short groups of data called packets. These packets contain addressing and error-detection information.

Phone — Emissions carrying speech or other sound information, such as FM, SSB or AM.

Public service — Activities involving Amateur Radio that hams perform to benefit their communities.

QRP — An abbreviation for low power.

QSL bureau — A system for sending and receiving Amateur Radio verification or "QSL" cards.

QSL cards — Cards that provide written confirmation of a communication between two hams.

QSO — A contact between amateurs.

QST — The monthly journal of the ARRL. *QST* means "calling all radio amateurs."

RACES (Radio Amateur Civil Emergency Service) — A radio service that uses amateur stations for civil defense communication during periods of local, regional or national civil emergencies.

RF (Radio frequency) — Electromagnetic radiation in the form of radio waves.

Radio (or Ham) shack — The room where Amateur Radio operators keep their station.

Radiotelegraphy — See **Morse code**.

Receiver — A device that converts radio signals into a form that can be heard or viewed.

Repeater — A typically unattended amateur station, typically located on a mountaintop, hilltop, or tall building, that automatically and simultaneously receives and retransmits the signals of other stations on a different channel or channels for greater range. Repeaters allow radio amateurs using low-power handheld transceivers to transmit over greater distances.

RTTY (radio teletype) — Narrow-band direct-printing radioteletype that uses a digital code.

Space station — An amateur station located more than 50 km above Earth's surface.

SSB (Single sideband) — A common mode of voice of Amateur Radio voice transmission.

SSTV (Slow-scan television) — An operating mode ham radio operators use to exchange still pictures from their stations.

SWL (Shortwave listener) — A person who enjoys listening to shortwave radio broadcasts or Amateur Radio conversations. (A *BCL* is someone who listens for distant AM stations on the Standard Broadcast Band. Some SWLs also are BCLs.)

TIS (Technical Information Service) — A service of the ARRL that helps hams solve technical problems (**www.arrl.org/tis**).

Transceiver — A radio transmitter and receiver combined in one unit.

Transmitter — A device that produces radio-frequency (RF) signals.

UHF (Ultra-high frequency) — The radio frequencies from 300 to 3000 MHz.

VE (Volunteer Examiner) — An Amateur Radio operator who is qualified to administer Amateur Radio licensing examinations.

VHF (Very-high frequency) — The radio frequency range from 30 to 300 MHz.

WAS (Worked All States) — An ARRL award that is earned when an Amateur Radio operator confirms two-way radio contact with other stations in all 50 US states.

Wavelength — A means of designating a frequency band, such as the 80 meter band.

Work — To contact another ham.

Contents

Chapter 2

Electrical Fundamentals

Collecting material on fundamental concepts from previous editions, this chapter summarizes the basic ideas of electricity and electronics. It covers the physical quantities, elementary circuits, basic components, and the laws that govern their behavior. These are the foundations on which all of electronics is constructed. Glossaries are included for each group of topics, as well.

Since many of the basic ideas are expressed or defined in term of mathematics, a tutorial "Radio Mathematics" and the compact summary "Radio Math Formulas and Notes" have been prepared. They are available in the *Handbook's* downloadable supplemental material (see the information on how to access that content at the front of this book). The tutorial includes sections on some of the mathematical techniques used in radio and electronics and a list of online math resources.

Chapter 2 — Downloadable Supplemental Content

- "Radio Mathematics" — information about math used in radio and a list of online resources and tutorials about common mathematics
- "Radio Math Formulas and Notes" — a "cheat sheet" for formulas and useful tables and online math resources
- "Hands-On Radio: Laying Down the Laws" by Ward Silver, NØAX
- "Hands-On Radio: Putting the Laws to Work" by Ward Silver, NØAX
- "Hands-On Radio: Kirchoff's Laws" by Ward Silver, NØAX
- "Hands-On Radio: Thevenin Equivalents" by Ward Silver, NØAX
- "Scientific and Engineering Notation" by Walter Banzhaf, WB1ANE
- "Understanding a Scientific Calculator" by Walter Banzhaf, WB1ANE

2.1 Introduction to Electricity

The *atom* is the primary building block of matter and is made up of a *nucleus*, containing *protons* and *neutrons*, surrounded by *electrons*. Protons have a positive electrical charge, electrons a negative charge, and neutrons have no electrical charge. An *element* (or *chemical element*) is a type of atom that has a specific number of protons, the element's *atomic number*. Each different element, such as iron, oxygen, silicon, or bromine has a distinct chemical and physical identity determined primarily by the number of protons. A *molecule* is two or more atoms bonded together and acting as a single particle.

Unless modified by chemical, mechanical, or electrical processes, all atoms are electrically neutral because they have the same number of electrons as protons. If an atom loses electrons, it has more protons than electrons and thus has a net positive charge. If an atom gains electrons, it has more electrons than protons and a net negative charge. Atoms or molecules with a positive or negative charge are called *ions*. Electrons not bound to any atom, or *free electrons*, can also be considered as ions because they have a negative charge.

2.1.1 Electric Charge, Voltage and Current

Any piece of matter that has a net positive or negative electrical charge is said to be *electrically charged*. An electrical force exists between electrically charged particles, pushing charges of the same type apart (like charges repel each other) and pulling opposite charges together (opposite charges attract). Moving charges in a magnetic field also generates an electrical force. This is the *electromotive force* (or EMF), the source of energy that causes charged particles to move. *Voltage* is the general term for the strength of the electromotive force or the difference in electrical potential between two points. Voltage and EMF are often used interchangeably in radio. A good diagram showing the relationship of EMF and voltage is available at **hyperphysics.phy-astr.gsu.edu/hbase/electric/elevol.html#c2**.

Under most conditions, the number of positive and negative charges in any volume of space is very close to balanced and so the region has no net charge. When there are extra positive ions in one region and extra negative ions (or electrons) in another region, the resulting EMF attracts the charges toward each other. The direction of the force, from the positive region to the negative region, is called its *polarity*. Because an imbalance of charge between two regions generates an EMF, its voltage is always measured between two points, with positive voltage defined as being in the direction from the positively-charged to the negatively-charged region.

If there is no path by which electric charge can move in response to an EMF (called a *conducting path*), the charges cannot move together and so remain separated. If a conducting path is available, then the electrons or ions will flow along the path, neutralizing the net imbalance of charge. The movement of electrical charge is called *electric current*. Materials through which current flows easily are called *conductors*. Most metals, such as copper or aluminum are good conductors. Materials in which it is difficult for current to flow are *insulators*. *Semiconductors*, such as silicon or germanium, are materials with much poorer conductivity than metals. Semiconductors can be chemically altered to acquire properties that make them useful in solid-state devices such as diodes, transistors and integrated circuits.

Voltage differences can be created in a variety of ways. For example, chemical ions can be physically separated to form a battery. The resulting charge imbalance creates a voltage difference at the battery terminals so that if a conductor is connected to both terminals at once, electrons flow between the terminals and gradually eliminate the charge imbalance, discharging the battery's stored energy. Mechanical means such as friction (static electricity, lightning) and moving conductors in a magnetic field (generators) can also produce voltages. Devices or systems that produce voltage are called *voltage sources*.

When Is E a V and V an E?

Beginners in electronics are often confused about the interchange of V and E to refer to voltage in a circuit. When should each be used? Unfortunately, there is no universal convention but *E* or *e* is usually used when referring to an electric field or the electromotive force in a circuit. *E* is also commonly used in the equation for Ohm's Law: $I = E/R$. *V* or *v* is used when describing the difference in voltage between two points in a circuit or the terminal voltage of a power supply or battery. Capital V is always used when referring to units of volts.

2.1.2 Electronic and Conventional Current

Electrons move in the direction of positive voltage — this is called *electronic current*. *Conventional current* takes the other point of view — of positive charges moving in the direction of negative voltage. Conventional current was the original model for electricity and results from an arbitrary decision made by Benjamin Franklin in the 18th century when the nature of electricity and atoms was still unknown. It can be imagined as electrons flowing "backward" and is completely equivalent to electronic current.

Conventional current is used in nearly all electronic literature and is the standard used in this book. The direction of conventional current direction establishes the polarity for most electronics calculations and circuit diagrams. The arrows in the drawing symbols for transistors point in the direction of conventional current, for example.

The Origin of Unit Names

Many units of measure carry names that honor scientists who made important discoveries in or advanced the state of scientific knowledge of electrical and radio phenomena. For example, Georg Ohm (1787-1854) discovered the relationship between current, voltage and resistance that now bears his name as Ohm's Law and as the unit of resistance, the ohm. The following table lists the most common electrical units, what they are used to measure, and the scientists for whom they are named. You can find more information on these and other notable scientists in encyclopedia entries on the units that bear their names.

Electrical Units and Their Namesakes

Unit	*Measures*	*Physical Quantities*	*Named for*
Ampere (A)	Current	Coulombs per second	Andree Ampere 1775-1836
Coulomb (C)	Charge		Charles Coulomb 1736-1806
Farad (F)	Capacitance	Coulombs per volt	Michael Faraday 1791-1867
Henry (H)	Inductance	Volts per amp per second	Joseph Henry 1797-1878
Hertz (Hz)	Frequency	Cycles per second	Heinrich Hertz 1857-1894
Ohm (Ω)	Resistance	Volts per amp	Georg Simon Ohm 1787-1854
Watt (W)	Power	Joules per second	James Watt 1736-1819
Volt (V)	Voltage	Joules per coulomb	Alessandro Volta 1745-1827

2.1.3 Units of Measurement

Measurement of electrical quantities is made in several standard units. Charge is measured in *coulombs* (C) and represented by *q* in equations. One coulomb is equal to 6.25×10^{18} electrons (or protons). Current, the flow of charge, is measured in *amperes* (A) and represented by *i* or *I* in equations. One ampere represents one coulomb of charge flowing past a point (or through a specific area) in one second so 1 A = 1 C/s. Electromotive force (EMF) is measured in *volts* (V) and represented by *e, E, v,* or *V* in equations. One volt is defined as the EMF required for one ampere of current to do one joule (J, a measure of energy) of work and 1 V = 1 J/C.

Schematic Diagrams

The drawing in Figure 2.1 is a *schematic diagram*. Schematics are used to show the electrical connections in a circuit without requiring a drawing of the actual components or wires, called a *pictorial diagram*. Pictorials are fine for very simple circuits like these, but quickly become too detailed and complex for everyday circuits. Schematics use lines and dots to represent the conducting paths and connections between them. Individual electrical devices and electronic components are represented by *schematic symbols* such as the resistors shown here. A set of the most common schematic symbols is provided in the **Component Data and References** chapter. You will find additional information on reading and drawing schematic diagrams in the ARRL website Technology section at **www.arrl.org/circuit-construction**.

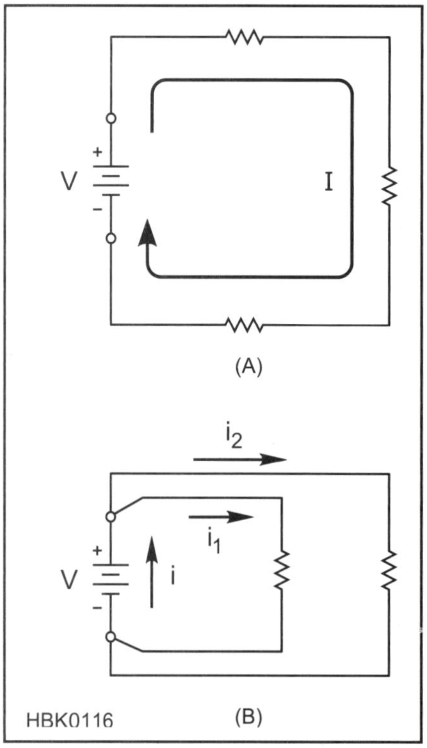

Figure 2.1 — A series circuit (A) has the same current through all components. Parallel circuits (B) apply the same voltage to all components.

2.1.4 Series and Parallel Circuits

A *circuit* is any conducting path through which current can flow between two points that have different voltages. An *open circuit* is a circuit in which a desired conducting path is interrupted, such as by a broken wire or a switch. A *short circuit* is a circuit in which a conducting path allows current to flow directly between the two points at different voltages.

The two fundamental types of circuits are shown in **Figure 2.1**. Part A shows a *series circuit* in which there is only one current path. The current in this circuit flows from the voltage source's positive terminal (the symbol for a battery is shown with its voltage polarity as + and –) in the direction shown by the arrow through three *resistors* (electronic components discussed later in this chapter) and back to the battery's negative terminal. Current is the same at every point in a series circuit.

Part B shows a *parallel circuit* in which there are multiple paths for the current to take. One terminal of both resistors is connected to the battery's positive terminal. The other terminal of both resistors is connected to the battery's negative terminal. Current flowing out of the battery's positive terminal divides into smaller currents that flow through the individual resistors and then recombine at the battery's negative terminal. All of the components in a parallel circuit experience the same voltage. All circuits are made up of series and parallel combinations of components and sources of voltage and current.

2.1.5 Direct and Alternating Current

A circuit is a complete conductive path for current to flow from a source, through a load and back to the source. If the source permits the current to flow in only one direction, the current is *dc* or *direct current*. If the source permits the current to change direction, the current is *ac* or *alternating current*. **Figure 2.2** illustrates the two types of circuits. Circuit A shows the source as a battery, a typical dc source. Circuit B shows a voltage source symbol to indicate ac such as from a generator or household power outlet. In an ac circuit, both the current and the voltage reverse direction. For nearly all ac signals in electronics and radio, the reversal is *periodic*, meaning that the change in direction occurs on a regular basis. The rate of reversal may range from a few times per second to many billion times per second.

Graphs of current or voltage, such as Figure 2.2, begin with a horizontal axis that represents time. The vertical axis represents the amplitude of the current or the voltage, whichever is graphed. Distance above the zero line indicates larger positive amplitude; distance below the zero line means larger negative amplitude. Positive and negative only designate the opposing directions in which current may flow in an alternating current circuit or the opposing *polarities* of an ac voltage.

If the current and voltage never change direction, then we have a dc circuit, even if the level of dc constantly changes. **Figure 2.3A** shows a current that is always positive with respect to 0. It varies periodically in amplitude, however. Whatever the shape of the variations, the current can be called *pulsating dc*. If the current periodically reaches 0, it can be called *intermittent dc*.

We can also look at intermittent and pulsating dc as a combination of an ac and a dc current (Figures 2.3B and 2.3C). Special circuits can separate the two currents into ac and dc *components* for separate analysis or use. There are circuits that combine ac and dc currents and voltages, as well.

2.1.6 Glossary — Basic Electricity

Alternating current (ac) — A flow of charged particles through a conductor, first in one direction, then in the other direction.

Ampere — A measure of flow of charged particles per unit of time. One ampere (A) represents one coulomb of charge flowing past a point in one second.

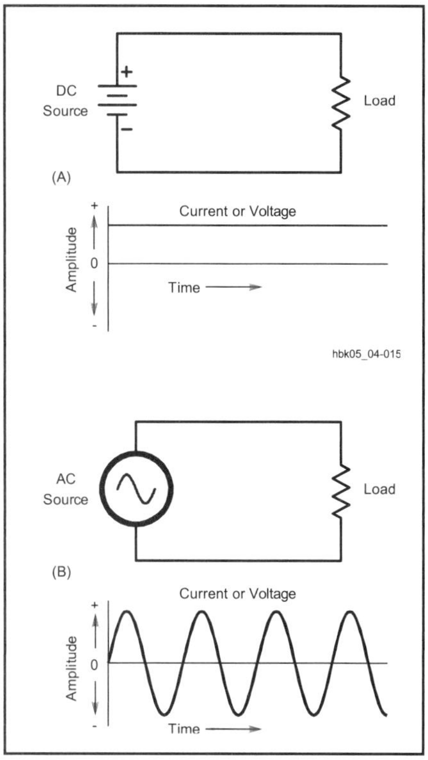

Figure 2.2 — Basic circuits for direct and alternating currents. With each circuit is a graph of the current, constant for the dc circuit, but periodically changing direction in the ac circuit.

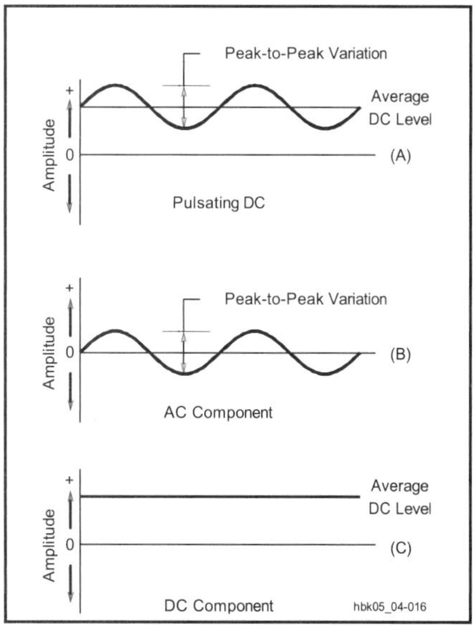

Figure 2.3 — A pulsating dc current (A) and its resolution into an ac component (B) and a dc component (C).

Atom — The smallest particle of matter that makes up a distinct chemical element. Atoms consist of protons and neutrons in the central region called the nucleus, with electrons surrounding the nucleus.

Circuit — Conducting path between two points of different voltage. In a *series circuit*, there is only one current path. In a *parallel circuit*, there are multiple current paths.

Conductor — Material in which electrons or ions can move easily.

Conventional current — Current defined as the flow of positive charges in the direction of positive to negative voltage. Conventional current flows in the opposite direction of electronic current, the flow of negative charges (electrons) from negative to positive voltage.

Coulomb — A unit of measure of a quantity of electrically charged particles. One coulomb (C) is equal to 6.25×10^{18} electrons.

Current (I) — The movement of electrical charge, measured in amperes and represented by *i* or *I* in equations.

Direct current (dc) — A flow of charged particles through a conductor in one direction only.

Electronic current — see **Conventional Current**

Electromotive force (EMF) — The source of energy that creates a force between charged particles or regions. define the force of attraction or repulsion between electrically-charged regions. Also see *voltage*.

Energy — Capability of doing work. It is usually measured in electrical terms as the number of watts of power consumed during a specific period of time, such as watt-seconds or kilowatt-hours.

Insulator — Material in which it is difficult for electrons or ions to move.

Ion — Atom or molecule with a positive or negative electrical charge.

Joule — Measure of a quantity of energy. One joule is defined as one newton (a measure of force) acting over a distance of one meter.

Polarity — The direction of EMF or voltage, from positive to negative.

Potential — See **voltage**

Power — Power is the rate at which work is done. One watt of power is equal to one volt of EMF causing a current of one ampere through a resistor.

Voltage — The general term for the difference in electrical potential energy between two points. Measured in volts or joules/coulomb.

Voltage source — Device or system that creates a voltage difference at its terminals.

2.2 Resistance and Conductance

2.2.1 Resistance and Resistors

Any conductor connected to points at different voltages will allow current to pass between the points. No conductor is perfect or lossless, however, at least not at normal temperatures. The moving electrons collide with the atoms making up the conductor and lose some of their energy by causing the atoms to vibrate, which is observed externally as heat. The property of energy loss due to interactions between moving charges and the atoms of the conductor is called *resistance*. The amount of resistance to current is measured in *ohms* (Ω) and is represented by *r* or *R* in equations.

Suppose we have two conductors of the same size and shape, but of different materials. Because all materials have different internal structures, the amount of energy lost by current flowing through the material is also different. The material's ability to impede current flow is its *resistivity*. Numerically, the resistivity of a material is given by the resistance, in ohms, of a cube of the material measuring one centimeter on each edge. The symbol for resistivity is the Greek letter rho, ρ.

The longer a conductor's physical path, the higher the resistance of that conductor. For direct current and low-frequency alternating currents (up to a few thousand hertz) the conductor's resistance is inversely proportional to the cross-sectional area of the conductor. Given two conductors of the same material and having the same length, but differing in cross-sectional area, the one with the larger area (for example, a thicker wire or sheet) will have the lower resistance.

One of the best conductors is copper, and it is frequently convenient to compare the resistance of a material under consideration with that of a copper conductor of the same size and shape. **Table 2.1** gives the ratio of the resistivity of various conductors to the resistivity of copper.

A package of material exhibiting a certain amount of resistance and made into a single unit or component is called a *resistor*. There are many types of resistors described in the **Circuits and Components** chapter, each suited to different applications and power levels. Next to the transistors built into microprocessors by the billion, resistors are the most common electronic component of all.

Table 2.1
Relative Resistivity of Metals

Material	*Resistivity Compared to Copper*
Aluminum (pure)	1.60
Brass	3.7-4.90
Cadmium	4.40
Chromium	8.10
Copper (hard-drawn)	1.03
Copper (annealed)	1.00
Gold	1.40
Iron (pure)	5.68
Lead	12.80
Nickel	5.10
Phosphor bronze	2.8-5.40
Silver	0.94
Steel	7.6-12.70
Tin	6.70
Zinc	3.40

Ohm's Law Timesaver

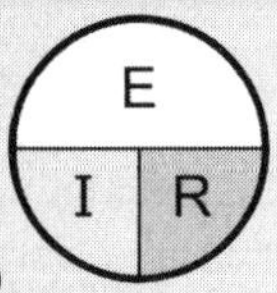

This simple diagram presents the mathematical equations relating voltage, current, and resistance. Cover the unknown quantity (E,I, or R) and the remaining symbols are shown as in the equation. For example, covering I shows E over R, as they would be written in the equation I=E/R.

When the current is small enough to be expressed in milliamperes, calculations are simplified if the resistance is expressed in kilohms rather than in ohms. With voltage in volts, if resistance in kilohms is substituted directly in Ohm's Law, the current will be milliamperes. Expressed as an equation: V = mA x kΩ.

2.2.2 Conductance

The reciprocal of resistance (1/R) is *conductance*. It is usually represented by the symbol G. A circuit having high conductance has low resistance, and vice versa. In radio work, the term is used chiefly in connection with electron-tube and field-effect transistor characteristics. The units of conductance are siemens (S). A resistance of 1 Ω has a conductance of 1 S, a resistance of 1000 Ω has a conductance of 0.001 S, and so on. A unit frequently used in regard to vacuum tubes and the field-effect transistor is the μS or one millionth of a siemens. It is the conductance of a 1-MΩ resistance. Siemens have replaced the obsolete unit *mho* (abbreviated as an upside-down Ω symbol).

2.2.3 Ohm's Law

The amount of current that will flow through a conductor when a given voltage is applied will vary with the resistance of the conductor. The lower the resistance, the greater the current for a given EMF. One ohm (Ω) is defined as the amount of resistance that allows one ampere of current to flow between two points that have a potential difference of one volt. This proportional relationship is known as *Ohm's Law*:

$$R = E / I$$

where

R = resistance in ohms,
E = voltage or EMF in volts and
I = current in amperes.

Rearranging the equation gives the other common forms of Ohm's Law as:

$$E = I \times R$$

and

$$I = E / R$$

All three forms of the equation are used often in electronics and radio. You must remember that the quantities are in volts, ohms and amperes; other units cannot be used in the equations without first being converted. For example, if the current is in milliamperes you must first change it to the equivalent fraction of an ampere before substituting the value into the equations.

The following examples illustrate the use of Ohm's Law in the simple circuit of **Figure 2.4**. If 150 V is applied to a circuit and the current is measured as 2.5 A, what is the resistance of the circuit? In this case R is the unknown, so we will use:

$$R = \frac{E}{I} = \frac{150\ V}{2.5\ A} = 60\ \Omega$$

No conversion of units was necessary because the voltage and current were given in volts and amperes.

If the current through a 20,000-Ω resistance is 150 mA, what is the voltage? To find voltage, use E = I × R. Convert the current from milliamperes to amperes by dividing by 1000 mA / A (or multiplying by 10^{-3} A / mA) so that 150 mA becomes 0.150 A. (Notice the conversion factor of 1000 does not limit the number of significant figures in the calculated answer.)

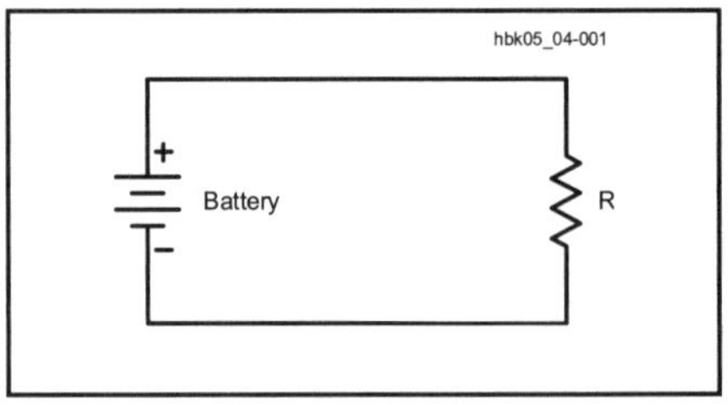

Figure 2.4 — A simple circuit consisting of a battery and a resistor.

$$I = \frac{150 \text{ mA}}{1000 \frac{\text{mA}}{\text{A}}} = 0.150 \text{ A}$$

Then:

$$E = 0.150 \text{ A} \times 20000\ \Omega = 3000 \text{ V}$$

In a final example, how much current will flow if 250 V is applied to a 5000-Ω resistor? Since I is unknown,

$$I = \frac{E}{R} = \frac{250 \text{ V}}{5000\ \Omega} = 0.05 \text{ A}$$

This value of current is more conveniently stated in mA, and 0.05 A × 1000 mA / A = 50 mA.

It is important to note that Ohm's Law applies in any portion of a circuit as well as to the circuit as a whole. No matter how many resistors are connected together or how they are connected together, the relationship between the resistor's value, the voltage across the resistor, and the current through the resistor still follows Ohm's Law.

2.2.4 Glossary — Conductance and Resistance

Conductance (G) — The reciprocal of resistance, measured in siemens (S).

Ohm — Unit of resistance. One ohm is defined as the resistance that will allow one ampere of current when one volt of EMF is impressed across the resistance.

Ohm's Law — The expression that describes resistance (R) as the proportional relationship between voltage (E) and current (I); R = E / I. Named for Georg Ohm who first described the relationship.

Resistance (R) — Opposition to current by conversion into other forms of energy, such as heat, measured in ohms (Ω).

2.3 Basic Circuit Principles

Circuits are composed of *nodes* and *branches*. A node is any point in the circuit at which current can divide between conducting paths. For example, in the parallel circuit of **Figure 2.5A**, the node is represented by the schematic dot. A branch is any unique conducting path between nodes. A series of branches that make a complete current path, such as the series circuit of Figure 2.1A, is called a *loop*.

Very few actual circuits are as simple as those shown in Figure 2.1. However, all circuits, no matter how complex, are constructed of combinations of these series and parallel circuits. We will now use these simple circuits of resistors and batteries to illustrate two fundamental rules for voltage and current, known as *Kirchoff's Laws.*

2.3.1 Kirchhoff's Current Law

Kirchhoff's Current Law (KCL) states, *"The sum of all currents flowing into a node and all currents flowing out of a node is equal to zero."* KCL is stated mathematically as:

$$(I_{in1} + I_{in2} + ...) - (I_{out1} + I_{out2} + ...) = 0$$

The dots indicate that as many currents as necessary may be added.

An equivalent way of stating KCL is that the sum of all currents flowing into a node must balance the sum of all currents flowing out of a node:

$$(I_{in1} + I_{in2} + ...) = (I_{out1} + I_{out2} + ...)$$

KCL is illustrated by the following example. Suppose three resistors (R1 = 5.0 kΩ, R2 = 20.0 kΩ, and R3 = 8.0 kΩ) are connected in parallel as shown in Figure 2.5A. The same voltage, 250 V, is applied to all three resistors. The current through R1 is I1, I2 is the current through R2, and I3 is the current through R3.

The current in each can be found from Ohm's Law, as shown below. For convenience, we can use resistance in kΩ, which gives current in milliamperes.

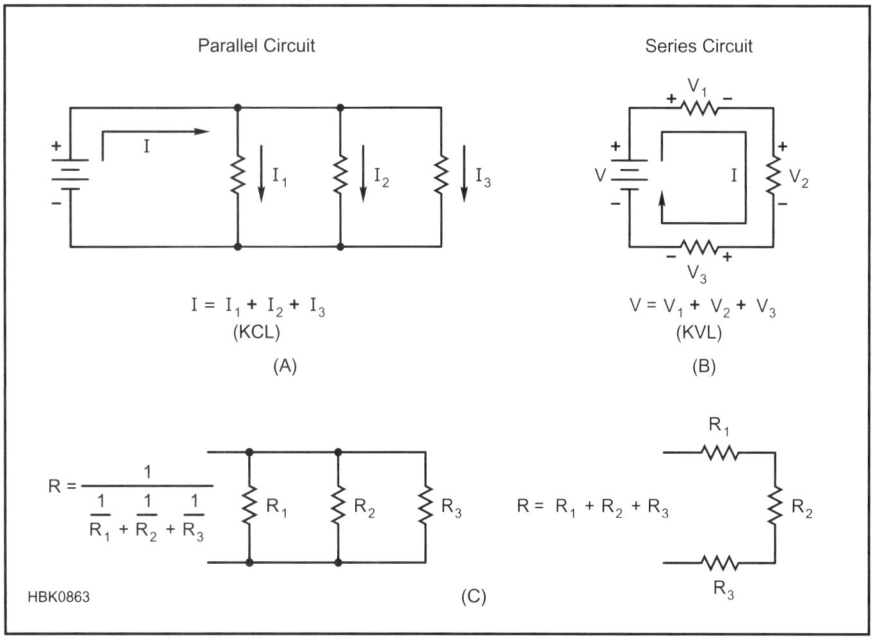

Figure 2.5 — An example of resistors in parallel (A) and series (B). In series circuits, the current is the same in all components, and voltages are summed. In parallel circuits, voltage across all components is the same and the sum of currents into and out of circuit junctions must be equal. Part C shows how to calculate equivalent values for series and parallel combinations.

$$I1 = \frac{E}{R1} = \frac{250\ V}{5.0\ k\Omega} = 50.0\ mA$$

$$I2 = \frac{E}{R2} = \frac{250\ V}{20.0\ k\Omega} = 12.5\ mA$$

$$I3 = \frac{E}{R3} = \frac{250\ V}{8.0\ k\Omega} = 31.2\ mA$$

Notice that the branch currents are inversely proportional to the resistances. The 20-kΩ resistor has a value four times larger than the 5-kΩ resistor, and has a current one-quarter as large. If a resistor has a value twice as large as another, it will have half as much current through it when they are connected in parallel.

Using the balancing form of KCL the current that must be supplied by the battery is:

$$I_{Batt} = I1 + I2 + I3$$

$$I_{Batt} = 50.0\ mA + 12.5\ mA + 31.2\ mA$$

$$I_{Batt} = 93.7\ mA$$

2.3.2 Resistors in Parallel

In a circuit made up of resistances in parallel, the resistors can be represented as a single *equivalent* resistance that has the same value as the parallel combination of resistors. In a parallel circuit, the equivalent resistance is less than that of the lowest resistance value present. This is because the total current is always greater than the current in any individual resistor. The formula for finding the equivalent resistance of resistances in parallel is:

$$R_{EQUIV} = \frac{1}{\frac{1}{R1} + \frac{1}{R2} + \frac{1}{R3} + \frac{1}{R4} \ldots}$$

where the dots indicate that any number of parallel resistors can be combined by the same method. The equation is often referred to as the "reciprocal of reciprocals." Figure 2.5C shows the general rule on a schematic.

In the example of the previous section, the equivalent resistance is:

$$R = \frac{1}{\frac{1}{5\ k\Omega} + \frac{1}{20\ k\Omega} + \frac{1}{8\ k\Omega}} = 2.67\ k\Omega$$

The notation "//" (two slashes) is frequently used to indicate "in parallel with." Using that notation, the preceding example would be given as "5.0 kΩ // 20 kΩ // 8.0 kΩ."

If all the resistors in parallel have the same value, divide the resistor value by the number of resistors, N, to get the parallel resistance. For example, for five 50-Ω resistors in parallel, the equivalent resistance is R = 50 / N = 50 / 5 = 10 Ω.

For only two resistances in parallel (a very common case) the formula can be reduced to the much simpler (and easier to remember):

$$R_{EQUIV} = \frac{R1 \times R2}{R1 + R2}$$

Example: If a 500-Ω resistor is connected in parallel with a 1200-Ω resistor, what is the total resistance?

$$R = \frac{R1 \times R2}{R1 + R2} = \frac{500\ \Omega \times 1200\ \Omega}{500\ \Omega + 1200\ \Omega}$$

$$R = \frac{600000\ \Omega^2}{1700\ \Omega} = 353\ \Omega$$

Any number of parallel resistors can be combined two at a time by using this equation until all have been combined into a single equivalent. This is a bit easier than using the general "reciprocal of reciprocals" equation to do the conversion in a single step.

2.3.3 Kirchhoff's Voltage Law

Kirchhoff's Voltage Law (KVL) states, *"The sum of the voltages around a closed current loop is zero."* Where KCL is somewhat intuitive, KVL is not as easy to visualize. In the circuit of Figure 2.5B, KVL requires that the battery's voltage must be balanced exactly by the voltages that appear across the three resistors in the circuit. If it were not, the "extra" voltage would create an infinite current with no limiting resistance, just as KCL prevents charge from "building up" at a circuit node. KVL is stated mathematically as:

$$E_1 + E_2 + E_3 + \ldots = 0$$

where each E represents a voltage encountered by current as it flows around the circuit loop.

This is best illustrated with an example. Although the current is the same in all three of the resistances in the previous example, the total voltage divides between them, just as current divides between resistors connected in parallel. The voltage appearing across each resistor (the *voltage drop*) can be found from Ohm's Law. (Voltage across a resistance is often referred to as a "drop" or "I-R drop" because the value of the voltage "drops" by the amount E = I × R.)

For the purpose of KVL, it is common to assume that if current flows *into* the more positive terminal of a component the voltage is treated as positive in the KVL equation. If the current flows *out* of a positive terminal, the voltage is treated as negative in the KVL. Positive voltages represent components that consume or "sink" power, such as resistors. Negative voltages represent components that produce or "source" power, such as batteries. This allows the KVL equation to be written in a balancing form, as well:

$$(E_{source1} + E_{source2} + \ldots) = (E_{sin\,k1} + E_{sin\,k2} + \ldots)$$

All of the voltages are treated as positive in this form, with the power sources (current flowing *out* of the more positive terminal) on one side and the power sinks (current flowing *into* the more positive terminal) on the other side.

Note that it doesn't matter what a component terminal's *absolute* voltage is with respect to ground, only which terminal of the component is more positive than the other. If one side of a resistor is at +1000 V and the other at +998 V, current flowing into the first terminal and out of the second experiences a +2 V voltage drop. Similarly, current supplied by a 9 V battery with its positive terminal at –100 V and its negative terminal at –108.5 V still counts for KVL as an 8.5 V power source. Also note that current can flow *into* a battery's positive terminal, such as during recharging, making the battery a power sink, just like a resistor.

Here's an example showing how KVL works: In Figure 2.5B, if the voltage across R1 is E1, that across R2 is E2 and that across R3 is E3, then:

$$-250 + I \times R1 + I \times R2 + I \times R3 = 0$$

This equation can be simplified to:

$$-250 + I\,(R1 + R2 + R3) =$$
$$-250 + I\,(33000\ \Omega) = 0$$

Solving for I gives I = 250 / 33000 = 0.00758 A = 7.58 mA. This allows us to calculate the value of the voltage across each resistor:

$$E1 = I \times R1 = 0.00758\ A \times 5000\ \Omega = 37.9\ V$$

$$E2 = I \times R2 = 0.00758\ A \times 20000\ \Omega = 152\ V$$

$$E3 = I \times R3 = 0.00758\ A \times 000\ \Omega = 60.6\ V$$

Verifying that the sum of E1, E2, and E3 does indeed equal the battery voltage of 250 V ignoring rounding errors:

$$E_{TOTAL} = E1 + E2 + E3$$

$$E_{TOTAL} = 37.9\ V + 152\ V + 60.6\ V$$

$$E_{TOTAL} = 250\ V$$

2.3.4 Resistors in Series

The previous example illustrated that in a circuit with a number of resistances connected in series, the equivalent resistance of the circuit is the sum of the individual resistances. If these are numbered R1, R2, R3 and so on, then:

$$R_{EQUIV} = R1 + R2 + R3 + R4 \ldots$$

Figure 2.5C shows the general rule on a schematic.

Example: Suppose that three resistors are connected to a source of voltage as shown in Figure 2.5B. The voltage is 250 V, R1 is 5.0 kΩ, R2 is 20.0 kΩ and R3 is 8.0 kΩ. The total resistance is then

$$R_{EQUIV} = R1 + R2 + R3$$

$$R_{EQUIV} = 5.0\ k\Omega + 20.0\ k\Omega + 8.0\ k\Omega$$

$$R_{EQUIV} = 33.0\ k\Omega$$

The current in the circuit is then

$$I = \frac{V}{R} = \frac{250\ V}{33.0\ k\Omega} = 7.58\ mA$$

2.3.5 Conductances in Series and Parallel

Since conductance is the reciprocal of resistance, G = 1/R, the formulas for combining resistors in series and in parallel can be converted to use conductance by substituting 1/G for R. Conductances in series are thus combined similarly to resistors in parallel:

$$G = \frac{1}{\frac{1}{G1} + \frac{1}{G2} + \frac{1}{G3} + \frac{1}{G4} \ldots}$$

and two conductances in series may be combined in a manner similar to two parallel resistors:

$$G_{EQUIV} = \frac{G1 \times G2}{G1 + G2}$$

Conductances in parallel are combined similarly to resistances in series:

$$G_{TOTAL} = G1 + G2 + G3 + G4 \ldots$$

This also shows that when faced with a large number of parallel resistances, converting them to conductances may make the math a little easier to deal with.

2.3.6 Equivalent Circuits

A circuit may have resistances both in parallel and in series, as shown in **Figure 2.6A**. In

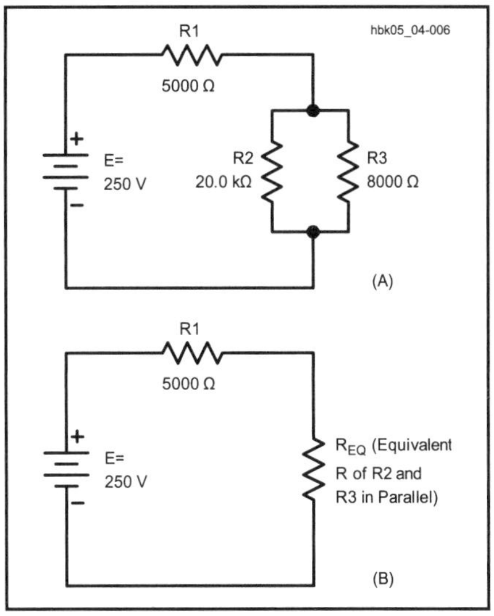

Figure 2.6 — At A, an example of resistors in series-parallel. The equivalent circuit is shown at B.

order to analyze the behavior of such a circuit, *equivalent circuits* are created and combined by using the equations for combining resistors in series and resistors in parallel. Each separate combination of resistors, series or parallel, can be reduced to a single equivalent resistor. The resulting combinations can be reduced still further until only a single resistor remains.

The simplest process begins with combining any two of the resistors into a single equivalent resistance using the formulas for series or parallel resistances. Then combine the resulting equivalent resistance with any single remaining resistor into a new equivalent resistance. Repeat the process of combining the equivalent resistance with a single resistor until all resistances have been combined into a single equivalent resistance. For example, to find the equivalent resistance for the circuit in Figure 2.5A: Combine R2 and R3 to create the equivalent single resistor, R_{EQ} whose value is equal to R2 and R3 in parallel.

$$R_{EQ} = \frac{R2 \times R3}{R2 + R3} = \frac{20000\ \Omega \times 8000\ \Omega}{20000\ \Omega + 8000\ \Omega}$$

$$= \frac{1.60 \times 10^8\ \Omega^2}{28000\ \Omega} = 5710\ \Omega = 5.71\ k\Omega$$

This resistance in series with R1 then forms a simple series circuit, as shown in Figure 2.5B. These two resistances can then be combined into a single equivalent resistance, R_{TOTAL}, for the entire circuit:

$$R_{TOTAL} = R1 + R_{EQ} = 5.0\ k\Omega + 5.71\ k\Omega$$

$$R_{TOTAL} = 10.71\ k\Omega$$

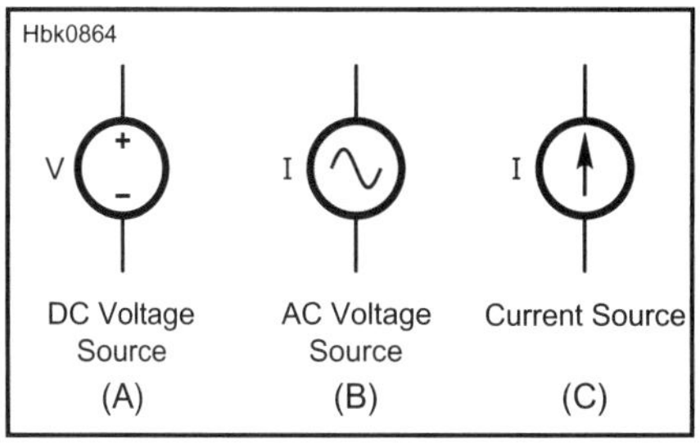

Figure 2.7— Voltage sources for dc (A) and ac (B) and current sources (C) are examples of ideal energy sources.

The battery current is then:

$$I = \frac{E}{R} = \frac{250\ V}{10.71\ k\Omega} = 23.3\ mA$$

The voltage drops across R1 and R_{EQ} are:

$$E1 = I \times R1 = 23.3\ mA \times 5.0\ k\Omega = 117\ V$$

$$E2 = I \times R_{EQ} = 23.3\ mA \times 5.71\ k\Omega = 133\ V$$

These two voltage drops total 250 V, as described by Kirchhoff's Voltage Law. E2 appears across both R2 and R3 so,

$$I2 = \frac{E2}{R2} = \frac{133\ V}{20.0\ k\Omega} = 6.65\ mA$$

$$I3 = \frac{E3}{R3} = \frac{133\ V}{8.0\ k\Omega} = 16.6\ mA$$

where

I2 = current through R2 and

I3 = current through R3.

The sum of I2 and I3 is equal to 23.3 mA, conforming to Kirchhoff's Current Law.

2.3.7 Voltage and Current Sources

In designing circuits and describing the behavior of electronic components, it is often useful to use *ideal sources*. The two most common types of ideal sources are the *voltage source* and the *current source*, symbols for which are shown in **Figure 2.7**. These sources are considered ideal because no matter what circuit is connected to their terminals, they continue to supply the specified amount of voltage or current. Practical voltage and current sources can approximate the behavior of an ideal source over certain ranges, but are limited in the amount of power they can supply and so under excessive load, their output will drop.

Voltage sources are defined as having zero *internal impedance*, where impedance is a more general form of resistance as described in the sections of this chapter dealing with alternating current. A short circuit across an ideal voltage source would result in the source providing an infinite amount of current. Practical voltage sources have non-zero internal impedance and this also limits the amount of power they can supply. For example, placing a short circuit across the terminals of a practical voltage source such as 1.5 V dry-cell battery may produce a current of several amperes, but the battery's internal impedance acts to limit the amount of current produced in accordance with Ohm's Law — as if the resistor in Figure 2.2 were inside of or internal to the battery.

Current sources are defined to have infinite internal impedance. This means that no matter what is connected to the terminals of an ideal current source, it will supply the same amount of current. An open circuit across the terminal of an ideal current source will result in the source generating an infinite voltage at its terminals. Practical current sources will raise their voltage until the internal power supply limits are reached and then reduce output current.

2.3.8 Thevenin's Theorem and Thevenin Equivalents

Thevenin's Voltage Theorem (usually just referred to as "Thevenin's Theorem") is a useful tool for simplifying electrical circuits or *networks* (the formal name for circuits) by allowing circuit designers to replace a circuit with a simpler equivalent circuit. Thevenin's Theorem states, "*Any two-terminal network made up of resistors and voltage or current sources can be replaced by an equivalent network made up of a single voltage source and a series resistor.*"

Thevenin's Theorem can be readily applied to the circuit of Figure 2.6A, to find the current through R3. In this example, illustrated in **Figure 2.8**, the circuit is redrawn to show R1 and R2 forming a voltage divider, with R3 as the load (Figure 2.8A). The current drawn by the load (R3) is simply the voltage across R3, divided by its resistance. Unfortunately, the value of R2 affects the voltage across R3, just as the presence of R3 affects the voltage appearing across R2. Some means of separating the two is needed; hence the *Thevenin-equivalent circuit* is constructed, replacing everything connected to terminals A and B with a single voltage source (the *Thevenin-equivalent voltage,* E_{THEV}) and series resistor (the *Thevenin-equivalent resistance,* R_{TH}).

The first step of creating the Thevenin-equivalent of the circuit is to determine its *open-circuit voltage,* measured when there is no load current drawn from either terminal A or B. Without a load connected between A and B, the total current through the circuit is (from Ohm's Law):

$$I = \frac{E}{R1 + R2}$$

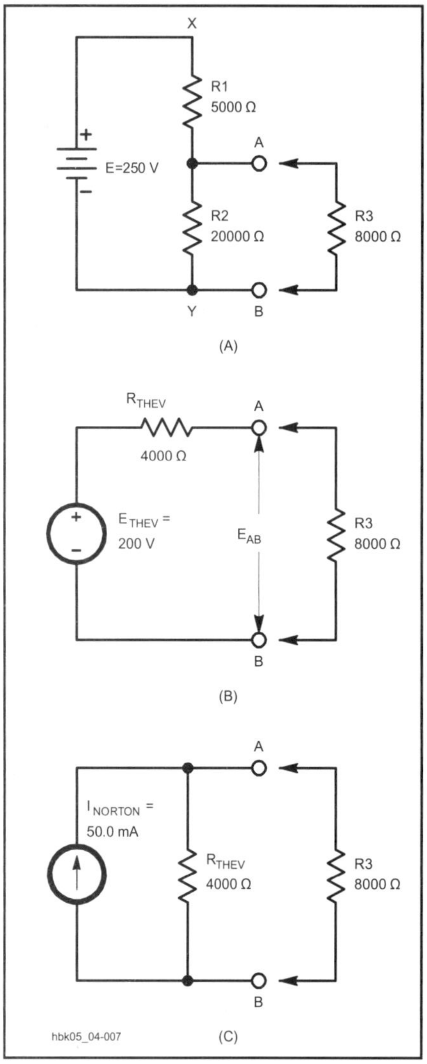

Figure 2.8 — Equivalent circuits for the circuit shown in Figure 2.6. A shows the circuit to be replaced by an equivalent circuit from the perspective of the resistor (R3 load). B shows the Thevenin-equivalent circuit, with a resistor and a voltage source in series. C shows the Norton-equivalent circuit, with a resistor

and the voltage between terminals A and B (E_{AB}) is:

$$E_{AB} = I \times R2$$

By substituting the equation for current for I, we have an expression for E_{AB} in which all values are known:

$$E_{AB} = \frac{R2}{R1 + R2} \times E$$

Using the values in our example, this becomes:

$$E_{AB} = \frac{20.0\ k\Omega}{25.0\ k\Omega} \times 250\ V = 200\ V$$

when nothing is connected to terminals A or B. E_{THEV} is equal to E_{AB} with no current drawn.

The equivalent resistance between terminals A and B is R_{THEV}. R_{THEV} is calculated as the equivalent circuit at terminals A and B with all sources, voltage or current, replaced by their internal impedances. The ideal voltage source, by definition, has zero internal resistance and is replaced by a short circuit. The ideal current source has infinite internal impedance and is replaced by an open circuit.

Assuming the battery to be a close approximation of an ideal source, replace it with a short circuit between points X and Y in the circuit of Figure 2.8A. R1 and R2 are then effectively placed in parallel, as viewed from terminals A and B. R_{THEV} is then:

$$R_{THEV} = \frac{R1 \times R2}{R1 + R2}$$

$$R_{THEV} = \frac{5000\ \Omega \times 20000\ \Omega}{5000\ \Omega + 20000\ \Omega}$$

$$R_{THEV} = \frac{1.0 \times 10^8\ \Omega^2}{25000\ \Omega} = 4000\ \Omega$$

This gives the Thevenin-equivalent circuit as shown in Figure 2.8B. The circuits of Figures 2.8A and 2.8B are completely equivalent from the perspective of R3, so the circuit becomes a simple series circuit.

Once R3 is connected to terminals A and B, there will be current through R_{THEV}, causing a voltage drop across R_{THEV} and reducing E_{AB}. The current through R3 is equal to

$$I3 = \frac{E_{THEV}}{R_{TOTAL}} = \frac{E_{THEV}}{R_{THEV} + R3}$$

Substituting the values from our example:

$$I3 = \frac{200\ V}{4000\ \Omega + 8000\ \Omega} = 16.7\ mA$$

This agrees with the value calculated earlier.

The Thevenin-equivalent circuit of an ideal voltage source in series with a resistance is a good model for a real voltage source with non-zero internal resistance. Using this more realistic model, the maximum current that a real voltage source can deliver is seen to be

$$I_{sc} = \frac{E_{THEV}}{R_{THEV}}$$

and the maximum output voltage is $V_{oc} = E_{THEV}$.

Sinusoidal voltage or current sources can be modeled in much the same way, keeping in mind that the internal impedance, Z_{THEV}, for such a source may not be purely resistive, but may have a reactive component that varies with frequency.

2.3.9 Norton's Theorem and Norton Equivalents

Norton's Theorem is another method of

creating an equivalent circuit. Norton's Theorem states, "*Any two-terminal network made up of resistors and current or voltage sources can be replaced by an equivalent network made up of a single current source and a parallel resistor.*" Norton's Theorem is to current sources what Thevenin's Theorem is to voltage sources. In fact, the Thevenin-resistance calculated previously is also the *Norton-equivalent resistance*.

The circuit just analyzed by means of Thevenin's Theorem can be analyzed just as easily by Norton's Theorem. The equivalent Norton circuit is shown in Figure 2.8C. The short circuit current of the equivalent circuit's current source, I_{NORTON}, is the current through terminals A and B with the load (R3) replaced by a short circuit. In the case of the voltage divider shown in Figure 2.8A, the short circuit completely bypasses R2 and the current is:

$$I_{AB} = \frac{E}{R1}$$

Substituting the values from our example, we have:

$$I_{AB} = \frac{E}{R1} = \frac{250\ V}{5000\ \Omega} = 50.0\ mA$$

The resulting Norton-equivalent circuit consists of a 50.0-mA current source placed in parallel with a 4000-Ω resistor. When R3 is connected to terminals A and B, one-third of the supply current flows through R3 and the remainder through R_{THEV}. This gives a current through R3 of 16.7 mA, again agreeing with previous conclusions.

A Norton-equivalent circuit can be transformed into a Thevenin-equivalent circuit and vice versa. The equivalent resistor, R_{THEV}, is the same in both cases; it is placed in series with the voltage source in the case of a Thevenin-equivalent circuit and in parallel with the current source in the case of a Norton-equivalent circuit. The voltage for the Thevenin-equivalent source is equal to the open-circuit voltage appearing across the resistor in the Norton-equivalent circuit. The current for a Norton-equivalent source is equal to the short circuit current provided by the Thevenin source. A Norton-equivalent circuit is a good model for a real current source that has a less-than infinite internal impedance.

2.4 Power and Energy

Regardless of how voltage is generated, energy must be supplied if current is drawn from the voltage source. The energy supplied may be in the form of chemical energy or mechanical energy. This energy is measured in joules (J). One joule is defined from classical physics as the amount of energy or *work* done when a force of one newton (a measure of force) is applied to an object that is moved one meter in the direction of the force.

Power is another important concept and measures the rate at which energy is generated or used. One *watt* (W) of power is defined as the generation (or use) of one joule of energy (or work) per second.

One watt is also defined as one volt of EMF causing one ampere of current to flow through a resistance. Thus,

$$P = I \times E$$

where

P = power in watts
I = current in amperes
E = EMF in volts.

(This discussion pertains only to direct current in resistive circuits. See the **Radio Fundamentals** chapter for a discussion about power in ac circuits, including reactive circuits.)

Common fractional and multiple units for power are the milliwatt (mW, one thousandth of a watt) and the kilowatt (kW, 1000 W).

Example: The plate voltage on a transmitting vacuum tube is 2000 V and the plate current is 350 mA. (The current must be changed to amperes before substitution in the formula, and so is 0.350 A.) Then:

$$P = I \times E = 2000\ V \times 0.350\ A = 700\ W$$

Power may be expressed in *horsepower* (hp) instead of watts, using the following conversion factor:

1 horsepower = 746 W

This conversion factor is especially useful if you are working with a system that converts electrical energy into mechanical energy, and vice versa, since mechanical power is often expressed in horsepower in the U.S. In metric countries, mechanical power is usually expressed in watts. All countries use the metric power unit of watts in electrical systems, however. The value 746 W/hp assumes lossless conversion between mechanical and electrical power; practical efficiency is taken up shortly.

2.4.1 Energy

When you buy electricity from a power company, you pay for electrical energy, not power. What you pay for is the work that the electrical energy does for you, not the rate at which that work is done. Like energy, work is equal to power multiplied by time. The common unit for measuring electrical energy is the *watt-hour* (Wh), which means that a power of one watt has been used for one hour. That is:

$$Wh = P \times t$$

where

Wh = energy in watt-hours
P = power in watts
t = time in hours.

Actually, the watt-hour is a fairly small energy unit, so the power company bills you for *kilowatt-hours* (kWh) of energy used. Another energy unit that is sometimes useful is the *watt-second* (Ws), which is equivalent to joules.

It is important to realize, both for calculation purposes and for efficient use of power resources, a small amount of power used for a long time can eventually result in a power bill that is just as large as if a large amount of power had been used for a very short time.

A common use of energy units in radio is in specifying the energy content of a battery. Battery energy is rated in *ampere-hours* (Ah) or *milliampere-hours* (mAh). While the multiplication of amperes and hours does not result in units of energy, the calculation assumes the result is multiplied by a specified (and constant) battery voltage. For example, a rechargeable NiMH battery rated to store 2000 mAh of energy is assumed to supply that energy at a terminal voltage of 1.5 V. Thus, after converting 2000 mA to 2 A, the actual energy stored is:

$$\text{Energy} = 1.5\ \text{V} \times 2\ \text{A} \times 1\ \text{hour} = 3\ \text{Wh}$$

Another common energy unit associated with batteries is *energy density*, with units of Ah per unit of volume or weight.

One practical application of energy units is to estimate how long a radio (such as a hand-held unit) will operate from a certain battery. For example, suppose a fully charged battery stores 900 mAh of energy and that the radio draws 30 mA on receive. A simple calculation indicates that the radio will be able receive 900 mAh / 30 mA = 30 hours with this battery, assuming 100% efficiency. You shouldn't expect to get the full 900 mAh out of the battery because the battery's voltage will drop as it is discharged, usually causing the equipment it powers to shut down before the last fraction of charge is used. Any time spent transmitting will also reduce the time the battery will last. The **Power Sources** chapter includes additional information about batteries and their charge/discharge cycles.

2.4.2 Generalized Definition of Resistance

Electrical energy is not always turned into heat. The energy used in running a motor, for example, is converted to mechanical motion. The energy supplied to a radio transmitter is largely converted into radio waves. Energy applied to a loudspeaker is changed into sound waves. In each case, the energy is converted to other forms and can be completely accounted for. None of the energy just disappears! These are examples of the Law of Conservation of Energy. When a device converts energy from one form to another, we often say it *dissipates* the energy, or power. (Power is energy divided by time.) Of course the device doesn't really "use up" the energy, or make it disappear, it just converts it to another form. Proper operation of electrical devices often requires that the power be supplied at a specific ratio of voltage to current. These features are characteristics of resistance, so it can be said that any device that "dissipates power" has a definite value of resistance.

This concept of resistance as something that absorbs power at a definite voltage-to-current ratio is very useful; it permits substituting a simple resistance for the load or power-consuming part of the device receiving power, often with considerable simplification of calculations. Of course, every electrical device has some resistance of its own in the more narrow sense, so a part of the energy supplied to it is converted to heat in that resistance even though the major part of the energy may be converted to another form.

2.4.3 Efficiency

In devices such as motors and transmitters, the objective is to convert the supplied energy (or power) into some form other than heat. In such cases, power converted to heat is considered to be a loss because it is not useful power. The efficiency of a device is the useful power output (in its converted form) divided by the power input to the device. In a transmitter, for example, the objective is to convert power from a dc source into ac power at some radio frequency. The ratio of the RF power output to the dc input is the *efficiency* (*Eff* or η) of the transmitter. That is:

$$\text{Eff} = \frac{P_O}{P_I}$$

where

Eff = efficiency (as a value or fraction between 0 and 1)

P_O = power output (W)

P_I = power input (W).

Example: If the dc input to the transmitter is 100 W, and the RF power output is 60 W, the efficiency is:

$$\text{Eff} = \frac{P_O}{P_I} = \frac{60\ \text{W}}{100\ \text{W}} = 0.6$$

Efficiency is usually expressed as a percentage — that is, it expresses what percent of the input power will be available as useful output. To calculate percent efficiency, multiply the value from equation 20 by 100%. The efficiency in the example above is 60%.

Suppose a mobile transmitter has an RF power output of 100 W with 52% efficiency at 13.8 V. The vehicle's alternator system charges the battery at a rate of 5.0 A at this voltage. Assuming an alternator efficiency of 68%, how much horsepower must the engine produce to operate the transmitter and charge the battery? Solution: To charge the battery, the alternator must produce 13.8 V × 5.0 A = 69 W. The transmitter dc input power is 100 W / 0.52 = 190 W. Therefore, the total electrical power required from the alternator is 190 + 69 = 259 W. The engine load then is:

$$P_I = \frac{P_O}{\text{Eff}} = \frac{259\ \text{W}}{0.68} = 381\ \text{W}$$

We can convert this to horsepower using the conversion factor given earlier to convert between horsepower and watts:

$$\frac{381\ \text{W}}{746\ \text{W / hp}} = 0.51\ \text{horsepower (hp)}$$

Ohm's Law and Power Circle

During the first semester of my *Electrical Power Technology* program, one of the first challenges issued by our dedicated instructor — Roger Crerie — to his new freshman students was to identify and develop 12 equations or formulas that could be used to determine voltage, current, resistance and power. Ohm's Law is expressed as R = E / I and it provided three of these equation forms while the basic equation relating power to current and voltage (P = I × E) accounted for another three. With six known equations, it was just a matter of applying mathematical substitution for his students to develop the remaining six. Together, these 12 equations compose the *circle* or *wheel* of voltage (E), current (I), resistance (R) and power (P) shown in **Figure 2.A1**. Just as Roger's previous students had learned at the Worcester Industrial Technical Institute (Worcester, Massachusetts), our Class of '82 now held the basic electrical formulas needed to proceed in our studies or professions. As can be seen in Figure 2.A1, we can determine any one of these four electrical quantities by knowing the value of any two others. You may want to keep this page bookmarked for your reference. You'll probably be using many of these formulas as the years go by — this has certainly been my experience. — *Dana G. Reed, W1LC*

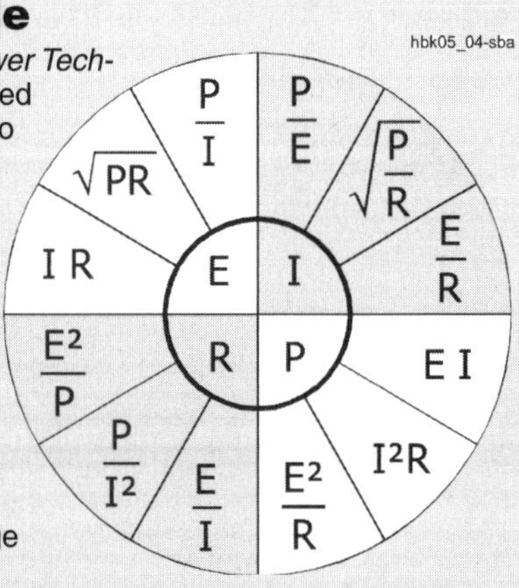

Figure 2.A1 — Electrical formulas

2.4.4 Ohm's Law and Power Formulas

Electrical power in a resistance is turned into heat. The greater the power, the more rapidly the heat is generated. By substituting the Ohm's Law equivalent for E and I, the following formulas are obtained for power:

$P = E^2 / R$

and

$P = I^2 \times R$

These formulas are useful in power calculations when the resistance and either the current or voltage (but not both) are known.

Example: How much power will be dissipated by (converted to heat in) a 4000-Ω resistor if the potential applied to it is 200 V?

$$P = \frac{E^2}{R} = \frac{40000\ V^2}{4000\ \Omega} = 10.0\ W$$

As another example, suppose a current of 20 mA flows through a 300-Ω resistor. Then:

$P = I^2 \times R = 0.020^2\ A^2 \times 300\ \Omega$

$P = 0.00040\ A^2 \times 300\ \Omega$

$P = 0.12\ W$

Note that the current was changed from milliamperes to amperes before substitution in the formula.

Resistors for radio work are made in many sizes, the smallest being rated to safely operate at power levels of about 1/16 W. The largest resistors commonly used in amateur equipment are rated at about 100 W. Large resistors, such as those used in dummy-load antennas, are often cooled with oil to increase their power-handling capability.

2.5 Circuit Control Components

2.5.1 Switches

Switches are used to allow or interrupt a current flowing in a particular circuit. Most switches are mechanical devices, although the same effect may be achieved with solid-state devices.

Switches come in many different forms and a wide variety of ratings. The most important ratings are the *voltage-handling* and *current-handling* capabilities. The voltage rating usually includes both the *breakdown voltage rating* and the *interrupt voltage rating*. The breakdown rating is the maximum voltage that the switch can withstand when it is open before the voltage will arc between the switch's terminals. The interrupt voltage rating is the maximum amount of voltage that the switch can interrupt without arcing. Normally, the interrupt voltage rating is the lower value, and therefore the one given for (and printed on) the switch.

Switches typically found in the home are usually rated for 125 V ac and 15 to 20 A. Switches in cars are usually rated for 12 V dc and several amperes. The breakdown voltage rating of a switch primarily depends on the insulating material surrounding the contacts and the separation between the contacts. Plastic or phenolic material normally provides both structural support and insulation. Ceramic material may be used to provide better insulation, particularly in rotary (wafer) switches.

A switch's current rating includes both the *current-carrying capacity* and the *interrupt capability*. The current-carrying capacity of the switch depends on the contact material and size, and on the pressure exerted to keep the contacts closed. It is primarily determined from the allowable contact temperature rise. On larger ac switches and most dc switches, the interrupt capability is usually lower than the current carrying value.

Most power switches are rated for alternating current use. Because ac current goes through zero twice in each cycle, switches can successfully interrupt much higher alternating currents than direct currents without arcing. A switch that has a 10-A ac current rating may arc and damage the contacts if used to turn off more than an ampere or two of dc.

Switches are normally designated by the number of *poles* (circuits controlled) and *throws* or *positions* (circuit path choices). The simplest switch is the on-off switch, which is a single-pole, single-throw (SPST) switch as shown in **Figure 2.9A**. The off position does not direct the current to another circuit. The next step would be to change the current path to another path. This would be a single-pole, double-throw (SPDT) switch as shown in Figure 2.9B. Adding an off position would give a single-pole, double-throw, center-off (ON-OFF-ON) switch as shown in Figure 2.9C.

Several such switches can be "ganged" to or actuated by the same mechanical activator to provide double-pole, triple-pole or even more, separate control paths all activated at once. Switches can be activated in a variety of ways. The most common methods include lever or toggle, push-button and rotary switches. Samples of these are shown in Figure 2.9D. Most switches stay in position once set, but some are spring-loaded so they only stay in

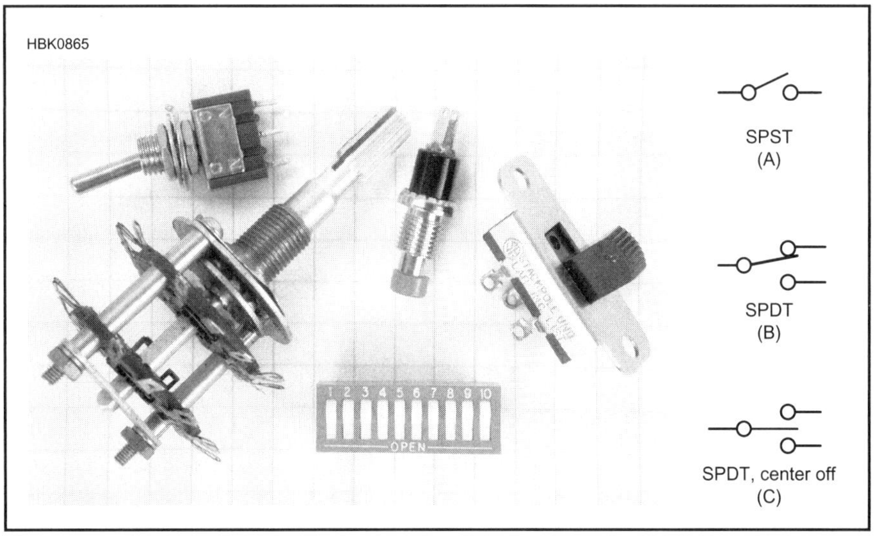

Figure 2.9 — Schematic diagrams of various types of switches. A is an SPST, B is an SPDT, and C is an SPDT switch with a center-off position. The photo (D) shows examples of various styles of switches. The ¼-inch-ruled graph paper background provides for size comparison.

the desired position while held there. These are called *momentary* switches.

Rotary/wafer switches can provide very complex switching patterns. Several poles (separate circuits) can be included on each wafer. Many wafers may be stacked on the same shaft. Not only may many different circuits be controlled at once, but by wiring different poles/positions on different wafers together, a high degree of circuit switching logic can be developed. Such switches can select different paths as they are turned and can also "short" together successive contacts to connect numbers of components or paths.

Rotary switches can also be designed to either break one contact before making another (*break-before-make*), or to short two contacts together before disconnecting the first one (*make-before-break*) to eliminate arcing or perform certain logic functions. The two types of switches are generally not interchangeable and may cause damage if inappropriately substituted for one another during circuit construction or repair. When buying rotary switches from a surplus or flea-market vendor, check to be sure the type of switch is correct.

Microswitches are designed to be actuated by the operation of machine components, opening or closing of a door, or some other mechanical movement. Instead of a handle or button-type actuator that would be used by a human, microswitches have levers or buttons more suitable for being actuated as part of an enclosure or machine.

In choosing a switch for a particular task, consideration should be given to function, voltage and current ratings, ease of use, availability and cost. If a switch is to be operated frequently, a better-quality switch is usually less costly over the long run. If signal noise or contact corrosion is a potential problem (usually in low-current signal applications), it is best to get gold-plated contacts. Gold does not oxidize or corrode, thus providing surer contact, which can be particularly important at very low signal levels. Gold plating will not hold up under high-current-interrupt applications, however.

2.5.2 Fuses and Circuit Breakers

Fuses self-destruct to protect circuit wiring or equipment. The fuse *element* that melts or *blows* is a carefully shaped piece of soft metal, usually mounted in a cartridge of some kind. The element is designed to safely carry a given amount of current and to melt at a current value that is a certain percentage above the rated value.

The most important fuse rating is the *nominal current rating* that it will safely carry for an indefinite period without blowing. A fuse's melting current depends on the type of material, the shape of the element and the heat dissipation capability of the cartridge and holder, among other factors.

Next most important are the timing characteristics, or how quickly the fuse element blows under a given current overload. Some fuses (*slow-blow*) are designed to carry an overload for a short period of time. They typically are used in motor-starting and power-supply circuits that have a large inrush current when first started. Other fuses are designed to blow very quickly to protect delicate instruments and solid-state circuits.

A fuse also has a voltage rating, both a value in volts and whether it is expected to be used in ac or dc circuits. The voltage rating is the amount of voltage an open fuse can withstand without arcing. While you should never substitute a fuse with a higher current rating than the one it replaces, you may use a fuse with a higher voltage rating.

Figure 2.10A shows typical cartridge-style cylindrical fuses likely to be encountered in ac-powered radio and test equipment. Automotive style fuses, shown in the lower half of Figure 2.10A, have become widely used in low voltage dc power wiring of amateur stations. These are called "blade" fuses. Rated for vehicle-level voltages, automotive blade fuses should never be used in ac line-powered circuits.

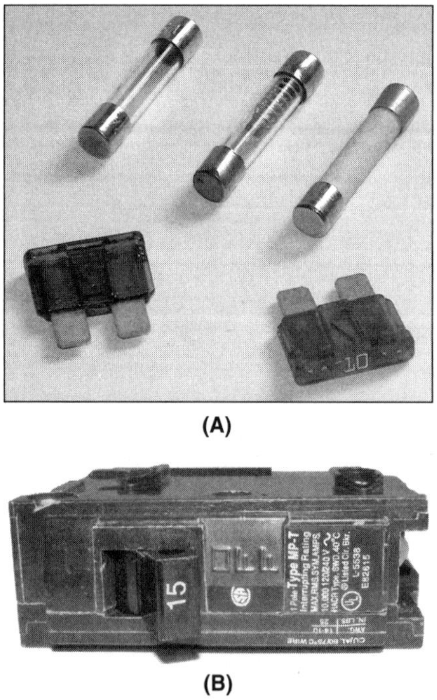

Figure 2.10 — These photos show examples of various styles of fuses. Cartridge-type fuses (A, top) can use glass or ceramic construction. The center fuse is a slow-blow type. Automotive blade-type fuses (A, bottom) are common for low-voltage dc use. A typical home circuit breaker for ac wiring is shown at B.

Circuit breakers perform the same function as fuses — they open a circuit and interrupt current flow when an overload occurs. Instead of a melting element, circuit breakers use spring-loaded magnetic mechanisms to open a switch when excessive current is present. Once the overload has been corrected, the circuit-breaker can be reset. Circuit breakers are generally used by amateurs in home ac wiring (a typical ac circuit breaker is shown in Figure 2.10B) and in dc power supplies.

A replacement fuse or circuit breaker should have the same current rating and the same characteristics as the fuse it replaces. Never substitute a fuse with a larger current rating. You may cause permanent damage (maybe even a fire) to wiring or circuit elements by allowing larger currents to flow when there is an internal problem in equipment. (Additional discussion of fuses and circuit breakers is provided in the chapter on **Safety**.)

Fuses blow and circuit breakers open for several reasons. The most obvious reason is that a problem develops in the circuit, causing too much current to flow. In this case, the circuit problem needs to be fixed. A fuse can fail from being cycled on and off near its current rating. The repeated thermal stress causes metal fatigue and eventually the fuse blows. A fuse can also blow because of a momentary power surge, or even by rapidly turning equipment with a large inrush current on and off several times. In these cases it is only necessary to replace the fuse with the same type and value.

Panel-mount fuse holders should be wired with the hot lead of an ac power circuit (the black wire of an ac power cord) connected to the end terminal, and the ring terminal is connected to the power switch or circuit inside the chassis. This removes voltage from the fuse as it is removed from the fuse holder. This also locates the line connection at the far end of the fuse holder where it is not easily accessible.

2.5.3 Relays and Solenoids

Relays are switches controlled by an electrical signal. *Electromechanical relays* consist of a electromagnetic *coil* and a moving *armature* attracted by the coil's magnetic field when energized by current flowing in the coil. Movement of the armature pushes the switch contacts together or apart. Many sets of contacts can be connected to the same armature, allowing many circuits to be controlled by a single signal. In this manner, the signal voltage that energizes the coil can control circuits carrying large voltages and/or currents.

Relays have two positions or *states* — *energized* and *de-energized*. Sets of contacts called *normally-closed* (NC) are closed when the relay is de-energized and open when it is energized. *Normally-open* (NO) contact sets

(A) (B) (C)

Figure 2.11 — These photos show examples of various styles and sizes of relays. Photo A shows a large reed relay, and a small reed relay in a package the size of an integrated circuit. The contacts and coil can clearly be seen in the open-frame relay. Photo B shows a relay inside a plastic case. Photo C shows a four-position coaxial relay-switch combination with SMA connectors. The ¼-inch-ruled graph paper background provides a size comparison.

are closed when the relay is energized.

Like switches, relay contacts have breakdown voltage, interrupting, and current-carrying ratings. These are not the same as the voltage and current requirements for energizing the relay's coil. Relay contacts (and housings) may be designed for ac, dc or RF signals. The most common control voltages for relays used in amateur equipment are 12 V dc or 120 V ac. Relays with 6, 24, and 28 V dc, and 24 V ac coils are also common. **Figure 2.11** shows some typical relays found in amateur equipment.

A relay's *pull-in voltage* is the minimum voltage at which the coil is guaranteed to cause the armature to move and change the relay's state. *Hold-in voltage* is the minimum voltage at which the relay is guaranteed to hold the armature in the energized position after the relay is activated. A relay's pull-in voltage is higher than its hold-in voltage due to magnetic hysteresis of the coil (see the section on magnetic materials later in this chapter).

Current-sensing relays activate when the current through the coil exceeds a specific value, regardless of the voltage applied to the coil. They are used when the control signal is a current rather than a voltage.

Latching relays have two coils; each moves the armature to a different position where it remains until the other coil is energized. These relays are often used in portable and low-power equipment so that the contact configuration can be maintained without the need to supply power to the relay continuously.

Reed relays have no armature. The contacts are attached to magnetic strips or "reeds" in a glass or plastic tube, surrounded by a coil. The reeds move together or apart when current is applied to the coil, opening or closing contacts. Reed relays can open and close very quickly and are often used in transmit-receive switching circuits.

Solid-state relays (SSR) use transistors instead of mechanical contacts and electronic circuits instead of magnetic coils. They are designed as substitutes for electromechanical relays in power and control circuits and are not used in low-level ac or dc circuits.

Coaxial relays have an armature and contacts designed to handle RF signals. The signal path in coaxial relays maintains a specific characteristic impedance for use in RF systems. Coaxial connectors are used for the RF circuits. Coaxial relays are typically used to control antenna system configurations or to switch a transceiver between a linear amplifier and an antenna.

A *solenoid* is very similar to a relay, except that instead of the moving armature actuating switch contacts, the solenoid moves a lever or rod to actuate some mechanical device. Solenoids are not commonly used in radio equipment, but may be encountered in related systems or devices.

2.6 Capacitance and Capacitors

It is possible to build up and hold an electrical charge in an *electrostatic field*. This phenomenon is called *capacitance*, and the devices that exhibit capacitance are called *capacitors*. (Old articles and texts use the obsolete term *condenser*.) **Figure 2.12** shows schematic symbols for capacitors: a fixed capacitor with a single value of capacitance (Figure 2.12A) and variable capacitors adjustable over a range of values (Figure 2.12B). If the capacitor is of a type that is *polarized*, meaning that dc voltages must be applied with a specific polarity, the straight line in the symbol should be connected to the most positive voltage, while the curved line goes to the more negative voltage. For clarity, the positive terminal of a polarized capacitor symbol is usually marked with a + symbol. The symbol for *non-polarized* capacitors may be two straight lines or the + symbol may be omitted. When in doubt, consult the capacitor's specifications or the circuits parts list.

2.6.1 Electrostatic Fields and Energy

An *electrostatic field* is created wherever a voltage exists between two points, such as two opposite electric charges or regions that contain different amounts of charge. The field causes electric charges (such as electrons or ions) in the field to feel a force in the direction of the field. If the charges are not free to move, as in an insulator, they store the field's energy as *potential energy*, just as a weight held in place by a surface stores gravitational energy. If the charges are free to move, the field's stored energy is converted to *kinetic energy* of motion just as if the weight is released to fall in a gravitational field.

The field is represented by *lines of force* that show the direction of the force felt by the electric charge. Each electric charge is surrounded by an electric field. The lines of force of the field begin on the charge and extend away from charge into space. The lines of force can terminate on another charge (such as lines of force between a proton and an electron) or they can extend to infinity.

The strength of the electrostatic field is measured in *volts per meter* (V/m). Stronger fields cause the moving charges to accelerate more strongly (just as stronger gravity causes weights to fall faster) and stores more energy in fixed charges. The stronger the field in V/m, the more force an electric charge in the field will feel. The strength of the electric field diminishes with the square of the distance from its source, the electric charge.

2.6.2 The Capacitor

Suppose two flat metal plates are placed close to each other (but not touching) and are connected to a battery through a switch, as illustrated in **Figure 2.13A**. At the instant the switch is closed, electrons are attracted from the upper plate to the positive terminal of the battery, while the same quantity is repelled from the negative battery terminal and pushed into the lower plate. This imbalance of charge creates a voltage between the plates. Eventually, enough electrons move into one plate and out of the other to make the voltage between the plates the same as the battery voltage. At this point, the voltage between the plates opposes further movement of electrons and no further current flow occurs.

If the switch is opened after the plates have been charged in this way, the top plate is left with a deficiency of electrons and the bottom plate with an excess. Since there is no current path between the two plates, they remain charged despite the fact that they are no longer connected to the battery which is the source of the voltage. In Figure 2.13B, the separated charges create an electrostatic field between the plates. The electrostatic field contains the energy that was expended by the battery in causing the electrons to flow off of or onto the plates. These two plates create a *capacitor*, a device that has the property of storing electrical energy in an electric field, a property called *capacitance*.

The amount of electric charge that is held on the capacitor plates is proportional to the applied voltage and to the capacitance of the capacitor:

$$Q = CV$$

where

Q = charge in coulombs,

C = capacitance in farads (F), and

V = electrical potential in volts. (The symbol E is commonly used instead of V in this and the following equation.)

The energy stored in a capacitor is also a function of voltage and capacitance:

$$W = \frac{V^2 C}{2}$$

where W = energy in joules (J) or watt-seconds.

If a wire is simultaneously touched to the two plates (short circuiting them), the voltage between the plates causes the excess electrons on the bottom plate to flow through the wire to the upper plate, restoring electrical neutrality. The plates are then *discharged*.

Figure 2.14 illustrates the voltage and current in the circuit, first, at the moment the switch is closed to charge the capacitor and, second, at the moment the shorting switch is closed to discharge the capacitor. Note that the periods of charge and discharge are very short, but that they are not zero. This finite charging and discharging time can be controlled and that will prove useful in the creation of timing circuits.

During the time the electrons are moving — that is, while the capacitor is being charged or discharged — a current flows in the circuit even though the circuit apparently is broken by the gap between the capacitor plates. The current flows only during the time of charge and discharge, however, and this time is usu-

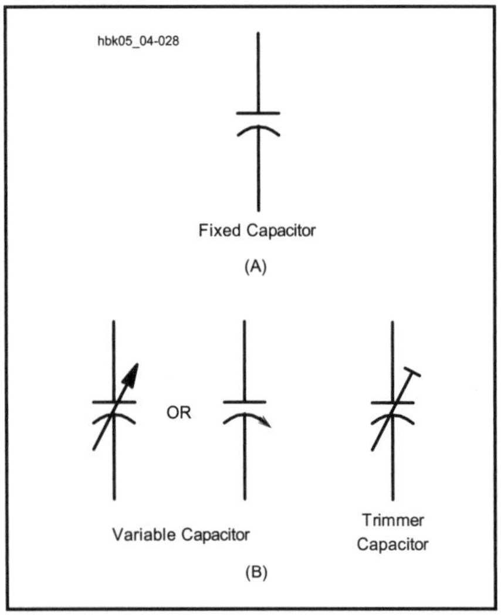

Figure 2.12 — Schematic symbol for a fixed capacitor is shown at A. The symbols for a variable capacitor are shown at B.

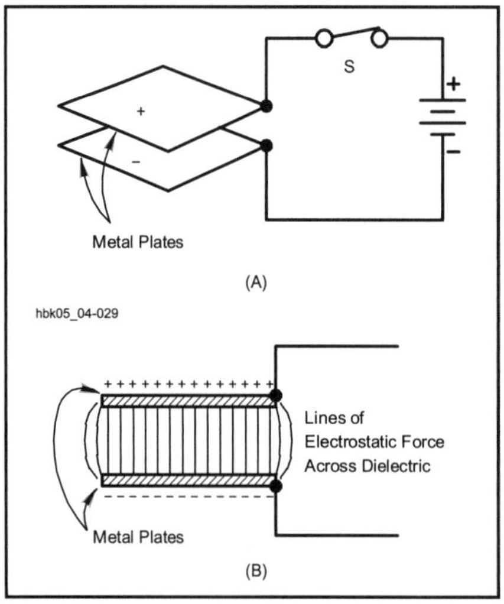

Figure 2.13 — A simple capacitor showing the basic charging arrangement at A, and the retention of the charge due to the electrostatic field at B.

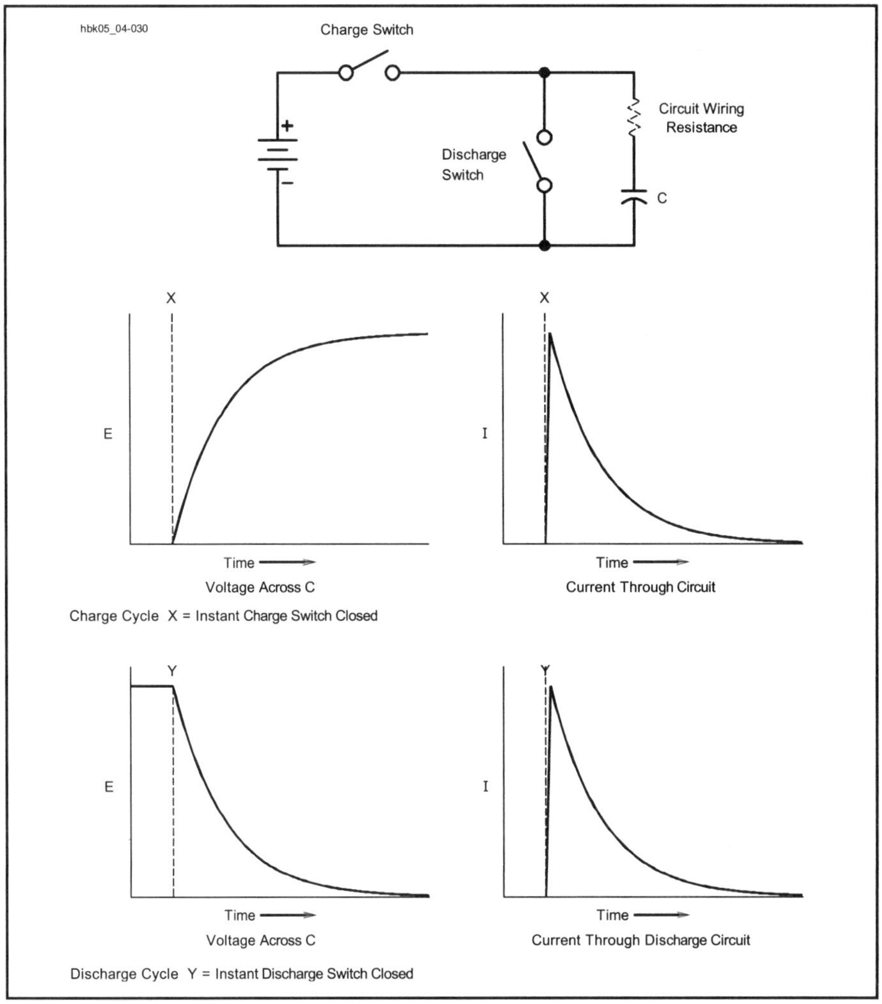

Figure 2.14 — The flow of current during the charge and discharge of a capacitor. The charging graphs assume that the charge switch is closed and the discharge switch is open. The discharging graphs assume just the opposite.

ally very short. There is no continuous flow of direct current through a capacitor.

Although dc cannot pass through a capacitor, alternating current can. At the same time one plate is charged positively by the positive excursion of the alternating current, the other plate is being charged negatively at the same rate. (Remember that conventional current is shown as the flow of positive charge, equal to and opposite the actual flow of electrons.) The reverse process occurs during the second half of the cycle as the changing polarity of the applied voltage causes the flow of charge to change direction, as well. The continual flow into and out of the capacitor caused by ac voltage appears as an ac current, although with a phase difference between the voltage and current flow as described below.

UNITS OF CAPACITANCE

The basic unit of capacitance, the ability to store electrical energy in an electrostatic field, is the *farad*. This unit is generally too large for practical radio circuits, although capacitors of several farads in value are used in place of small batteries or as a power supply filter for automotive electronics. Capacitance encountered in radio and electronic circuits is usually measured in microfarads (abbreviated µF), nanofarads (abbreviated nF) or picofarads (pF). The microfarad is one millionth of a farad (10^{-6} F), the nanofarad is one thousandth of a microfarad (10^{-9} F) and the picofarad is one millionth of a microfarad (10^{-12} F). Old articles and texts use the obsolete term micromicrofarad (mmF or µµF) in place of picofarad.

CAPACITOR CONSTRUCTION

An idealized capacitor is a pair of parallel metal plates separated by an insulating or *dielectric* layer, ideally a vacuum. The capacitance of a vacuum-dielectric capacitor is given by

$$C = \frac{A\, \varepsilon_r\, \varepsilon_0}{d}$$

where

C = capacitance, in farads
A = area of plates, in cm^2
d = spacing of the plates in cm
ε_r = dielectric constant of the insulating material
ε_0 = permittivity of free space, 8.85×10^{-14} F/cm.

The actual capacitance of such a parallel-plate capacitor is somewhat higher due to *end effect* caused by the electric field that exists just outside the edges of the plates.

The *larger* the plate area and the *smaller* the spacing between the plates, the *greater* the amount of energy that can be stored for a given voltage, and the *greater* the capacitance. The more general name for the capacitor's plates is *electrodes*. However, amateur literature generally refers to a capacitor's clectrodes as plates and that is the convention in this text.

The amount of capacitance also depends on the material used as insulating material between the plates; capacitance is smallest with air or a vacuum as the insulator. Substituting other insulating materials for air may greatly increase the capacitance.

The ratio of the capacitance with a material other than a vacuum or air between the plates to the capacitance of the same capacitor with air insulation is called the *dielectric constant* (ε_r or K), of that particular insulating material. The dielectric constants of a number of materials commonly used as dielectrics in capacitors are given in **Table 2.2**. For example, if polystyrene is substituted for air in a capacitor, the capacitance will be 2.6 times greater.

In practice, capacitors often have more than two plates, with alternating plates being connected in parallel to form two sets, as shown in **Figure 2.15**. This practice makes it possible to obtain a fairly large capacitance in a small space, since several plates of smaller individual area can be stacked to form the equivalent of a single large plate of the same total area. Also, all plates except the two on the ends of the stack are exposed to plates of the other group on both sides, and so are twice as effective in increasing the capacitance.

The formula for calculating capacitance from these physical properties is:

$$C = \frac{0.2248\, K\, A\, (n-1)}{d}$$

where

C = capacitance in pF,
K = dielectric constant of material between plates,
A = area of one side of one plate in square inches,
d = separation of plate surfaces in inches, and
n = number of plates.

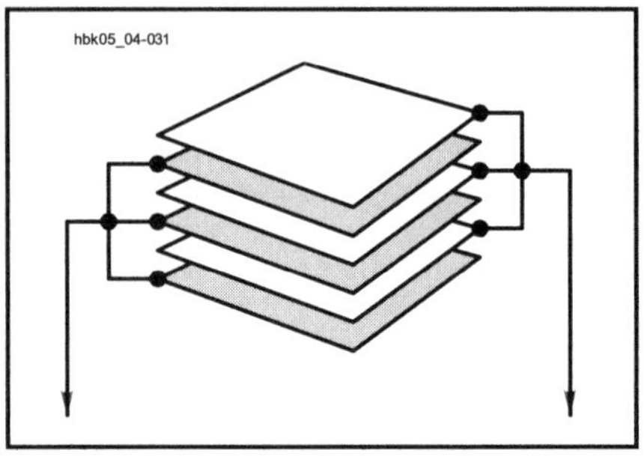

Figure 2.15 — A multiple-plate capacitor. Alternate plates are connected to each other, increasing the total area available for storing charge.

Table 2.2
Relative Dielectric Constants of Common Capacitor Dielectric Materials

Material	*Dielectric Constant (k)*	*(O)rganic or (I)norganic*
Vacuum	1 (by definition)	I
Air	1.0006	I
Ruby mica	6.5 - 8.7	I
Glass (flint)	10	I
Barium titanate (class I)	5 - 450	I
Barium titanate (class II)	200 - 12000	I
Kraft paper	≈ 2.6	O
Mineral Oil	≈ 2.23	O
Castor Oil	≈ 4.7	O
Halowax	≈ 5.2	O
Chlorinated diphenyl	≈ 5.3	O
Polyisobutylene	≈ 2.2	O
Polytetrafluoroethylene	≈ 2.1	O
Polyethylene terephthalate	≈ 3	O
Polystyrene	≈ 2.6	O
Polycarbonate	≈ 3.1	O
Aluminum oxide	≈ 8.4	I
Tantalum pentoxide	≈ 28	I
Niobium oxide	≈ 40	I
Titanium dioxide	≈ 80	I

(Adapted from: Charles A. Harper, *Handbook of Components for Electronics*, p 8-7.)

If the area (A) is in square centimeters and the separation (d) is in centimeters, then the formula for capacitance becomes

$$C = \frac{0.0885\ K\ A\ (n-1)}{d}$$

If the plates in one group do not have the same area as the plates in the other, use the area of the smaller plates.

Example: What is the capacitance of two copper plates, each 1.50 square inches in area, separated by a distance of 0.00500 inch, if the dielectric is air?

$$C = \frac{0.2248\ K\ A\ (n-1)}{d}$$

$$C = \frac{0.2248 \times 1 \times 1.50\ (2-1)}{0.00500}$$

$$C = 67.4\ \text{pF}$$

What is the capacitance if the dielectric is mineral oil? (See Table 2.2 for the appropriate dielectric constant.)

$$C = \frac{0.2248 \times 2.23 \times 1.50\ (2-1)}{0.00500}$$

$$C = 150.3\ \text{pF}$$

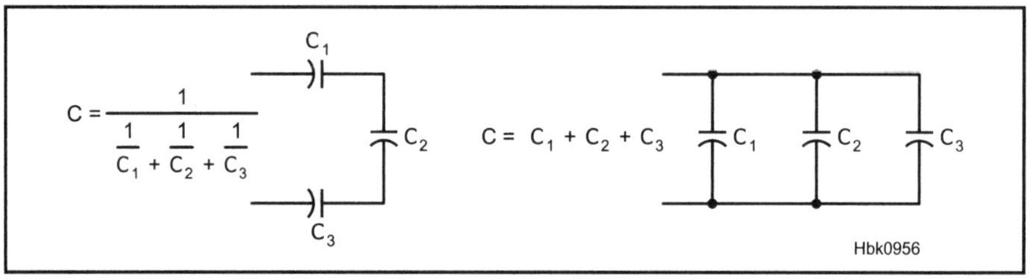

Figure 2.16 — Capacitors in series and parallel.

2.6.3 Capacitors in Series and Parallel

When a number of capacitors are connected in parallel, as in the right side of **Figure 2.16**, the total capacitance of the group is equal to the sum of the individual capacitances:

$$C_{total} = C1 + C2 + C3 + C4 \ldots + C_n)$$

When two or more capacitors are connected in series, as in the left side of Figure 2.16, the total capacitance is less than that of the smallest capacitor in the group. The rule for finding the capacitance of a number of series-connected capacitors is the same as that for finding the resistance of a number of parallel-connected resistors.

$$C_{total} = \frac{1}{\frac{1}{C1} + \frac{1}{C2} + \frac{1}{C3} + \ldots + \frac{1}{C_n}}$$

For only two capacitors in series, the formula becomes:

$$C_{total} = \frac{C1 \times C2}{C1 + C2}$$

The same units must be used throughout; that is, all capacitances must be expressed in µF, nF or pF, etc. Different units cannot be combined in the same equation.

Capacitors are often connected in parallel to obtain a larger total capacitance than is available in one unit. The voltage rating of capacitors connected in parallel is the lowest voltage rating of any of the capacitors.

When capacitors are connected in series, the applied voltage is divided between them according to Kirchhoff's Voltage Law. The situation is much the same as when resistors are in series and there is a voltage drop across each. The voltage that appears across each series-connected capacitor is inversely proportional to its capacitance, as compared with the capacitance of the whole group. (This assumes ideal capacitors.)

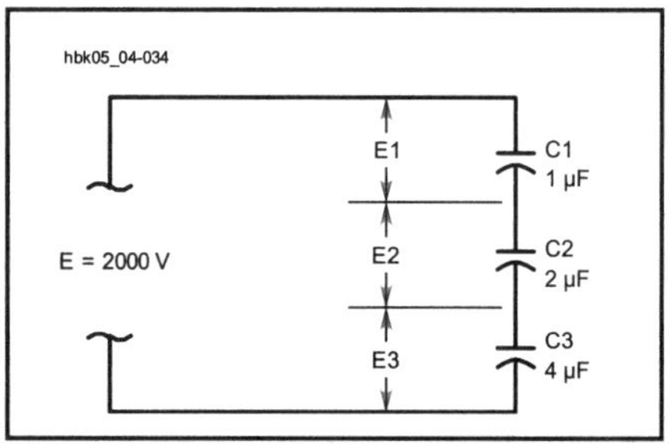

Figure 2.17 — An example of capacitors connected in series. The text shows how to find the voltage drops, E1 through E3.

Example: Three capacitors having capacitances of 1, 2 and 4 µF, respectively, are connected in series as in **Figure 2.17**. The voltage across the entire series is 2000 V. What is the total capacitance? (Since this is a calculation using theoretical values to illustrate a technique, we will not follow the rules of significant figures for the calculations.)

$$C_{total} = \frac{1}{\frac{1}{C1} + \frac{1}{C2} + \frac{1}{C3}}$$

$$= \frac{1}{\frac{1}{1\ \mu F} + \frac{1}{2\ \mu F} + \frac{1}{4\ \mu F}}$$

$$= \frac{1}{\frac{7}{4\ \mu F}} = \frac{4\ \mu F}{7} = 0.5714\ \mu F$$

The voltage across each capacitor is proportional to the total capacitance divided by the capacitance of the capacitor in question. So the voltage across C1 is:

$$E1 = \frac{0.5714\ \mu F}{1\ \mu F} \times 2000\ V = 1143\ V$$

Similarly, the voltages across C2 and C3 are:

$$E2 = \frac{0.5714\ \mu F}{2\ \mu F} \times 2000\ V = 571\ V$$

and

$$E3 = \frac{0.5714\ \mu F}{4\ \mu F} \times 2000\ V = 286\ V$$

The sum of these three voltages equals 2000 V, the applied voltage.

Capacitors may be connected in series to enable the group to withstand a larger voltage than any individual capacitor is rated to withstand. The trade-off is a decrease in the total capacitance. As shown by the previous example, the applied voltage does not divide equally between the capacitors except when all the capacitances are precisely the same. Use care to ensure that the voltage rating of any capacitor in the group is not exceeded. If you use capacitors in series to withstand a higher voltage, you should also connect an "equalizing resistor" across each capacitor as described in the **Power Sources** chapter.

2.6.4 RC Time Constant

Connecting a dc voltage source directly to the terminals of a capacitor charges the capacitor to the full source voltage almost instantaneously. Any resistance added to the circuit (as R in **Figure 2.18A)** limits the current, lengthening the time required for the voltage between the capacitor plates to build up to the source-voltage value. During this charging period, the current flowing from the source into the capacitor gradually decreases from its initial value. The increasing voltage stored in the capacitor's electric field offers increasing opposition to the steady source voltage.

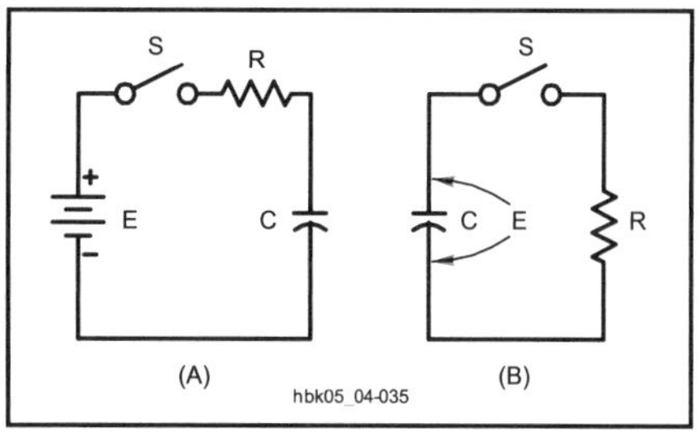

Figure 2.18 — An RC circuit. The series resistance delays the process of charging (A) and discharging (B) when the switch, S, is closed.

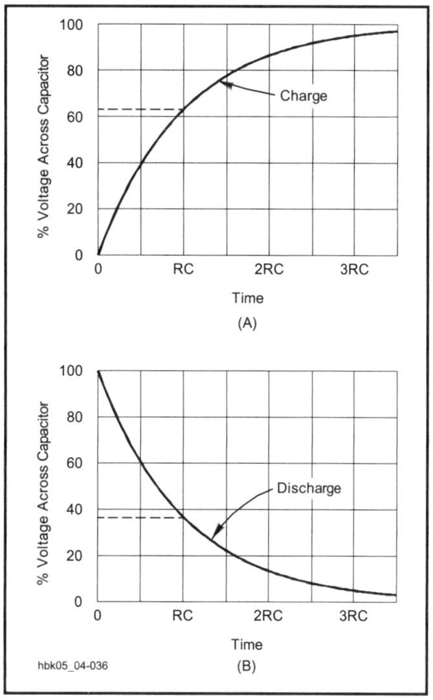

Figure 2.19 — At A, the curve shows how the voltage across a capacitor rises, with time, when charged through a resistor. The curve at B shows the way in which the voltage decreases across a capacitor when discharging through the same resistance. For practical purposes, a capacitor may be considered charged or discharged after five RC periods.

While it is being charged, the voltage between the capacitor terminals is an exponential function of time, and is given by:

$$V(t) = E\left(1 - e^{-\frac{t}{RC}}\right)$$

where

V(t) = capacitor voltage at time t,

E = power source potential in volts,

t = time in seconds after initiation of charging current,

e = natural logarithmic base = 2.718,

R = circuit resistance in ohms, and

C = capacitance in farads.

(References that explain exponential equations, e, and other mathematical topics are found in the "Radio Mathematics" article in this book's downloadable supplemental information.)

By letting t = RC, the above equation becomes:

$$V(RC) = E\,(1 - e^{-1}) \cong 0.632\ E$$

The product of R in ohms times C in farads is called the *time constant* (also called the *RC time constant*) of the circuit and is the time in seconds required to charge the capacitor to 63.2% of the applied voltage. (The lower-case Greek letter tau, τ, is often used to represent the time constant in electronics circuits.) After two time constants ($t = 2\tau$) the capacitor charges another 63.2% of the difference between the capacitor voltage at one time constant and the applied voltage, for a total charge of 86.5%. After three time constants the capacitor reaches 95% of the applied voltage, and so on, as illustrated in the curve of **Figure 2.19A**. After five time constants, a capacitor is considered fully charged, having reached 99.24% of the applied voltage. Theoretically, the charging process is never really finished, but eventually the charging current drops to an immeasurably small value and the voltage is effectively constant.

If a charged capacitor is discharged through a resistor, as in Figure 2.18B, the same time constant applies to the decay of the capacitor voltage. A direct short circuit applied between the capacitor terminals would discharge the capacitor almost instantly. The resistor, R, limits the current, so a capacitor discharging through a resistance exhibits the same time-constant characteristics (calculated in the same way as above) as a charging capacitor. The voltage, as a function of time while the capacitor is being discharged, is given by:

$$V(t) = E\left(e^{-\frac{t}{RC}}\right)$$

where t = time in seconds after initiation of discharge and E is the fully-charged capacitor voltage prior to beginning discharge.

Again, by letting t = RC, the time constant of a discharging capacitor represents a decrease in the voltage across the capacitor of about 63.2%. After five time-constants, the capacitor is considered fully discharged, since the voltage has dropped to less than 1% of the full-charge voltage. Figure 2.19B is a graph of the discharging capacitor voltage in terms of time constants..

Time constant calculations have many uses in radio work. The following examples are all derived from practical-circuit applications.

Example 1: A 100-μF capacitor in a high-voltage power supply is shunted by a 100-kΩ

RC Timesaver

When calculating time constants, it is handy to remember that if R is in units of MΩ and C is in units of μF, the result of R × C will be in seconds. Expressed as an equation: MΩ × μF = seconds

resistor. What is the minimum time before the capacitor may be considered fully discharged? Since full discharge is approximately five RC periods,

$$t = 5 \times RC = 5 \times 100 \times 10^3\ \Omega \times 100 \times 10^{-6}\ F = 50000 \times 10^{-3} = 50\ s$$

Caution: Although waiting almost a minute for the capacitor to discharge seems safe in this high-voltage circuit, *never* rely solely on capacitor-discharging resistors (often called *bleeder resistors*). Be certain the power source is removed and the capacitors are totally discharged before touching any circuit components. (See the **Power Sources** chapter for more information on bleeder resistors.)

Example 2: Smooth CW keying without clicks requires both the rising and falling edges of the waveform to take approximately 5 ms (0.005 s). If an RC delay circuit in a keyed voltage line is used to set the rise and fall time, what values of R and C should be used? Since full charge and discharge require 5 RC periods,

$$RC = \frac{t}{5} = \frac{0.005\ s}{5} = 0.001\ s$$

Any combination of resistor and capacitor whose values, when multiplied together, equal 0.001 would do the job. A typical capacitor might be 0.05 μF. In that case, the necessary resistor would be:

$$R = \frac{0.001\ s}{0.05 \times 10^{-6}\ F}$$

$$= 0.02 \times 10^{6}\ \Omega = 20000\ \Omega = 20\ k\Omega$$

In practice, a builder would use the calculated value as a starting point. The final value would be selected by monitoring the waveform on an oscilloscope.

Example 3: The popular 555 timer IC activates its output pin with the trigger input reaches 0.667 of the supply voltage. What value of capacitor and resistor would be required for a 4.5-second timing period?

First we will solve the charging equation for the time constant, RC. The threshold voltage is 0.667 times the supply voltage, so we use this value for V(t).

$$V(t) = E\left(1 - e^{-\frac{t}{RC}}\right)$$

$$0.667\ E = E\left(1 - e^{-\frac{t}{RC}}\right)$$

$$e^{-\frac{t}{RC}} = 1 - 0.667$$

$$\ln\left(e^{-\frac{t}{RC}}\right) = \ln(0.333)$$

$$-\frac{t}{RC} = -1.10$$

We want to find a capacitor and resistor combination that will produce a 4.5 s timing period, so we substitute that value for t.

$$RC = \frac{4.5\ s}{1.10} = 4.1\ s$$

If we select a value of 10 μF, we can solve for R.

$$R = \frac{4.1\ s}{10 \times 10^{-6}\ F} = 0.41 \times 10^{6}\ \Omega = 410\ k\Omega$$

A 1% tolerance resistor and capacitor will give good results. You could also use a variable resistor and an accurate method of measuring time to set the circuit to a 4.5 s period.

2.7 Inductance and Inductors

A second way to store electrical energy is in a *magnetic field*. This phenomenon is called *inductance*, and the devices that exhibit inductance are called *inductors*. Inductance is derived from some basic underlying magnetic properties.

2.7.1 Magnetic Fields and Magnetic Energy Storage

As an electric field surrounds an electric charge, magnetic fields surround *magnets*. You are probably familiar with metallic bar, disc, or horseshoe-shaped magnets. **Figure 2.20** shows a bar magnet, but particles of matter as small as an atom can also be magnets.

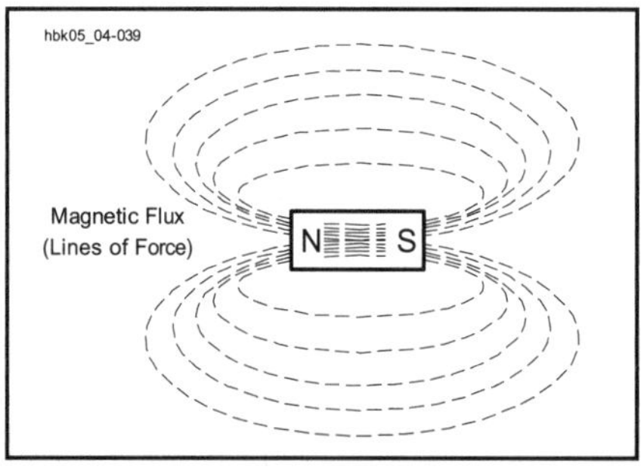

Figure 2.20 — The magnetic field and poles of a permanent magnet. The magnetic field direction is from the north to the south pole.

Figure 2.20 also shows the magnet surrounded by lines of force called *magnetic flux*, representing a *magnetic field*. (More accurately, a *magnetostatic field*, since the field is not changing.) Similar to those of an electric field, magnetic lines of force (or *flux lines*) show the direction in which a magnet would feel a force in the field.

There is no "magnetic charge" comparable to positive and negative electric charges. All magnets and magnetic fields have a polarity, represented as *poles*, and every magnet — from atoms to bar magnets — possesses both a *north* and *south pole*. The size of the source of the magnetism makes no difference. The north pole of a magnet is defined as the one attracted to the Earth's north magnetic pole. (Confusingly, this definition means the Earth's North Magnetic Pole is magnetically a south pole!) Like conventional current, the direction of magnetic lines of force was assigned arbitrarily by early scientists as pointing *from* the magnet's north pole *to* the south pole.

An electric field is *open* — that is, its lines of force have one end on an electric charge and can extend to infinity. A magnetic field is *closed* because all magnetic lines of force form a loop passing through a magnet's north and south poles.

Magnetic fields exist around two types of materials; *permanent magnets* and *electromagnets*. Permanent magnets consist of *ferromagnetic* and *ferrimagnetic* materials whose atoms are or can be aligned so as to produce a magnetic field. Ferro- or ferrimagnetic materials are strongly attracted to magnets. They can be *magnetized*, meaning to be made magnetic, by the application of a magnetic field. Lodestone, magnetite, and ferrites are examples of ferrimagnetic materials. Iron, nickel, cobalt, Alnico alloys and other materials are ferromagnetic. Magnetic materials with high *retentivity* form permanent magnets because they retain their magnetic properties for long periods. Other materials, such as soft iron, yield temporary magnets that lose their magnetic properties rapidly.

Paramagnetic substances are very weakly attracted to a magnet and include materials such as platinum, aluminum, and oxygen. *Diamagnetic* substances, such as copper, carbon, and water, are weakly repelled by a magnet.

The second type of magnet is an electrical conductor with a current flowing through it. As shown in **Figure 2.21**, moving electrons are surrounded by a closed magnetic field, illustrated as the circular lines of force around the wire lying in planes perpendicular to the current's motion. The magnetic needle of a compass placed near a wire carrying direct current will be deflected as its poles respond to the forces created by the magnetic field around the wire.

If the wire is coiled into a *solenoid* as shown in **Figure 2.22**, the magnetic field greatly intensifies. This occurs as the magnetic fields from each successive turn in the coil add together because the current in each turn is flowing in the same direction.

Note that the resulting *electromagnet* has magnetic properties identical in principle to those of a permanent magnet, including poles and lines of force or flux. The strength of the magnetic field depends on several factors: the number and shape of turns of the coil, the magnetic properties of the materials surrounding the coil (both inside and out), the length of the coil and the amplitude of the current.

Magnetic fields and electric current have a special two-way connection: voltage causing an electrical current (moving charges) in a conductor will produce a magnetic field and a moving magnetic field will create an electrical field (voltage) that produces current in a conductor. This is the principle behind motors and generators, converting mechanical energy into electrical energy and vice-versa. **Table 2.3** shows the similarities: magnetic quantities and circuits have analogues in electrical quantities and circuits. This illustrates the deep relationship between electricity and magnetism, two sides of the same coin.

The Right-Hand Rule

How do you remember which way the magnetic field around a current is pointing? Luckily, there is a simple method, called the *right-hand rule.* Make your right hand into a fist, then extend your thumb, as in the figure below. If your thumb is pointing in the direction of conventional current flow, then your fingers curl in the same direction as the magnetic field. (If you are dealing with electronic current, use your left hand, instead!)

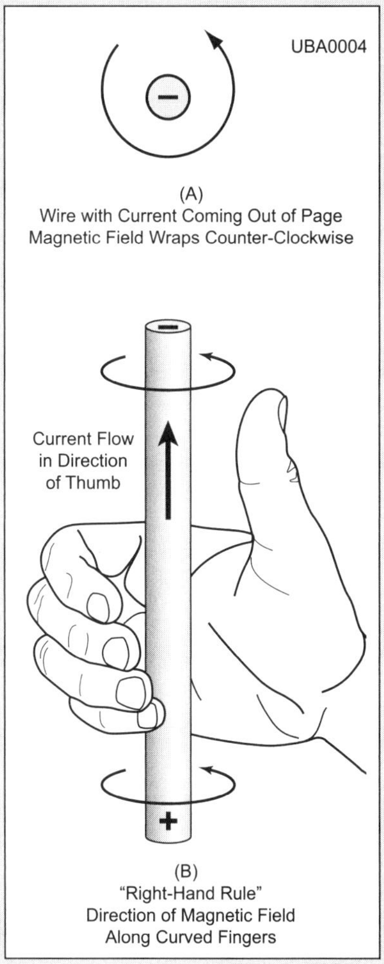

Figure 2.A2 — Use the right-hand rule to determine magnetic field direction from the direction of current flow.

MAGNETIC FLUX

Magnetic flux is measured in the SI unit (International System of Units) of the weber, which is a volt-second (Wb = V-s). In the *centimeter-gram-second* (*cgs*) metric system

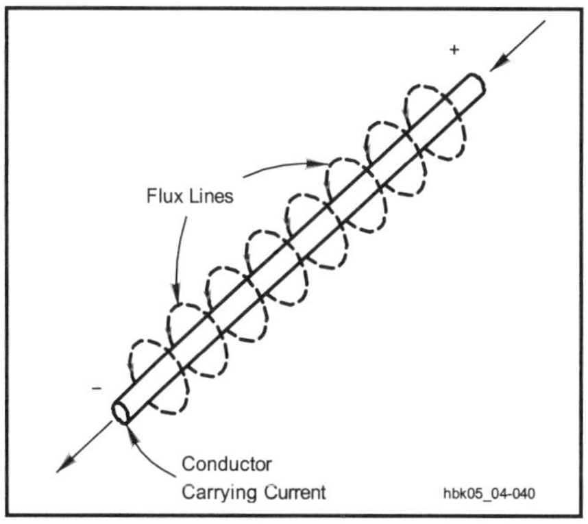

Figure 2.21 — The magnetic field around a conductor carrying an electrical current. If the thumb of your right hand points in the direction of the conventional current (plus to minus), your fingers curl in the direction of the magnetic field around the wire.

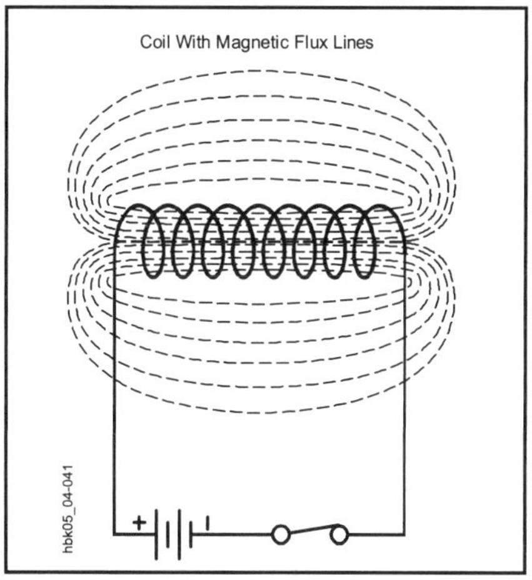

Figure 2.22 — Cross section of an inductor showing its flux lines and overall magnetic field.

Table 2.3

Magnetic Quantities

Value	*Symbol*	*MKS*	*cgs*
Magnetic Flux	lines	Weber, Wb = V-s	Maxwell, Mx = 10^{-8} Wb
Magnetic Flux Density	B	Tesla, T = Wb/m^2	Gauss, G = Mx/ cm^2 T = 10,000 G
Magnetomotive Force	[T]	Amp-turn = A	Gilbert, Gb = 0.79577 A
Magnetic Field Strength	H	A / meter	Oersted, Oe = Gb/cm = 79.58 A/m

Magnetic Circuit Analogies

Electric Circuit	*Magnetic Circuit*
Voltage drop V	Hl magnetovoltage drop
Voltage source V	nI magnetomotive force
Current I	psi = BA magnetic flux

Note – Magnetic circuit analogies as described by Shen and Kong, Applied Electromagnetism units, magnetic flux is measured in maxwells (1 Mx = 10^{-8} Wb). The volt-second is used because of the relationship described in the previous paragraph: 1 volt of electromotive force will be created in a loop of wire in which magnetic flux through the loop changes at the rate of 1 weber per second. The relationship between current and magnetic fields is one of motion and change.

Magnetic field intensity, known as *flux density*, decreases with the square of the distance from the source, either a magnet or current. Flux density (B) is represented in gauss (G), where one gauss is equivalent to one line of force (1 Mx) per square centimeter of area measured perpendicularly to the direction of the field (G = Mx / cm^2). The Earth's magnetic field at the surface is approximately one gauss. The gauss is a *cgs* unit. In SI units, flux density is represented by the tesla (T), which is one weber per square meter (T = Wb/m^2 and 1T = 10,000 G).

Magnetomotive Force and Field Strength

The magnetizing or *magnetomotive force* ($\Im$) that produces a flux or total magnetic field is measured in gilberts (Gb). Magnetomotive force is analogous to electromotive force in that it produces the magnetic field. The SI unit of magnetomotive force is the ampere-turn, abbreviated A, just like the ampere. (1 Gb = 0.79577 A)

$$\Im = \frac{10\,N\,I}{4\pi}$$

where

$\Im$ = magnetomotive strength in gilberts,

N = number of turns in the coil creating the field,

I = dc current in amperes in the coil, and

π = 3.1416.

The magnetic field strength (H) measured in oersteds (Oe) produced by any particular magnetomotive force (measured in gilberts) is given by:

$$H = \frac{\Im}{\ell} = \frac{10\,N\,I}{4\,\pi\,\ell}$$

where

H = magnetic field strength in oersteds, and

ℓ = mean magnetic path length in centimeters.

The *mean magnetic path length* is the average length of the lines of magnetic flux. If the inductor is wound on a closed core as shown in the next section, l is approximately the average of the inner and outer circumferences of the core. The SI unit of magnetic field strength is the ampere-turn per meter. (1 Oe = 79.58 A/m)

2.7.2 Magnetic Core Properties

PERMEABILITY

The nature of the material within the coil of an electromagnet, where the lines of force are most concentrated, has the greatest effect upon the magnetic field established by the coil. All core materials are compared relatively to air. The ratio of flux density produced by a given material compared to the flux density produced by an air core is the *permeability* (μ) of the material. Air and non-magnetic materials have a permeability of one.

Suppose the coil in **Figure 2.23** is wound on an iron core having a cross-sectional area of 2 square inches. When a certain current is sent through the coil, it is found that there are 80,000 lines of force in the core. Since the area is 2 square inches, the magnetic flux density is 40,000 lines per square inch. Now suppose that the iron core is removed and the same current is maintained in the coil. Also suppose the flux density without the iron core is found to be 50 lines per square inch. The ratio of these flux densities, iron core to air, is 40,000 / 50 or 800. This ratio is the core's permeability.

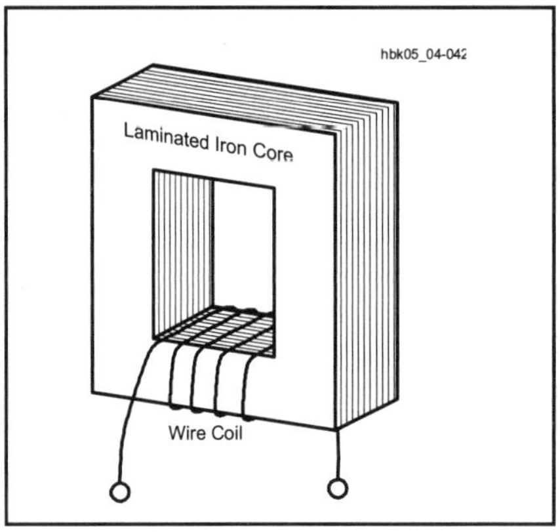

Figure 2.23 — A coil of wire wound around a laminated iron core.

Permeabilities as high as 10^6 have been attained. The three most common types of materials used in magnetic cores are:

A) stacks of thin steel laminations (for power and audio applications, see the discussion on eddy currents below);

B) various ferrite compounds (for cores shaped as rods, toroids, beads and numerous other forms); and

C) powdered iron (shaped as slugs, toroids and other forms for RF inductors).

The permeability of silicon-steel power-transformer cores approaches 5000 in high-quality units. Powdered-iron cores used in RF tuned circuits range in permeability from 3 to about 35, while ferrites of nickel-zinc and manganese-zinc range from 20 to 15,000. Not all materials have permeabilities higher than air. Brass has a permeability of less than one. A brass core inserted into a coil will decrease the magnetic field compared to an air core.

Table 2.4 lists some common magnetic materials, their composition and their permeabilities. Core materials are often frequency sensitive, exhibiting excessive losses outside the frequency band of intended use. (Ferrite materials are discussed separately in a later section of the chapter on **RF Techniques**.)

As a measure of the ease with which a magnetic field may be established in a material as compared with air, permeability (μ) corresponds roughly to electrical conductivity. Higher permeability means that it is easier to establish a magnetic field in the material.

Table 2.4

Properties of Some High-Permeability Materials

Material	*Approximate Percent Composition*					*Maximum Permeability*
	Fe	Ni	Co	Mo	Other	
Iron	99.91	—	—	—	—	5000
Purified Iron	99.95	—	—	—	—	180,000
4% silicon-iron	96	—	—	—	4 Si	7000
45 Permalloy	54.7	45	—	—	0.3 Mn	25,000
Hipernik	50	50	—	—	—	70,000
78 Permalloy	21.2	78.5	—	—	0.3 Mn	100,000
4-79 Permalloy	16.7	79	—	—	0.3 Mn	100,000
Supermalloy	15.7	79	—	5	0.3 Mn	800,000
Permendur	49.7	—	50	—	0.3 Mn	5000
2V Permendur	49	—	49	—	2 V	4500
Hiperco	64	—	34	—	2 Cr	10,000
2-81 Permalloy*	17	81	—	2	—	130
Carbonyl iron*	99.9	—	—	—	—	132
Ferroxcube III**	($MnFe_2O_4$ + $ZnFe_2O_4$)			1500		

Note: all materials in sheet form except * (insulated powder) and ** (sintered powder).
(Reference: L. Ridenour, ed., *Modern Physics for the Engineer*, p 119.)

Permeability is given as:

$$\mu = \frac{B}{H}$$

where

B is the flux density in gauss, and

H is the magnetic field strength in oersteds.

RELUCTANCE

That a force (the magnetomotive force) is required to produce a given magnetic field strength implies that there is some opposition to be overcome. This opposition to the creation of a magnetic field is called *reluctance*. Reluctance ($\Re$) is the reciprocal of permeability and corresponds roughly to resistance in an electrical circuit. Carrying the electrical resistance analogy a bit further, the magnetic equivalent of Ohm's Law relates reluctance, magnetomotive force, and flux density: $\Re = \Im / B$.

HYSTERESIS

Retentivity in magnetic core materials is caused by atoms retaining their alignment from an applied magnetizing force. Retentivity is desirable if the goal is to create a permanent magnet. In an electronic circuit, however, the changes caused by retentivity cause the properties of the core material to depend on the history of how the magnetizing force was applied.

Figure 2.24 illustrates the change of flux density (*B*) with a changing magnetizing force (*H*). From starting point A, with no flux in the core, the flux reaches point B at the maximum magnetizing force. As the force decreases, so too does the flux, but it does not reach zero simultaneously with the force at point D. As the force continues in the opposite direction, it brings the flux density to point C. As the force decreases to zero, the flux once more lags behind. This occurs because some of the atoms in core retain their alignment, even after the external magnetizing force is removed. This creates *residual flux* that is present even with no applied magnetizing force. This is the property of *hysteresis*.

In effect, a *coercive force* is necessary to reverse or overcome the residual magnetism retained by the core material. If a circuit carries a large ac current (that is, equal to or larger than saturation), the path shown in Figure 2.24 will be retraced with every cycle and the reversing force each time. The result is a power loss to the magnetic circuit, which appears as heat in the core material. Air cores are immune to hysteresis effects and losses.

SATURATION

Unlike electrical conductivity, which is independent of other electrical parameters, the permeability of a magnetic material varies with the flux density. At low flux densities (or with an air core), increasing the current through the coil will cause a proportionate increase in flux. This occurs because the current passing through the coil forces the atoms of the iron (or other material) to line up, just like many small compass needles. The magnetic field that results from the atomic alignment is *much* larger than that produced by the current with no core. As more and more atoms align, the magnetic flux density also increases.

At very high flux densities, increasing the current beyond a certain point may cause no appreciable change in the flux because all of the atoms are aligned. At this point, the core is said to be *saturated*. Saturation causes a rapid decrease in permeability, because it decreases the ratio of flux lines to those obtainable with the same current using an air core. **Figure 2.25** displays a typical permeability curve, showing the region of saturation. The saturation point varies with the makeup of different magnetic materials. Air and other nonmagnetic materials do not saturate.

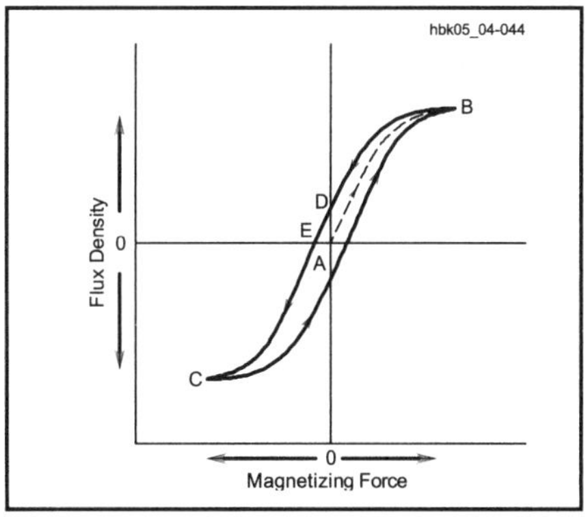

Figure 2.24 — A typical hysteresis curve for a magnetic core, showing the additional energy needed to overcome residual flux.

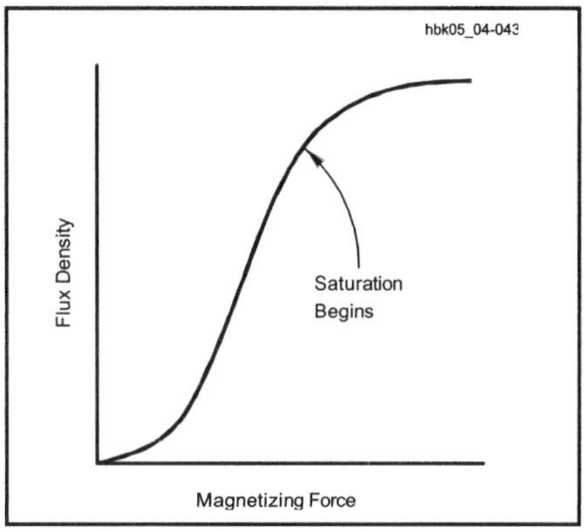

Figure 2.25 — A typical permeability curve for a magnetic core, showing the point where saturation begins.

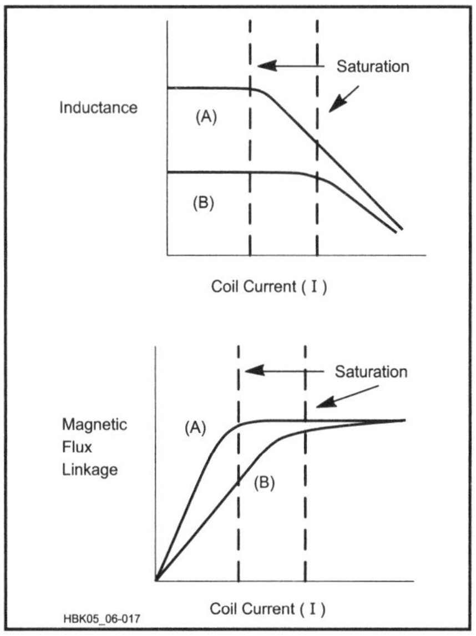

Figure 2.26 — Magnetic flux linkage and inductance plotted versus coil current for (A) a typical iron-core inductor. As the flux linkage Nϕ in the coil saturates, the inductance begins to decrease since inductance = flux linkage / current. The curves marked B show the effect of adding an air gap to the core. The current-handling capability has increased, but at the expense of reduced inductance.

EFFECTS OF SATURATION

An important concept for using inductors is that as long as the coil current remains below saturation, the inductance of the coil is essentially constant. **Figure 2.26** shows graphs of magnetic flux linkage (ψ) and inductance (L) vs. current (I) for a typical iron-core inductor both saturated and non-saturated. These quantities are related by the equation

$$\psi = N\phi = LI$$

where

ψ = the flux linkage

N = number of turns,

ϕ = flux density in webers

L = inductance in henrys, and

I = current in amperes.

In the lower graph, a line drawn from any point on the curve to the (0,0) point will show the effective inductance, $L = N\phi / I$, at that current. These results are plotted on the upper graph.

Note that below saturation, the inductance is constant because both ψ and I are increasing at a steady rate. Once the saturation current is reached, the inductance decreases because ψ does not increase anymore (except for the tiny additional magnetic field the current itself provides).

One common method of increasing the saturation current level is to cut a small air gap in the core (see **Figure 2.27**). This gap forces the flux lines to travel through air for a short distance, reducing the permeability of the core. Since the saturation flux linkage of the core is unchanged, this method works by requiring a higher current to achieve

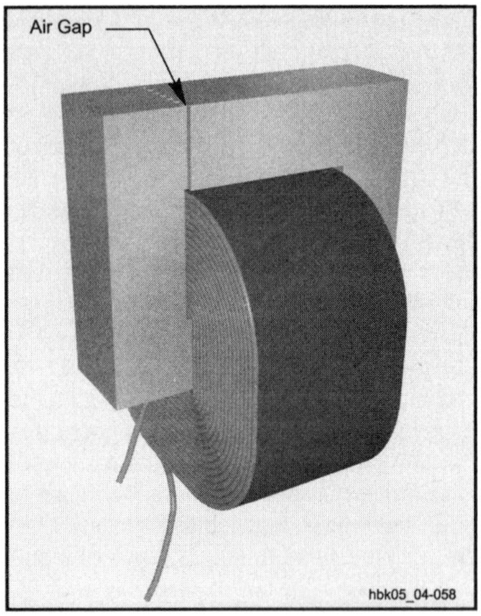

Figure 2.27 — Typical construction of a magnetic-core inductor. The air gap greatly reduces core saturation at the expense of reducing inductance. The insulating laminations between the core layers help to minimize eddy currents, as well.

saturation. The price that is paid is a reduced inductance below saturation. The curves in Figure 2.26B show the result of an air gap added to that inductor.

Manufacturer's data sheets for magnetic cores usually specify the saturation flux density. Saturation flux density (ϕ) in gauss can be calculated for ac and dc currents from the following equations:

$$\varphi_{ac} = \frac{3.49\ V}{fNA}$$

$$\varphi_{dc} = \frac{NIA_L}{10A}$$

where

V = RMS ac voltage
f = frequency, in MHz
N = number of turns
A = equivalent area of the magnetic path in square inches (from the data sheet)
I = dc current, in amperes, and
A_L = inductance index (also from the data sheet).

EDDY CURRENT

Since magnetic core material is usually conductive, the changing magnetic field produced by an ac current in an inductor also induces a voltage in the core. This voltage causes a current to flow in the core. This *eddy current* (so-named because it moves in a closed path, similarly to eddy currents in water) serves no useful purpose and results in energy being dissipated as heat from the core's resistance. Eddy currents are a particular problem in inductors with iron cores. Cores made of thin strips of magnetic material, called *laminations*, are used to reduce eddy currents. (See also the section on Practical Inductors in the **Circuits and Components** chapter.)

2.7.3 Inductance and Direct Current

In an electrical circuit, any element whose operation is based on the transfer of energy into and out of magnetic fields is called an *inductor* for reasons to be explained shortly. **Figure 2.28** shows schematic-diagram symbols and photographs of a few representative inductors. The photograph shows an air-core inductor, a slug-tuned (variable-core) inductor with a nonmagnetic core and an inductor with a magnetic (iron) core. Inductors are often called *coils* because of their construction.

As explained above, when current flows through any conductor — even a straight wire — a magnetic field is created. The transfer of energy to the magnetic field represents work performed by the source of the voltage. Power is required for doing work, and since power is equal to current multiplied by voltage, there must be a voltage drop across the inductor while energy is being stored in the field. This voltage drop, exclusive of any voltage drop caused by resistance in the conductor, is the result of an opposing voltage created in the conductor while the magnetic field is building up to its final value. Once the field becomes constant, the *induced voltage* or *back-voltage* disappears, because no further energy is being stored. Back voltage is analogous to the opposition to current flow in a capacitor from the increasing capacitor voltage.

The induced voltage opposes the voltage of the source, preventing the current from rising rapidly when voltage is applied. **Figure 2.29A** illustrates the situation of energizing an inductor or magnetic circuit, showing the relative amplitudes of induced voltage and the delayed rise in current to its full value.

The amplitude of the induced voltage is proportional to the rate at which the current changes (and consequently, the rate at which the magnetic field changes) and to a constant associated with the inductor itself, *inductance* (*L*). (*Self-inductance* is sometimes used, distinguishing it from *mutual inductance*, as described below.) The basic unit of inductance is the *henry* (abbreviated H).

$$V = -L\frac{\Delta I}{\Delta t}$$

where

V is the induced voltage in volts,
L is the inductance in henries, and
ΔI/Δt is the rate of change of the current in amperes per second.

An inductance of 1 H generates an induced voltage of one volt when the inducing current is varying at a rate of one ampere per second. The minus sign (–) indicates that the induced voltage has a polarity opposing the change in current.

The energy stored in the magnetic field of an inductor is given by the formula:

$$W = \frac{I^2\ L}{2}$$

where

W = energy in joules,
I = current in amperes, and
L = inductance in henrys.

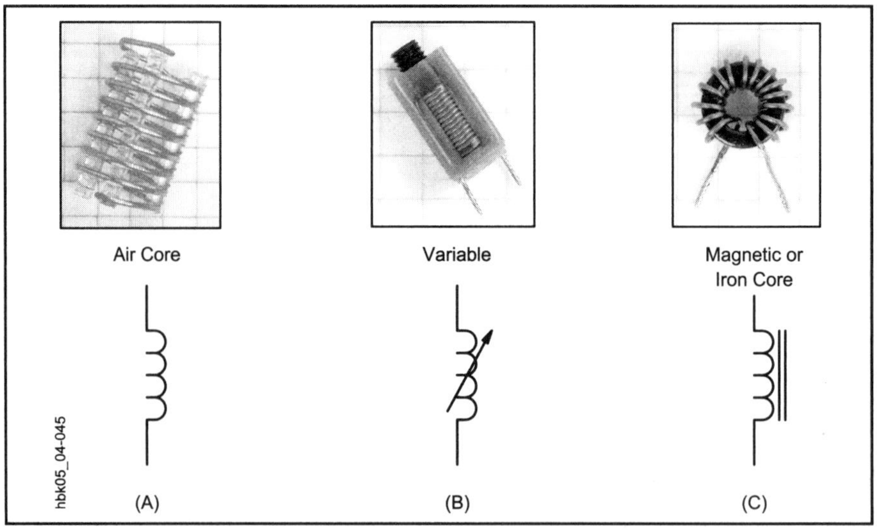

Figure 2.28 — Photos and schematic symbols for representative inductors. A, an air-core inductor; B, a variable inductor with a nonmagnetic slug and C, an inductor with a toroidal magnetic core. The ¼-inch-ruled graph paper background provides a size comparison.

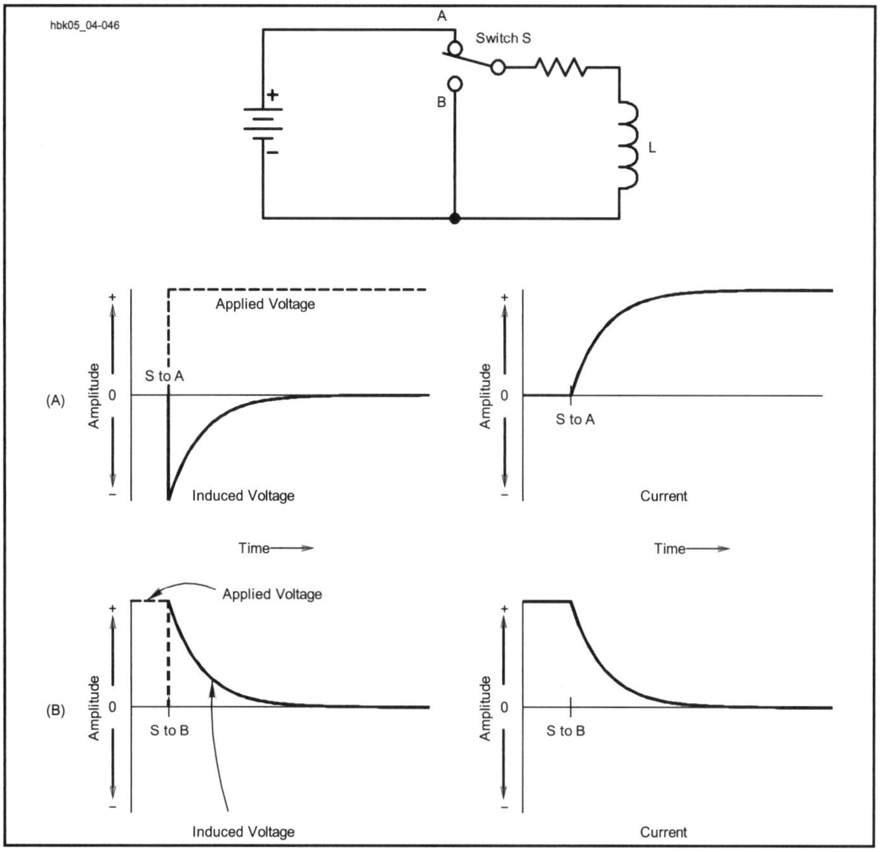

Figure 2.29 — Inductive circuit showing the generation of induced voltage and the rise of current when voltage is applied to an inductor at A, and the decay of current as the coil shorted at B.

This formula corresponds to the energy-storage formula for capacitors: energy storage is a function of current squared. Inductance is proportional to the amount of energy stored in an inductor's magnetic field for a given amount of current. The magnetic field strength, H, is proportional to the number of turns in the inductor's winding, N, (see the equation for magnetic field strength given previously) and for a given amount of current, to the value of μ for the core. Thus, inductance is directly proportional to both N and μ.

The polarity of the induced voltage is always such as to oppose any change in the circuit current. (This is why the term "back" is used, as in back-voltage or *back-EMF* for this reason.) This means that when the current in the circuit is increasing, work is being done against the induced voltage by storing energy in the magnetic field. Likewise, if the current in the circuit tends to decrease, the stored energy of the field returns to the circuit, and adds to the energy being supplied by the voltage source. The net effect of storing and releasing energy is that inductors oppose changes in current just as capacitors oppose changes in voltage. This phenomenon tends to keep the current flowing even though the applied voltage may be decreasing or be removed entirely. Figure 2.29B illustrates the decreasing but continuing flow of current caused by the induced voltage after the source voltage is removed from the circuit.

Inductance depends on the physical configuration of the inductor. All conductors, even straight wires, have inductance. Coiling a conductor increases its inductance. In effect, the growing (or shrinking) magnetic field of each turn produces magnetic lines of force that — in their expansion (or contraction) — intercept the other turns of the coil, inducing a voltage in every other turn. (Recall the two-way relationship between a changing magnetic field and the voltage it creates in a conductor.) The mutuality of the effect, called *magnetic flux linkage* (ψ), multiplies the ability of the coiled conductor to store magnetic energy.

A coil of many turns will have more inductance than one of few turns, if both coils are otherwise physically similar. Furthermore, if an inductor is placed around a magnetic core, its inductance will increase in proportion to the permeability of that core, if the circuit current is below the point at which the core saturates.

In various aspects of radio work, inductors may take values ranging from a fraction of a nanohenry (nH) through millihenrys (mH) up to about 20 H.

Rate of Change

The symbol Δ represents change in the following variable, so that ΔI represents "change in current" and Δt "change in time." A rate of change per unit of time is often expressed in this manner. When the amount of time over which the change is measured becomes very small, the letter *d* replaces Δ in both the numerator and denominator to indicate infinitesimal changes. This notation is used in the derivation and presentation of the functions that describe the behavior of electric circuits.

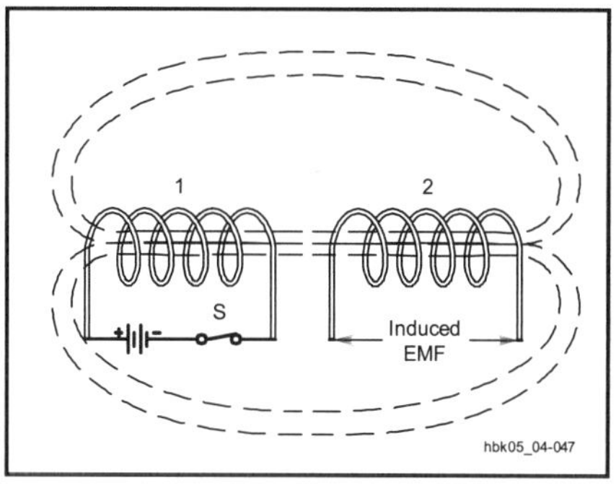

Figure 2.30 — Mutual inductance: When S is closed, current flows through coil number 1, setting up a magnetic field that induces a voltage in the turns of coil number 2.

2.7.4 Mutual Inductance and Magnetic Coupling

When two inductors are arranged with their axes aligned as shown in **Figure 2.30**, current flowing in through inductor 1 creates a magnetic field that intercepts inductor 2. Consequently, a voltage will be induced in inductor 2 whenever the field strength of inductor 1 is changing. This induced voltage is similar to the voltage of self-induction, but since it appears in the second inductor because of current flowing in the first, it is a mutual effect and results from the *mutual inductance* between the two inductors.

When all the flux set up by one coil intercepts all the turns of the other coil, the mutual inductance has its maximum possible value. If only a small part of the flux set up by one coil intercepts the turns of the other, the mutual inductance is relatively small. Two inductors having mutual inductance are said to be *coupled*.

The ratio of actual mutual inductance to the maximum possible value that could theoretically be obtained with two given inductors is called the *coefficient of coupling* between the inductors. It is expressed as a percentage or as a value between 0 and 1. Inductors that have nearly the maximum possible mutual inductance (coefficient = 1 or 100%) are said to be closely, or tightly, coupled. If the mutual inductance is relatively small the inductors are said to be loosely coupled. The degree of coupling depends upon the physical spacing between the inductors and how they are placed with respect to each other. Maximum coupling exists when they have a common or parallel axis and are as close together as possible (for example, one wound over the other). The coupling is least when the inductors are far apart or are placed so their axes are at right angles.

The maximum possible coefficient of coupling is closely approached when the two inductors are wound on a closed iron core. The coefficient with air-core inductors may run as high as 0.6 or 0.7 if one inductor is wound over the other, but will be much less if the two inductors are separated. Although unity coupling is suggested by Figure 2.30, such coupling is possible only when the inductors are wound on a closed magnetic core.

Coupling between inductors can be minimized by using separate closed magnetic cores for each. Since an inductor's magnetic field is contained almost entirely in a closed core, two inductors with separate closed cores, such as the toroidal inductor in Figure 2.28C, can be placed close together in almost any relative orientation without coupling.

UNWANTED COUPLING

The inductance of a short length of straight wire is small, but it may not be negligible. (In free-space, round wire has an inductance on the order of 1 μH/m, but this is affected by wire diameter and the total circuit's physical configuration.) Appreciable voltage may be induced in even a few inches of wire carrying ac by changing magnetic fields with a frequency on the order of 100 MHz or higher. At much lower frequencies or at dc, the inductance of the same wire might be ignored because the induced voltage would be very small.

There are many phenomena, both natural and man-made, that create sufficiently strong or rapidly-changing magnetic fields to induce voltages in conductors. Many of them create brief but intense pulses of energy called *transients* or "spikes." The magnetic fields from these transients intercept wires leading into and out of — and wires wholly within — electronic equipment, inducing unwanted voltages by mutual coupling.

Lightning is a powerful natural source of magnetically-coupled transients. Strong transients can also be generated by sudden changes in current in nearby circuits or wiring. High-speed digital signals and pulses can also induce voltages in adjacent conductors.

2.7.5 Inductances in Series and Parallel

When two or more inductors are connected in series (left side of **Figure 2.31**), the total inductance is equal to the sum of the individual inductances, provided that the inductors are sufficiently separated so that there is no coupling between them (see the preceding section):

$$L_{total} = L1 + L2 + L3 \ldots + L_n$$

If inductors are connected in parallel (right side of Figure 2.31), again assuming no mutual coupling, the total inductance is given by:

$$L_{total} = \frac{1}{\frac{1}{L1} + \frac{1}{L2} + \frac{1}{L3} + \ldots + \frac{1}{L_n}}$$

For only two inductors in parallel, the formula becomes:

$$L_{total} = \frac{L1 \times L2}{L1 + L2}$$

Thus, the rules for combining inductances in series and parallel are the same as those for resistances, assuming there is no coupling between the inductors. When there is coupling between the inductors, the formulas given above will not yield correct results.

2.7.6 RL Time Constant

As with capacitors, the time dependence of inductor current is a significant property. A comparable situation to an RC circuit exists when resistance and inductance are connected in series. In **Figure 2.32**, first consider the case in which R is zero. Closing S1 sends a current through the circuit. The instantaneous transition from no current to a finite value, however small, represents a rapid change in current, and an opposing voltage is induced in L. The value of the opposing voltage is almost equal to the applied voltage, so the resulting initial current is very small.

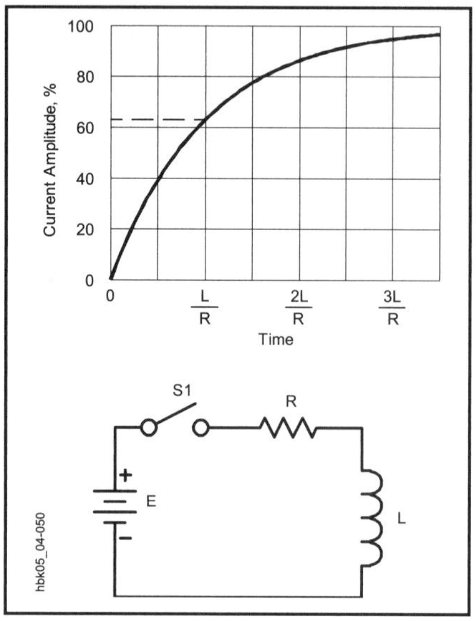

Figure 2.32 — Time constant of an RL circuit being energized.

The opposing voltage is created by change in the inductor current and would cease to exist if the current did not continue to increase. With no resistance in the circuit, the current would increase forever, always growing just fast enough to keep the self-induced opposing voltage just below the applied voltage.

When resistance in the circuit limits the current, the opposing voltage induced in L must only equal the difference between E and the drop across R, because that is the voltage actually applied to L. This difference becomes smaller as the current approaches its final value, limited by Ohm's Law to I = E/R. Theoretically, the opposing voltage never quite disappears, and so the current never quite reaches the Ohm's Law limit. In practical terms, the difference eventually becomes insignificant, just as described above for capacitors charging to an applied voltage through a resistor.

The inductor current at any time after the switch in Figure 2.32 has been closed, can be found from:

$$I(t) = \frac{E}{R}\left(1 - e^{-\frac{tR}{L}}\right)$$

where

I(t) = current in amperes at time t,
E = power source potential in volts,
t = time in seconds after application of voltage,
e = natural logarithmic base = 2.718,
R = circuit resistance in ohms, and
L= inductance in henrys.

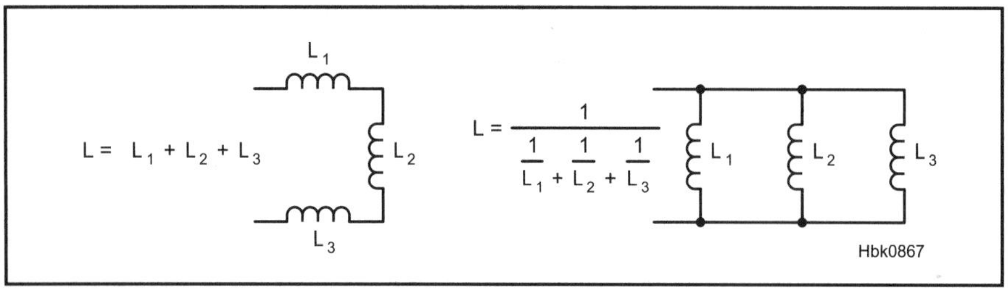

Figure 2.31 — Inductors in series and parallel.

(References that explain exponential equations, e, and other mathematical topics are found in the "Radio Mathematics" article in this book's downloadable supplemental information.) The term E/R in this equation represents the dc value of I, or the value of I(t) when t becomes very large; this is the *steady-state value* of I. If t = L/R, the above equation becomes:

$$V(L/R) = \frac{E}{R}(1 - e^{-1}) \approx 0.632\frac{E}{R}$$

The time in seconds required for the current to build up to 63.2% of the maximum value is called the *time constant* (also the *RL time constant*), and is equal to L/R, where L is in henrys and R is in ohms. (Time constants are also discussed in the section on RC circuits above.) After each time interval equal to this constant, the current increases by an additional 63.2% closer to the final value of E/R. This behavior is graphed in Figure 2.32. As is the case with capacitors, after five time constants the current is considered to have reached its maximum value. As with capacitors, we use the lower-case Greek tau (τ) to represent the time constant.

Example: If a circuit has an inductor of 5.0 mH in series with a resistor of 10 Ω, how long will it take for the current in the circuit to reach full value after power is applied? Since achieving maximum current takes approximately five time constants,

$$t = \frac{5\,L}{R} = \frac{5 \times 5.0 \times 10^{-3}\ \text{H}}{10\ \Omega}$$

$$= 2.5 \times 10^{-3}\ \text{seconds} = 2.5\ \text{ms}$$

Note that if the inductance is increased to 5.0 H, the required time increases by a factor of 1000 to 2.5 seconds. Since the circuit resistance didn't change, the final current is the same for both cases in this example. Increasing inductance increases the time required to reach full current.

Zero resistance would prevent the circuit from ever achieving full current. All practical inductors have some resistance in the wire making up the inductor.

An inductor cannot be discharged in the simple circuit of Figure 2.32 because the magnetic field ceases to exist or "collapses" as soon as the current ceases. Opening S1 does not leave the inductor charged in the way that a capacitor would remain charged. Energy storage in a capacitor depends on the separated charges staying in place. Energy storage in an inductor depends on the charges continuing to move as current.

The energy stored in the inductor's magnetic field attempts to return instantly to the circuit when S1 is opened. The rapidly changing (collapsing) field in the inductor causes a very large voltage to be induced across the inductor. Because the change in current is now in the opposite direction, the induced voltage also reverses polarity. This induced voltage (called *inductive kick-back*) is usually many times larger than the originally applied voltage, because the induced voltage is proportional to the rate at which the field changes.

The common result of opening the switch in such a circuit is that a spark or arc forms at the switch contacts during the instant the switch opens. When the inductance is large and the current in the circuit is high, large amounts of energy are released in a very short time. It is not at all unusual for the switch contacts to burn or melt under such circumstances.

The spark or arc at the opened switch can be reduced or suppressed by connecting a suitable capacitor and resistor in series across the contacts to absorb the energy non-destructively. Such an RC combination is called a *snubber network*. The current rating for a switch may be significantly reduced if it is used in an inductive circuit.

Transistor switches connected to and controlling inductors, such as relays and solenoids, also require protection from the high kick-back voltages. In most cases, a small power diode connected across the relay coil so that it does not conduct current when the inductor is energized (called a *kick-back diode*) will protect the transistor.

If the excitation is removed without breaking the circuit, as shown in **Figure 2.33**, the current will decay according to the formula:

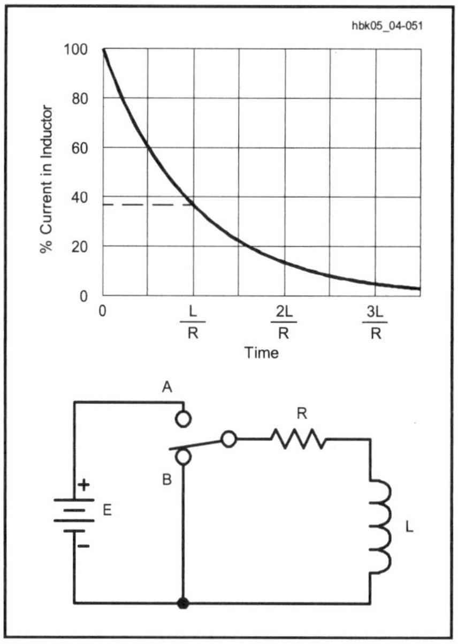

Figure 2.33 — Time constant of an RL circuit being de-energized. This is a theoretical model only, since a mechanical switch cannot change state instantaneously.

$$I(t) = \frac{E}{R}\left(e^{-\frac{tR}{L}}\right)$$

where t = time in seconds after removal of the source voltage.

After one time constant the current will decay by 63.2% of its steady-state value. (It will decay to 36.8% of the steady-state value.) The graph in Figure 2.33 shows the current-decay waveform to be identical to the voltage-discharge waveform of a capacitor. Be careful about applying the terms *charge* and *discharge* to an inductive circuit, however. These terms refer to energy storage in an electric field. An inductor stores energy in a magnetic field and the usual method of referring to the process is *energize* and *de-energize* (although it is not always followed).

2.8 Semiconductor Devices

2.8.1 Introduction to Semiconductors

In a conductor, such as a metal, some of the outer, or *valence*, electrons of each atom are free to move about between atoms. These *free electrons* are the constituents of electrical current. In a good conductor, the concentration of these free electrons is very high, on the order of 10^{22} electrons/cm^3. In an insulator, nearly all the electrons are tightly held by their atoms and the concentration of free electrons is very small — on the order of 10 electrons/cm^3.

Between the classes of materials considered to be conductors and insulators is a class of elements called *semiconductors*, materials with conductivity much poorer than metals and much better than insulators. (In electronics, "semiconductor" means a device made from semiconductor elements that have been chemically manipulated as described below, leading to interesting properties that create useful applications.)

Semiconductor atoms (silicon, Si, is the most widely used) share their valence electrons in a chemical bond that holds adjacent atoms together, forming a three-dimensional *lattice* that gives the material its physical characteristics. A lattice of pure semiconductor material (one type of atom or molecule) can form a crystal, in which the lattice structure and orientation is preserved throughout the material. *Monocrystalline* or "single-crystal" is the type of material used in electronic semiconductor devices. *Polycrystalline* material is made of up many smaller crystals with their own individual lattice orientations.

Crystals of pure semiconductor material are called *intrinsic* semiconductors. When energy, generally in the form of heat, is added to a semiconductor crystal lattice, some electrons are liberated from their bonds and move freely throughout the lattice. The bond that loses an electron is then unbalanced and the space that the electron came from is referred to as a *hole*. In these materials the number of free electrons is equal to the number of holes.

Electrons from adjacent bonds can leave their positions to fill the holes, thus leaving behind a hole in their old location. As a consequence of the electron moving, two opposite movements can be said to occur: negatively charged electrons move from bond to bond in one direction and positively charged holes move from bond to bond in the opposite direction. Both of these movements represent forms of electrical current, but this is very different from the current in a conductor. While a conductor has free electrons that flow independently from the bonds of the crystalline lattice, the current in a pure semiconductor is constrained to move from bond to bond.

Impurities can be added to intrinsic semiconductors (by a process called *doping*) to enhance the formation of electrons or holes and thus improve conductivity. These materials are *extrinsic* semiconductors. Since the additional electrons and holes can move, their movement is current and they are called *carriers*. The type of carrier that predominates in the material is called the *majority carrier*. In N-type material the majority carriers are electrons and in P-type material, holes.

There are two types of impurities that can be added: a *donor impurity* with five valence electrons donates free electrons to the crystalline structure; this is called an *N-type* impurity, for the negative charge of the majority carriers. Some examples of donor impurities are antimony (Sb), phosphorus (P) and arsenic (As). N-type extrinsic semiconductors have more electrons and fewer holes than intrinsic semiconductors. *Acceptor impurities* with three valence electrons accept free electrons from the lattice, adding holes to the overall structure. These are called P-type impurities, for the positive charge of the majority carriers; some examples are boron (B), gallium (Ga) and indium (In).

It is important to note that even though N-type and P-type material have different numbers of holes and free electrons than intrinsic material, they are still electrically neutral. When an electron leaves an atom, the positively-charged atom that remains in place in the crystal lattice electrically balances the roaming free electron. Similarly, an atom gaining an electron acquires a negative charge that balances the positively-charged atom it left. At no time does the material acquire a net electrical charge, positive or negative.

Compound semiconductor material can be formed by combining equal amounts of N-type and P-type impurity materials. Some examples of this include gallium-arsenide (GaAs), gallium-phosphate (GaP) and indium-phosphide (InP). To make an N-type compound semiconductor, a slightly higher amount of N-type material is used in the mixture. A P-type compound semiconductor has a little more P-type material in the mixture.

Impurities are introduced into intrinsic semiconductors by diffusion, the same physical process that lets you smell cookies baking from several rooms away. (Molecules diffuse through air much faster than through solids.) Rates of diffusion are proportional to temperature, so semiconductors are doped with impurities at high temperature to save time. Once the doped semiconductor material is cooled, the rate of diffusion of the impurities is so low that they are essentially immobile for many years to come. If an electronic device made from a structure of N- and P-type materials is raised to a high temperature, such as by excessive current, the impurities can again migrate and the internal structure of the device may be destroyed. The maximum operating temperature for semiconductor devices is specified at a level low enough to limit additional impurity diffusion.

The conductivity of an extrinsic semiconductor depends on the charge density (in other words, the concentration of free electrons in N-type, and holes in P-type, semiconductor material). As the energy in the semiconductor increases, the charge density also increases. This is the basis of how all semiconductor devices operate: the major difference is the way in which the energy level is increased. Variations include: The *transistor*, where conductivity is altered by injecting current into the device via a wire; the *thermistor*, where the level of heat in the device is detected by its conductivity, and the *photoconductor*, where light energy that is absorbed by the semiconductor material increases the conductivity.

2.8.2 The PN Semiconductor Junction

If a piece of N-type semiconductor material is placed against a piece of P-type semiconductor material, the location at which they join is called a *PN junction*. The junction has characteristics that make it possible to develop diodes and transistors. The action of the junction is best described by a diode operating as a rectifier.

Initially, when the two types of semiconductor material are placed in contact, each type of material will have only its majority carriers: P-type will have only holes and N-type will have only free electrons. The presence of the positive charges (holes) in the P-type material attracts free electrons from the N-type material immediately across the junction. The opposite is true in the N-type material.

These attractions lead to diffusion of some of the majority carriers across the junction, which combine with and neutralize the majority carriers immediately on the other side (a process called *recombination*). As distance from the junction increases, the attraction quickly becomes too small to cause the carriers to move. The region close to the junction is then *depleted* of carriers, and so is named the *depletion region* (also the *space-charge region* or the *transition region*). The width of the depletion region is very small, on the order of 0.5 µm.

If the N-type material (the *cathode*) is placed at a more negative voltage than the P-type material (the *anode*), current will pass through the junction because electrons are attracted from the lower potential to the higher potential and holes are attracted in the opposite direction. This *forward bias* forces the majority carriers toward the junction where recombination occurs with the opposite type of majority carrier. The source of voltage supplies replacement electrons to the N-type material and removes electrons from the P-type material so that the majority carriers are continually replenished. Thus, the net effect is a *forward current* flowing through the semiconductor, across the PN junction. The *forward resistance* of a diode conducting current is typically very low and varies with the amount of forward current.

When the polarity is reversed, majority-carriers are attracted away from the junction, not toward it. Very little current flows across the PN junction — called *reverse leakage current* — in this case. Allowing only unidirectional current flow is what allows a semiconductor diode to act as rectifier.

2.8.3 Junction Semiconductors

Semiconductor devices that operate using the principles of a PN junction are called *junction semiconductors*. These devices can have one or several junctions. The properties of junction semiconductors can be tightly controlled by the characteristics of the materials used and the size and shape of the junctions.

SEMICONDUCTOR DIODES

Diodes are commonly made of silicon and occasionally germanium. Although they act similarly, they have slightly different characteristics. The *junction threshold voltage*, or *junction barrier voltage,* is the forward bias voltage (V_F) at which current begins to pass through the device. This voltage is different for the two kinds of diodes. In the diode response curve of **Figure 2.34**, V_F corresponds to the voltage at which the positive portion of the curve begins to rise sharply from the x-axis. Most silicon diodes have a junction threshold voltage of about 0.7 V, while the voltage for germanium diodes is typically 0.3 V. Reverse leakage current is much lower for silicon diodes than for germanium diodes.

The characteristic curve for a semiconductor diode junction is given by the following equation (slightly simplified) called the *Fundamental Diode Equation* because it describes the behavior of all semiconductor PN junctions.

$$I = I_S \left(e^{\frac{V}{\eta V_t}} - 1 \right)$$

where

I = diode current

V = diode voltage

I_s = reverse-bias saturation current

V_t = kT/q, the thermal equivalent of voltage (about 25 mV at room temperature)

η = emission coefficient.

The value of I_s varies with the type of semiconductor material, with the value of 10^{-12} used for silicon. η also varies from 1 to 2 with the type of material and method of fabrication. (η is close to 1 for silicon at normal current values, increasing to 2 at high currents.) This curve is shown in **Figure 2.35B**.

The obvious differences between Figure 2.35A and B are that the semiconductor diode has a finite *turn-on* voltage — it requires a small but nonzero forward bias voltage before it begins conducting. Furthermore, once conducting, the diode voltage continues to increase very slowly with increasing current, unlike a true short circuit. Finally, when the applied voltage is negative, the reverse current is not exactly zero but very small (microamperes). The reverse current flow rapidly reaches a level that varies little with the reverse bias voltage. This is the *reverse-bias saturation current*, I_s.

For bias (dc) circuit calculations, a useful model for the diode that takes these two effects into account is shown by the artificial I-V curve in Figure 2.35C. This model neglects the negligible reverse bias current I_s.

When converted into an equivalent circuit, the model in Figure 2.35C yields the circuit in Figure 2.35D. The ideal voltage source V_a represents the turn-on voltage and R_f represents the effective resistance caused by the small increase in diode voltage as the diode current increases. The turn-on voltage is material-dependent: approximately 0.3 V for germanium diodes and 0.7 for silicon. R_f is typically on the order of 10 Ω, but it can vary according to the specific component. R_f can often be completely neglected in comparison to the other resistances in the circuit. This very common simplification leaves only a pure *voltage drop* for the diode model.

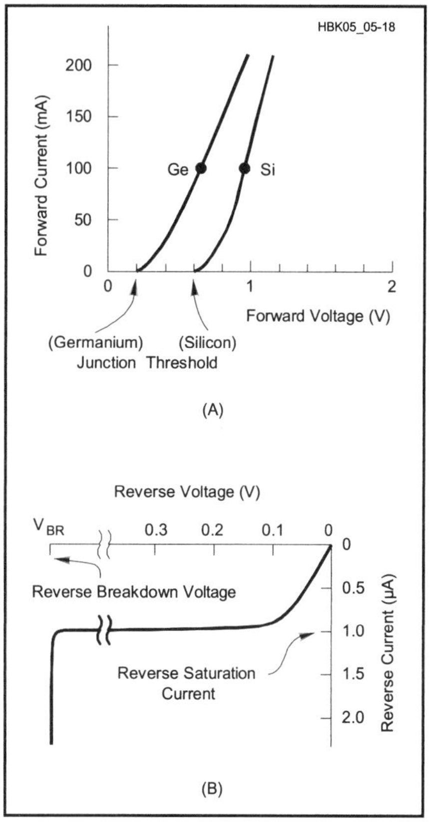

Figure 2.34 — Semiconductor diode (PN junction) characteristic curve. (A) Forward- biased (anode voltage higher than cathode) response for Germanium (Ge) and Silicon (Si) devices. Each curve breaks away from the X-axis at its junction threshold voltage. The slope of each curve is its forward resistance. (B) Reverse-biased response. Very small reverse current increases until it reaches the reverse saturation current (I_0). The reverse current increases suddenly and drastically when the reverse voltage reaches the reverse breakdown voltage, V_{BR}.

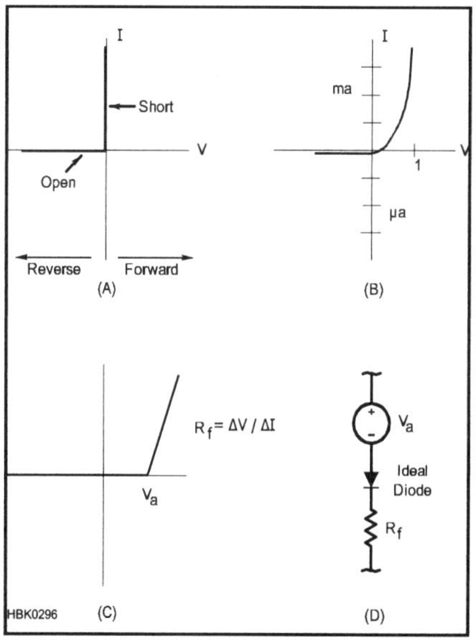

Figure 2.35 — Circuit models for rectifying switches (diodes). A: I-V curve of the ideal rectifier. B: I-V curve of a typical semiconductor diode showing the typical small leakage current in the reverse direction. Note the different scales for forward and reverse current. C shows a simplified diode I-V curve for dc-circuit calculations (at a much larger scale than B). D is an equivalent circuit for C.

BIPOLAR TRANSISTOR

A bipolar transistor is formed when two PN junctions are placed next to each other. If N-type material is surrounded by P-type material, the result is a PNP transistor. Alternatively, if P-type material is in the middle of two layers of N-type material, the NPN transistor is formed (**Figure 2.36**).

Physically, we can think of the transistor as two PN junctions back-to-back, such as two diodes connected at their *anodes* (the positive terminal) for an NPN transistor or two diodes connected at their *cathodes* (the negative terminal) for a PNP transistor. The connection point is the base of the transistor. (You can't actually make a transistor this way — this is a representation for illustration only.)

A transistor conducts when the base-emitter junction is forward biased and the base-collector is reverse biased. Under these conditions, the emitter region emits majority carriers into the base region, where they become minority carriers because the materials of the emitter and base regions have opposite polarity. The excess minority carriers in the base are then attracted across the very thin base to the base-collector junction, where they are collected and are once again considered majority carriers before they can flow to the base terminal.

The flow of majority carriers from emitter to collector can be modified by the application of a bias current to the base terminal. If the bias current causes majority carriers to be injected into the base material (electrons flowing into an N-type base or out of a P-type base) the emitter-collector current increases. In this way, a transistor allows a small base current to control a much larger collector current.

As in a semiconductor diode, the forward biased base-emitter junction has a threshold voltage (V_{BE}) that must be exceeded before the emitter current increases. As the base-emitter current continues to increase, the point is reached at which further increases in base-emitter current cause no additional change in collector current. This is the condition of *saturation*. Conversely, when base-emitter current is reduced to the point at which collector current ceases to flow, that is the situation of *cutoff*.

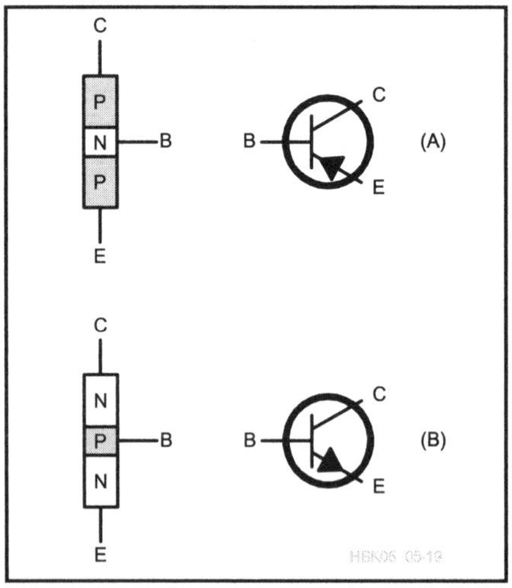

Figure 2.36 — Bipolar transistors. (A) A layer of N-type semiconductor sandwiched between two layers of P-type semiconductor makes a PNP device. The schematic symbol has three leads: collector (C), base (B) and emitter (E), with the arrow pointing in toward the base. (B) A layer of P-type semiconductor sandwiched between two layers of N-type semiconductor makes an NPN device. The schematic symbol has three leads: collector (C), base (B) and emitter (E), with the arrow pointing out away from the base.

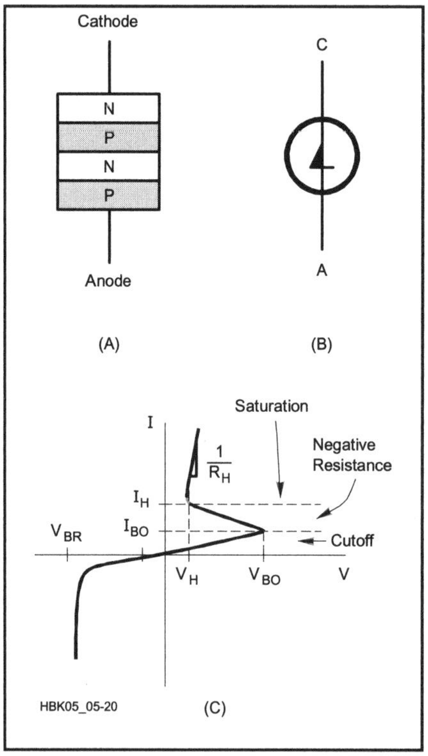

Figure 2.37 — PNPN diode. (A) Alternating layers of P-type and N-type semiconductor. (B) Schematic symbol with cathode (C) and anode (A) leads. (C) I-V curve. Reverse-biased response is the same as normal PN junction diodes. Forward biased response acts as a hysteresis switch. Resistance is very high until the bias voltage reaches V_{BO} (where the center junction breaks over) and exceeds the cutoff current, I_{BO}. The device exhibits a negative resistance when the current increases as the bias voltage decreases until a voltage of V_H and saturation current of I_H is reached. After this, the resistance is very low, with large increases in current for small voltage increases.

THYRISTORS

Thyristors are semiconductors made with four or more alternating layers of P- and N-type semiconductor material. In a four-layer thyristor, when the anode is at a higher potential than the cathode, the first and third junctions are forward biased and the center junction reverse biased. In this state, there is little current, just as in the reverse-biased diode. The different types of thyristor have different ways in which they turn on to conduct current and in how they turn off to interrupt current flow.

PNPN Diode

The simplest thyristor is a PNPN (usually pronounced like *pinpin*) diode with three junctions (see **Figure 2.37**). As the forward bias voltage is increased, the current through the device increases slowly until the *breakover (or firing) voltage*, V_{BO}, is reached and the flow of current abruptly increases. The PNPN diode is often considered to be a switch that is off below V_{BO} and on above it.

Bilateral Diode Switch (Diac)

A semiconductor device similar to two

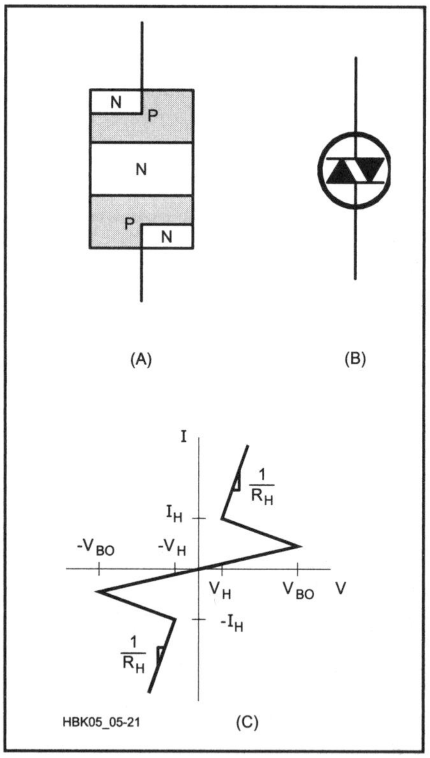

Figure 2.38 — Bilateral switch. (A) Alternating layers of P-type and N-type semiconductor. (B) Schematic symbol. (C) I-V curve. The right-hand side of the curve is identical to the PNPN diode response in Figure 2.37. The device responds identically for both forward and reverse bias so the left-hand side of the curve is symmetrical with the right-hand side.

PNPN diodes facing in opposite directions and attached in parallel is the *bilateral diode switch* or *diac*. This device has the characteristic curve of the PNPN diode for both positive and negative bias voltages. Its construction, schematic symbol and characteristic curve are shown in **Figure 2.38**.

Silicon Controlled Rectifier (SCR)

Another device with four alternate layers of P-type and N-type semiconductor is the *silicon controlled rectifier (SCR)*. (Some sources refer to an SCR as a thyristor, as well.) In addition to the connections to the outer two layers, two other terminals can be brought out for the inner two layers. The connection to the P-type material near the cathode is called the *cathode gate* and the N-type material near the anode is called the *anode gate*. In nearly all commercially available SCRs, only the cathode gate is connected (**Figure 2.39**).

Like the PNPN diode switch, the SCR is used to abruptly start conducting when the voltage exceeds a given level. By biasing the gate terminal appropriately, the breakover voltage can be adjusted.

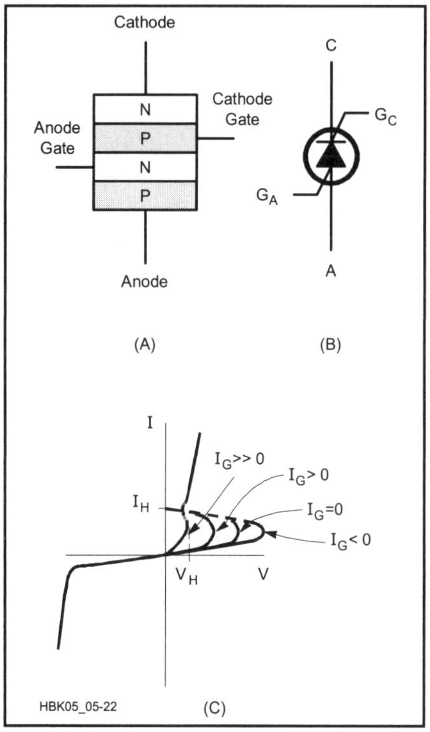

Figure 2.39 — SCR. (A) Alternating layers of P-type and N-type semiconductor. This is similar to a PNPN diode with gate terminals attached to the interior layers. (B) Schematic symbol with anode (A), cathode (C), anode gate (G_A) and cathode gate (G_C). Many devices are constructed without G_A. (C) I-V curve with different responses for various gate currents. I_G = 0 has a similar response to the PNPN diode.

Triac

A five-layered semiconductor whose operation is similar to a bidirectional SCR is the *triac* (**Figure 2.40**). This is also similar to a bidirectional diode switch with a bias control gate. The gate terminal of the triac can control both positive and negative breakover voltages and the devices can pass both polarities of voltage.

Thyristor Applications

The SCR is highly efficient and is used in power control applications. SCRs are available that can handle currents of greater than 100 A and voltage differentials of greater than 1000 V, yet can be switched with gate currents of less than 50 mA. Because of their high current-handling capability, SCRs are used as "crowbars" in power supply circuits, to short the output to ground and blow a fuse when an overvoltage condition exists.

SCRs and triacs are often used to control ac power sources. A sine wave with a given RMS value can be switched on and off at preset points during the cycle to decrease the RMS voltage. When conduction is delayed until after the peak (as **Figure 2.41** shows) the peak-to-peak voltage is reduced. If conduction starts before the peak, the RMS voltage is reduced, but the peak-to-peak value remains the same. This method is used to operate light dimmers and 240 V ac to 120 V ac converters. The sharp switching transients created when these devices turn on are common sources of RF interference. (See the chapter on **RF Interference** for information on dealing with interference from thyristors.)

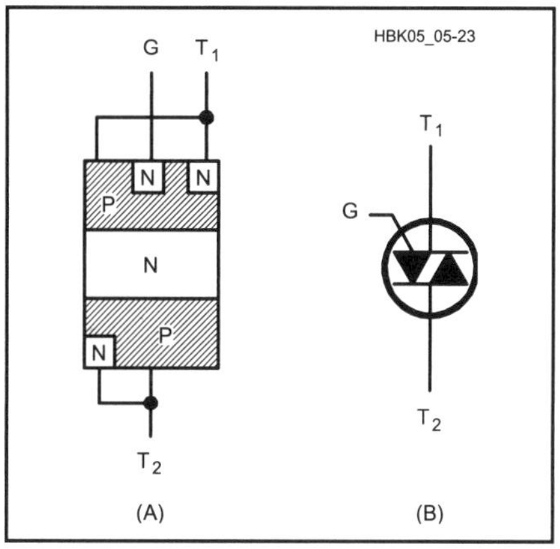

Figure 2.40 — Triac. (A) Alternating layers of P-type and N-type semiconductor. This behaves as two SCR devices facing in opposite directions with the anode of one connected to the cathode of the other and the cathode gates connected together. (B) Schematic symbol.

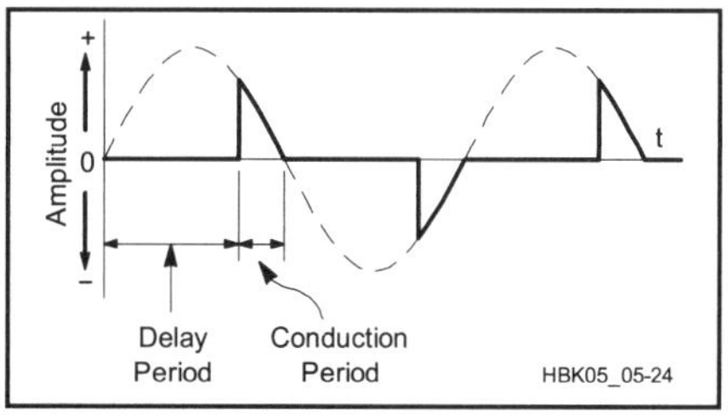

Figure 2.41 — Triac operation on sine wave. The dashed line is the original sine wave and the solid line is the portion that conducts through the triac. The relative delay and conduction period times are controlled by the amount or timing of gate current, I_G. The response of an SCR is the same as this for positive voltages (above the X-axis) and with no conduction for negative voltages.

2.8.4 Field-Effect Transistors (FET)

The *field-effect transistor (FET)* controls the current between two points but does so differently than the bipolar transistor. The FET operates by the effects of an electric field on the flow of electrons through a single type of semiconductor material. This is why the FET is sometimes called a *unipolar* transistor. Unlike bipolar semiconductors that can be arranged in many configurations to provide diodes, transistors, photoelectric devices, temperature sensitive devices and so on, the field effect technique is usually only used to make transistors, although FETs are also available as special-purpose diodes, for use as constant current sources.

FET devices are constructed on a *substrate* of doped semiconductor material. The channel is formed within the substrate and has the opposite polarity (a P-channel FET has N-type substrate). Most FETs are constructed with silicon.

Within the FET, current moves in a *channel* as shown in **Figure 2.42**. The channel is made

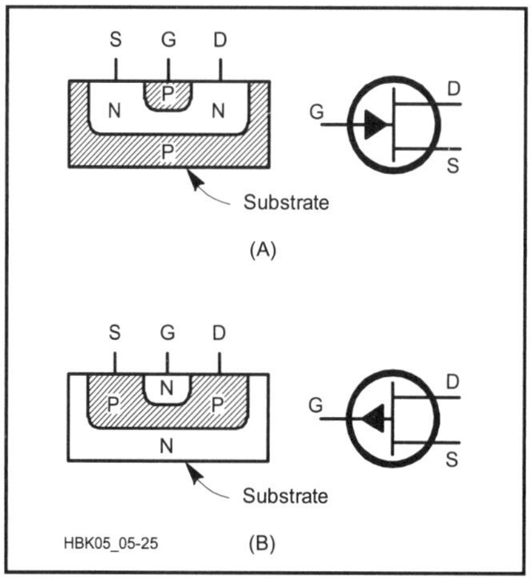

Figure 2.42 — JFET devices with terminals labeled: source (S), gate (G) and drain (D). (A) Pictorial of N-type channel embedded in P-type substrate and schematic symbol. (B) P-channel embedded in N-type substrate and schematic symbol.

of either N-type or P-type semiconductor material; an FET is specified as either an N-channel or P-channel device. Current flows from the *source* terminal (where majority carriers are injected) to the *drain* terminal (where majority carriers are removed). A *gate* terminal generates an electric field that controls the current in the channel.

In N-channel devices, the drain potential must be higher than that of the source ($V_{DS} > 0$) for electrons (the majority carriers) to flow in channel. In P-channel devices, the flow of holes requires that $V_{DS} < 0$. The polarity of the electric field that controls current in the channel is determined by the majority carriers of the channel, ordinarily positive for P-channel FETs and negative for N-channel FETs.

Variations of FET technology are based on different ways of generating the electric field. In all of these, however, electrons at the gate are used only for their charge in order to create an electric field around the channel. There is a minimal flow of electrons through the gate. This leads to a very high dc input resistance in devices that use FETs for their input circuitry. There may be quite a bit of capacitance between the gate and the other FET terminals, however, causing the input impedance to be quite low at high frequencies.

The current through an FET only has to pass through a single type of semiconductor material. Depending on the type of material and the construction of the FET, drain-source resistance when the FET is conducting ($r_{DS(ON)}$) may be anywhere from a few hundred ohms to much less than an ohm. The output impedance of devices made with FETs is generally quite low. If a gate bias voltage is added to operate the transistor near cutoff, the circuit output impedance may be much higher.

In order to achieve a higher gain-bandwidth product, other materials have been used. Gallium-arsenide (GaAs) has *electron mobility* and *drift velocity* (both are measures of how easily electrons are able to move through the crystal lattice) far higher than the standard doped silicon. Amplifiers designed with GaAsFET devices operate at much higher frequencies and with a lower noise factor at VHF and UHF than those made with silicon FETs (although silicon FETs have improved dramatically in recent years).

JFET

One of two basic types of FET, the *junction FET (JFET)* gate material is made of the opposite polarity semiconductor to the channel material (for a P-channel FET the gate is made of N-type semiconductor material). The gate-channel junction is similar to a diode's PN junction with the gate material in direct contact with the channel. JFETs are used with the junction reverse-biased, since any current in the gate is undesirable. The reverse bias of the junction creates an electric field that "pinches" the channel. Since the magnitude of the electric field is proportional to the reverse-bias voltage, the current in the channel is reduced for higher reverse gate bias voltages. When current in the channel is completely halted by the electric field, this is called *pinch-off* and it is analogous to cutoff in a bipolar transistor. The channel in a JFET is at its maximum conductivity when the gate and source voltages are equal ($V_{GS} = 0$).

Because the gate-channel junction in a JFET is similar to a bipolar junction diode, this junction must never be forward biased; otherwise large currents will pass through the gate and into the channel. For an N-channel JFET, the gate must always be at a lower potential than the source ($V_{GS} < 0$). The prohibited condition is for $V_{GS} > 0$. For P-channel JFETs these conditions are reversed (in normal operation $V_{GS} > 0$ and the prohibited condition is for $V_{GS} < 0$).

MOSFET

Placing an insulating layer between the gate and the channel allows for a wider range of control (gate) voltages and further decreases the gate current (and thus increases the device input resistance). The insulator is typically made of an oxide (such as silicon dioxide, SiO_2). This type of device is called a *metal-oxide-semiconductor FET (MOSFET)* or *insulated-gate FET (IGFET)*.

The substrate is often connected to the source internally. The insulated gate is on the opposite side of the channel from the substrate (see **Figure 2.43**). The bias voltage on the gate terminal either attracts or repels the majority carriers of the substrate across its PN-junction with the channel. This narrows (*depletes*) or widens (*enhances*) the channel, respectively, as V_{GS} changes polarity. For example, in the N-channel enhancement-mode MOSFET, positive gate voltages with respect to the substrate and the source ($V_{GS} > 0$) repel holes from the channel into the substrate, thereby widening the channel and

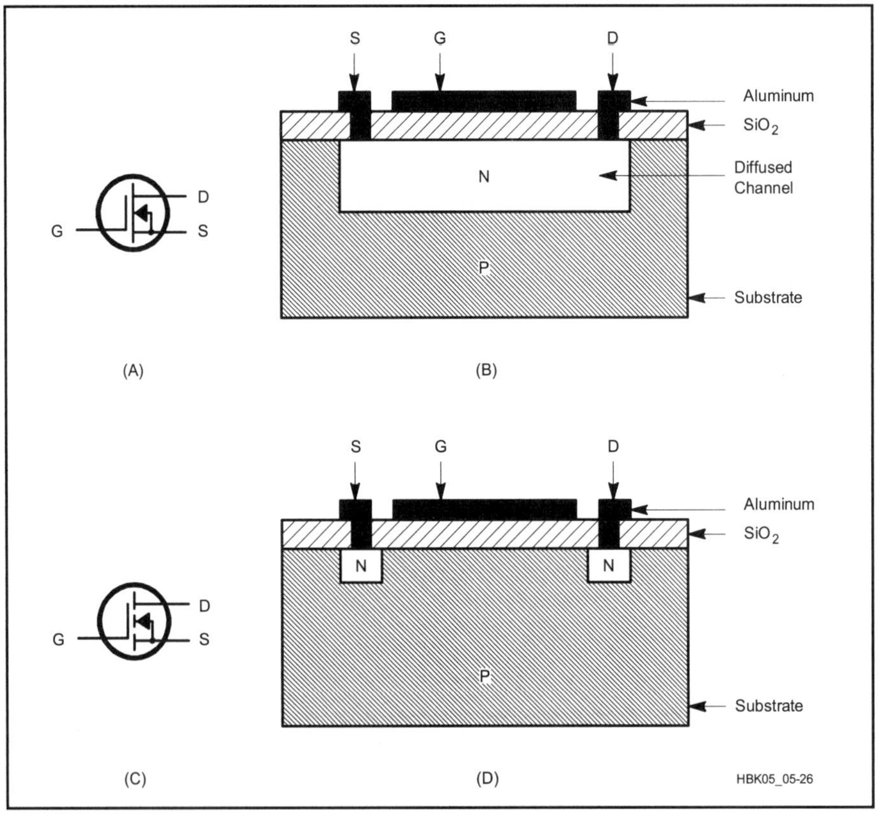

Figure 2.43 — MOSFET devices with terminals labeled: source (S), gate (G) and drain (D). N-channel devices are pictured. P-channel devices have the arrows reversed in the schematic symbols and the opposite type semiconductor material for each of the layers. (A) N-channel depletion mode device schematic symbol and (B) pictorial of P-type substrate, diffused N-type channel, SiO_2 insulating layer and aluminum gate region and source and drain connections. The substrate is connected to the source internally. A negative gate potential narrows the channel. (C) N-channel enhancement mode device schematic and (D) pictorial of P-type substrate, N-type source and drain wells, SiO_2 insulating layer and aluminum gate region and source and drain connections. Positive gate potential forms a channel between the two N-type wells by repelling the P-carriers away from the channel region in the substrate.

decreasing channel resistance. Conversely, $V_{GS} < 0$ causes holes to be attracted from the substrate, narrowing the channel and increasing the channel resistance. Once again, the polarities discussed in this example are reversed for P-channel devices. The common abbreviation for an N-channel MOSFET is *NMOS*, and for a P-channel MOSFET, *PMOS*.

Because of the insulating layer next to the gate, input resistance of a MOSFET is usually greater than $10^{12}\ \Omega$ (a million megohms). Since MOSFETs can both deplete the channel, like the JFET, and also enhance it, the construction of MOSFET devices differs based on the channel size in the quiescent state, $V_{GS} = 0$.

A *depletion mode* device (also called a *normally-on MOSFET*) has a channel in the quiescent state that gets smaller as a reverse bias is applied; this device conducts current with no bias applied (see Figure 2.43A and B). An *enhancement mode* device (also called a *normally-off MOSFET*) is built without a channel and does not conduct current when $V_{GS} = 0$; increasing forward bias forms a temporary channel that conducts current (see Figure 2.43C and D).

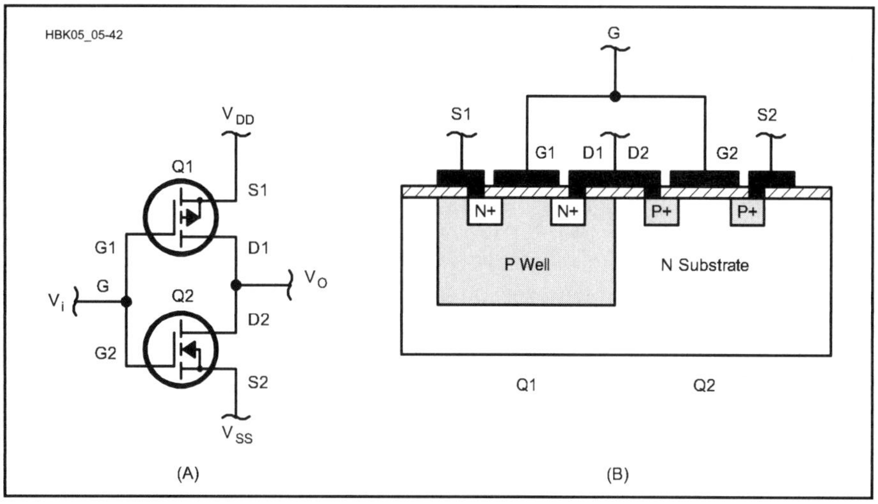

Figure 2.44 — Complementary metal oxide semiconductor (CMOS). (A) CMOS device is made from a pair of enhancement mode MOS transistors. The upper is a P-channel device, and the lower is an N-channel device. When one transistor is biased on, the other is biased off; therefore, there is minimal current from V_{DD} to ground. (B) Implementation of a CMOS pair as an integrated circuit.

Complementary Metal Oxide Semiconductors (CMOS)

Power dissipation in a circuit can be reduced to very small levels (on the order of a few nanowatts) by using MOSFET devices in complementary pairs (CMOS). Each amplifier is constructed of a series circuit of MOSFET devices, as in **Figure 2.44**. The gates are tied together for the input signal, as are the drains for the output signal. In saturation and cutoff, only one of the devices conducts. The current drawn by the circuit under no load is equal to the OFF leakage current of either device and the voltage drop across the pair is equal to V_{DD}, so the steady-state power used by the circuit is always equal to $V_{DD} \times I_{D(OFF)}$. Power is only consumed during the switching process, so for ac signals, power consumption is proportional to frequency.

CMOS circuitry could be built with discrete components, but the number of extra parts and the need for the complementary components to be matched has made that an unusual design technique. The low power consumption and ease of fabrication has made CMOS the most common of all IC technologies. Although CMOS is most commonly used in digital integrated circuitry, its low power consumption has also been put to work by manufacturers of analog ICs, as well as digital ICs.

2.9 References and Bibliography

BOOKS AND ARTICLES

Alexander and Sadiku, *Fundamentals of Electric Circuits* (McGraw-Hill)

Banzhaf, W., WB1ANE, *Understanding Basic Electronics*, 2nd ed (ARRL)

Glover, T., *Pocket Ref* (Sequoia Publishing)

Horowitz and Hill, *The Art of Electronics* (Cambridge University Press)

Kaplan, S., *Wiley Electrical and Electronics Dictionary* (Wiley Press)

Orr, W., *Radio Handbook* (Newnes)

W. Silver, NØAX, "Experiment #117 — Laying Down the Laws," *QST*, Oct 2012, pp 60-61

W. Silver, NØAX, "Experiment #118 — The Laws at Work," *QST*, Nov 2012, pp 70-71

W. Silver, NØAX, "Experiment #138 — E vs V," *QST*, Jul 2014, pp 59-60

Terman, F., *Radio Engineer's Handbook* (McGraw-Hill)

WEBSITES

Rohde & Schwarz, "dB or not dB? Everything you ever wanted to know about decibels but were afraid to ask…," Application Note 1MA98, **www.rohde-schwarz.us/en/applications/db-or-not-db-application-note_56280-15534.html**

Contents

Chapter 3 — Downloadable Supplemental Content

Articles

- "Digital Electronic Basics" by Dale Botkin, NØXAS (from previous editions)
- "Hands-On Radio: Maxwell's Equations — Grad, Div and Curl" by Ward Silver, NØAX
- "Hands-On Radio: Maxwell's Equations — The Wave Emerges" by Ward Silver, NØAX
- "Hands-On Radio: The Effects of Gain-Bandwidth Product" by Ward Silver, NØAX
- "Maxwell Without Tears — A Fresh Look at His Infamous Equations" by Paul Schuch, N6TX
- "Radio Mathematics" — supplemental information about math used in radio and a list of online resources and tutorials about common mathematics
- "Radio Math Formulas and Notes" — a "cheat sheet" for formulas and useful tables and online math resources

Tools

- Frequency Response Spreadsheet

Chapter 3

Radio Fundamentals

Radio begins with an understanding of alternating current waveforms and how they are measured. This chapter also examines the relationship between ac voltage and current in energy-storing components like capacitors and inductors that defines reactance and impedance. We can then explore quality factor (Q) and the properties of resonant circuits.

Analog system concepts are introduced to explain the concepts and techniques of working with electronic circuits in radio. Finally, we discuss electromagnetic waves that carry information between stations.

As for the previous chapter, additional mathematics resources are available in the article "Radio Mathematics" in this book's downloadable supplemental information.

3.1 AC Waveforms

A *waveform* is the pattern of *amplitudes* reached by voltage or current measured over time, including combinations of ac and dc voltages and currents results. For example, **Figure 3.1** shows two ac waveforms fairly close in frequency and their combination. **Figure 3.2** shows two ac waveforms dissimilar in both frequency and wavelength, along with the resultant combined waveform.

3.1.1 Sine Waves and Rotation

Not only is a sine wave the most fundamental ac waveform — energy at a single frequency — it also describes rotation. The cyclical nature of the sine wave is at the heart of much of radio technology, whether analog or digital. A good grasp of the sine wave and the closely related cosine wave are key to understanding the techniques that make up radio. (Sine and cosine functions as well as vectors and phasors are discussed in the "Radio Mathematics" article in this book's downloadable supplemental information.)

Figure 3.3 illustrates the relationship. Imagine a rotating wheel with a visible dot at a point anywhere along the circumference (rim) of the wheel. If you spin the wheel at a constant rate and watch the wheel on-edge as in Figure 3.3A, the dot will just move up and down. If

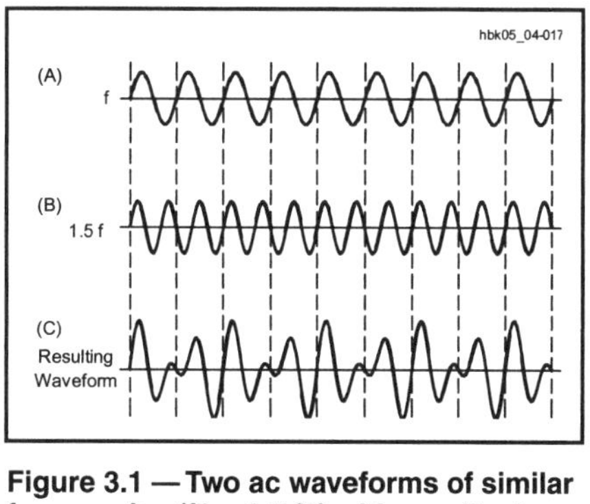

Figure 3.1 — Two ac waveforms of similar frequencies (f1 = 1.5 f2) with amplitudes added together to form a composite wave. Note the points where the positive peaks of the two waves combine to create high composite peaks at a frequency that is the difference between f1 and f2. The beat note frequency is 1.5f – f = 0.5f and is visible in the drawing.

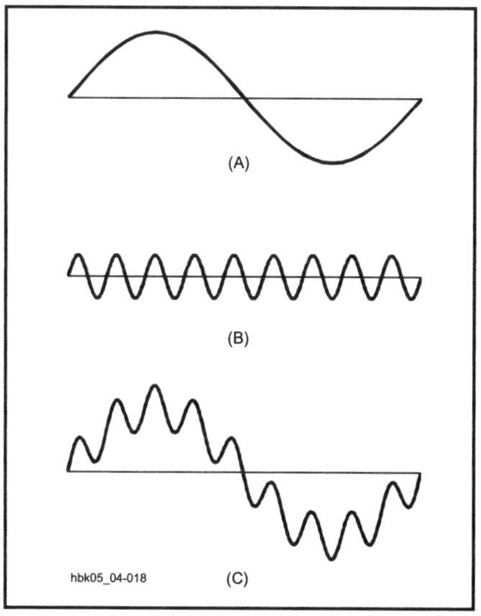

Figure 3.2 — Two ac waveforms of widely different frequencies and amplitudes form a composite wave in which one wave appears to ride upon the other.

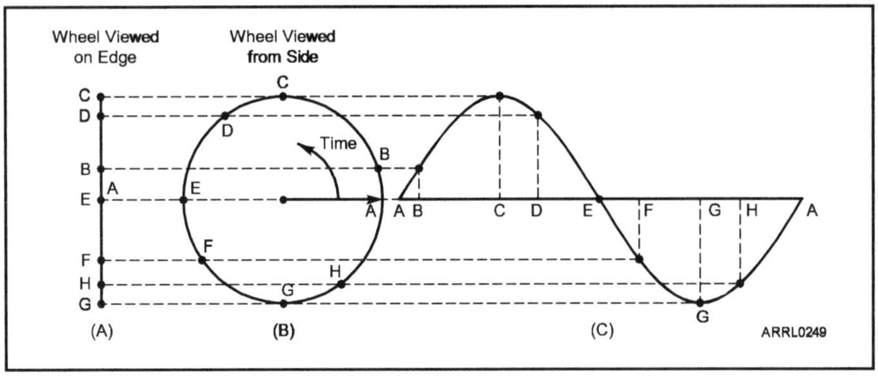

Figure 3.3 — This diagram illustrates the relationship between a sine wave and circular rotation. You can see how various points on the circle correspond to values on the sine wave.

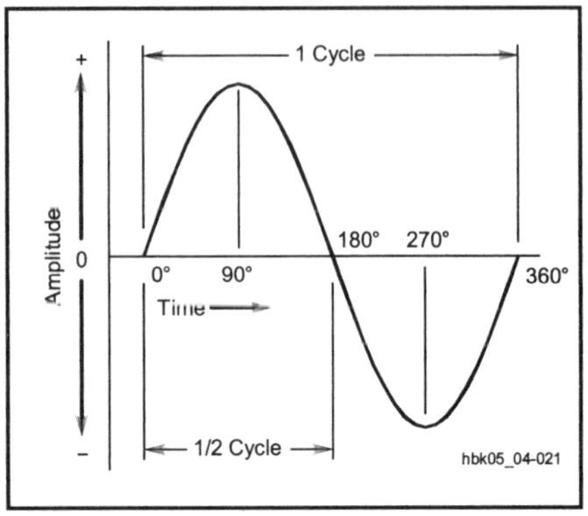

Figure 3.4 — An ac cycle is divided into 360 degrees that are used as a measure of time or phase.

we designate the height at point C as +1 and at point G as –1, then make a table of values as the wheel rotates through 360°, the height values will correspond exactly to the values of the sine function (*sin*). When the wheel is at 0° in position A, sin (0°) = 0; when at 90° in position C, sin (90°) = 1, and so forth all the way around.

Now look at the wheel from the side as in Figure 3.3B. Plotting the dot's height around its circular path against degrees on the horizontal axis will then trace out a sine wave as in Figure 3.3C. Each rotation of the wheel corresponds to one *cycle* of the sine wave. The amplitude (A) of the sine wave is equal to the sine of the wheel's *angular position* in degrees (θ):

$$A = \sin(\theta)$$

Figure 3.4 shows how each cycle of a sine wave is divided into 360° to measure angular position.

3.1.2 Frequency, Period, and Harmonics

With a continuously rotating generator, alternating current or voltage will pass through many equal cycles over time. This is a *periodic waveform*, composed of repeated identical cycles. An arbitrary point on any one cycle can be used as a marker of position on a periodic waveform. For this discussion, the positive peak of the waveform will work as an unambiguous marker. The number of times per second that the current (or voltage) reaches this positive peak in any one second is called the *frequency* of the waveform. In other words, frequency expresses the *rate* at which current (or voltage) cycles occur. The unit of frequency is *cycles per second*, or *hertz*—abbreviated Hz (after Heinrich Hertz, the 19th century physicist who demonstrated the existence of radio waves).

If the sine wave has a constant frequency, every complete cycle takes the same amount of time, the *period*, T, as in **Figure 3.5**. The signal's period is the reciprocal of its frequency:

$$\text{Frequency (f) in Hz} = \frac{1}{\text{Period (T) in seconds}}$$

and

$$\text{Period (T) in seconds} = \frac{1}{\text{Frequency (f) in Hz}}$$

Example: What is the period of 60 Hz ac current?

$$T = \frac{1}{f} = \frac{1}{60\ \text{Hz}} = 0.01666\ \text{s} = 16.6\ \text{ms}$$

To calculate the amplitude, A, of the sine wave at any point in time, t, we need to be able to convert time to the angle, θ:

$$\theta = 360\frac{t}{T}$$

The sine wave equation is now:

$$A = \sin\left(360\frac{t}{T}\right) = \sin\left(360 \times \frac{1}{T} \times t\right) = \sin(360 \times f \times t)$$

HARMONICS

A *harmonic* is a signal with a frequency that is some integer multiple (2, 3, 4 and so on) of a signal at a *fundamental frequency*. Figure 3.5 shows a simple example of harmonics. The harmonic at twice the fundamental's frequency is called the *second harmonic*, at three times the fundamental frequency the *third harmonic*, and so forth. There is no "first harmonic." For example, if a complex waveform is made up of sine waves with frequencies of 10, 20, and 30 kHz, 10 kHz is the fundamental and the other two are harmonics. Signals at the frequency of harmonics are said to be *harmonically related* to the fundamental.

3.1.3 Phase

Now let's make the connection between angular position and time. Although time is measurable in parts of a second, it is more convenient to treat each cycle as a complete time unit divided into 360°. The conventional starting point for phase in a sinusoidal wave-

Degrees, Radians, and Angular Frequency

While most electronic and radio mathematics use degrees as a measure of phase, you will occasionally encounter radians. Radians are used because they are more convenient mathematically in certain types of equations and computations. There are 2π radians in a circle, just as there are 360°, so one radian = 360/2π ≈ 57.3°. In this book, unless it is specifically noted otherwise, the convention will be to use degrees in all calculations of phase or angle.

In engineering textbooks and other electronic references, you will often encounter the symbol ω used to represent angular frequency. The sine wave equation would then be written:

$$A = \sin(2\ \omega\ ft) = \sin(\omega\ t)$$

where ω=2πf. The use of angular frequency is more straightforward in many types of engineering calculations. Radians are used for angular position when angular frequency (ω) is being used.

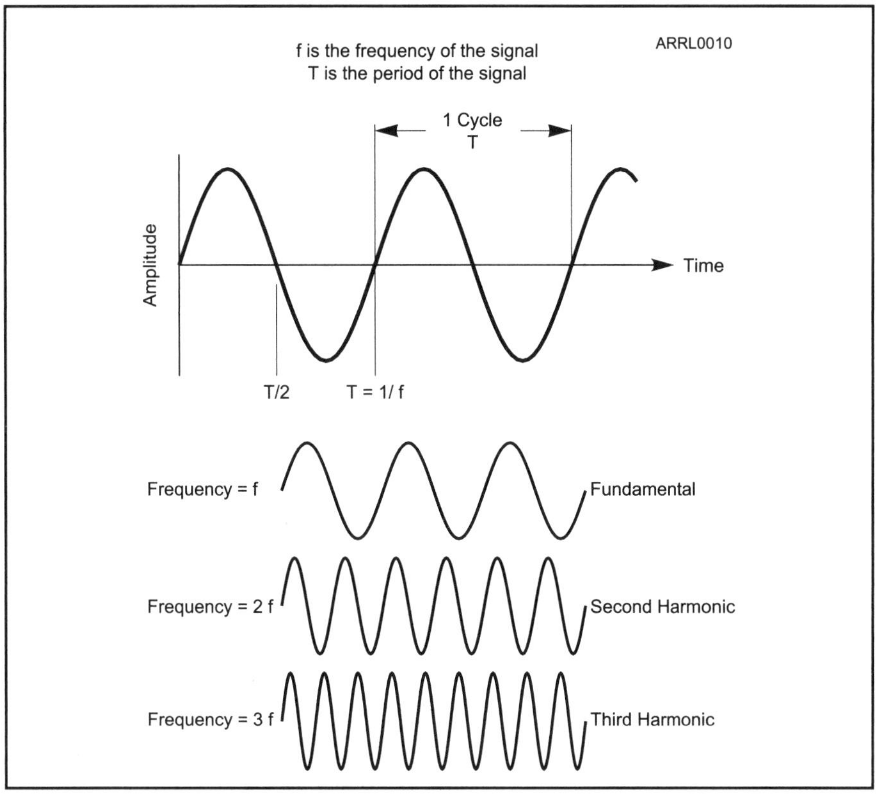

Figure 3.5 — The frequency of a signal and its period are reciprocals. A higher frequency means a shorter period and vice versa. Harmonics are signals with frequencies that are integer multiples of a fundamental frequency.

Phase versus Polarity

It is important to distinguish between polarity and phase. Polarity is the assigned conventions or directions for positive and negative voltage or current. Phase is a function of time or position in a waveform. It is quite possible for two signals to have opposite polarities, but still be in phase, for example. In a multi-phase ac power system, "phase" refers to one of the distinct voltage waveforms generated by the utility.

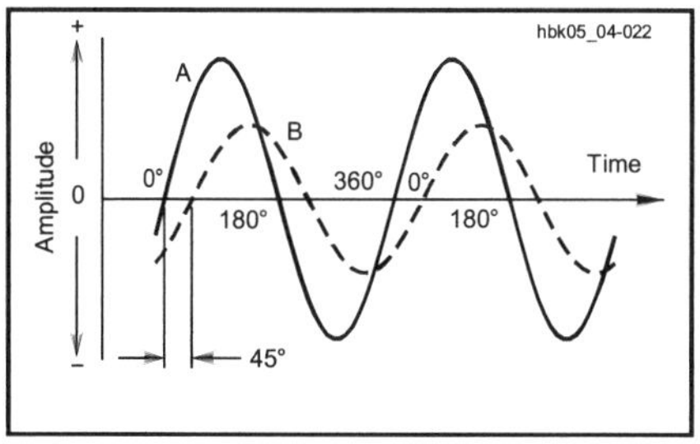

Figure 3.6 — When two waves of the same frequency start their cycles at slightly different times, the time difference or phase difference is measured in degrees. In this drawing, wave B starts 45° (one-eighth cycle) later than wave A, and so lags 45° behind A.

form is the *zero point* at which the positive *half cycle* begins as shown in Figure 3.4.

The advantage of treating the ac cycle in this way is that many calculations and measurements can be taken and recorded in a manner that is independent of frequency. The positive peak voltage or current occurs at 90° into the cycle. Relative to the starting point, 90° is the *phase* of the ac at that point. Phase is the position within an ac cycle expressed in degrees or *radians*. Thus, a complete description of an ac voltage or current involves reference to three properties: frequency, amplitude, and phase.

Each degree of phase represents the same amount of time. For example, a sine wave with a frequency of four cycles per second has a period T = 0.25 second and each degree of phase is equivalent to T/360 = 0.25 / 360 = 0.00069 second.

Phase relationships also permit the comparison of two ac voltages or currents at the same frequency. If the zero point of two signals with the frequency occur at the same time, there is zero phase difference between the signals and they are said to be *in phase.*

Figure 3.6 illustrates two waveforms with a constant phase difference. Since B crosses the zero point in the positive direction after A has already done so, there is a *phase difference* between the two waves. In the example, B *lags* A by 45°, or A *leads* B by 45°. If A and B occur in the same circuit, their composite waveform will also be a sine wave at an intermediate phase angle relative to each. Adding any number of sine waves of the same frequency always results in a sine wave at that frequency. Adding sine waves of different frequencies, as in Figure 3.1, creates a complex waveform with a *beat frequency* that is the difference between the two sine waves.

Figure 3.6 might equally apply to a voltage and a current measured in the same ac circuit. Either A or B might represent the voltage; that is, in some instances voltage will lead the current and in others voltage will lag the current.

Two important special cases appear in **Figure 3.7**. In Part A, line B lags 90° behind line A. Its cycle begins exactly one quarter cycle later than the A cycle. When one wave is passing through zero, the other just reaches its maximum value. In this example, the two sine waves are said to be *in quadrature*. If waveform B is a sine wave, waveform A is a *cosine wave*, leading waveform B by 90°. Quadrature signals form the basis of I/Q modulation, as is described in the **Modulation** chapter. (I and Q stand for In-Phase and Quadrature.)

In Part B, lines A and B are 180° *out of phase*, sometimes called *anti-phase*. In this

Vectors and Phasors

In Figure 3.3B, the arrow drawn from the center of the wheel to point A is a *vector* which has both an amplitude (its length) and direction (its angular position). The amplitude of the vector is equal to its length, which we arbitrarily decided would be 1 when constructing the table of sine values. Since the vector is pointing exactly along the horizontal axis, its direction is 0°. Thus, the vector is described as "1 at an angle of 0°" or "1 with a phase of 0°." In the *phasor notation* commonly used in radio, this is written $1\angle0°$. The rotation of the wheel and the repeated cycles of the sine wave can also be described by a vector that is rotating (spinning around like the hand of a clock) at the frequency of the sine wave. You can find more information about vectors and phasors in the ARRL's "Radio Mathematics" article in the downloadable supplemental information for this book.

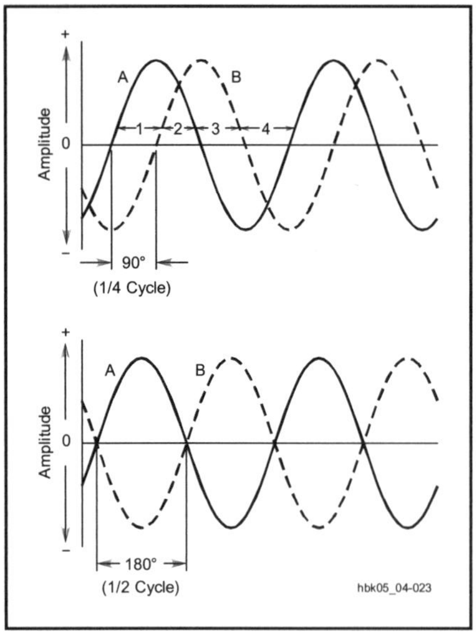

Figure 3.7 — Two important special cases of phase difference: In the upper drawing, the phase difference between A and B is 90°; in the lower drawing, the phase difference is 180°.

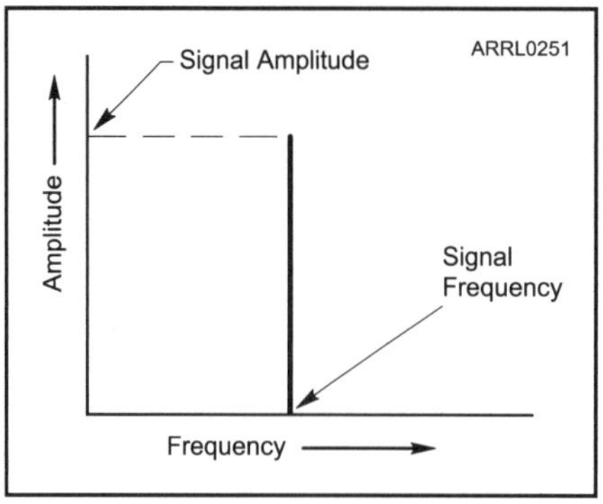

Figure 3.8 — A frequency domain or spectrum graph shows a sine wave as a single vertical line. The horizontal axis represents frequency and the vertical axis represents amplitude. The height of the line representing the sine wave shows its amplitude.

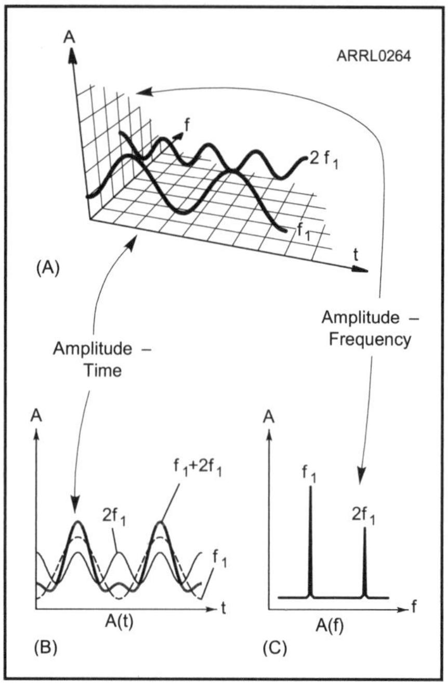

Figure 3.9 — This diagram shows how a complex waveform may be displayed in either the time domain or frequency domain. Part A is a three-dimensional display of amplitude, time, and frequency. At B, this information is shown in the time domain as on an oscilloscope. At C, the signal's frequency domain information

case, it does not matter which one is considered to lead or lag. Line B is always positive while line A is negative, and vice versa. If the two waveforms are of two voltages or two currents in the same circuit and if they have the same amplitude, they will cancel each other completely.

3.1.4 Time and Frequency Domain

To this point in the chapter, our discussions and illustrations have been in the *time domain* in which some characteristic of the signal (usually amplitude) is presented in relation to time. On a graph, this means the horizontal axis represents time. Events to the right take place later; events to the left occur earlier. For pure sinusoids (sine waves), this is enough to describe the signal.

For a complex signal with more than one sine wave, the time domain is insufficient to describe the necessary frequency and time information. The *frequency domain* is better for showing the characteristics of these signals as shown in **Figure 3.8**. A sine wave signal is shown as a vertical line, with the height of the line showing the signal's amplitude. Note that a sine wave signal occupies a single frequency.

To better understand the relationship between the time and frequency domains, refer to **Figure 3.9**. In Figure 3.9A, the three-dimensional coordinates show time (as the line sloping toward the bottom right); frequency (as the line sloping toward the top right); and amplitude (as the vertical axis). The two frequencies shown are harmonically related (f_1 and $2f_1$). The time domain is represented in Figure 3.9B, in which all frequency components are added together. If the two frequencies were applied to the input of an oscilloscope, we would see the bold line that represents the amplitudes of the signals added together. The frequency domain contains information not found in the time domain, and vice versa.

The display shown in Figure 3.9C is typical of a spectrum analyzer's display of a complex waveform. (The spectrum analyzer is described in the **Test Equipment and Measurements** chapter.) In the figure the signal is separated into its individual frequency components, and a measurement made of the amplitude of each signal component. A signal's amplitude can be represented on the vertical scale as its voltage or as its power. You can see that using the frequency domain gives more information about the composition of the signal.

3.1.5 Complex Waveforms

A signal composed of more than one sine wave is called a *complex waveform*. A simple example of a complex waveform is the signaling waveform used by telephones when dialing. This waveform is composed of two different sine wave tones, thus the name "dual-tone multi-frequency" or DTMF for that signaling system. Listen carefully next time you dial and you will hear the two tones of different frequencies.

There are certain well-known and common complex waveforms that are made up of a sine wave and its harmonics. These are termed *regular* waveforms because the harmonic relationship of all the sine waves results in a waveform with a single overall frequency and period. A waveform that is made of sine waves that are not harmonically related, such as human speech, is an *irregular* waveform. Whether regular or irregular, the sine waves that make up a complex waveform are called its *components*. (Analysis of complex signals in terms of its individual components is addressed in the **DSP and SDR Fundamentals** chapter.)

It is common for complex ac signals to contain a fundamental signal and a series of harmonics. Which harmonics are combined with the fundamental and the relative amplitude of each determine the final shape of the waveform as you will see in the following two sections. The set of all components that make up a signal is called the signal's *spectrum*. (More than one spectrum is *spectra*.)

SAWTOOTH WAVES

A *sawtooth* waveform, as shown in **Figure 3.10**, has a significantly faster *rise time* (the time it takes for the wave to reach a maximum value) compared to its *fall time* (the time it takes for the wave to reach a minimum value). A sawtooth wave is made up of a sine wave at its fundamental frequency and all of its harmonics. The sawtooth's spectrum is shown in Figure 3.10. The *ramp* waveform is similar to the sawtooth but slowly rises (the ramp) then has a fast fall, the opposite of the sawtooth.

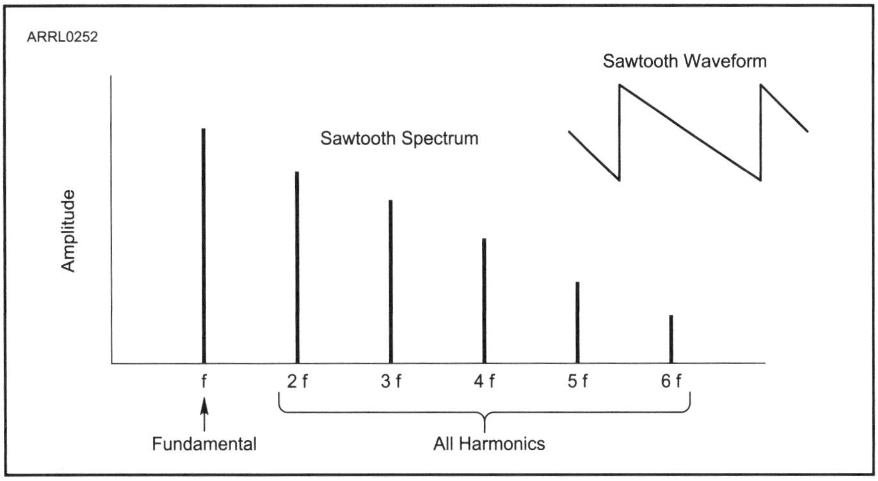

Figure 3.10 — The sawtooth waveform is made up of sine waves at the fundamental frequency and all of its harmonics. The amplitude of the harmonics decreases as their frequency increases.

Both the sawtooth and ramp waveforms are useful in timing circuits.

SQUARE WAVES

A square wave is one that abruptly changes back and forth between two voltage levels and remains an equal time at each level as in **Figure 3.11**. (If the wave spends an unequal time at each level, it is known as a *rectangular wave*.) A square wave is made up of sine waves at the fundamental and all the *odd* harmonic frequencies as shown in Figure 3.11.

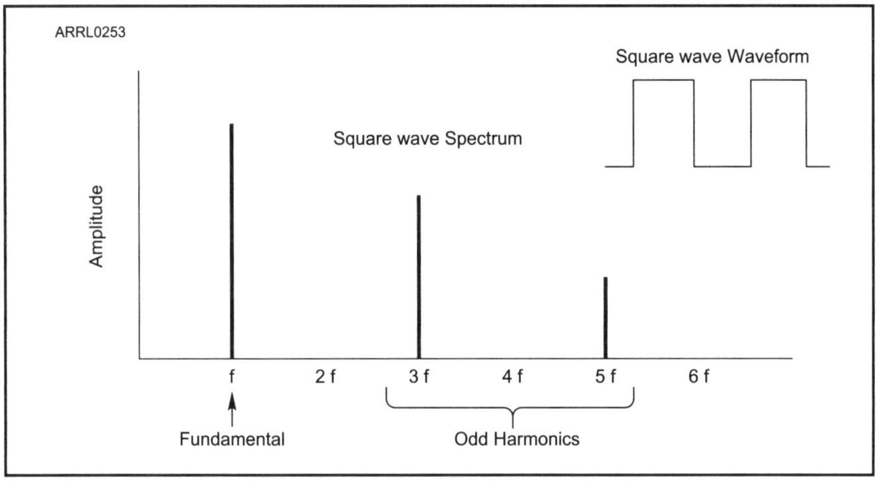

Figure 3.11 — The square wave is made up of sine waves at the fundamental frequency and only the odd harmonics. amplitude of the harmonics decreases as their frequency increases.

3.2 Measuring AC Voltage, Current and Power

Measuring the voltage or current in a dc circuit is straightforward, as **Figure 3.12A** demonstrates. Since the current flows in only one direction, the voltage and current have constant values until the resistor values are changed.

Figure 3.12B illustrates a perplexing problem encountered when measuring voltages and currents in ac circuits — the current and voltage continuously change direction and value. Which values are meaningful? How are measurements performed? In fact, there are several methods of measuring sine-wave voltage and current in ac circuits with each method providing different information about the waveform. Note that the following sections assume the waveform is a sine wave unless otherwise noted.

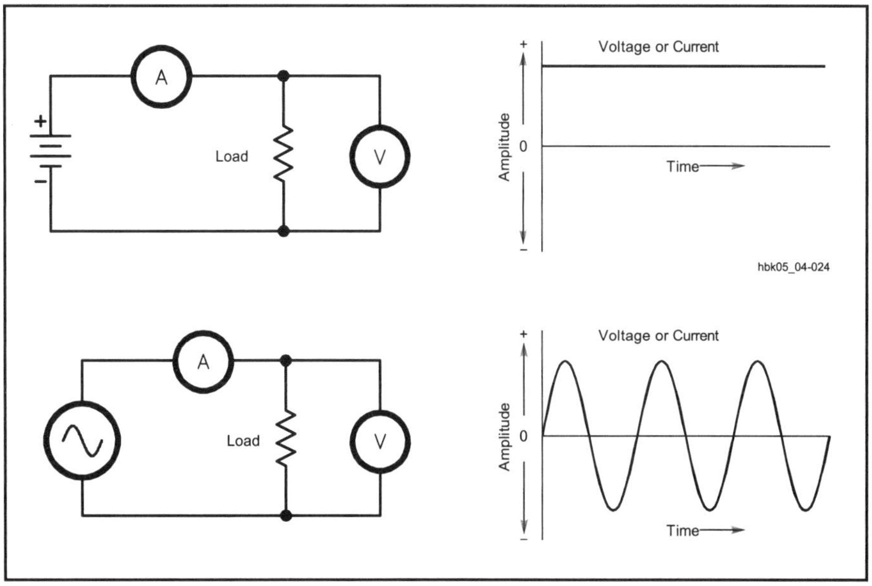

Figure 3.12 — Voltage and current measurements in dc (A) and ac circuits (B).

3.2.1 Instantaneous Values

By far, the most common waveform associ-

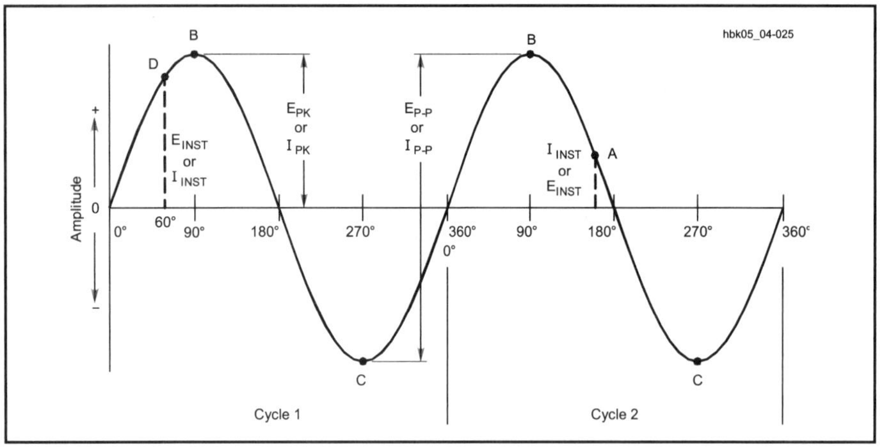

Figure 3.13 — Two cycles of a sine wave to illustrate instantaneous, peak, and peak-to-peak ac voltage and current values.

ated with ac of any frequency is the sine wave. Unless otherwise noted, it is safe to assume that measurements of ac voltage or current are of a sinusoidal waveform. **Figure 3.13** shows a sine wave representing a voltage or current of some arbitrary frequency and amplitude. The *instantaneous* voltage (or current) is the value at one instant in time. If a series of instantaneous values are plotted against time, the resulting graph will show the waveform.

In the sine wave of Figure 3.13, the instantaneous value of the waveform at any point in time is a function of three factors: the maximum value of voltage (or current) along the curve (point B, E_{max}), the frequency of the wave, f, and the time elapsed from the preceding positive-going zero crossing, t, in seconds or fractions of a second. Thus,

$$E_{inst} = E_{max} \sin (ft)$$

assuming all sine calculations are done in degrees. (See the sidebar "Degrees, Radians and Angular Frequency." If the sine calculation is done in radians, substitute $2\pi ft$ for ft in the equation.)

If the point's phase is known — the position along the waveform — the instantaneous voltage at that point can be calculated directly as:

$$E_{inst} = E_{max} \sin \theta$$

where θ is the number of degrees of phase difference from the beginning of the cycle.

Example: What is the instantaneous value of voltage at point D in Figure 3.13, if the maximum voltage value is 120 V and point D's phase is 60.0°?

$$E_{inst} = 120 \text{ V} \times \sin 60° = 120 \times 0.866 = 104 \text{ V}$$

3.2.2 Peak and Peak-to-Peak Values

The most important of an ac waveform's instantaneous values are the maximum or *peak values* reached on each positive and negative half cycle. In Figure 3.13, points B and C represent the positive and negative peaks. Peak values (indicated by a "pk" or "p" subscript) are especially important with respect to component ratings, which the voltage or current in a circuit must not exceed without danger of component failure.

The *peak power* in an ac circuit is the product of the peak voltage and the peak current, or

$$P_{pk} = E_{pk} \times I_{pk}$$

The span from points B to C in Figure 3.13 represents the largest difference in value of the sine wave. Designated the *peak-to-peak* value (indicated by a "P-P" or "pk-pk" subscript), this span is equal to twice the peak value of the waveform. Thus, peak-to-peak voltage is:

$$E_{P-P} = 2\, E_{pk}$$

3.2.3 RMS Values

The *root mean square* or *RMS* values of voltage and current are the most common values encountered in electronics. Sometimes called *effective* values, the RMS value of an ac voltage or current is the value of a dc voltage or current that would cause a resistor to dissipate the same average amount of power as the ac waveform. This measurement became widely used in the early days of electrification when both ac and dc power utility power were in use. Even today, the values of the ac line voltage available from an electrical power outlet are given as RMS values. Unless otherwise specified, unlabeled ac voltage and current values found in most electronics literature are normally RMS values.

The RMS values of voltage and current get their name from the mathematical method used to derive their value relative to peak voltage and current. This procedure provides the RMS value for any type of periodic waveform, sinusoidal or not. Start by *squaring* the individual values of all the instantaneous values of voltage or current during an entire single cycle of ac. Take the average (*mean*) of these squares (this is done by computing an integral of the waveform) and then find the square *root* of that average.

SINE WAVE RMS VALUES

This section applies only when the waveform in question is a sine wave. The simple formulas and conversion factors in this sec-

Measuring Nonsinusoidal Waveforms

Making measurements of ac waveforms is covered in more detail in the **Test Equipment and Measurements** chapter. However, this is a good point in the discussion to reinforce the dependence of RMS and values on the nature of the waveform being measured.

Analog meters and other types of instrumentation that display RMS values may only be calibrated for sine waves, those being the most common type of ac waveform. Using that instrumentation to accurately measure waveforms other than sine waves — such as speech, intermittent sine waves (such as CW from a transmitter), square waves, triangle waves or noise — requires the use of *calibration factors* or the measurement may not be valid.

To make calibrated, reliable measurements of the RMS or value of these waveforms requires the use of *true-RMS* instruments. These devices may use a balancing approach to a known dc value or if they are microprocessor-based, may actually perform the full root-mean-square calculation on the waveform. Be sure you know the characteristics of your test instruments if an accurate RMS value is important.

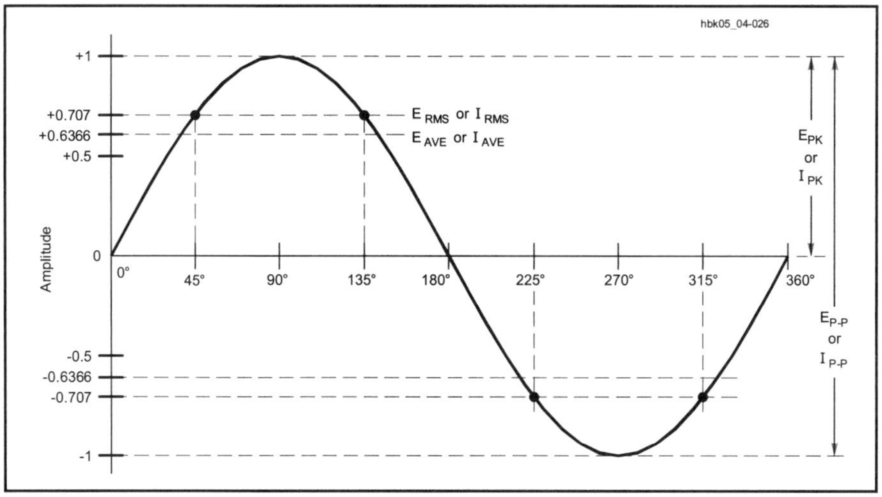

Figure 3.14 — The relationships between RMS, average, peak, and peak-to-peak values of ac voltage and current for a sine wave. The numeric constants are different for non-sinusoidal waveforms.

tion are generally *not* true for non-sinusoidal waveforms such as square or triangle waves (see the sidebar "Measuring Non-Sinusoidal Waveforms"). The following formulas are true *only* if the waveform is a sine wave and the circuit is *linear* — that is, raising or lowering the voltage will raise or lower the current proportionally. If those conditions are true, the following conversion factors have been computed and can be used without any additional mathematics.

For a sine wave to produce heat equivalent to a dc waveform the peak ac power required is twice the dc power. Therefore, the average ac power equivalent to a corresponding dc power is half the peak ac power.

$$P_{ave} = \frac{P_{pk}}{2}$$

A sine wave's RMS voltage and current values needed to arrive at average ac power are related to their peak values by the conversion factors:

$$E_{RMS} = \frac{E_{pk}}{\sqrt{2}} = \frac{E_{pk}}{1.414} = E_{pk} \times 0.707$$

$$E_{RMS} = \frac{E_{pk}}{\sqrt{2}} = \frac{E_{pk}}{1.414} = E_{pk} \times 0.707$$

RMS voltages and currents are what is displayed by most volt and ammeters.

If the RMS voltage is the peak voltage divided by $\sqrt{2}$, then the peak voltage must be the RMS voltage multiplied by $\sqrt{2}$, or

$$E_{pk} = E_{RMS} \times 1.414$$

$$I_{pk} = I_{RMS} \times 1.414$$

Example: What is the peak voltage and the peak-to-peak voltage at the usual household ac outlet, if the RMS voltage is 120 V?

$$E_{pk} = 120 \text{ V} \times 1.414 = 170 \text{ V}$$

$$E_{P\text{-}P} = 2 \times 170 \text{ V} = 340 \text{ V}$$

In the time domain of a sine wave, the instantaneous values of voltage and current correspond to the RMS values at the 45°, 135°, 225° and 315° points along the cycle shown in **Figure 3.14**. (The sine of 45° is approximately 0.707.) The instantaneous value of voltage or current is greater than the RMS value for half the cycle and less than the RMS value for half the cycle.

Since circuit specifications will most commonly list only RMS voltage and current values, these relationships are important in finding the peak voltages or currents that will stress components.

Example: What is the peak voltage across a capacitor if the RMS voltage of a sinusoidal waveform signal across it is 300 V ac?

$$E_{pk} = 300 \text{ V} \times 1.414 = 424 \text{ V}$$

The capacitor must be able to withstand this higher voltage, plus a safety margin. (The capacitor must also be rated for ac use because of the continually reversing polarity and ac current flow.) In power supplies that convert ac to dc and use capacitive input filters, the output voltage will approach the peak value of the ac voltage rather than the RMS value. (See the **Power Sources** chapter for more information on specifying components in this application.)

3.2.4 Average Values of AC Waveforms

Certain kinds of circuits respond to the *average* voltage or current (not power) of an ac waveform. Among these circuits are analog electrodynamic meter movements and power supplies that convert ac to dc and use heavily inductive ("choke") input filters, both of which work with the pulsating dc output of a full-wave rectifier. The average value of each ac half cycle is the *mean* of all the instantaneous values in that half cycle. (The average value of a sine wave or any symmetric ac waveform over an entire cycle is zero!) Related to the peak values of voltage and current, average values for each half-cycle

Table 3.1
Conversion Factors for Sinusoidal AC Voltage or Current

From	*To*	*Multiply By*
Peak	Peak-to-Peak	2
Peak-to-Peak	Peak	0.5
Peak	RMS	$1/\sqrt{2}$ or 0.707
RMS	Peak	$\sqrt{2}$ or 1.414
Peak-to-Peak	RMS	$1/(2 \times \sqrt{2})$ or 0.35355
RMS	Peak-to-Peak	$2 \times \sqrt{2}$ or 2.828
Peak	Average	$2/\pi$ or 0.6366
Average	Peak	$\pi/2$ or 1.5708
RMS	Average	$(2 \times \sqrt{2})/\pi$ or 0.90
Average	RMS	$\pi/(2 \times \sqrt{2})$ or 1.11

Note: These conversion factors apply only to continuous pure sine waves.

Sine and Square Wave Measurement Definitions

Since square waves are very common waveforms, the following table provides definitions for the two types of waveforms. These are *not* conversion factors between two measurements unless a true-RMS instrument is used.

AC Measurements for Sine and Square Waves

	Sine Wave	*Square Wave*
Peak-to-Peak	2 × Peak	2 × Peak
Peak	0.5 × Peak-to-Peak	0.5 × Peak-to-Peak
RMS	0.707 × Peak	Peak
Peak	1.414 × RMS	RMS
Average	0 (full cycle)	0 (full cycle)
	0.637 × Peak (half cycle)	0.5 × Peak (half cycle)

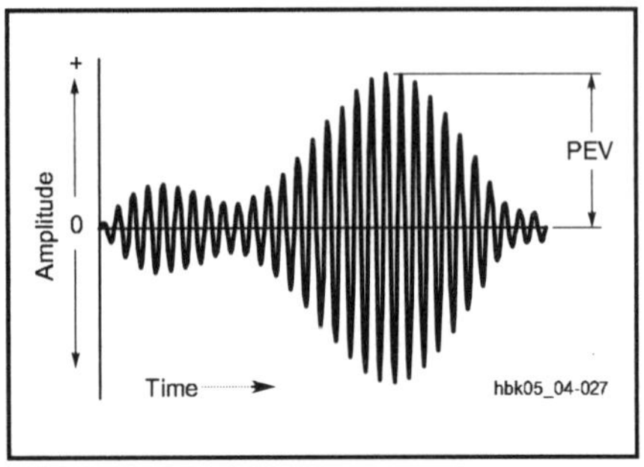

Figure 3.15 — The peak envelope voltage (PEV) for a composite waveform.

of a sine wave are 2/π (or 0.6366) times the peak value.

$E_{ave} = 0.6366\ E_{pk}$

$I_{ave} = 0.6366\ I_{pk}$

For convenience, **Table 3.1** summarizes the relationships between all of the common ac values. All of these relationships apply *only* to sine waves in linear circuits.

3.2.5 Complex Waveforms and Peak Envelope Values

Complex waveforms, as shown earlier in Figures 3.10 and 3.11, differ from sine waves. For speech signals, the peak voltage may vary significantly from one cycle to the next, for example. Therefore, other amplitude measures are required, especially for accurate measurement of voltage and power with transmitted speech or data waveforms.

An SSB waveform (either speech or data) contains an RF ac waveform with a frequency many times that of the audio-frequency ac waveform with which it is combined. Therefore, the resultant *composite* waveform appears as an amplitude envelope superimposed upon the RF waveform as illustrated by **Figure 3.15**. For a complex waveform such as this, the *peak envelope voltage* (PEV) is the maximum or peak value of voltage anywhere in the waveform.

Peak envelope voltage is used in the calculation of *peak envelope power* (PEP). The Federal Communications Commission (FCC) sets the maximum power levels for amateur transmitters in terms of peak envelope power. PEP is the *average* power supplied to the antenna transmission line by the transmitter during one RF cycle at the crest of the modulation envelope, taken under normal operating conditions. That is, the average power for the RF cycle during which PEV occurs.

Since calculation of PEP requires the average power of the cycle, and the deviation of the modulated RF waveform from a sine wave is very small, the error incurred by using the conversion factors for sine waves is insignificant. Multiply PEV by 0.707 to obtain an RMS value. Then calculate PEP by using the square of the voltage divided by the load resistance.

$$PEP = \frac{(PEV \times 0.707)^2}{R}$$

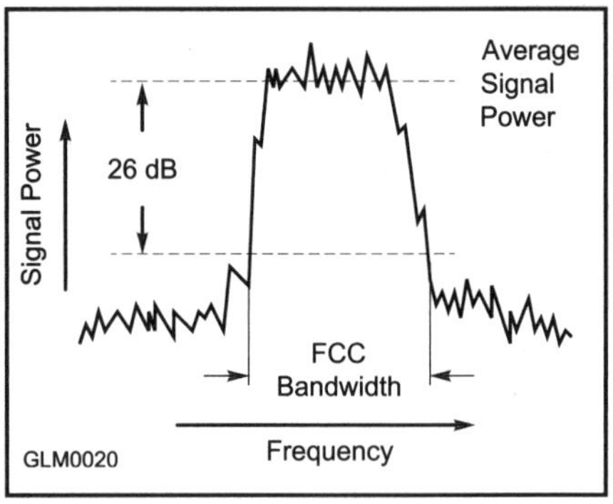

Figure 3.16 — The FCC defines bandwidth as "the width of a frequency band outside of which the mean (average) power of the transmitted signal is attenuated at least 26 dB below the mean power." (FCC §97.3(a)(8))

Example: What is the PEP of a transmitter's output with a PEV of 100 V into a 50-ohm load?

$$PEP = \frac{(100 \times 0.707)^2}{R} = \frac{(70.7)^2}{50} = 100\ W$$

COMPOSITE WAVEFORMS AND BANDWIDTH

Composite signals are groups of individual signals that combine to create a complex signal. Composite signals have *components* that generally cover a range of frequencies. The general definition of a signal's *bandwidth* is the difference in frequency between the two points at which the signal's amplitude falls to 3 dB below its peak value. For some kinds of very simple and very complex signals this may not be a useful definition.

The FCC has a more specific definition of bandwidth in section §97.3(a)(8): "*Bandwidth.* The width of a frequency band outside of which the mean [average] power of the transmitted signal is attenuated at least 26 dB below the mean power within the band." **Figure 3.16** illustrates how this measurement is made. This definition is used when evaluating a signal's occupied bandwidth to determine whether it satisfies FCC rules.

3.3 Effective Radiated Power

When evaluating total station performance, accounting for the effects of the entire system is important, including antenna gain. This allows you to evaluate the effects of changes to the station. Transmitting performance is usually computed as *effective radiated power* (*ERP*). ERP is calculated with respect to a reference antenna system — usually a dipole but occasionally an isotropic antenna — and answers the question, "How much power does my station radiate as compared to that if my antenna was a simple dipole?" Effective isotropic radiated power (EIRP) results when an isotropic antenna is used as the reference. If no antenna reference is specified, assume a dipole reference antenna.

ERP is especially useful in designing and coordinating repeater systems. The effective power radiated from the antenna helps establish the coverage area of the repeater. In addition, the height of the repeater antenna as compared to buildings and mountains in the surrounding area (*height above average terrain*, or *HAAT*) has a large effect on the repeater coverage. In general, for a given coverage area, with a greater antenna HAAT, less effective radiated power (ERP) is needed. A frequency coordinator may even specify a maximum ERP for a repeater, to help reduce interference between stations using the same frequencies.

ERP calculations begin with the *transmitter power output* (*TPO*). (This is assumed to be the output of the final power amplification stage if an external power amplifier is used.) Then the *system gain* of the entire antenna system including the antenna, the transmission line, and all transmission line components is applied to TPO to compute the entire station's output power.

System Gain = Transmission Line Loss – Transmission Components Loss + Antenna Gain

There is always some power lost in the feed line and often there are other devices inserted in the line, such as a filter or an impedance-matching network. In the case of a repeater system, there is usually a duplexer so the transmitter and receiver can use the same antenna and perhaps a circulator to reduce the possibility of intermodulation interference. These devices also introduce some loss to the system. The antenna system then usually returns some gain to the system. (See the **Antennas** chapter for information on antenna gain and the **Transmission Lines** chapter for information on feed line loss.)

ERP = TPO × System Gain

Since the system gains and losses are usually expressed in decibels, they can simply be added together, with losses written as negative values. System gain must then be converted back to a linear value from dB to calculate ERP.

$$ERP = TPO \times \log^{-1}\left(\frac{\text{System Gain (dB)}}{10}\right)$$

It is also common to work entirely in dBm and dB until the final result for ERP is obtained and then converted back to watts. (dBm represents "decibels with respect to one mW" such that 0 dBm = 1 mW, 30 dBm = 1 W, and so forth.)

ERP (in dBm) = TPO (in dBm) + System Gain (in dB)

Suppose we have a repeater station that uses a 50 W transmitter and a feed line with 4 dB of loss. There is a duplexer in the line that exhibits 2 dB of loss and a circulator that adds another 1 dB of loss. This repeater uses an antenna that has a gain of 6 dBd. Our total system gain looks like:

System gain = –4 dB + –2 dB + –1 dB + 6 dBd = –1 dB

Note that this is a loss of 1 dB total for the system from TPO to radiated power. The effect on the 50 W of TPO results in:

$$ERP = 50\ W \times \log^{-1}\left(\frac{\text{system gain (dB)}}{10}\right)$$

$$= 50 \times \log^{-1}(-0.1) = 50 \times 0.79 = 39.7\ W$$

This is consistent with the expectation that with a 1 dB system loss we would have somewhat less ERP than transmitter output power.

As another example, suppose we have a transmitter that feeds a 100 W output signal into a feed line that has 1 dB of loss. The feed line connects to an antenna that has a gain of 6 dBd. What is the effective radiated power from the antenna? To calculate the total system gain (or loss) we add the decibel values given:

System gain = – 1 dB + 6 dBd = 5 dB

and

$$ERP = 100\ W \times \log^{-1}\left(\frac{\text{system gain (dB)}}{10}\right)$$

$$= 100 \times \log^{-1}(0.5) = 100 \times 3.16 = 316\ W$$

The total system has positive gain, so we should have expected a larger value for ERP than TPO. Keep in mind that the gain antenna concentrates more of the signal in a desired direction, with less signal in undesired directions. So the antenna doesn't really increase the total available power. If directional antennas are used, ERP will change with direction.

Example: What is the effective radiated power of a repeater station with 150 W transmitter power output, 2 dB feed line loss, 2.2 dB duplexer loss and 7 dBd antenna gain?

System gain = –2 dB – 2.2 dB + 7 dBd = 2.8 dB

$$ERP = 150\ W \times \log^{-1}\left(\frac{\text{system gain (dB)}}{10}\right)$$

$$= 150 \times \log^{-1}(0.28) = 150 \times 1.9 = 285\ W$$

Example: What is the effective radiated power of a repeater station with 200 W transmitter power output, 4 dB feed line loss, 3.2 dB duplexer loss, 0.8 dB circulator loss and 10 dBd antenna gain?

System gain = –4 – 3.2 – 0.8 + 10 = 2 dB

$$ERP = 200\ W \times \log^{-1}\left(\frac{\text{system gain (dB)}}{10}\right)$$

$$= 200 \times \log^{-1}(0.2) = 200 \times 1.58 = 317\ W$$

What is the effective isotropic radiated power of a repeater station with 200 W transmitter power output, 2 dB feed line loss, 2.8 dB duplexer loss, 1.2 dB circulator loss and 7 dBi antenna gain?

System gain = –2 – 2.8 – 1.2 + 7 = 1 dB

$$ERP = 200\ W \times \log^{-1}\left(\frac{\text{system gain (dB)}}{10}\right)$$

$$= 100 \times \log^{-1}(0.1) = 200 \times 1.26 = 252\ W$$

The Decibel

The decibel (dB) is discussed in the section on Gain, later in this chapter. It is also covered in the "Radio Mathematics" item in the downloadable supplemental information.

3.4 AC in Capacitors and Inductors

Both capacitors and inductors can store electrical or magnetic energy, respectively. When an ac signal is applied to them, the storing and releasing of energy results in a phase shift between the current and voltage waveforms. The phase shift varies with frequency and makes capacitors and inductors behave differently than resistors. They also interact to create frequency-sensitive tuned circuits, filters, impedance-matching circuits, and more.

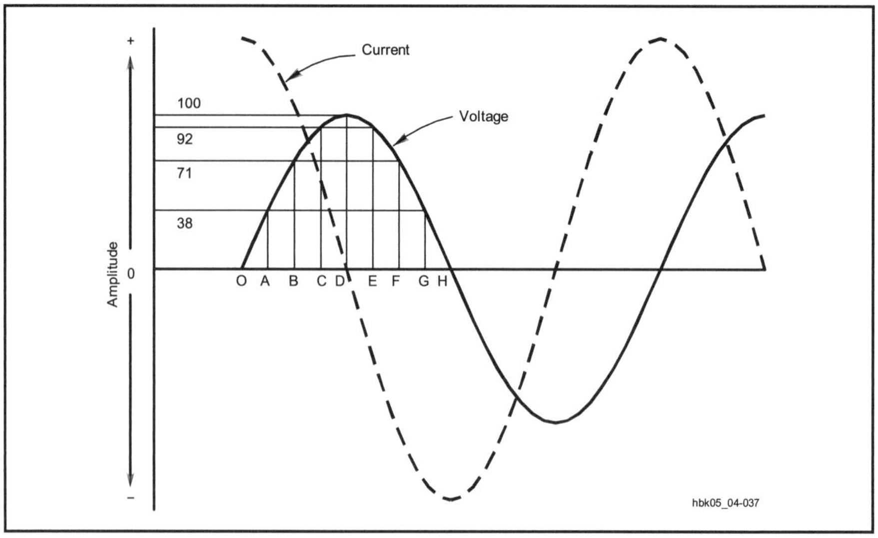

Figure 3.17 — Voltage and current phase relationships when an alternating current is applied to a capacitor.

3.4.1 Alternating Current in Capacitance

While a capacitor in a dc circuit will appear as an open circuit except for the brief charge and discharge periods, the same capacitor in an ac circuit will both pass and oppose current. A capacitor in an ac circuit does not handle electrical energy like a resistor, however. Instead of converting the energy to heat and dissipating it, capacitors store electrical energy when the applied voltage is greater than that across the capacitor and return it to the circuit when the opposite is true.

In **Figure 3.17** a sine-wave ac voltage having a maximum value of 100 V is applied to a capacitor. In the period OA, the applied voltage increases from 0 to 38, storing energy in the capacitor; at the end of this period the capacitor is charged to that voltage. In interval AB the voltage increases to 71; that is, by an additional 33 V. During this interval a smaller quantity of charge has been added than in OA, because the voltage rise during interval AB is smaller. Consequently the average current during interval AB is smaller than during OA. In the third interval, BC, the voltage rises from 71 to 92, an increase of 21 V. This is less than the voltage increase during AB, so the quantity of charge added is less; in other words, the average current during interval BC is still smaller. In the fourth interval, CD, the voltage increases only 8 V; the charge added is smaller than in any preceding interval and therefore the current also is smaller.

By dividing the first quarter-cycle into a very large number of such intervals, it can be shown that the current charging the capacitor has the shape of a sine wave, just as the applied voltage does. The current is largest at the beginning of the cycle and becomes zero at the maximum value of the voltage, so there is a phase difference of 90° between the voltage and the current. During the first quarter-cycle the current is flowing in the original (positive) direction through the circuit as indicated by the dashed line in Figure 3.17, since the capacitor is being charged. The increasing capacitor voltage indicates that energy is being stored in the capacitor.

In the second quarter-cycle — that is, in the time from D to H — the voltage applied to the capacitor decreases. During this time the capacitor loses charge, returning the stored energy to the circuit. Applying the same reasoning, it is evident that the current is small in interval DE and continues to increase during each succeeding interval. The current is flowing *against* the applied voltage, however, because the capacitor is returning energy to (discharging into) the circuit. The current thus flows in the *negative* direction during this quarter-cycle.

The third and fourth quarter-cycles repeat the events of the first and second, respectively, although the polarity of the applied voltage has reversed, and so the current changes to correspond. In other words, an alternating current flows in the circuit because of the alternate charging and discharging of the capacitance. As shown in Figure 3.17, the current starts its cycle 90° before the voltage, so the current in a capacitor *leads* the applied voltage by 90°. You might find it helpful to remember the word "ICE" as a mnemonic because the current (I) in a capacitor (C) comes before voltage (E). (See the sidebar "ELI the ICE man" in the section on inductors.) We can also turn this statement around, to say the voltage in a capacitor *lags* the current by 90°.

Capacitive Reactance Timesaver

The fundamental units for frequency and capacitance (hertz and farads) are too cumbersome for practical use in radio circuits. If the capacitance is specified in microfarads (μF) and the frequency is in megahertz (MHz), however, the reactance is calculated in ohms (Ω).

3.4.2 Capacitive Reactance and Susceptance

The quantity of electric charge that can be placed on a capacitor is proportional to the applied voltage and the capacitance. If the applied voltage is ac, this amount of charge moves back and forth in the circuit once each cycle. Therefore, the rate of movement of charge (the current) is proportional to voltage, capacitance and frequency. Stated in another way, capacitor current is proportional to capacitance for a given applied voltage and frequency.

When the effects of capacitance and frequency are considered together, they form a quantity called *reactance* that relates voltage and current in a capacitor, similar to the role of resistance in Ohm's Law. Because the reactance is created by a capacitor, it is called *capacitive reactance*. The units for reactance are ohms, just as in the case of resistance. Although the units of reactance are ohms, there is no power dissipated in reactance. The energy stored in the capacitor during one portion of the cycle is simply returned to the circuit in the next.

The formula for calculating the magnitude of the capacitive reactance is:

$$X_C = \frac{1}{2\,\pi\,f\,C}$$

where:

X_C = magnitude of capacitive reactance in ohms,
f = frequency in hertz,
C = capacitance in farads
π = 3.1416

By convention, capacitive reactance is assigned a negative value whereas inductive reactance (discussed below) is assigned a positive value.

Note: In many references and texts, angular frequency $\omega=2\pi f$ is used and the equation would read:

$$X_C = \frac{1}{\omega\,C}$$

Example: What is the reactance of a capacitor of 470 pF (0.000470 μF) at a frequency of 7.15 MHz?

$$X_C = \frac{1}{2\,\pi\,f\,C}$$

$$= \frac{1}{2\,\pi \times 7.15\text{ MHz} \times 0.000470\ \mu\text{F}}$$

$$= \frac{1\,\Omega}{0.0211} = 47.4\,\Omega$$

Example: What is the reactance of the same capacitor, 470 pF (0.000470 μF), at a frequency of 14.29 MHz?

$$X_C = \frac{1}{2\,\pi\,f\,C}$$

$$= \frac{1}{2\,\pi \times 14.3\text{ MHz} \times 0.000470\ \mu\text{F}}$$

$$= \frac{1\,\Omega}{0.0422} = 23.7\,\Omega$$

Current in a capacitor is directly related to the rate of change of the capacitor voltage. The maximum rate of change of voltage in a sine wave increases directly with the frequency, even if its peak voltage remains fixed. Therefore, the maximum current in the capacitor must also increase directly with frequency. Since, if voltage is fixed, an increase in current is equivalent to a decrease in reactance, the reactance of any capacitor decreases proportionally as the frequency increases. **Figure 3.18** illustrates the decrease in reactance of an arbitrary-value capacitor with respect to increasing frequency. The only limitation on the application of the graph is the physical construction of the capacitor, which may favor low-frequency uses or high-frequency applications.

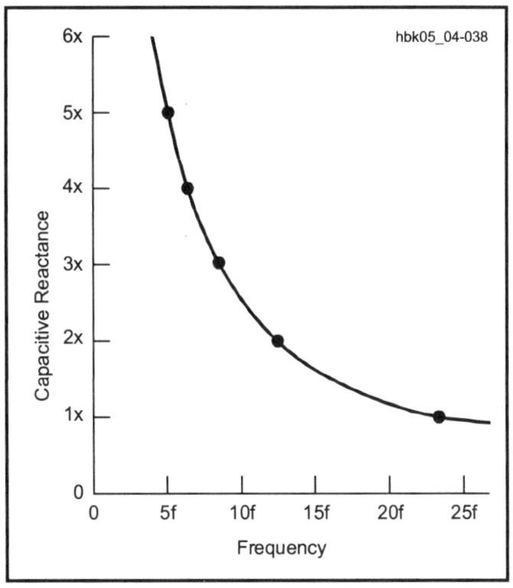

Figure 3.18 — A graph showing the general relationship of reactance to frequency for a fixed value of capacitance.

CAPACITIVE SUSCEPTANCE

Just as conductance is sometimes the most useful way of expressing a resistance's ability to conduct current, the same is true for capacitors and ac current. This ability is called *susceptance* (abbreviated *B*). The units of susceptance are siemens (S), the same as that of conductance and admittance.

Susceptance in a capacitor is *capacitive susceptance*, abbreviated B_C. In an ideal capacitor with no losses, susceptance is simply the reciprocal of reactance. Hence,

$$B_C = \frac{1}{X_C}$$

where

X_C is the capacitive reactance, and
B_C is the capacitive susceptance.

3.4.3 Alternating Current in Inductors

For reasons similar to those that cause a phase difference between current and voltage in a capacitor, when an alternating voltage is applied to an ideal inductance with no resistance, the current is 90° out of phase with the applied voltage. In the case of an inductor, however, the current *lags* 90° behind the voltage as shown in **Figure 3.19**, the opposite of the capacitor current-voltage relationship. (Here again, we can also say the voltage across an inductor *leads* the current by 90°.) Interpreting Figure 3.19 begins with understanding that the cause for current lag in an inductor is the opposing voltage that is induced in the inductor and that the amplitude of the opposing voltage is proportional to the rate at which the inductor current changes.

In time segment OA, when the applied voltage is at its positive maximum, the rate at which the current is changing is also the highest, a 38% change. This means that the opposing voltage is also maximum, allowing the least current to flow. In the segment AB, as a result of the decrease in the applied voltage, current changes by only 33% inducing a smaller opposing voltage. The process continues in time segments BC and CD, the latter producing only an 8% rise in current as the applied and induced opposing voltage approach zero.

In segment DE, the applied voltage changes polarity, causing current to begin to decrease, returning stored energy to the circuit from the inductor's magnetic field. As the current rate of change is now negative (decreasing) the induced opposing voltage also changes polarity. Current flow is still in the original

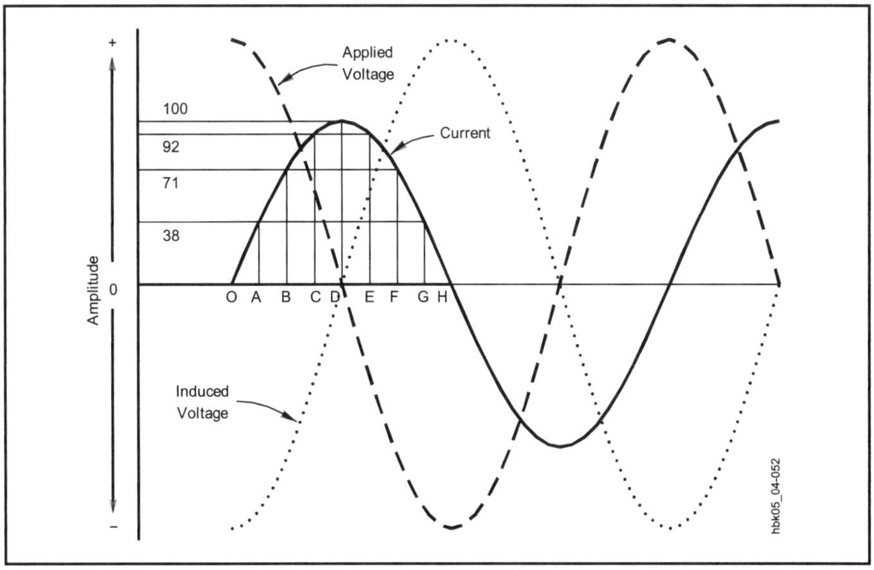

Figure 3.19 — Phase relationships between voltage and current when an alternating current is applied to an inductance.

ELI the ICE Man

If you have difficulty remembering the phase relationships between voltage and current with inductors and capacitors, you may find it helpful to think of the phrase, "ELI the ICE man." This will remind you that voltage across an inductor leads the current through it, because the E comes before (leads) I, with an L between them, as you read from left to right. (The letter L represents inductance.) Similarly, I comes before (leads) E with a C between them.

direction (positive), but is decreasing as less energy is stored in the inductor.

As the applied voltage continues to increase negatively, the current — although still positive — continues to decrease in value, reaching zero as the applied voltage reaches its negative maximum. The energy once stored in the inductor has now been completely returned to the circuit. The negative half-cycle then continues just as the positive half-cycle.

Similarly to the capacitive circuit discussed earlier, by dividing the cycle into a large number of intervals, it can be shown that the current and voltage are both sine waves, although with a difference in phase.

Compare Figure 3.19 with Figure 3.17. Whereas in a pure capacitive circuit, the current *leads* the voltage by 90°, in a pure inductive circuit, the current *lags* the voltage by 90°. These phenomena are especially important in circuits that combine inductors and capacitors. Remember that the phase difference between voltage and current in both types of circuits is a result of energy being stored and released as voltage across a capacitor and as current in an inductor.

3.4.4 Inductive Reactance and Susceptance

The amount of current that can be created in an inductor is proportional to the applied voltage but inversely proportional to the inductance because of the induced opposing voltage. If the applied voltage is ac, the rate of change of the current varies directly with the frequency and this rate of change also determines the amplitude of the induced or reverse voltage. Hence, the opposition to the flow of current increases proportionally to frequency. Stated in another way, inductor current is inversely proportional to inductance for a given applied voltage and frequency.

The combined effect of inductance and frequency is called *inductive reactance*, which — like capacitive reactance — is expressed in ohms. As with capacitive reactance, no power is dissipated in inductive reactance. The energy stored in the inductor during one portion of the cycle is returned to the circuit in the next portion.

The formula for calculating the magnitude of the inductive reactance is:

$$X_L = 2 \pi f L$$

where

X_L = magnitude of inductive reactance in ohms,

f = frequency in hertz,

L = inductance in henrys, and

$\pi = 3.1416$.

(If $\omega = 2 \pi f$, then $X_L = \omega L$.)

Example: What is the reactance of an inductor having an inductance of 8.0 H at a frequency of 120 Hz?

$$X_L = 2 \pi f L$$

$$= 6.2832 \times 120 \text{ Hz} \times 8.0 \text{ H}$$

$$= 6030\ \Omega$$

Example: What is the reactance of a 15.0-microhenry inductor at a frequency of 14.0 MHz?

$$X_L = 2 \pi f L$$

$$= 6.2832 \times 14.0 \text{ MHz} \times 15.0\ \mu\text{H}$$

$$= 1320\ \Omega$$

The resistance of the wire used to make the inductor has no effect on the reactance, but simply acts as a separate resistor connected in series with the inductor.

Example: What is the reactance of the same inductor at a frequency of 7.0 MHz?

$$X_L = 2 \pi f L$$

$$= 6.2832 \times 7.0 \text{ MHz} \times 15.0\ \mu\text{H}$$

$$= 660\ \Omega$$

The direct relationship between frequency and reactance in inductors, combined with the inverse relationship between reactance and frequency in the case of capacitors, will be of fundamental importance in creating resonant circuits.

INDUCTIVE SUSCEPTANCE

As a measure of the ability of an inductor to limit the flow of ac in a circuit, inductive reactance is similar to capacitive reactance in having a corresponding susceptance, or ability to pass ac current in a circuit. In an ideal inductor with no resistive losses — that is, no energy lost as heat — susceptance is simply the reciprocal of reactance.

$$B = 1 / X_L$$

where

X_L = reactance, and

B = susceptance.

The unit of susceptance for both inductors and capacitors is the *siemens*, abbreviated S.

Inductive Reactance Timesaver

Similarly to the calculation of capacitive reactance, if inductance is specified in microhenrys (μH) and the frequency is in megahertz (MHz), the reactance is calculated in ohms (Ω). The same is true for the combination of mH and kHz.

3.4.5 Glossary — AC Theory and Reactance

Frequency (f) — The rate of change of an ac voltage or current, measured in cycles per second, or hertz (Hz).

Fundamental — The lowest frequency in a series of sine waves whose frequencies have an integer relationship.

Harmonic — A sine wave whose frequency is an integer multiple of a fundamental frequency.

Peak (voltage or current) — The maximum value relative to zero that an ac voltage or current attains during any cycle.

Peak-to-peak (voltage or current) — The value of the total swing of an ac voltage or current from its peak negative value to its peak positive value, ordinarily twice the value of the peak voltage or current.

Period (T) — The duration of one ac voltage or current cycle, measured in seconds (s).

Power (P) — The rate of electrical-energy use, measured in watts (W).

Reactance (X) — Opposition to alternating current by storage in an electrical field (by a capacitor) or in a magnetic field (by an inductor), measured in ohms (Ω).

RMS (voltage or current) — Literally, "root mean square," the square root of the average of the squares of the instantaneous values for one cycle of a waveform. A dc voltage or current that will produce the same heating effect as the waveform. For a sine wave, the RMS value is equal to 0.707 times the peak value of ac voltage or current.

Time constant (τ) — The time required for the voltage in an RC circuit or the current in an RL circuit to rise from zero to approximately 63.2% of its maximum value or to fall from its maximum value 63.2% toward zero.

3.5 Working with Reactance

3.5.1 Ohm's Law for Reactance

Only ac circuits containing capacitance or inductance (or both) have reactance. Despite the fact that the voltage in such circuits is 90° out of phase with the current, circuit reactance does oppose the flow of ac current in a manner that corresponds to resistance. That is, in a capacitor or inductor, reactance is equal to the ratio of ac voltage to ac current and the equations relating voltage, current and reactance take the familiar form of Ohm's Law:

$$E = I X$$

$$I = E / X$$

$$X = E / I$$

where

E = RMS ac voltage in volts,

I = RMS ac current in amperes, and

X = inductive or capacitive reactance in ohms.

Example: What is the voltage across a capacitor of 200 pF at 7.15 MHz, if the current through the capacitor is 50 mA?

Since the reactance of the capacitor is a function of both frequency and capacitance, first calculate the reactance:

$$X_C = \frac{1}{2 \pi f C}$$

$$= \frac{1}{2 \times 3.1416 \times 7.15 \times 10^6 \text{ Hz} \times 200 \times 10^{-12} \text{ F}}$$

$$= \frac{10^6 \ \Omega}{8980} = 111 \ \Omega$$

Next, use:

$$E = I \times X_C = 0.050 \text{ A} \times 111 \ \Omega = 5.6 \text{ V}$$

Example: What is the current through an 8.0-H inductor at 120 Hz, if 420 V is applied?

$$X_L = 2 \pi f L$$

$$= 2 \times 3.1416 \times 120 \text{ Hz} \times 8.0 \text{ H}$$

$$= 6030 \ \Omega$$

$$I = E / X_L = 420 / 6030 = 69.6 \text{ mA}$$

Figure 3.20 charts the reactances of capacitors from 1 pF to 100 µF, and the reactances of inductors from 0.1 µH to 10 H, for frequencies between 100 Hz and 100 MHz. Approximate values of reactance can be read or interpolated from the chart. The formulas will produce more exact values, however. (The chart can also be used to find the frequency at which an inductor and capacitor have equal reactances, creating resonance as described in the section "Reactances At and Near Resonance" below.)

Although both inductive and capacitive reactance oppose the flow of ac current, the two types of reactance differ. With capacitive reactance, the current *leads* the voltage by 90°, whereas with inductive reactance, the current *lags* the voltage by 90°. The convention for charting the two types of reactance appears in **Figure 3.21**. On this graph, inductive reactance is plotted along the +90° vertical line, while capacitive reactance is plotted along the –90° vertical line. This convention of assigning a positive value to inductive reactance and a negative value to capacitive reactance results from the mathematics used for working with impedance as described elsewhere in this chapter.

3.5.2 Reactances in Series and Parallel

If a circuit contains two reactances of the same type, whether in series or in parallel, the resulting reactance can be determined by applying the same rules as for resistances in series and in parallel. Series reactance is given by the formula

$$X_{total} = X1 + X2 + X3 ... + X_n$$

Example: Two noninteracting inductances are in series. Each has a value of 4.0 µH, and the operating frequency is 3.8 MHz. What is the resulting reactance?

The reactance of each inductor is:

$$X_L = 2 \pi f L$$

$$= 2 \times 3.1416 \times 3.8 \times 10^6 \text{ Hz} \times 4 \times 10^{-6} \text{ H}$$

$$= 96 \ \Omega$$

$$X_{total} = X1 + X2 = 96 \ \Omega + 96 \ \Omega = 192 \ \Omega$$

We might also calculate the total reactance by first adding the inductances:

$$L_{total} = L1 + L2 = 4.0 \ \mu\text{H} + 4.0 \ \mu\text{H} = 8.0 \ \mu\text{H}$$

$$X_{total} = 2 \pi f L$$

$$= 2 \times 3.1416 \times 3.8 \times 10^6 \text{ Hz} \times 8.0 \times 10^{-6} \text{ H}$$

$$= 191 \ \Omega$$

(The fact that the last digit differs by one illustrates the uncertainty of the calculation caused by the limited precision of the measured values in the problem, and differences caused by rounding off the calculated values. This also shows why it is important to follow the rules for significant figures.)

Example: Two noninteracting capacitors are in series. One has a value of 10.0 pF, the other of 20.0 pF. What is the resulting reactance in a circuit operating at 28.0 MHz?

$$X_{C1} = \frac{1}{2 \pi f C}$$

$$= \frac{1}{2 \times 3.1416 \times 28.0 \times 10^6 \text{ Hz} \times 10.0 \times 10^{-12} \text{ F}}$$

$$= \frac{10^6 \ \Omega}{1760} = 568 \ \Omega$$

$$X_{C2} = \frac{1}{2 \pi f C}$$

$$= \frac{1}{2 \times 3.1416 \times 28.0 \times 10^6 \text{ Hz} \times 20.0 \times 10^{-12} \text{ F}}$$

$$= \frac{10^6 \ \Omega}{3520} = 284 \ \Omega$$

$$X_{total} = X_{C1} + X_{C2} = 568 \ \Omega + 284 \ \Omega = 852 \ \Omega$$

Alternatively, combining the series capacitors first, the total capacitance is 6.67×10^{-12} F or 6.67 pF. Then:

$$X_{total} = \frac{1}{2 \pi f C}$$

$$= \frac{1}{2 \times 3.1416 \times 28.0 \times 10^6 \text{ Hz} \times 6.67 \times 10^{-12} \text{ F}}$$

$$= \frac{10^6 \ \Omega}{1170} = 855 \ \Omega$$

(Within the uncertainty of the measured values and the rounding of values in the calculations, this is the same result as the 852 Ω

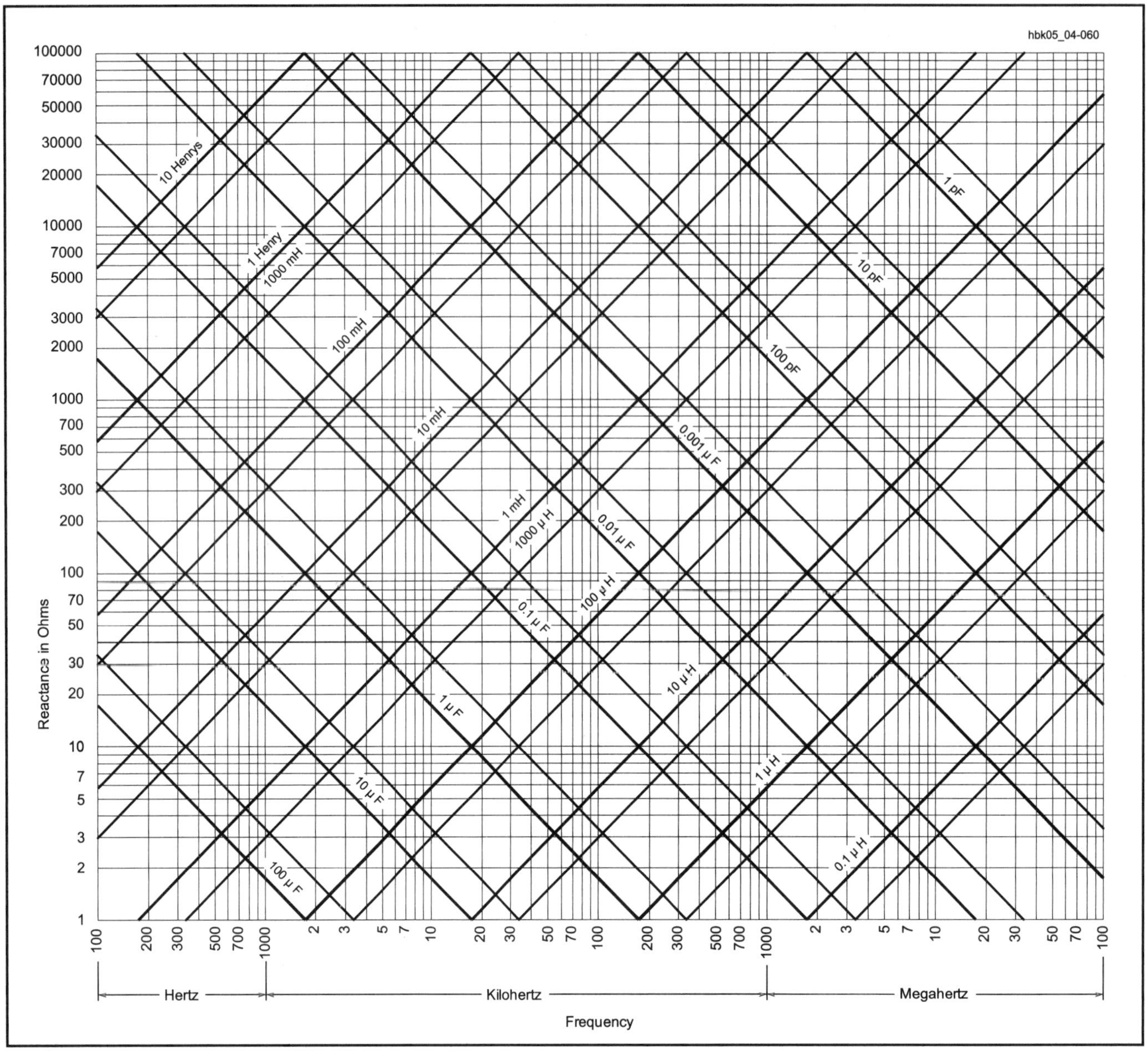

Figure 3.20 — Inductive and capacitive reactance vs frequency. Heavy lines represent multiples of 10, intermediate lines multiples of 5. For example, the light line between 10 μH and 100 μH represents 50 μH; the light line between 0.1 μF and 1 μF represents 0.5 μF, and so on. Other values can be extrapolated from the chart. For example, the reactance of 10 H at 60 Hz can be found by taking the reactance of 10 H at 600 Hz and dividing by 10 for the 10 times decrease in frequency. (Originally from Terman, *Radio Engineer's Handbook*. See references.)

we obtained with the first method.)

This example serves to remind us that *series capacitance* is not calculated in the manner used by other series resistance and inductance, but *series capacitive reactance* does follow the simple addition formula.

For reactances of the same type in parallel, the general formula is:

$$X_{total} = \frac{1}{\frac{1}{X1} + \frac{1}{X2} + \frac{1}{X3} + \ldots + \frac{1}{X_n}}$$

or, for exactly two reactances in parallel

$$X_{total} = \frac{X1 \times X2}{X1 + X2}$$

Example: Place the capacitors in the last example (10.0 pF and 20.0 pF) in parallel in the 28.0 MHz circuit. What is the resultant reactance?

$$X_{total} = \frac{X1 \times X2}{X1 + X2}$$

$$= \frac{568\ \Omega \times 284\ \Omega}{568\ \Omega + 284\ \Omega} = 189\ \Omega$$

Alternatively, two capacitors in parallel can be combined by adding their capacitances.

$$C_{total} = C_1 + C_2 = 10.0\text{ pF} + 20.0\text{ pF} = 30\text{ pF}$$

$$X_C = \frac{1}{2\pi f C}$$

$$= \frac{1}{2 \times 3.1416 \times 28.0 \times 10^6\text{ Hz} \times 30 \times 10^{-12}\text{ F}}$$

$$= \frac{10^6\ \Omega}{5280} = 189\ \Omega$$

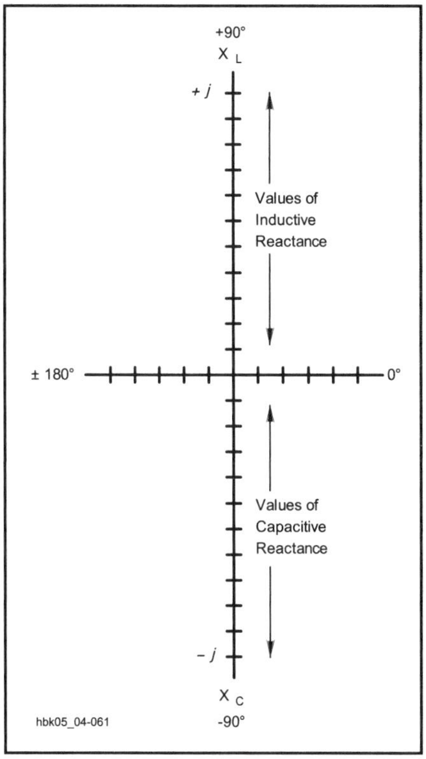

Figure 3.21 — The conventional method of plotting reactances on the vertical axis of a graph, using the upward or "plus" direction for inductive reactance and the downward or "minus" direction for capacitive reactance. The horizontal axis will be used for resistance in later examples.

Example: Place the series inductors above (4.0 μH each) in parallel in a 3.8-MHz circuit. What is the resultant reactance?

$$X_{total} = \frac{X_{L1} \times X_{L2}}{X_{L1} + X_{L2}}$$

$$= \frac{96\ \Omega \times 96\ \Omega}{96\ \Omega + 96\ \Omega} = 48\ \Omega$$

Of course, a number (N) of equal reactances (or resistances) in parallel yields a reactance that is the value of one of them divided by N, or:

$$X_{total} = \frac{X}{N} = \frac{96\ \Omega}{2} = 48\ \Omega$$

All of these calculations apply only to reactances of the same type; that is, all capacitive or all inductive. Mixing types of reactances requires a different approach.

UNLIKE REACTANCES IN SERIES

When combining unlike reactances — that is, combinations of inductive and capacitive reactance — in series, it is necessary to take into account that the voltage-to-current phase relationships differ for the different types of reactance. **Figure 3.22** shows a series circuit with both types of reactance. Since the reactances are in series, the current must be the same in both. The voltage across each circuit element differs in phase, however. The voltage E_L *leads* the current by 90°, and the voltage E_C *lags* the current by 90°. Therefore, E_L and E_C have opposite polarities and cancel each other in whole or in part. The line E in Figure 3.22 approximates the resulting voltage, which is the *difference* between E_L and E_C.

Since for a constant current the reactance is directly proportional to the voltage, the net reactance is still the sum of the individual reactances. Because inductive reactance is considered to be positive and capacitive reactance negative, the resulting reactance can be either positive (inductive) or negative (capacitive) or even zero (no reactance).

$$X_{total} = X_L - X_C$$

The convention of using absolute values for the reactances and building the sense of positive and negative into the formula is the preferred method used by hams and will be used in all of the remaining formulas in this chapter. Nevertheless, before using any formulas that include reactance, determine whether this convention is followed before assuming that the absolute values are to be used.

Example: Using Figure 3.22 as a visual aid, let $X_C = 20.0\ \Omega$ and $X_L = 80.0\ \Omega$. What is the resulting reactance?

$$X_{total} = X_L - X_C$$

$$= 80.0\ \Omega - 20.0\ \Omega = +60.0\ \Omega$$

Since the result is a positive value, total reactance is inductive. Had the result been a negative number, the total reactance would have been capacitive.

When reactance types are mixed in a series circuit, the resulting reactance is always smaller than the larger of the two reactances. Likewise, the resulting voltage across the series combination of reactances is always smaller than the larger of the two voltages across individual reactances.

Every series circuit of mixed reactance types with more than two circuit elements can be reduced to this simple circuit by combining all the reactances into one inductive and one capacitive reactance. If the circuit has more than one capacitor or more than one inductor in the overall series string, first use the formulas given earlier to determine the total series inductance alone and the total series capacitance alone (or their respective reactances). Then combine the resulting single capacitive reactance and single inductive reactance as shown in this section.

UNLIKE REACTANCES IN PARALLEL

The situation of parallel reactances of mixed type appears in **Figure 3.23**. Since the elements are in parallel, the voltage is common to both reactive components. The current through the capacitor, I_C, *leads* the voltage by 90°, and the current through the inductor, I_L, *lags* the voltage by 90°. In this case, it is the currents that are 180° out of phase and thus cancel each other in whole or in part. The total current is the difference between the individual currents, as indicated by the line I in Figure 3.23.

Since reactance is the ratio of voltage to current, the total reactance in the circuit is:

$$X_{total} = \frac{E}{I_L - I_C}$$

In the drawing, I_C is larger than I_L, and the resulting differential current retains the phase of I_C. Therefore, the overall reactance, X_{total}, is capacitive in this case. The total reactance

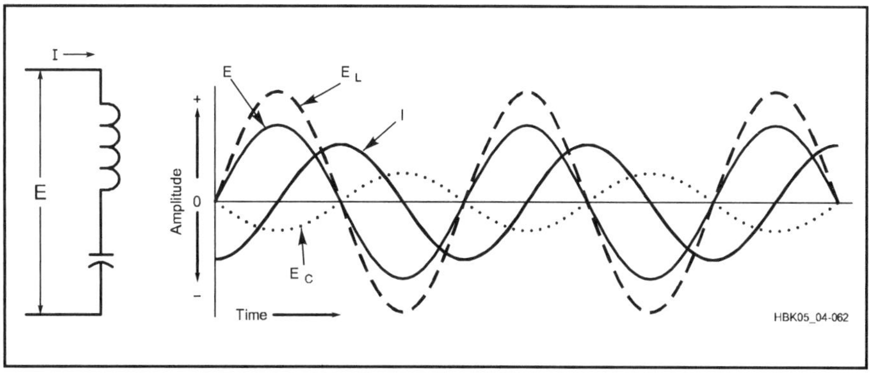

Figure 3.22 — A series circuit containing both inductive and capacitive components, together with representative voltage and current relationships.

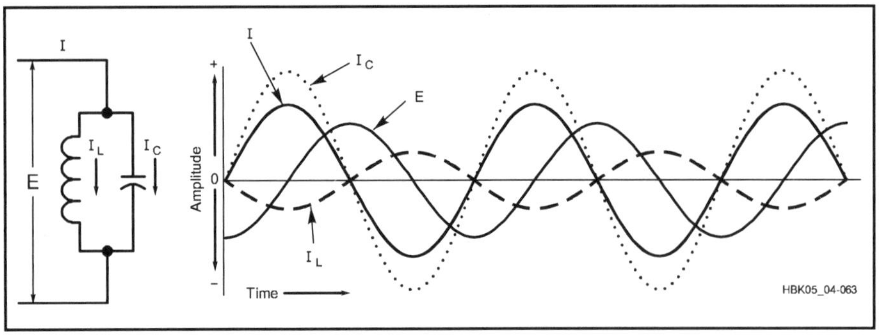

Figure 3.23 — A parallel circuit containing both inductive and capacitive components, together with representative voltage and current relationships.

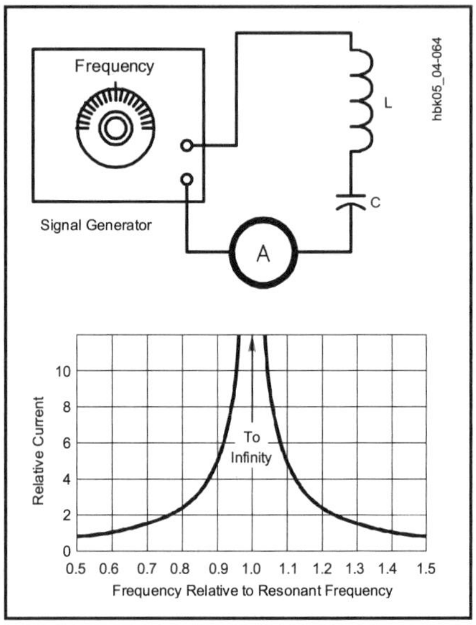

Figure 3.24 — The relative generator current with a fixed voltage in a series circuit containing inductive and capacitive reactances as the frequency approaches and departs from resonance.

of the circuit will be smaller than the larger of the individual reactances, because the total current is smaller than the larger of the two individual currents.

In parallel circuits, reactance and current are inversely proportional to each other for a constant voltage and the equation for two reactances in parallel can be used, carrying the positive and negative signs:

$$X_{total} = \frac{X_L \times (-X_C)}{X_L - X_C} = \frac{-X_L \times X_C}{X_L - X_C}$$

As with the series formula for mixed reactances, follow the convention of using absolute values for the reactances, since the minus signs in the formula account for capacitive reactance being negative. If the solution yields a negative number, the resulting reactance is capacitive, and if the solution is positive, then the reactance is inductive.

Example: Using Figure 3.23 as a visual aid, place a capacitive reactance of 10.0 Ω in parallel with an inductive reactance of 40.0 Ω. What is the resulting reactance?

$$X_{total} = \frac{-X_L \times X_C}{X_L - X_C}$$

$$= \frac{-40.0\ \Omega \times 10.0\ \Omega}{40.0\ \Omega - 10.0\ \Omega}$$

$$= \frac{-400\ \Omega}{30.0\ \Omega} = -13.3\ \Omega$$

The reactance is capacitive, as indicated by the negative solution. Moreover, like resistances in parallel, the resultant reactance is always smaller than the larger of the two individual reactances.

As with the case of series reactances, if each leg of a parallel circuit contains more than one reactance, first simplify each leg to a single reactance. If the reactances are of the same type in each leg, the series reactance formulas for reactances of the same type will apply. If the reactances are of different types, then use the formulas shown above for mixed series reactances to simplify the leg to a single value and type of reactance.

3.5.3 Reactances At and Near Resonance

Any series or parallel circuit in which the values of the two unlike reactances are equal is said to be *resonant*. For any given inductance or capacitance, it is theoretically possible to find a value of the opposite reactance type to produce a resonant circuit for any desired frequency.

When a series circuit like the one shown in Figure 3.22 is resonant, the voltages E_C and E_L are equal and cancel; their sum is zero. This is a *series-resonant* circuit. Since the reactance of the circuit is proportional to the sum of these voltages, the net reactance also goes to zero. Theoretically, the current, as shown in **Figure 3.24**, can become infinite. In fact, it is limited only by losses in the components and other resistances that would exist in a real circuit of this type. As the frequency of operation moves slightly off resonance and the reactances no longer cancel completely, the net reactance climbs as shown in the figure. Similarly, away from resonance the current drops to a level determined by the net reactance.

In a *parallel-resonant* circuit of the type in Figure 3.23, the current I_L and I_C are equal and cancel to zero. Since the reactance is inversely proportional to the current, as the current approaches zero, the reactance becomes infinite. As with series circuits, component losses and other resistances in the circuit prevent the current from reaching zero. **Figure 3.25** shows the theoretical current curve near and at resonance for a purely reactive parallel-resonant circuit. Note that in both Figure 3.24 and Figure 3.25, the departure of current from the resonance value is close to, but not quite, symmetrical above and below the resonant frequency.

Example: What is the reactance of a series L-C circuit consisting of a 56.04-pF capacitor and an 8.967-μH inductor at 7.00, 7.10 and 7.20 MHz? Using the formulas from earlier in this chapter, we calculate a table of values:

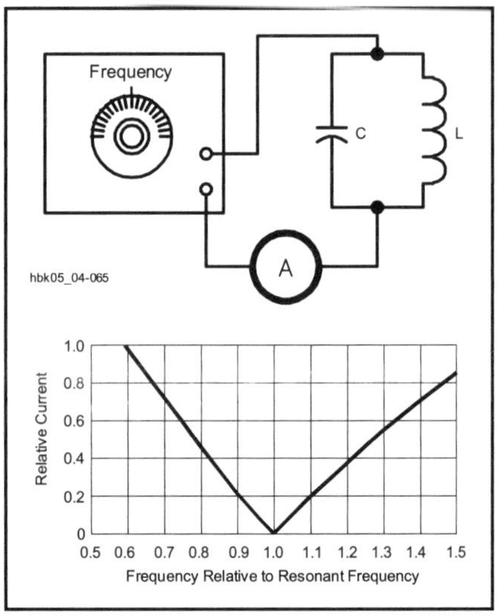

Figure 3.25 — The relative generator current with a fixed voltage in a parallel circuit containing inductive and capacitive reactances as the frequency approaches and departs from resonance. (The circulating current through the parallel inductor and capacitor is a maximum at resonance.)

Frequency (MHz)	X_L (Ω)	X_C (Ω)	X_{total} (Ω)
7.000	394.4	405.7	−11.3
7.100	400.0	400.0	0
7.200	405.7	394.4	11.3

The exercise shows the manner in which the reactance rises rapidly as the frequency moves above and below resonance. Note that in a series-resonant circuit, the reactance at frequencies below resonance is capacitive, and above resonance, it is inductive. **Figure 3.26** displays this fact graphically. In a parallel-resonant circuit, where the reactance becomes infinite at resonance, the opposite condition exists: above resonance, the reactance is capacitive and below resonance it is inductive, as shown in **Figure 3.27**. Of course, all graphs and calculations in this section are theoretical and presume a purely reactive circuit. Real circuits are never purely reactive; they contain some resistance that modifies their performance considerably. Real resonant circuits will be discussed later in this chapter.

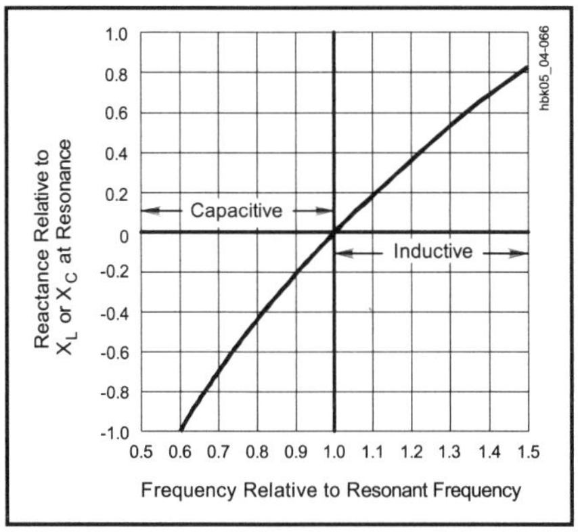

Figure 3.26 — The transition from capacitive to inductive reactance in a series-resonant circuit as the frequency passes resonance.

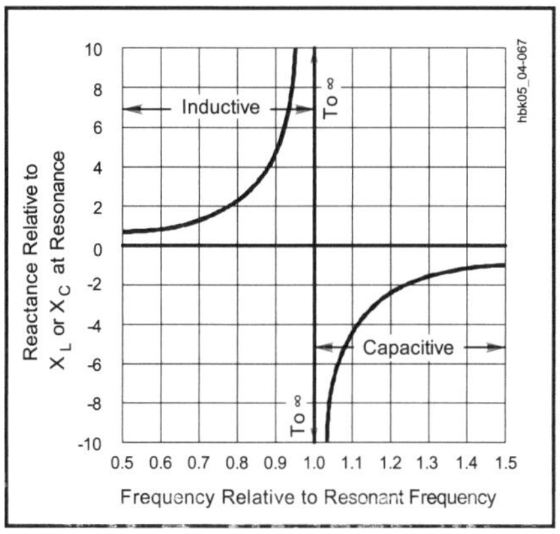

Figure 3.27 — The transition from inductive to capacitive reactance in a parallel-resonant circuit as the frequency passes resonance.

3.5.4 Reactance and Complex Waveforms

All of the formulas and relationships shown in this section apply to alternating current in the form of regular sine waves. Complex wave shapes complicate the reactive situation considerably. A complex or nonsinusoidal wave can be treated as a sine wave of some fundamental frequency and a series of harmonic frequencies whose amplitudes depend on the original wave shape. When such a complex wave — or collection of sine waves — is applied to a reactive circuit, the current through the circuit will not have the same wave shape as the applied voltage. The difference results because the reactance of an inductor and capacitor depend in part on the applied frequency.

For the second-harmonic component of the complex wave, the reactance of the inductor is twice and the reactance of the capacitor is half their respective values at the fundamental frequency. A third-harmonic component produces inductive reactances that are triple and capacitive reactances that are one-third those at the fundamental frequency. Thus, the overall circuit reactance is different for each harmonic component.

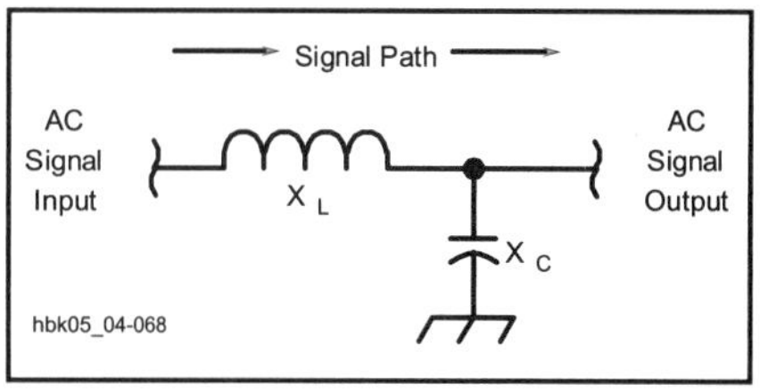

Figure 3.28 — A signal path with a series inductor and a shunt capacitor. The circuit presents different reactances to an ac signal and to its harmonics.

The frequency sensitivity of a reactive circuit to various components of a complex wave shape creates both difficulties and opportunities. On the one hand, calculating the circuit reactance in the presence of highly variable as well as complex waveforms, such as speech, is difficult at best. On the other hand, the frequency sensitivity of reactive components and circuits lays the foundation for filtering, that is, for separating signals of different frequencies or acting upon them differently. For example, suppose a coil is in the series path of a signal and a capacitor is connected from the signal line to ground, as represented in **Figure 3.28**. The reactance of the coil to the second harmonic of the signal will be twice that at the fundamental frequency and oppose more effectively the flow of harmonic current. Likewise, the reactance of the capacitor to the harmonic will be half that to the fundamental, allowing the harmonic an easier current path away from the signal line toward ground. The result is a low-pass filter that attenuates the harmonic more than the fundamental signal. (See the **Analog and Digital Filtering** chapter for detailed information on filter theory and construction.)

3.6 Impedance

When a circuit contains both resistance and reactance, the combined opposition to current is called *impedance*. Symbolized by the letter Z, impedance is a more general term than either resistance or reactance. Frequently, the term is used even for circuits containing only resistance or reactance. Qualifications such as "resistive impedance" are sometimes added to indicate that a circuit has only resistance, however.

The reactance and resistance comprising an impedance may be connected either in series or in parallel, as shown in **Figure 3.29**. In these circuits, the reactance is shown as a box to indicate that it may be either inductive or capacitive. In the series circuit at A, the current is the same in both elements, with (generally) different voltages appearing across the resistance and reactance. In the parallel circuit at B, the same voltage is applied to both elements, but different currents may flow in the two branches.

In a resistance, the current is in phase with the applied voltage, while in a reactance it is 90° out of phase with the voltage. Thus, the phase relationship between current and voltage in the circuit as a whole may be anything between zero and 90°, depending on the relative amounts of resistance and reactance.

As shown in Figure 3.21 in the preceding section, reactance is graphed on the vertical axis to record the phase difference between the voltage and the current.

Figure 3.30 adds resistance to the graph. Since the voltage is in phase with the current, resistance is recorded on the horizontal axis, using the positive or right side of the scale.

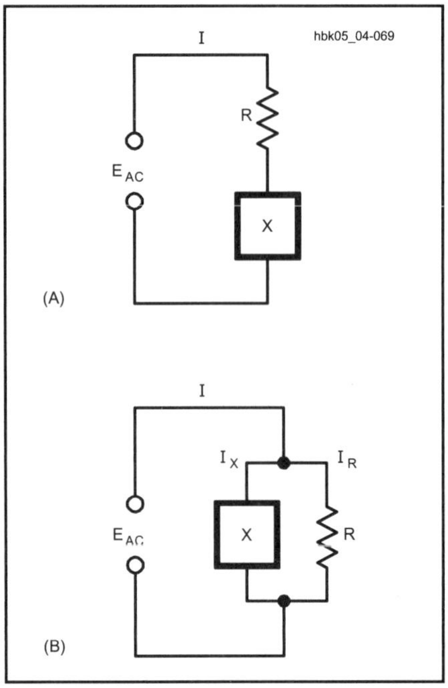

Figure 3.29 — Series and parallel circuits containing resistance and reactance.

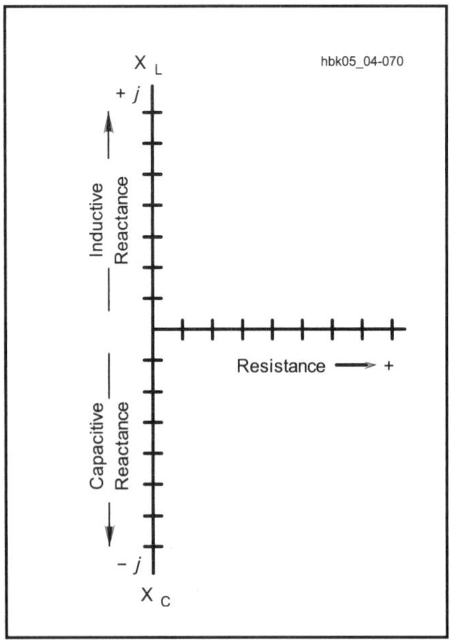

Figure 3.30 — The conventional method of charting impedances on a graph, using the vertical axis for reactance (the upward or "plus" direction for inductive reactance and the downward or "minus" direction for capacitive reactance), and using the horizontal axis for resistance.

3.6.1 Calculating Z from R and X in Series Circuits

Impedance is the complex combination of resistance and reactance. Since there is a 90° phase difference between resistance and reactance (whether inductive or capacitive), simply adding the two values does not correspond to what actually happens in a circuit and will not give the correct result. Therefore, expressions such as "$Z = R + X$" are incorrect because they show resistance and reactance being added directly. The correct expression is "$Z = R + jX$" showing that complex mathematics must be used. In pure mathematics, "*i*" indicates an imaginary number. Because *i* represents current in electronics, we use the letter "*j*" for the same mathematical operator, although there is nothing imaginary about what it represents in electronics. (References to explain imaginary numbers, rectangular coordinates, polar coordinates and how to work with them are provided in the "Radio Mathematics" article in this book's downloadable supplemental information.) With respect to resistance and reactance, the letter *j* is normally assigned to those figures on the vertical axis, 90° out of phase with the horizontal axis. The presence of *j* means that impedance is a vector and calculating impedance from resistance and reactance involves *vector addition*.

As noted earlier, a vector is a value with both magnitude and direction, such as velocity; "10 meters/second to the north." Impedance also has a "direction" derived from the phase differences between voltage and current as described below. In vector addition, the result of combining two values with a phase difference is a quantity different from the simple *algebraic addition* of the two values. The result will have a phase difference intermediate between two vectors.

RECTANGULAR FORM OF IMPEDANCE

Because this form for impedances, $Z = R \pm jX$, can be plotted on a graph using rectangular coordinates, this is the *rectangular form* of impedance. The rectangular coordinate system in which one axis represents real number and the other axis imaginary numbers is called the *complex plane* and impedance with both real (R) and imaginary (X) components is called *complex impedance*. Unless specifically noted otherwise, assume that "impedance" means "complex impedance" and that both R and X may be present.

Consider **Figure 3.31**, a series circuit consisting of an inductive reactance and a resistance. As given, the inductive reactance is 100 Ω and the resistance is 50 Ω. Using *rectangular coordinates*, the impedance becomes

$$Z = R + jX$$

where
Z = the impedance in ohms,
R = the resistance in ohms, and
X = the reactance in ohms.

In the present example,

$$Z = 50 + j100\ \Omega$$

This point is located at the tip of the arrow drawn on the graph where the dashed lines cross.

POLAR FORM OF IMPEDANCE AND PHASE ANGLE

As the graph in Figure 3.31 shows, the impedance that results from combining R and X can also be represented by a line completing a right triangle whose sides are the resistance and reactance. The point at the end of the line — the complex impedance — can be described by how far it is from the origin of the graph where the axes cross (the *magnitude* of the impedance indicated by vertical bars around the variable, |Z|) and the angle made by the line with the horizontal axis representing 0° (the *phase angle* of the impedance, θ).

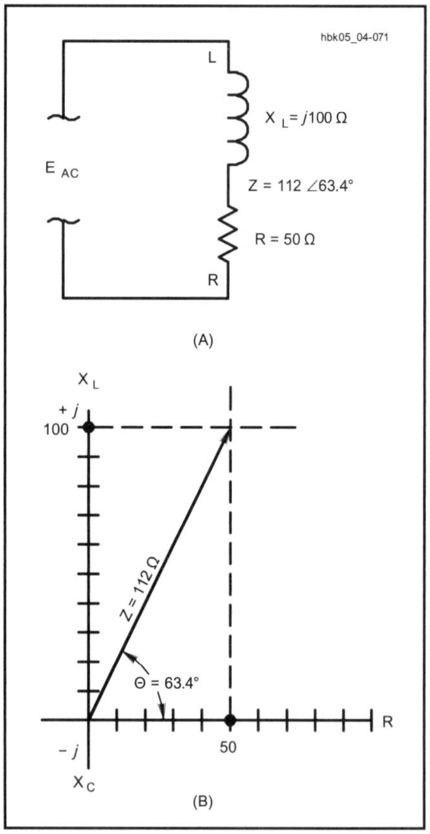

Figure 3.31 — A series circuit consisting of an inductive reactance of 100 Ω and a resistance of 50 Ω. At B, the graph plots the resistance, reactance, and impedance.

This is the *polar form* of impedance and it is written in the form

$$Z = |Z| \angle\theta$$

Occasionally, θ may be given in radians. The convention in this handbook is to use degrees unless specifically noted otherwise.

The length of the hypotenuse of the right triangle represents the magnitude of the impedance and can be calculated using the formula for calculating the hypotenuse of a right triangle, in which the square of the hypotenuse equals the sum of the squares of the two sides:

$$|Z| = \sqrt{R^2 + X^2}$$

In this example:

$$|Z| = \sqrt{(50\ \Omega)^2 + (100\ \Omega)^2}$$

$$= \sqrt{2500\ \Omega^2 + 10000\ \Omega^2}$$

$$= \sqrt{12500\ \Omega^2} = 112\ \Omega$$

The magnitude of the impedance that results from combining 50 Ω of resistance with 100 Ω of inductive reactance is 112 Ω. From trigonometry, the tangent of the phase angle is the side opposite the angle (X) divided by the side adjacent to the angle (R), or

$$\tan\theta = \frac{X}{R}$$

where
X = the reactance, and
R = the resistance.

Find the angle by taking the inverse tangent, or arctan:

$$\theta = \arctan\frac{X}{R}$$

Calculators sometimes label the inverse tangent key as "$\tan^{-1}$". Remember to be sure your calculator is set to use the right angular units, either degrees or radians.

In the example shown in Figure 3.31,

$$\theta = \arctan\frac{100\ \Omega}{50\ \Omega} = \arctan 2.0 = 63.4°$$

Using the information just calculated, the complex impedance in polar form is:

$$Z = 112\ \Omega \angle 63.4°$$

This is stated verbally as "112 ohms at an angle of 63 point 4 degrees."

POLAR TO RECTANGULAR CONVERSION

The expressions $R \pm jX$ and $|Z| \angle\theta$ both provide the same information, but in two different forms. The procedure just given permits conversion from rectangular coordinates into polar coordinates. The reverse procedure is also important. **Figure 3.32** shows an impedance composed of a capacitive reactance and a resistance. Since capacitive reactance appears as a negative value, the impedance will be at a negative phase angle, in this case, 12.0 Ω at a phase angle of – 42.0° or Z = |12.0 Ω | ∠ – 42.0°.

Remember that the impedance forms a triangle with the values of X and R from the rectangular coordinates. The reactance axis forms the side opposite the angle θ.

$$\sin\theta = \frac{\text{side opposite}}{\text{hypotenuse}} = \frac{X}{|Z|}$$

Solving this equation for reactance, we have:

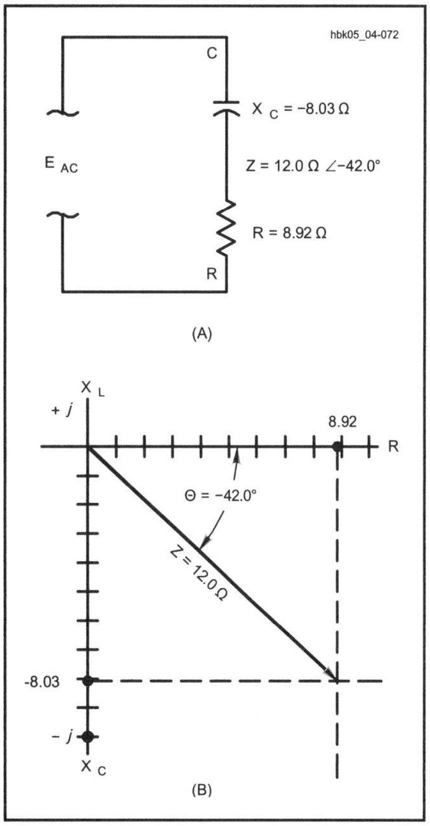

Figure 3.32 — A series circuit consisting of a capacitive reactance and a resistance: the impedance is given as 12.0 Ω at a phase angle θ of –42 degrees. At B, the graph plots the resistance, reactance, and impedance.

$$X = |Z| \times \sin\theta\ \text{(ohms)}$$

Likewise, the resistance forms the side adjacent to the angle.

$$\sin\theta = \frac{\text{side opposite}}{\text{hypotenuse}} = \frac{X}{|Z|}$$

Solving for resistance, we have:

$$R = |Z| \times \cos\theta\ \text{(ohms)}$$

Then from our example:

$$X = 12.0\ \Omega \times \sin(-42°)$$
$$= 12.0\ \Omega \times -0.669 = -8.03\ \Omega$$

$$R = 12.0\ \Omega \times \cos(-42°)$$
$$= 12.0\ \Omega \times 0.743 = 8.92\ \Omega$$

Since X is a negative value, it is plotted on the lower vertical axis, as shown in Figure 3.32, indicating capacitive reactance. In rectangular form, Z = 8.92 Ω – *j*8.03 Ω.

In performing impedance and related calculations with complex circuits, rectangular coordinates are most useful when formulas require the addition or subtraction of values. Polar notation is most useful for multiplying and dividing complex numbers. (See the article "Radio Mathematics" in this book's downloadable supplemental material for references dealing with the mathematics of complex numbers.)

All of the examples shown so far in this section presume a value of reactance that contributes to the circuit impedance. Reactance is a function of frequency, however, and many impedance calculations may begin with a value of capacitance or inductance and an operating frequency. In terms of these values, |Z| can be calculated in either of two ways, depending on whether the reactance is inductive or capacitive:

$$|Z| = \sqrt{R^2 + (2\pi f L)^2}$$

$$|Z| = \sqrt{R^2 + \left(\frac{1}{2\pi f C}\right)^2}$$

Example: What is the impedance of a circuit like Figure 3.31 with a resistance of 100 Ω and a 7.00-µH inductor operating at a frequency of 7.00 MHz? Using the equation appropriate for inductive reactance,

$$|Z| = \sqrt{R^2 + (2 \pi f L)^2}$$

$$= \sqrt{(100\ \Omega)^2 + (2 \pi \times 7.0 \times 10^{-6}\ H \times 7.0 \times 10^6\ Hz)^2}$$

$$= \sqrt{10000\ \Omega^2 + (308\ \Omega)^2}$$

$$= \sqrt{10000\ \Omega^2 + 94900\ \Omega^2}$$

$$= \sqrt{104900\ \Omega^2} = 323.9\ \Omega$$

Since 308 Ω is the value of inductive reactance of the 7.00-μH coil at 7.00 MHz, the phase angle calculation proceeds as given in the earlier example:

$$\theta = \arctan \frac{X}{R} = \arctan \left(\frac{308.0\ \Omega}{100.0\ \Omega} \right)$$

= arctan (3.08) = 72.0°

Since the reactance is inductive, the phase angle is positive.

3.6.2 Calculating Z from R and X in Parallel Circuits

In a parallel circuit containing reactance and resistance, such as shown in **Figure 3.33**, calculation of the resultant impedance from the values of R and X does not proceed by direct combination as for series circuits. The general formula for parallel circuits is:

$$|Z| = \frac{RX}{\sqrt{R^2 + X^2}}$$

where the formula uses the absolute (unsigned) reactance value. The phase angle for the parallel circuit is given by:

$$\theta = \arctan \left(\frac{R}{X} \right)$$

The sign of θ has the same meaning in both series and parallel circuits: if the parallel reactance is capacitive, then θ is a negative angle, and if the parallel reactance is inductive, then θ is a positive angle.

Example: An inductor with a reactance of 30.0 Ω is in parallel with a resistor of 40.0 Ω. What is the resulting impedance and phase angle?

$$|Z| = \frac{RX}{\sqrt{R^2 + X^2}} = \frac{30.0\ \Omega \times 40.0\ \Omega}{\sqrt{(30.0\ \Omega)^2 + (40.0\ \Omega)^2}}$$

$$= \frac{1200\ \Omega^2}{\sqrt{900\ \Omega^2 + 1600\ \Omega^2}} = \frac{1200\ \Omega^2}{\sqrt{2500\ \Omega^2}}$$

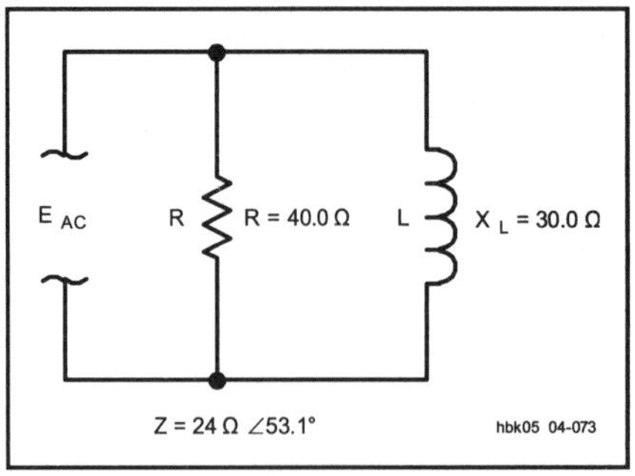

Figure 3.33 — A parallel circuit containing an inductive reactance of 30.0 Ω and a resistor of 40.0 Ω. No graph is given, since parallel impedances cannot be manipulated graphically in the simple way of series impedances.

$$= \frac{1200\ \Omega^2}{50.0\ \Omega} = 24.0\ \Omega$$

$$\theta = \arctan \left(\frac{R}{X} \right) = \arctan \left(\frac{40.0\ \Omega}{30.0\ \Omega} \right)$$

$$\theta = \arctan (1.33) = 53.1°$$

Since the parallel reactance is inductive, the resultant angle is positive.

Example: A capacitor with a reactance of 16.0 Ω is in parallel with a resistor of 12.0 Ω. What is the resulting impedance and phase angle? (Remember that capacitive reactance is negative when used in calculations.)

$$|Z| = \frac{RX}{\sqrt{R^2 + X^2}} \frac{-16.0\ \Omega \times 12.0\ \Omega}{\sqrt{(-16.0\ \Omega)^2 + (12.0\ \Omega)^2}}$$

$$= \frac{-192\ \Omega^2}{\sqrt{256\ \Omega^2 + 144\ \Omega^2}} = \frac{-192\ \Omega^2}{\sqrt{400\ \Omega^2}}$$

$$= \frac{-192\ \Omega^2}{20.0\ \Omega} = -9.60\ \Omega$$

$$\theta = \arctan \left(\frac{R}{X} \right) = \arctan \left(\frac{12.0\ \Omega}{-16.0\ \Omega} \right)$$

$$\theta = \arctan (-0.750) = -36.9°$$

Because the parallel reactance is capacitive and the reactance negative, the resultant phase angle is negative.

3.6.3 Admittance

Just as the inverse of resistance is conductance (*G*) and the inverse of reactance is susceptance (B), so, too, impedance has an inverse: *admittance* (*Y*), measured in siemens (S). Thus,

$$Y = 1 / Z$$

Since resistance, reactance and impedance are inversely proportional to the current (Z = E / I), conductance, susceptance and admittance are directly proportional to current. That is,

$$Y = I / E$$

Admittance can be expressed in rectangular and polar forms, just like impedance,

$$Y = G \pm jB = |Y| \angle \theta$$

The phase angle for admittance has the same sign convention as for impedance; if the susceptance component is inductive, the phase angle is positive, and if the susceptive component is capacitive, the phase angle is negative.

One handy use for admittance is in simplifying parallel circuit impedance calculations. Similarly to the rules stated previously for combining conductance, the admittance of a parallel combination of reactance and resistance is the vector addition of susceptance and conductance. In other words, for parallel circuits:

$$|Y| = \sqrt{G^2 + B^2}$$

where

|Y| = magnitude of the admittance in siemens,
G = conductance or 1 / R in siemens, and
B = susceptance or 1 / X in siemens.

Example: An inductor with a reactance of 30.0 Ω is in parallel with a resistor of 40.0 Ω. What is the resulting impedance and phase angle? The susceptance is 1 / 30.0 Ω = 0.0333 S and the conductance is 1 / 40.0 Ω = 0.0250 S.

$$Y = \sqrt{(0.0333\ S)^2 + (0.0250\ S)^2}$$

$$Y = \sqrt{0.00173\ S^2} = 0.0417\ S$$

$$Z = \frac{1}{Y} = \frac{1}{0.0417\ S} = 24.0\ \Omega$$

The phase angle in terms of conductance and susceptance is:

$$\theta = \arctan \left(\frac{B}{G} \right)$$

In this example,

$$\theta = \arctan\left(\frac{0.0333\ S}{0.0250\ S}\right) = \arctan(1.33) = 53.1°$$

Again, since the reactive component is inductive, the phase angle is positive. For a capacitively reactive parallel circuit, the phase angle would have been negative. Compare these results with the example calculation of the impedance for the same circuit earlier in the section.

Conversion between resistance, reactance and impedance and conductance, susceptance and admittance is very useful in working with complex circuits and in impedance matching of antennas and transmission lines. There are many on-line calculators that can perform these operations and many programmable calculators and suites of mathematical computer software have these functions built-in. Knowing when and how to use them, however, demands some understanding of the fundamental strategies shown here.

3.6.4 More than Two Elements in Series or Parallel

When a circuit contains several resistances or several reactances in series, simplify the circuit before attempting to calculate the impedance. Resistances in series add, just as in a purely resistive circuit. Series reactances of the same kind — that is, all capacitive or all inductive — also add, just as in a purely reactive circuit. The goal is to produce a single value of resistance and a single value of reactance that can be used in the impedance calculation.

Figure 3.34 illustrates a more difficult case in which a circuit contains two different reactive elements in series, along with a series resistance. The series combination of X_C and X_L reduce to a single value using the same rules of combination discussed in the section on purely reactive components. As Figure 3.34B demonstrates, the resultant reactance is the difference between the two series reactances.

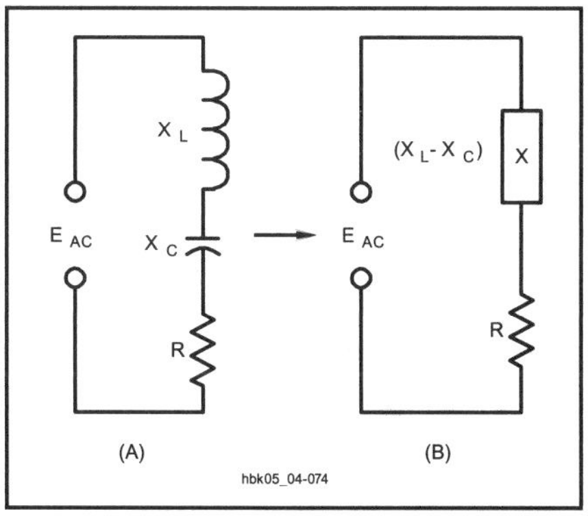

Figure 3.34 — A series impedance containing mixed capacitive and inductive reactances can be reduced to a single reactance plus resistance by combining the reactances algebraically.

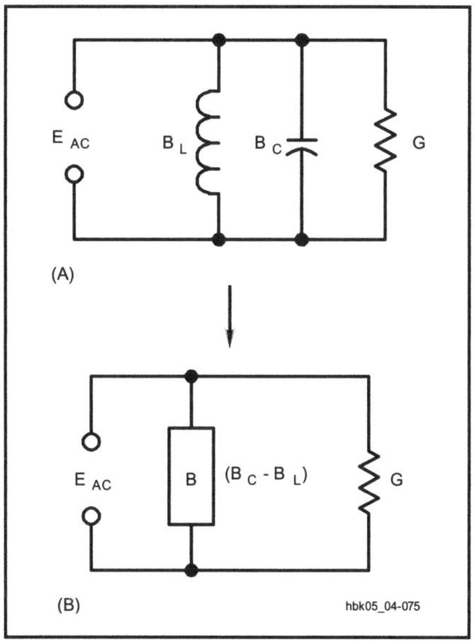

Figure 3.35 — A parallel impedance containing mixed capacitive and inductive reactances can be reduced to a single reactance plus resistance using formulas shown earlier in the chapter. By converting reactances to susceptances, as shown in A, you can combine the susceptances algebraically into a single susceptance, as shown in B.

For parallel circuits with multiple resistances or multiple reactances of the same type, use the rules of parallel combination to reduce the resistive and reactive components to single elements. Where two or more reactive components of different types appear in the same circuit, they can be combined using formulas shown earlier for pure reactances. As **Figure 3.35** suggests, however, they can also be combined as susceptances. Parallel susceptances of different types add, with attention to their differing signs. The resulting single susceptance can then be combined with the conductance to arrive at the overall circuit admittance whose inverse is the final circuit impedance.

3.6.5 Equivalent Series and Parallel Circuits

The two circuits shown in Figure 3.29 are equivalent if the same current flows when a given voltage of the same frequency is applied, and if the phase angle between voltage and current is the same in both cases. It is possible, in fact, to transform any given series circuit into an equivalent parallel circuit, and vice versa.

A series RX circuit can be converted into its parallel equivalent by means of the formulas:

$$R_P = \frac{R_S^2 + X_S^2}{R_S}$$

$$X_P = \frac{R_S^2 + X_S^2}{X_S}$$

where the subscripts P and S represent the parallel- and series-equivalent values, respectively. If the parallel values are known, the equivalent series circuit can be found from:

$$R_S = \frac{R_P\ X_P^2}{R_P^2 + X_P^2}$$

and

$$X_S = \frac{R_P^2\ X_P}{R_P^2 + X_P^2}$$

Example: Let the series circuit in Figure 3.29 have a series reactance of –50.0 Ω (indicating a capacitive reactance) and a resistance of 50.0 Ω. What are the values of the equivalent parallel circuit?

$$R_P = \frac{R_S^2 + X_S^2}{R_S} = \frac{(50.0\ \Omega)^2 + (-50.0\ \Omega)^2}{50.0\ \Omega}$$

$$= \frac{2500\ \Omega^2 + 2500\ \Omega^2}{50.0\ \Omega} = \frac{5000\ \Omega^2}{50\ \Omega} = 100\ \Omega$$

$$X_P = \frac{R_S^2 + X_S^2}{X_S} = \frac{(50.0\ \Omega)^2 + (-50.0\ \Omega)^2}{-50.0\ \Omega}$$

$$= \frac{2500\ \Omega^2 + 2500\ \Omega^2}{-50.0\ \Omega} = \frac{5000\ \Omega^2}{-50\ \Omega} = -100\ \Omega$$

A capacitive reactance of 100 Ω in parallel with a resistance of 100 Ω is the equivalent circuit to the series circuit.

3.6.6 Ohm's Law for Impedance

Ohm's Law applies to circuits containing impedance just as readily as to circuits having resistance or reactance only. The formulas are:

$$E = I\ Z$$

$$I = E / Z$$

$$Z = E / I$$

where

E = voltage in volts,

I = current in amperes, and

Z = impedance in ohms.

Z must now be understood to be a complex number, consisting of resistive and reactive components. If Z is complex, then so are E and I, with a magnitude and phase angle. The rules of complex mathematics are then applied and the variables are written in boldface type as **Z**, **E**, and **I**, or an arrow is added above them to indicate that they are complex, such as,

$$\vec{E} = \vec{I}\,\vec{Z}$$

If only the magnitude of impedance, voltage, and currents are important, however, then the magnitudes of the three variables can be combined in the familiar ways without regard to the phase angle. In this case E and I are assumed to be RMS values (or some other steady-state value such as peak, peak-to-peak, or average). **Figure 3.36** shows a simple circuit consisting of a resistance of 75.0 Ω and a reactance of 100 Ω in series. From the series-impedance formula previously given, the impedance is

$$Z = \sqrt{R^2 + {X_L}^2} = \sqrt{(75.0\ \Omega)^2 + (100\ \Omega)^2}$$

$$= \sqrt{5630\ \Omega^2 + 10000\ \Omega^2}$$

$$= \sqrt{15600\ \Omega^2} = 125\ \Omega$$

If the applied voltage is 250 V, then

$$I = \frac{E}{Z} = \frac{250\ V}{125\ \Omega} = 2.0\ A$$

This current flows through both the resistance and reactance, so the voltage drops are:

$$E_R = I\,R = 2.0\ A \times 75.0\ \Omega = 150\ V$$

$$E_{XL} = I\,X_L = 2.0\ A \times 100\ \Omega = 200\ V$$

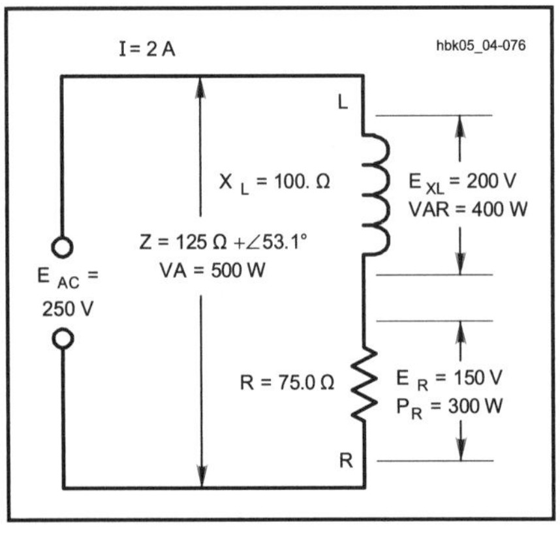

Figure 3.36 — A series circuit consisting of an inductive reactance of 100 Ω and a resistance of 75.0 Ω. Also shown is the applied voltage, voltage drops across the circuit elements, and the current.

AC Component Summary

	Resistor	*Capacitor*	*Inductor*
Basic Unit	ohm (Ω)	farad (F)	henry (H)
Units Commonly Used		microfarads (µF) picofarads (pF)	millihenrys (mH) microhenrys (µH)
Time constant	(None)	RC	L/R
Voltage-Current Phase	In phase	Current leads voltage Voltage lags current	Voltage leads current Current lags voltage
Resistance or Reactance	Resistance	$X_C = 1 / 2\pi fC$	$X_L = 2\pi fL$
Change with increasing frequency	No	Reactance decreases	Reactance increases
Q of circuit	Not defined	X_C / R	X_L / R

Illustrating one problem of working only with RMS values, the simple arithmetical sum of these two drops, 350 V, is greater than the applied voltage because the two voltages are 90° out of phase. When phase is taken into account,

$$E = \sqrt{(150\ V)^2 + (200\ V)^2}$$

$$= \sqrt{22500\ V^2 + 40000\ V^2}$$

$$= \sqrt{62500\ V^2} = 250\ V$$

3.6.7 Reactive Power and Power Factor

Although purely reactive circuits, whether simple or complex, show a measurable ac voltage and current, we cannot simply multiply the two together to arrive at power. Power is the rate at which energy is consumed by a circuit, and purely reactive circuits do not consume energy. The charge placed on a capacitor during part of an ac cycle is returned to the circuit during the next part of a cycle. Likewise, the energy stored in the magnetic field of an inductor returns to the circuit later in the ac cycle. A reactive circuit simply cycles and recycles energy into and out of the reactive components. If a purely reactive circuit were possible in reality, it would consume no energy at all.

In reactive circuits, circulation of energy accounts for seemingly odd phenomena. For example, in a series circuit with capacitance and inductance, the voltages across the components may exceed the supply voltage. That condition can exist because, while energy is being stored by the inductor, the capacitor is returning energy to the circuit from its previously charged state, and vice versa. In a parallel circuit with inductive and capacitive branches, the current circulating through the components may exceed the current drawn from the source. Again, the phenomenon occurs because the inductor's collapsing magnetic field supplies current to the capacitor, and the discharging capacitor provides current to the inductor.

To distinguish between the non-dissipated energy circulating in a purely reactive circuit and the dissipated or *real power* in a resistive circuit, thc unit of *reactive power* is callcd thc *volt-ampere reactive*, or *VAR*. The term watt is not used and sometimes reactive power is called "wattless" power. VAR has only limited use in radio circuits. Formulas similar to those for resistive power are used to calculate VAR:

$$VAR = I \times E$$

$$VAR = I^2 \times X$$

$$VAR = E^2 / X$$

where E and I are RMS values of voltage and current.

Real, or dissipated, power is measured in watts. *Apparent power* is the product of the voltage across and the current through an impedance. To distinguish apparent power from real power, apparent power is measured in *volt-amperes* (*VA*).

In the circuit of Figure 3.36, an applied voltage of 250 V results in a current of 2.00 A, giving an apparent power of 250 V × 2.00 A = 500 W. Only the resistance actually consumes power, however. The real power dissipated by the resistance is:

$$E = I^2\,R = (2.0\ A)^2 \times 75.0\ V = 300\ W$$

and the reactive power is:

$$VAR = I^2 \times X_L = (2.0\ A)^2 \times 100\ \Omega = 400\ VA$$

The ratio of real power to the apparent power is called the circuit's *power factor* (PF).

$$PF = \frac{P_{consumed}}{P_{apparent}} = \frac{R}{Z}$$

Power factor is frequently expressed as a percentage. The power factor of a purely resistive circuit is 100% or 1, while the power factor of a pure reactance is zero. In the example of Figure 3.36 the power factor would be 300 W / 500 W = 0.600 or 60%.

Apparent power has no direct relationship to the power actually dissipated unless the power factor of the circuit is known.

$$P = \text{Apparent Power} \times \text{Power Factor}$$

An equivalent definition of power factor is:

$$PF = \cos\theta$$

where θ is the phase angle of the circuit impedance.

Since the phase angle in the example equals:

$$\theta = \arctan\left(\frac{X}{R}\right) = \arctan\left(\frac{100\ \Omega}{75.0\ \Omega}\right)$$

$$\theta = \arctan(1.33) = 53.1°$$

and the power factor is:

$$PF = \cos 53.1° = 0.600$$

as the earlier calculation confirms.

Since power factor is always rendered as a positive number, the value must be followed by the words "leading" or "lagging" to identify the phase of the voltage with respect to the current. Specifying the numerical power factor is not always sufficient. For example, many dc-to-ac power inverters can safely operate loads having a large net reactance of one sign but only a small reactance of the opposite sign. Hence, the final calculation of the power factor in this example would be reported as "0.600, leading."

3.7 Quality Factor (Q) of Components

Components that store energy, such as capacitors and inductors, may be compared in terms of *quality factor* or *Q factor*, abbreviated *Q*. The concept of *Q* originated in 1914 (then dubbed *K*) and first appeared in print in 1923 when Kenneth S. Johnson used it to represent the ratio of reactance to resistance as a "figure of merit" for inductors in US patent 1,628,983. For a series or parallel representation of a reactive circuit element:

$$Q = \frac{X_S}{R_S} = \frac{R_P}{X_P}$$

where for series-connected reactance and its series loss resistance (such as an inductor)

Q = quality factor (no units),

X_S = series reactance of the component (in ohms), and

R_S = the sum of all series resistances associated with the energy losses in the component (in ohms).

For a parallel connected reactance and its parallel loss resistance (such as a capacitor)

Q = quality factor (no units),

X_P = parallel-connected reactance of the component (in ohms), and

R_P = the total parallel resistance associated with the energy losses in the component (in ohms).

Several exactly equivalent formulas for Q may be seen in **Table 3.2**. In Table 3.2, equation [a] most naturally represents the Q of an inductor, while equation [b] is useful for a capacitor. Both representations are equivalent to equation [c] which relates the energy storage to energy losses in inductors and capacitors. Note that in a series circuit representation, the series resistance is proportional to energy loss, and the series reactance is proportional to stored energy. In a parallel circuit, however, the reciprocal of the resistance is proportional to the lost energy and the reciprocal of the reactance is proportional to the stored energy. The Q of a tuned circuit may be found by measuring the upper and lower frequencies where the resistance equals the magnitude of the reactance, and applying equation [d]. The geometrical mean frequency is

$$f = \sqrt{f_U f_L}$$

and may be replaced by the center frequency for high-Q circuits. In circuits having several reactive components, such as the tuned circuits in Figure 3.42 later in this chapter, the circuit Q is the parallel combination of the individual Q factors. For example:

$$Q = 1 / \left(\frac{1}{Q_C} + \frac{1}{Q_L}\right)$$

where Q_C is the capacitor Q (sometimes specified by a manufacturer) and the inductor Q is Q_L.

The Q of capacitors is ordinarily high. Good quality ceramic capacitors and mica capacitors may have Q values of 1200 or more. Microwave capacitors can have poor Q values — 10 or less at 10 GHz and higher frequencies because X_C will be low. Capacitors are subject to predominantly dielectric losses which are modeled as a parallel loss resistance across

Table 3.2
Equivalent Formulas for Expressing Q and Their Uses

[a]	$Q = \frac{\text{Series Reactance}}{\text{Series Resistance}}$	Johnson's historical definition of Q for inductors, used for series circuits
[b]	$Q = \frac{\text{Parallel Resistance}}{\text{Parallel Reactance}}$	Parallel equivalent circuit definition of Q, useful for capacitors.
[c]	$Q = \frac{2\pi \times \text{Stored energy}}{\text{Energy lost in one cycle}}$	Fundamental energy definition, useful with antennas, reactive components, and mechanical systems.
[d]	$Q = \frac{\sqrt{f_U f_L}}{f_U - f_L} = \frac{\text{Frequency}}{\text{Bandwidth}}$	Bandwidth formula for simple resonant circuits. Impedance Z = R + *j*X, and f_U is the upper frequency where R = X, and f_L is the lower frequency where R = –X, and $f_U - f_L$ represents the –3 dB bandwidth.

the capacitive reactance. Capacitors also have a series loss resistance associated with the conductor leads and capacitor plates, but this loss is often small enough to ignore.

Inductors are subject to several types of electrical energy losses such as wire resistance (including skin effect) and core losses. All electrical conductors have some resistance through which electrical energy is lost as heat. Wire conductors suffer additional ac losses because alternating current tends to flow on the conductor surface due to the skin effect discussed in the chapter on **RF Techniques**. If the inductor's core is iron, ferrite or brass, the core will introduce additional losses of energy. Note that core losses for inductors are modeled as a resistor in parallel with the inductor (analogous to capacitor dielectric losses). The specific details of these losses are discussed in connection with each type of core material.

The sum of all core losses may be depicted by showing an equivalent series connected resistor with the inductor (see the section on Practical Inductors in the **Circuits and Components** chapter), although there is no separate component represented by the resistor symbol. As a result of inherent energy losses, inductor Q rarely approaches capacitor Q in a circuit where both components work together. Although many circuits call for the highest Q inductor obtainable, other circuits may call for a specific Q, even a very low one.

Q is also discussed in the following section on Resonant Circuits. For these circuits, Q is closely related to circuit bandwidth and selectivity. In addition, the circuit Q depends on whether or not a load is attached.

3.8 Resonant Circuits

A circuit containing both an inductor and a capacitor — and therefore, both inductive and capacitive reactance — is often called a *tuned circuit* or a *resonant circuit.* For any such circuit, there is a particular frequency at which the inductive and capacitive reactances are the same, that is, $X_L = X_C$. For most purposes, this is the *resonant frequency* of the circuit. At the resonant frequency — or at *resonance*, for short:

$$X_L = 2 \pi f L = X_C = \frac{1}{2 \pi f C}$$

By solving for f, we can find the resonant frequency of any combination of inductor and capacitor from the formula:

$$f = \frac{1}{2 \pi \sqrt{L C}}$$

where

f = frequency in hertz (Hz),
L = inductance in henrys (H),
C = capacitance in farads (F), and
π = 3.1416.

For most high-frequency (HF) radio work, smaller units of inductance and capacitance and larger units of frequency are more convenient. The basic formula becomes:

$$f = \frac{10^3}{2 \pi \sqrt{L C}}$$

where

f = frequency in megahertz (MHz),
L = inductance in microhenrys (μH),
C = capacitance in picofarads (pF), and
π = 3.1416.

Example: What is the resonant frequency of a circuit containing an inductor of 5.0 μH and a capacitor of 35 pF?

$$f = \frac{10^3}{2 \pi \sqrt{L C}} = \frac{10^3}{6.2832 \sqrt{5.0 \times 35}}$$

$$= \frac{10^3}{83} = 12 \text{ MHz}$$

To find the matching component (inductor or capacitor) when the frequency and one component is known (capacitor or inductor) for general HF work, use the formula:

$$f^2 = \frac{1}{4 \pi^2 L C}$$

where f, L and C are in basic units. For HF work in terms of MHz, μH and pF, the basic relationship rearranges to these handy formulas:

$$L = \frac{25{,}330}{f^2 C}$$

$$C = \frac{25{,}330}{f^2 L}$$

where

f = frequency in MHz,
L = inductance in μH, and
C = capacitance in pF

For most radio work, these formulas will permit calculations of frequency and component values well within the limits of component tolerances.

Example: What value of capacitance is needed to create a resonant circuit at 21.1 MHz, if the inductor is 2.00 μH?

$$C = \frac{25{,}330}{f^2 L} = \frac{25{,}330}{(21.1^2 \times 2.0)}$$

$$= \frac{25{,}330}{890} = 28.5 \text{ pF}$$

Figure 3.20 can also be used if an approximate answer is acceptable. From the horizontal axis, find the vertical line closest to the desired resonant frequency. Every pair of diagonals that cross on that vertical line represent a combination of inductance and capacitance that will resonate at that frequency. For example, if the desired frequency is 10 MHz, the pair of diagonals representing 5 μH and 50 pF cross quite close to that frequency. Interpolating between the given diagonals will provide more resolution — remember that all three sets of lines are spaced logarithmically.

Resonant circuits have other properties of importance, in addition to the resonant frequency, however. These include impedance, voltage drop across components in series-resonant circuits, circulating current in parallel-resonant circuits, and bandwidth. These properties determine such factors as the selectivity of a tuned circuit and the component ratings for circuits handling significant amounts of power. Although the basic determination of the tuned-circuit resonant frequency ignored any resistance in the circuit, that resistance will play a vital role in the circuit's other characteristics.

3.8.1 Series-Resonant Circuits

Figure 3.37 presents a basic schematic diagram of a *series-resonant circuit.* Although most schematic diagrams of radio circuits would show only the inductor and the capacitor, resistance is always present in such circuits. The most notable resistance is associated with the series resistance losses in the inductor at HF. The dominant losses in the capacitor may be modeled as a parallel resistance (not shown), but these losses are low enough at HF to be ignored. The current meter shown in the circuit is a reminder that in

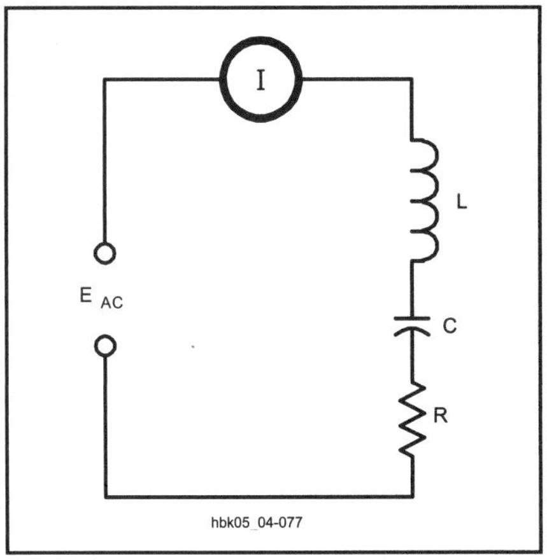

Figure 3.37 — A series circuit containing L, C, and R is resonant at the applied frequency when the reactance of C is equal to the reactance of L. The I in the circle is the schematic symbol for an ammeter.

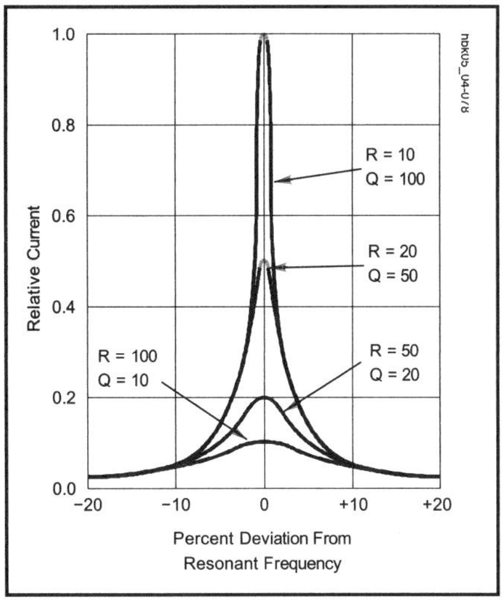

Figure 3.38 — Relative current in series-resonant circuits with various values of series resistance and Q. (An arbitrary maximum value of 1.0 represents current at resonance.) The reactance at resonance for all curves is 1000 Ω. Note that the current is hardly affected by the resistance in the circuit at frequencies more than 10% away from the resonant frequency.

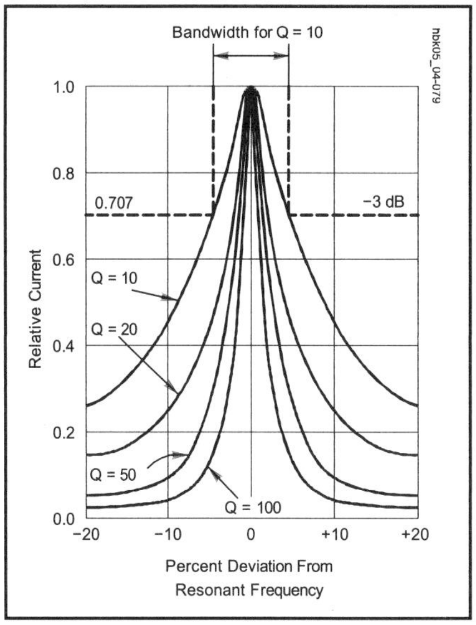

Figure 3.39 — Relative current in series-resonant circuits having different values of Q_U. The current at resonance is normalized to the same level for all curves in order to show the rate of change of decrease in current for each value of Q_U. The half-power points are shown to indicate relative bandwidth of the response for each curve. The bandwidth is indicated for a circuit with a Q_U of 10.

series circuits, the same current flows through all elements.

At resonance, the reactance of the capacitor cancels the reactance of the inductor. The voltage and current are in phase with each other, and the impedance of the circuit is determined solely by the resistance. The actual current through the circuit at resonance, and for frequencies near resonance, is determined by the formula:

$$I = \frac{E}{Z} = \frac{E}{\sqrt{R^2 + \left[2\pi f L - \frac{1}{(2\pi f C)}\right]^2}}$$

where all values are in basic units.

At resonance, the reactive factor in the formula is zero (the bracketed expression under the square root symbol). As the frequency is shifted above or below the resonant frequency without altering component values, however, the reactive factor becomes significant, and the value of the current becomes smaller than at resonance. At frequencies far from resonance, the reactive components become dominant, and the resistance no longer significantly affects the current amplitude.

The exact curve created by recording the current as the frequency changes depends on the ratio of reactance to resistance. When the reactance of either the coil or capacitor is of the same order of magnitude as the resistance, the current decreases rather slowly as the frequency is moved in either direction away from resonance. Such a curve is said to be *broad*. Conversely, when the reactance is considerably larger than the resistance, the current decreases rapidly as the frequency moves away from resonance, and the circuit is said to be *sharp*. A sharp circuit will respond a great deal more readily to the resonant frequency than to frequencies quite close to resonance; a broad circuit will respond almost equally well to a group or band of frequencies centered around the resonant frequency.

Both types of resonance curves are useful. A sharp circuit gives good selectivity — the ability to respond strongly (in terms of current amplitude) at one desired frequency and to discriminate against others. A broad circuit is used when the apparatus must give about the same response over a band of frequencies, rather than at a single frequency alone.

Figure 3.38 presents a family of curves, showing the decrease in current as the frequency deviates from resonance. In each case, the inductive and capacitive reactances are assumed to be 1000 Ω. The maximum current, shown as a relative value on the graph, occurs with the lowest resistance, while the lowest peak current occurs with the highest resistance. Equally important, the rate at which the current decreases from its maximum value also changes with the ratio of reactance to resistance. It decreases most rapidly when the ratio is high and most slowly when the ratio is low.

UNLOADED Q

As noted in equation [a] of Table 3.2 earlier in this chapter, Q is the ratio of series reactance representing 2π times the stored energy (equation [c] in Table 3.2) to series resistance or consumed energy. Since both terms of the ratio are measured in ohms, Q has no units and is known as the *quality factor* (and less frequently, the *figure of merit* or the *multiplying factor*). The series resistive losses of the coil often dominate the energy consumption in HF series-resonant circuits, so the inductor Q largely determines the resonant-circuit Q. Since this value of Q is independent of any external load to which the circuit might transfer power, it is called the *unloaded Q* or Q_U of the circuit.

Example: What is the unloaded Q of a series-resonant circuit with a series loss resistance of 5 Ω and inductive and capacitive components having a reactance of 500 Ω each? With a reactance of 50 Ω each?

$$Q_{U1} = \frac{X1}{R} = \frac{500\ \Omega}{5\ \Omega} = 100$$

$$Q_{U2} = \frac{X2}{R} = \frac{50\ \Omega}{5\ \Omega} = 10$$

BANDWIDTH

Figure 3.39 is an alternative way of drawing the family of curves that relate current to frequency for a series-resonant circuit. By assuming that the peak current of each curve is the same, the rate of change of current for various values of Q_U and the associated ratios of reactance to resistance are more easily compared. From the curves, it is evident that the lower Q_U circuits pass current across a greater *bandwidth* of frequencies than the circuits with a higher Q_U. For the purpose of comparing tuned circuits, bandwidth is often defined as the frequency spread between the two frequencies at which the current amplitude decreases to 0.707 (or $\sqrt{2} / 2$) times the maximum value. Since the power consumed by the resistance, R, is proportional to the square of the current, the power at these points is half the maximum power at resonance, assuming that R is constant for the calculations. The half-power, or –3 dB, points are marked on Figure 3.39.

For Q values of 10 or greater, the curves shown in Figure 3.39 are approximately symmetrical. On this assumption, bandwidth (BW) can be easily calculated by inverting equation [d] in Table 3.2, and approximating the geometrical mean –3 dB frequency by f:

$$BW = \frac{f}{Q_U}$$

where BW and f are in the same units, that is, in Hz, kHz or MHz.

Example: What is the 3 dB bandwidth of a series-resonant circuit operating at 14 MHz with a Q_U of 100?

$$BW = \frac{f}{Q_U} = \frac{14\ \text{MHz}}{100} = 0.14\ \text{MHz} = 140\ \text{kHz}$$

The relationship between Q_U, f and BW provides a means of determining the value of circuit Q when inductor losses may be difficult to measure. By constructing the series-resonant circuit and measuring the current as the frequency varies above and below resonance, the half-power points can be determined. Then:

$$Q_U = \frac{f}{BW}$$

Example: What is the Q_U of a series-resonant circuit operating at 3.75 MHz, if the –3 dB bandwidth is 375 kHz?

$$Q_U = \frac{f}{BW} = \frac{3.75\ \text{MHz}}{0.375\ \text{MHz}} = 10.0$$

If the loss resistance of the inductor is much greater than of the capacitor (the usual case), BW is approximately R/L. The Q of a series resonant circuit can also be stated

$$Q_U = \frac{f_0}{BW} = \frac{1}{R}\sqrt{\frac{L}{C}}$$

The illustrations the relationship between Q and bandwidth at **hyperphysics.phy-astr.gsu.edu/hbase/electric/serres.html** are helpful in understanding the concept. **Table 3.3** provides some simple formulas for estimating the maximum current and phase angle for various bandwidths, if both f and Q_U are known.

Table 3.3
The Selectivity of Resonant Circuits

Approximate percentage of current at resonance[1] or of impedance at resonance[2]	*Bandwidth (between half-power or –3 dB points on response curve)*	*Series circuit current phase angle (degrees)*
95	f / 3Q	18.5
90	f / 2Q	26.5
70.7	f / Q	45
44.7	2f / Q	63.5
24.2	4f / Q	76
12.4	8f / Q	83

[1]For a series resonant circuit
[2]For a parallel resonant circuit

VOLTAGE DROP ACROSS COMPONENTS

The voltage drop across the coil and across the capacitor in a series-resonant circuit are each proportional to the reactance of the component for a given current (since E = I X). These voltages may be many times the applied voltage for a high-Q circuit. In fact, at resonance, the voltage drop is:

$$E_X = Q_U E_{AC}$$

where

E_X = the voltage across the reactive component,
Q_U = the circuit unloaded Q, and
E_{AC} = the applied voltage in Figure 3.37.

(Note that the voltage drop across the inductor is the vector sum of the voltages across the resistance and the reactance; however, for Q greater than 10, the error created by using this is not ordinarily significant.) Since the calculated value of E_X is the RMS voltage, the peak voltage will be higher by a factor of 1.414. Antenna couplers and other high-Q circuits handling significant power may experience arcing from high values of E_X, even though the source voltage to the circuit is well within component ratings.

CAPACITOR LOSSES

Although capacitor energy losses tend to be insignificant compared to inductor losses up to about 30 MHz, the losses may affect circuit Q in the VHF range. Leakage resistance, principally in the solid dielectric that forms the insulating support for the capacitor plates, appears as a resistance in parallel with the capacitor plates. Instead of forming a series resistance, capacitor leakage usually forms a parallel resistance with the capacitive reactance. If the leakage resistance of a capacitor is significant enough to affect the Q of a series-resonant circuit, the parallel resistance (R_P) may be converted to an equivalent series resistance (R_S) before adding it to the inductor's resistance.

$$R_S = \frac{X_C^2}{R_P} = \frac{1}{R_P \times (2\,\pi\, f\, C)^2}$$

Example: A 10.0 pF capacitor has a leakage resistance of 10,000 Ω at 50.0 MHz. What is the equivalent series resistance?

$$R_S = \frac{1}{R_P \times (2\,\pi\, f\, C)^2}$$

$$= \frac{1}{1.0 \times 10^4 \times (6.283 \times 50.0 \times 10^6 \times 10.0 \times 10^{-12})^2}$$

$$= \frac{1}{1.0 \times 10^4 \times 9.87 \times 10^{-6}}$$

$$= \frac{1}{0.0987} = 10.1\ \Omega$$

In calculating the impedance, current and bandwidth for a series-resonant circuit in which this capacitor might be used, the series-equivalent resistance of the unit is added to the loss resistance of the coil. Since inductor losses tend to increase with frequency because of skin effect in conductors, and capacitor dielectric losses also tend to increase with frequency, the combined losses in the capacitor and the inductor can seriously reduce circuit Q.

3.8.2 Parallel-Resonant Circuits

Although series-resonant circuits are common, the vast majority of resonant circuits used in radio work are *parallel-resonant circuits*. **Figure 3.40** represents a typical HF parallel-resonant circuit. As is the case for series-resonant circuits, the inductor is the chief source of resistive losses (that is, the parallel loss resistance across the capacitor is not shown), and these losses appear in series with the coil. Because current through parallel-resonant circuits is lowest at resonance, and

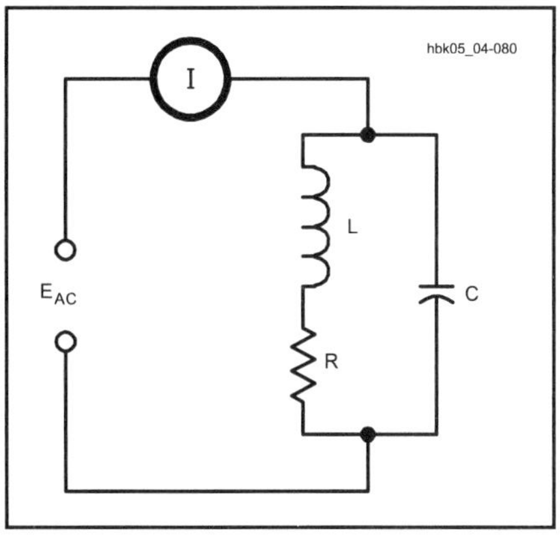

Figure 3.40 — A typical parallel-resonant circuit, with the resistance shown in series with the inductive leg of the circuit. Below a Q_U of 10, resonance definitions may lead to three separate frequencies which converge at higher Q_U levels. See text.

impedance is highest, they are sometimes called *antiresonant* circuits. (You may encounter the old terms *acceptor* and *rejector* referring to series- and parallel-resonant circuits, respectively.)

Because the conditions in the two legs of the parallel circuit in Figure 3.40 are not the same — the resistance is shown in only one of the legs — all of the conditions by which series resonance is determined do not occur simultaneously in a parallel-resonant circuit. **Figure 3.41** graphically illustrates the situation by showing the currents through the two components. (Currents are drawn in the manner of complex impedances shown previously to show the phase angle for each current.) When the inductive and capacitive reactances are identical, the condition defined for series resonance is met as shown at point (a). The impedance of the inductive leg is composed of both X_L and R, which yields an impedance greater than X_C and that is not 180° out of phase with X_C. The resultant current is greater than the minimum possible value and is not in phase with the voltage.

By altering the value of the inductor slightly (and holding the Q constant), a new frequency can be obtained at which the current reaches its minimum. When parallel circuits are tuned using a current meter as an indicator, this point (b) is ordinarily used as an indication of resonance. The current "dip" indicates a condition of maximum impedance and is sometimes called the *antiresonant* point or *maximum impedance resonance* to distinguish it from the condition at which $X_C = X_L$. Maximum impedance is achieved at this point by vector addition of X_C, X_L and R, however, and the result is a current somewhat out of phase with the voltage.

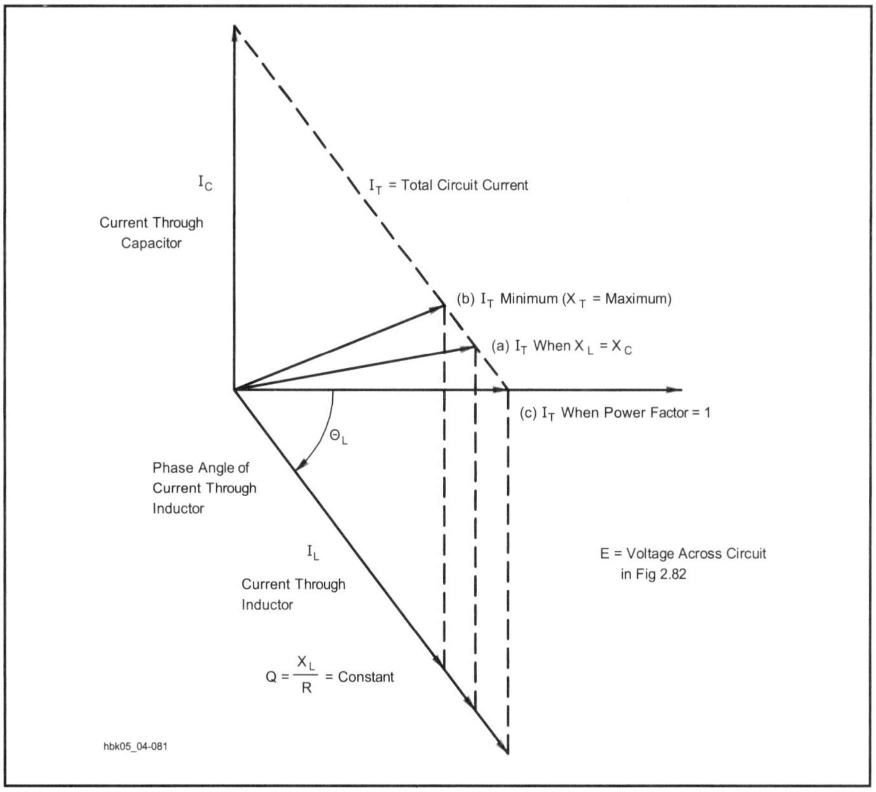

Figure 3.41 — Resonant conditions for a low- Q_U parallel circuit. Resonance may be defined as (a) $X_L = X_C$ (b) minimum current flow and maximum impedance or (c) voltage and current in phase with each other. With the circuit of Figure 3.40 and a Q_U of less than 10, these three definitions may represent three distinct frequencies.

Point (c) in the figure represents the *unity-power-factor* resonant point. Adjusting the inductor value and hence its reactance (while holding Q constant) produces a new resonant frequency at which the resultant current is in phase with the voltage. The new value of inductive reactance is the value required for a parallel-equivalent inductor and its parallel-equivalent resistor (calculated according to the formulas in the last section) to just cancel the capacitive reactance. The value of the parallel-equivalent inductor is always smaller than the actual inductor in series with the resistor and has a proportionally smaller reactance. (The parallel-equivalent resistor, conversely, will always be larger than the coil-loss resistor shown in series with the inductor.) The result is a resonant frequency slightly different from the one for minimum current and the one for $X_L = X_C$.

The points shown in the graph in Figure 3.41 represent only one of many possible situations, and the relative positions of the three resonant points do not hold for all possible cases. Moreover, specific circuit designs can draw some of the resonant points together, for example, compensating for the resistance of the coil by retuning the capacitor. The differences among these resonances are significant for circuit Q below 10, where the inductor's series resistance is a significant percentage of the reactance. Above a Q of 10, the three points converge to within a percent of the frequency and the differences between them can be ignored for practical calculations. Tuning for minimum current will not introduce a sufficiently large phase angle between voltage and current to create circuit difficulties.

PARALLEL CIRCUITS OF MODERATE TO HIGH Q

The resonant frequencies defined above converge in parallel-resonant circuits with Q higher than about 10. Therefore, a single set of formulas will sufficiently approximate circuit performance for accurate predictions. Indeed, above a Q of 10, the performance of a parallel circuit appears in many ways to be simply the inverse of the performance of a series-resonant circuit using the same components.

Accurate analysis of a parallel-resonant circuit requires the substitution of a parallel-equivalent resistor for the actual inductor-loss series resistor, as shown in **Figure 3.42**. Sometimes called the *dynamic resistance* of the parallel-resonant circuit, the parallel-equivalent resistor value will increase with circuit Q, that is, as the series resistance value decreases. To calculate the approxi-

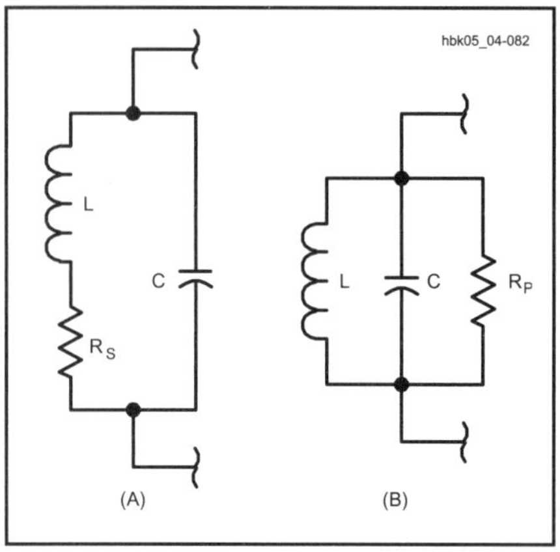

Figure 3.42 — Series and parallel equivalents when both circuits are resonant. The series resistance, R_S in A, is replaced by the parallel resistance, R_p in B, and vice versa. $R_P = X_L^2 / R_S$.

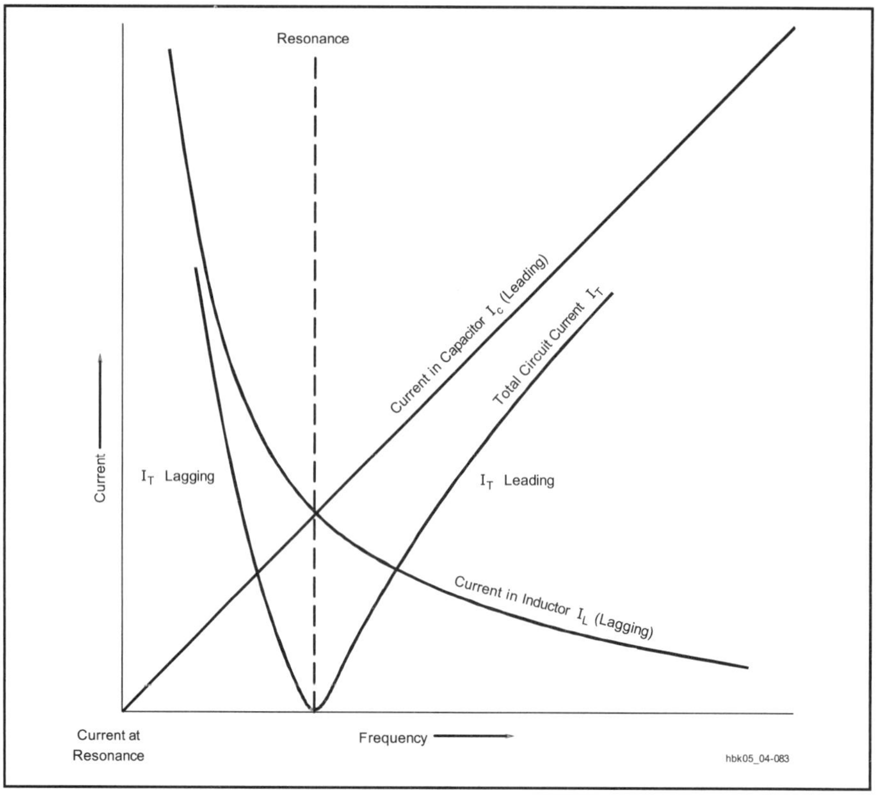

Figure 3.43 — The currents in a parallel-resonant circuit as the frequency moves through resonance. Below resonance, the current lags the voltage; above resonance the current leads the voltage. The base line represents the current level at resonance, which depends on the impedance of the circuit at that frequency.

mate parallel-equivalent resistance, use the formula:

$$R_P = \frac{{X_L}^2}{R_S} = \frac{(2 \pi f L)^2}{R_S} = Q_U X_L$$

for $R_S << X_U << R_P$ and $X_P \approx X_S$ in the equations for series-parallel conversion in the section on Impedance.

Example: What is the parallel-equivalent resistance for a coil with an inductive reactance of 350 Ω and a series resistance of 5.0 Ω at resonance?

$$R_P = \frac{{X_L}^2}{R_S} = \frac{(350\ \Omega)^2}{5.0\ \Omega}$$

$$= \frac{122{,}500\ \Omega^2}{5.0\ \Omega} = 24{,}500\ \Omega$$

Since the coil Q_U remains the inductor's reactance divided by its series resistance, the coil Q_U is 70. Multiplying Q_U by the reactance also provides the approximate parallel-equivalent resistance of the coil series resistance.

At resonance, where $X_L = X_C$, R_P defines the impedance of the parallel-resonant circuit. The reactances just equal each other, leaving the voltage and current in phase with each other. In other words, the circuit shows only the parallel resistance. Therefore, the equation for R_P can be rewritten as:

$$Z = \frac{{X_L}^2}{R_S} = \frac{(2 \pi f L)^2}{R_S} = Q_U X_L$$

In this example, the circuit impedance at resonance is 24,500 Ω.

At frequencies below resonance the current through the inductor is larger than that through the capacitor, because the reactance of the coil is smaller and that of the capacitor is larger than at resonance. There is only partial cancellation of the two reactive currents, and the total current therefore is larger than the current taken by the resistance alone. At frequencies above resonance the situation is reversed and more current flows through the capacitor than through the inductor, so the total current again increases.

The current at resonance, being determined wholly by R_P, will be small if R_P is large, and large if R_P is small. **Figure 3.43** illustrates the relative current flows through a parallel-tuned circuit as the frequency is moved from below resonance to above resonance. The base line represents the minimum current level for the particular circuit. The actual current at any frequency off resonance is simply the vector sum of the currents through the parallel equivalent resistance and through the reactive components.

To obtain the impedance of a parallel-tuned circuit either at or off the resonant frequency, apply the general formula:

$$Z = \frac{Z_C\, Z_L}{Z_S}$$

where

Z = overall circuit impedance

Z_C = impedance of the capacitive leg (usually, the reactance of the capacitor),

Z_L = impedance of the inductive leg (the vector sum of the coil's reactance and resistance), and

Z_S = series impedance of the capacitor-inductor combination as derived from the equation for current in a series-resonant circuit.

After using vector calculations to obtain Z_L and Z_S, converting all the values to polar form — as described earlier in this chapter — will ease the final calculation. Of course, each impedance may be derived from the resistance and the application of the basic reactance formulas on the values of the inductor and capacitor at the frequency of interest.

Since the current rises away from resonance, the parallel-resonant-circuit impedance must fall. It also becomes complex, resulting in an ever-greater phase difference between the voltage and the current. The rate at which the impedance falls is a function of Q_U. **Figure 3.44** presents a family of curves showing the impedance drop from resonance for circuit Q ranging from 10 to 100. The curve family for parallel-circuit impedance is essentially the same as the curve family for series-circuit current.

As with series-resonant circuits, the higher the Q of a parallel-tuned circuit, the sharper will be the response peak. Likewise, the lower the Q, the wider the band of frequencies to which the circuit responds. Using the

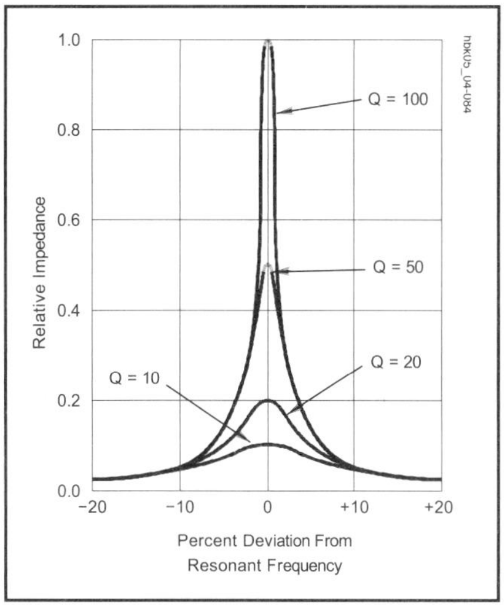

Figure 3.44 — Relative impedance of parallel-resonant circuits with different values of Q_U. The curves are similar to the series-resonant circuit current level curves of Figure 3.38. The effect of Q_U on impedance is most pronounced within 10% of the resonance frequency.

Table 3.4
The Performance of Parallel-Resonant Circuits

A. High- and Low-Q Circuits (in relative terms)

Characteristic	*High-Q Circuit*	*Low-Q Circuit*
Selectivity	high	low
Bandwidth	narrow	wide
Impedance	high	low
Total current	low	high
Circulating current	high	low

B. Off-Resonance Performance for Constant Values of Inductance and Capacitance

Characteristic	*Above Resonance*	*Below Resonance*
Inductive reactance	increases	decreases
Capacitive reactance	decreases	increases
Circuit resistance	unchanged*	unchanged*
Relative impedance	decreases	decreases
Total current	increases	increases
Circulating current	decreases	decreases
Circuit impedence	capacitive	inductive

*This is true for frequencies near resonance. At distant frequencies, skin effect may alter the resistive losses of the inductor.

half-power (–3 dB) points as a comparative measure of circuit performance as in series-resonant circuits, $BW = f / Q_U$ and $Q_U = f / BW$, where the resonant frequency and the bandwidth are in the same units. Also similarly to the series-resonant circuit:

$$Q_U = R\sqrt{\frac{C}{L}}$$

As a handy reminder, **Table 3.4** summarizes the performance of parallel-resonant circuits at high and low Q and above and below resonant frequency.

It is possible to use either series- or parallel-resonant circuits to do the same work in many circuits, thus giving the designer considerable flexibility. **Figure 3.45** illustrates this general principle by showing a series-resonant circuit in the signal path and a parallel-resonant circuit shunted from the signal path to ground. Assume both circuits are resonant at the same frequency, f, and have the same Q. The series-resonant circuit at A has its lowest impedance at f, permitting the maximum possible current to flow along the signal path. At all other frequencies, the impedance is greater and the current at those frequencies is less. The circuit passes the desired signal and tends to impede signals at undesired frequencies. The parallel circuit at B provides the highest impedance at resonance, f, making the signal path the lowest impedance path for the signal. At frequencies off resonance, the parallel-resonant circuit presents a lower impedance, thus presenting signals with a path to ground and away from the signal path. In theory, the effects will be the same relative to a signal current on the signal path. In actual circuit design exercises, of course, many other variables will enter the design picture to make one circuit preferable to the other.

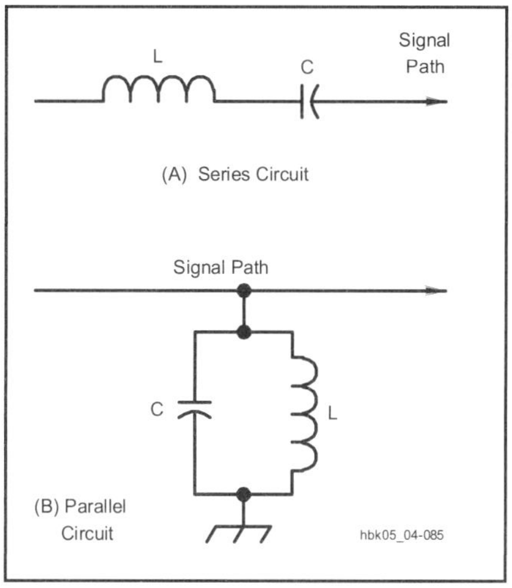

Figure 3.45 — Series- and parallel-resonant circuits configured to perform the same theoretical task: passing signals in a narrow band of frequencies along the signal path. A real design example would consider many other factors.

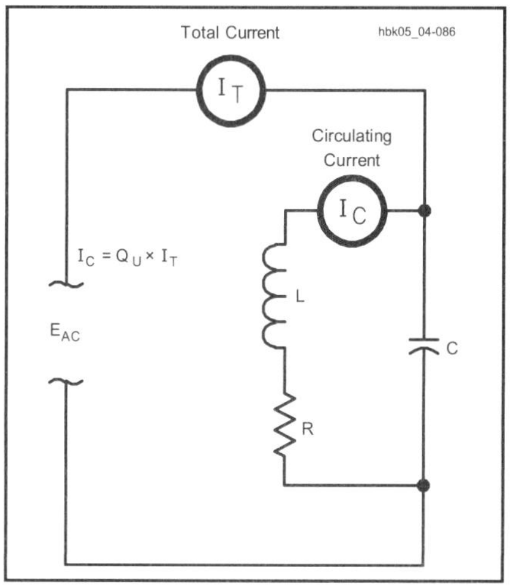

Figure 3.46 — A parallel-resonant circuit redrawn to illustrate both the total current and the circulating current.

CIRCULATING CURRENT

In a parallel-resonant circuit, the source voltage is the same for all the circuit elements. The current in each element, however, is a function of the element's reactance. **Figure 3.46** redraws the parallel-resonant circuit to indicate the total current and the current circulating between the coil and the capacitor. The current drawn from the source may be low, because the overall circuit impedance is high. The current through the individual elements may be high, however, because there is little resistive loss as the current circulates through the inductor and capacitor. For parallel-resonant circuits with an unloaded Q of 10 or greater, this *circulating current* is approximately:

$$I_C = Q_U I_T$$

where

I_C = circulating current in A, mA or μA,
Q_U = unloaded circuit Q, and
I_T = total current in the same units as I_C.

Example: A parallel-resonant circuit permits an ac or RF total current of 30 mA and has a Q of 100. What is the circulating current through the elements?

$I_X = Q_U I = 100 \times 30\text{ mA} = 3000\text{ mA} = 3\text{ A}$

Circulating currents in high-Q parallel-tuned circuits can reach a level that causes component heating and power loss. Therefore, components should be rated for the anticipated circulating currents, and not just the total current.

LOADED Q

In many resonant-circuit applications, the only power lost is that dissipated in the resistance of the circuit itself. At frequencies below 30 MHz, most of this resistance is in the coil. Within limits, increasing the number of turns in the coil increases the reactance faster than it raises the resistance, so coils for circuits in which the Q must be high are made with relatively large inductances for the frequency.

When the circuit delivers energy to a load (as in the case of the resonant circuits used in transmitters), the energy consumed in the circuit itself is usually negligible compared with that consumed by the load. The equivalent of such a circuit is shown in **Figure 3.47**, where the parallel resistor, R_L, represents the load to which power is delivered. If the power dissipated in the load is at least 10 times as great as the power lost in the inductor and capacitor, the parallel impedance of the resonant circuit itself will be so high compared with the resistance of the load that for all practical purposes the impedance of the combined circuit is equal to the load impedance. Under these conditions, the load resistance replaces the circuit impedance in calculating Q. The Q of a parallel-resonant circuit loaded by a resistive impedance is:

$$Q_L = \frac{R_L}{X}$$

where

Q_L = circuit loaded Q,
R_L = parallel load resistance in ohms, and
X = reactance in ohms of either the inductor or the capacitor.

Example: A resistive load of 3000 Ω is connected across a resonant circuit in which the inductive and capacitive reactances are each 250 Ω. What is the circuit Q?

$$Q_L = \frac{R_L}{X} = \frac{3000\ \Omega}{250\ \Omega} = 12$$

The effective Q of a circuit loaded by a parallel resistance increases when the reactances are decreased. A circuit loaded with a relatively low resistance (a few thousand ohms) must have low-reactance elements (large capacitance and small inductance) to have reasonably high Q. Many power-handling circuits, such as the output networks of transmitters, are designed by first choosing a loaded Q for the circuit and then determining component values. See the chapter on **RF Power Amplifiers** for more details.

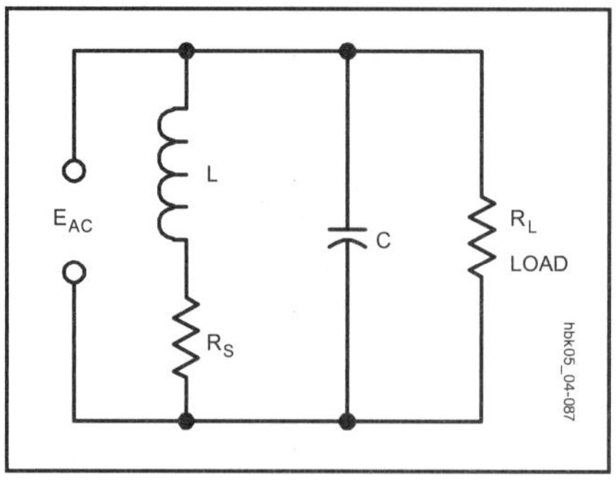

Figure 3.47 — A loaded parallel-resonant circuit, showing both the inductor-loss resistance and the load, R_L. If smaller than the inductor resistance, R_L will control the loaded Q of the circuit (Q_L).

Parallel load resistors are sometimes added to parallel-resonant circuits to lower the circuit Q and increase the circuit bandwidth. By using a high-Q circuit and adding a parallel resistor, designers can tailor the circuit response to their needs. Since the parallel resistor consumes power, such techniques ordinarily apply to receiver and similar low-power circuits, however.

Example: Specifications call for a parallel-resonant circuit with a bandwidth of 400 kHz at 14.0 MHz. The circuit at hand has a Q_U of 70.0 and its components have reactances of 350 Ω each. What is the parallel load resistor that will increase the bandwidth to the specified value? The bandwidth of the existing circuit is:

$$BW = \frac{f}{Q_U} = \frac{14.0\text{ MHz}}{70.0} = 0.200\text{ MHz}$$

$= 200\text{ kHz}$

The desired bandwidth, 400 kHz, requires a circuit with a Q of:

$$Q = \frac{f}{BW} = \frac{14.0\text{ MHz}}{0.400\text{ MHz}} = 35.0$$

Since the desired Q is half the original value, halving the resonant impedance or parallel-resistance value of the circuit is in order. The present impedance of the circuit is:

$Z = Q_U X_L = 70.0 \times 350\ \Omega = 24500\ \Omega$

The desired impedance is:

$Z = Q_U X_L = 35.0 \times 350\ \Omega$

$= 12250\ \Omega = 12.25\text{ k}\Omega$

or half the present impedance.

A parallel resistor of 24,500 Ω, or the nearest lower value (to guarantee sufficient bandwidth), will produce the required reduction in Q and bandwidth increase. Although this example simplifies the situation encountered in real design cases by ignoring such factors as the shape of the band-pass curve, it illustrates the interaction of the ingredients that determine the performance of parallel-resonant circuits.

IMPEDANCE TRANSFORMATION

An important application of the parallel-resonant circuit is as an impedance matching device. Circuits and antennas often need to be connected to other circuits or feed lines that do not have the same impedance. To transfer power effectively requires a circuit that will convert or "transform" the impedances so that each connected device or system can operate properly.

Figure 3.48 shows such a situation where the source, E_{AC}, operates at a high impedance, but the load, R_L, operates at a low impedance. The technique of impedance transformation shown in the figure is to connect the parallel-resonant circuit, which has a high impedance, across the source, but connect the load across only a portion of the coil. (This is called *tapping the coil* and the connection point is a *tap*.) The coil acts as an *autotransformer*, described in the following section, with the magnetic field of the coil shared between what are effectively two coils in series, the upper coil having many turns and the lower coil fewer turns. Energy stored in the field induces larger voltages in the many-turn coil than it does in the fewer-turn coil, "stepping down" the

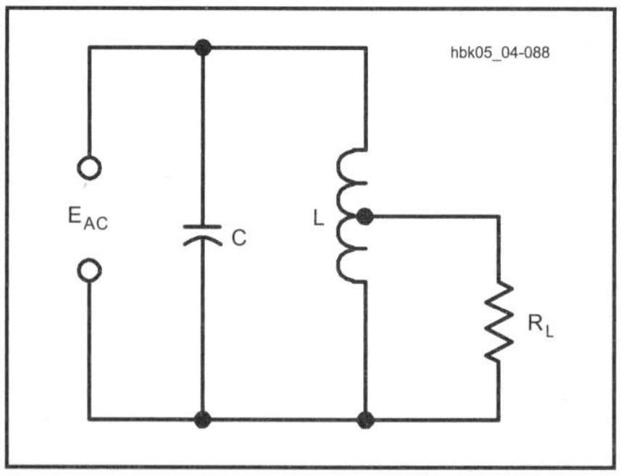

Figure 3.48 — A parallel-resonant circuit with a tapped inductor to effect an impedance match. Although the impedance presented to E_{AC} is very high, the impedance at the connection of the load, R_L, is lower.

input voltage so that energy can be extracted by the load at the required lower voltage-to-current ratio (which is impedance). The correct tap point on the coil usually has to be experimentally determined, but the technique is very effective.

When the load resistance has a very low value (say below 100 Ω) it may be connected in series in the resonant circuit (such as R_S in Figure 3.42A, for example), in which case the series L-R circuit can be transformed to an equivalent parallel L-R circuit as previously described. If the Q is at least 10, the equivalent parallel impedance is:

$$Z_R = \frac{X^2}{R_L}$$

where

Z_R = resistive parallel impedance at resonance,

X = reactance (in ohms) of either the coil or the capacitor, and

R_L = load resistance inserted in series.

If the Q is lower than 10, the reactance will have to be adjusted somewhat — for the reasons given in the discussion of low-Q parallel resonant circuits — to obtain a resistive impedance of the desired value.

These same techniques work in either "direction" — with a high-impedance source and low-impedance load or vice versa. Using a parallel-resonant circuit for this application does have some disadvantages. For instance, the common connection between the input and the output provides no dc isolation. Also, the common ground is sometimes troublesome with regard to ground-loop currents. Consequently, a circuit with only mutual magnetic coupling is often preferable. With the advent of ferrites, constructing impedance transformers that are both broadband and permit operation well up into the VHF portion of the spectrum has become relatively easy. The basic principles of broadband impedance transformers appear in the **RF Techniques** chapter.

3.9 Analog Signal Processing

The term *analog signal* refers to voltages, currents and waves that make up ac radio and audio signals, dc measurements, even power. The essential characteristic of an analog signal is that the information or energy it carries is continuously variable. Even small variations of an analog signal affect its value or the information it carries. This stands in contrast to *digital signals* that have values only within well-defined and separate ranges called *states*. To be sure, at the fundamental level all circuits and signals are analog: Digital signals are created by designing circuits that restrict the values of analog signals to those discrete states.

Analog signal processing involves various electronic stages to perform functions on analog signals such as amplifying, filtering, modulation and demodulation. A piece of electronic equipment, such as a radio, is constructed by combining a number of these circuits. How these stages interact with each other and how they affect the signal individually and in tandem is the subject of sections later in the chapter.

3.9.1 Terminology

A similar terminology is used when describing active electronic devices. The letter V or v stands for voltages and I or i for currents. Capital letters are often used to denote dc or bias values (bias is discussed later in this chapter). Lower-case often denotes instantaneous or ac values.

Voltages generally have two subscripts indicating the terminals between which the voltage is measured (V_{BE} is the dc voltage between the base and the emitter of a bipolar transistor). Currents have a single subscript indicating the terminal into which the current flows (I_C is the dc current into the collector of a bipolar transistor). If the current flows out of the device, it is generally treated as a negative value.

Resistance is designated with the letter R or r, and impedance with the letter Z or z. For example, r_{DS} is resistance between drain and source of an FET and Z_i is input impedance. For some parameters, values differ for dc and ac signals. This is indicated by using capital letters in the subscripts for dc and lower-case subscripts for ac. For example, the common-emitter dc current gain for a bipolar transistor is designated as h_{FE}, and h_{fe} is the ac current gain. (See the section on transistor amplifiers in the **Circuits and Components** chapter for a discussion of the common-emitter circuit.) Qualifiers are sometimes added to the subscripts to indicate certain operating modes of the device. SS for saturation, BR for breakdown, ON and OFF are all commonly used.

Power supply voltages have two subscripts that are the same, indicating the terminal to which the voltage is applied. V_{DD} would represent the power supply voltage applied to the drain of a field-effect transistor.

Since integrated circuits are collections of semiconductor components, the abbreviations for the type of semiconductor used also apply to the integrated circuit. For example, V_{CC} is a power supply voltage for an integrated circuit made with bipolar transistor technology in which voltage is applied to transistor collectors.

3.9.2 Linearity

The premier properties of analog signals are *superposition* and *scaling*. Superposition is the property by which signals are combined, whether in a circuit, in a piece of wire, or even in air, as the sum of the individual signals. This is to say that at any one point in time, the voltage of the combined signal is the sum of the voltages of the original signals at the same time. In a *linear system* any number of signals will add in this way to give a single combined signal. (Mathematically, this is a *linear combination*.) For this reason, analog signals and components are often referred to as *linear signals* or *linear components*. A linear system whose characteristics do not change, such as a resistive voltage divider, is called *time-invariant*. If the system changes with time, it is *time-varying*. The variations may be random, intermittent (such as being adjusted by an operator) or periodic.

One of the more important features of superposition, for the purposes of signal processing, is that signals that have been combined by superposition can be separated back into the original signals. This is what allows multiple signals that have been received by an antenna to be separated back into individual signals by a receiver.

3.9.3 Linear Operations

Any operation that modifies a signal and obeys the rules of superposition and scaling is a *linear operation*. The following sections explain the basic linear operations from which linear systems are made.

AMPLIFICATION AND ATTENUATION

Amplification and *attenuation* scale signals to be larger and smaller, respectively. The operation of *scaling* is the same as multiplying the signal at each point in time by a constant value; if the constant is greater than one then the signal is amplified, if less than one then the signal is attenuated.

An *amplifier* is a circuit that increases the amplitude of a signal. Schematically, a generic amplifier is signified by a triangular symbol, its input along the left face and its output at the point on the right (see **Figure 3.49**).

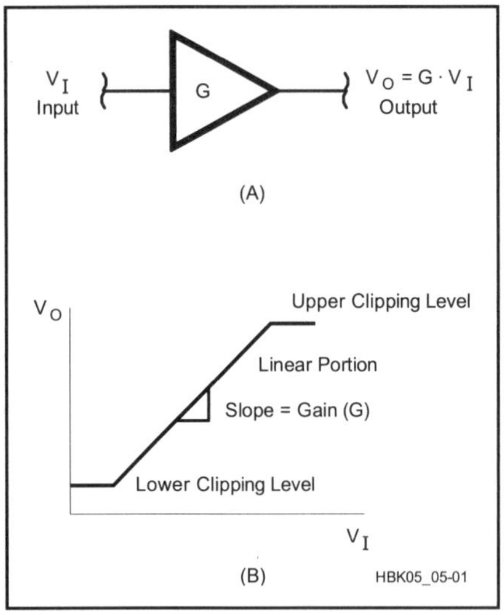

Figure 3.49 — Generic amplifier. (A) Symbol. For the linear amplifier, gain is the constant value, G, and the output voltage is equal to the input voltage times G; (B) Transfer function, input voltage along the x-axis is converted to the output voltage along the y-axis. The linear portion of the response is where the plot is diagonal; its slope is equal to the gain, G. Above and below this range are the clipping limits, where the response is not linear and the output signal is clipped.

The Decibel

The decibel (dB) is the standard unit for comparing two quantities, such as power or voltage, as a ratio. It is logarithmic so very large and very small ratios are easy to work with. The formula for calculating decibels is:

$$dB = 10\log\left(\frac{P_2}{P_1}\right) = 20\log\left(\frac{V_2}{V_1}\right)$$

For more on working with decibels, read the articles "Radio Mathematics" found in this book's downloadable supplemental information. Rohde & Schwarz has published Application Note IMA98 "dB or not dB? Everything you ever wanted to know about decibels but were afraid to ask..." at the website listed in the References and Bibliography section of this chapter.

The linear amplifier multiplies every value of a signal by a constant value. Amplifier gain is often expressed as a multiplication factor (× 5, for example).

$$\text{Gain} = V_o/V_i$$

where V_o is the output voltage from an amplifier when an input voltage, V_i, is applied.

An *attenuator* is a circuit that reduces the amplitude of a signal. Attenuators can be constructed from passive circuits, such as the attenuators built using resistors, described in the chapter on **Test Equipment and Measurements**. Active attenuator circuits include amplifiers whose gain is less than one or circuits with adjustable resistance in the signal path, such as a PIN diode attenuator or amplifier with gain is controlled by an external voltage.

GAIN AND TRANSCONDUCTANCE

The operation of an amplifier is specified by its *gain.* Gain in this sense is defined as the change (Δ) in the output parameter divided by the corresponding change in the input parameter. If a particular device measures its input and output as currents, the gain is called a *current gain.* If the input and output are voltages, the amplifier is defined by its *voltage gain. Power gain* is often used, as well. Gain is technically unit-less, but is often given in V/V. Decibels are often used to specify gain, particularly power gain. (Gain is often expressed in decibels (dB) — see the sidebar "The Decibel".)

If an amplifier's input is a voltage and the output is a current, the ratio of the change in output current to the change in input voltage is called *transconductance,* g_m.

$$g_m = \frac{\Delta I_o}{\Delta V_i}$$

Transconductance has the same units as conductance and admittance, siemens (S), but is only used to describe the operation of active devices, such as transistors or vacuum tubes.

Ideal linear amplifiers have the same gain for all parts of a signal. Thus, a gain of 10 changes 10 V to 100 V, 1 V to 10 V and –1 V to –10 V. (Gain can also be less than one.) The ability of an amplifier to change a signal's level is limited by the amplifier's *dynamic range,* however. An amplifier's dynamic range is the range of signal levels over which the amplifier

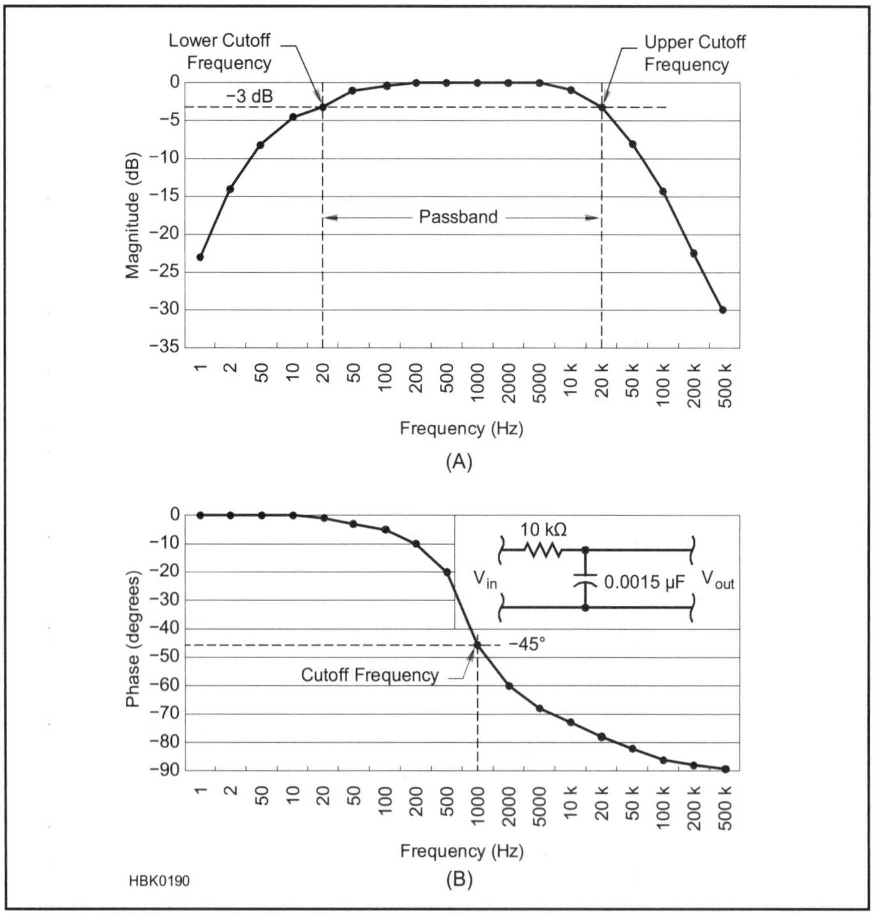

Figure 3.50 — Bode plot of (A) band-pass filter magnitude response and (B) an RC low-pass filter phase response.

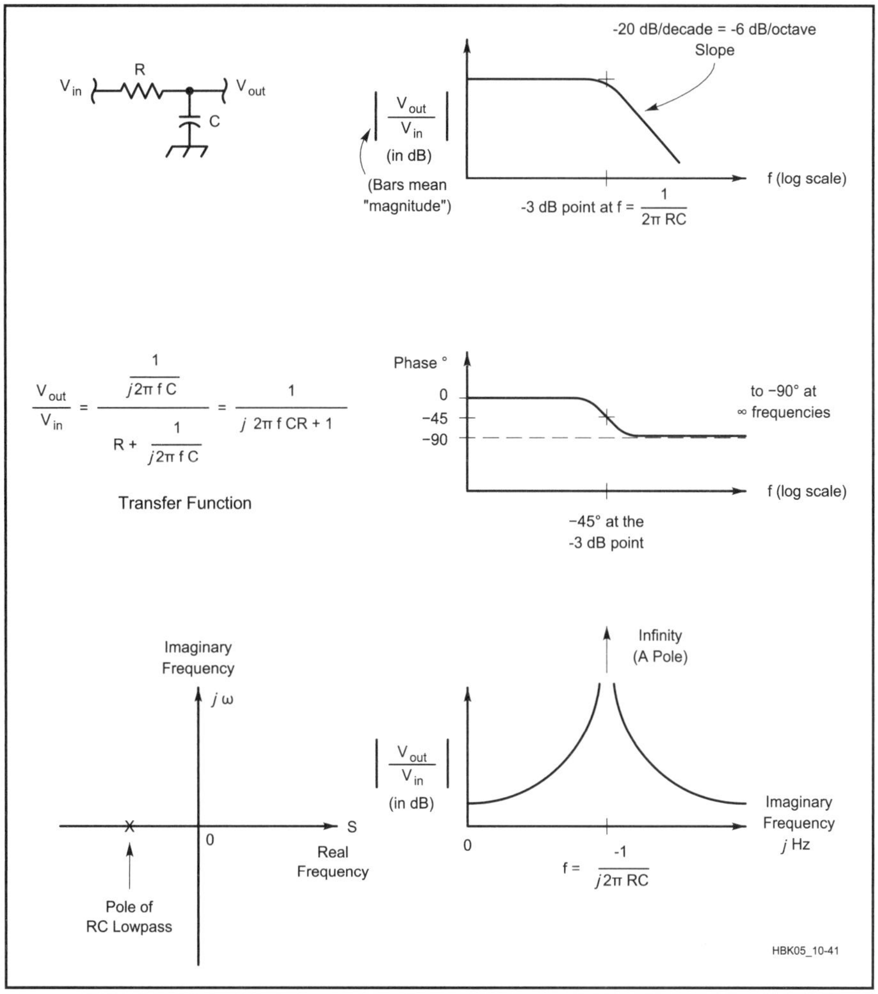

Figure 3.51 — The transfer function for a circuit describes both the magnitude and phase response of a circuit. The RC circuit shown at the upper left has a pole at f = 2πRC, the filter's –3 dB or cutoff frequency, at which the phase response is a 45° lagging phase shift. Poles cause an infinite response on the imaginary frequency axis.

produces the required gain without distortion. Dynamic range is limited for small signals by noise, distortion and other nonlinearities.

Dynamic range is limited for large signals because an amplifier can only produce output voltages (and currents) that are within the range of its power supply. (Power-supply voltages are also called the *rails* of a circuit.) As the amplified output approaches one of the rails, the output cannot exceed a given voltage near the rail and the operation of the amplifier becomes nonlinear as described below in the section on Clipping and Rectification.

Another similar limitation on amplifier linearity is called *slew rate*. Applied to an amplifier, this term describes the maximum rate at which a signal can change levels and still be accurately amplified in a particular device. *Input slew rate* is the maximum rate of change to which the amplifier can react linearly. *Output slew rate* refers to the maximum rate at which the amplifier's output circuit can change. Slew rate is an important concept, because there is a direct correlation between a signal level's rate of change and the frequency content of that signal. The amplifier's ability to react to or reproduce that rate of change affects its frequency response and dynamic range.

FREQUENCY RESPONSE AND BODE PLOTS

Another important characteristic of a circuit is its *frequency response*, a description of how it modifies a signal of any frequency. Frequency response can be stated in the form of a mathematical equation called a *transfer function*, but it is more conveniently presented as a graph of gain vs frequency. The ratio of output amplitude to input amplitude is often called the circuit's *magnitude* or *amplitude response*. Plotting the circuit's magnitude response in dB versus frequency on a logarithmic scale, such as in **Figure 3.50A**, is called a *Bode plot* (after Henrik Wade Bode). The combination of decibel and log-frequency scales is used because the behavior of most circuits depends on ratios of amplitude and frequency and thus appears linear on a graph in which both the vertical and horizontal scales are logarithmic.

Most circuits also affect a signal's phase along with its amplitude. This is called *phase shift*. A plot of phase shift from the circuit's input to its output is called the *phase response*, seen in Figure 3.50B. Positive phase greater than 0° indicates that the output signal *leads* the input signal, while *lagging* phase shift has a negative phase. The combination of an amplitude and phase response plot gives a good picture of what effect the circuit has on signals passing through it.

TRANSFER CHARACTERISTICS

Transfer characteristics are the ratio of an output parameter to an input parameter, such as output current divided by input current, h_{FE}. There are different families of transfer characteristics, designated by letters such as h, s, y or z. Each family compares parameters in specific ways that are useful in certain design or analysis methods. The most common transfer characteristics used in radio are the h-parameter family (used in transistor models) and the s-parameter family (used in RF design, particularly at VHF and above). See the **RF Techniques** chapter for more discussion of transfer characteristics.

COMPLEX FREQUENCY

We are accustomed to thinking of frequency as a real number — so many cycles per second — but frequency can also be a complex number, s, with both a real part, designated by σ, and an imaginary part, designated by $j\omega$. (ω is also equal to 2πf.) The resulting complex frequency is written as $s = \sigma + j\omega$. At the lower left of **Figure 3.51** a pair of real and imaginary axes are used to plot values of s. This is called the *s-plane*. Complex frequency is used in Laplace transforms, a mathematical technique used for circuit and signal analysis. (Thorough treatments of the application of complex frequency can be found in college-level textbooks on circuit and signal analysis.)

When complex frequency is used, a sinusoidal signal is described by Ae^{st}, where A is the amplitude of the signal and t is time. Because s is complex, $Ae^{st} = Ae^{(\sigma+j\omega)t} = A(e^{\sigma t})(e^{j\omega t})$. The two exponential terms describe independent characteristics of the signal. The second term, $e^{j\omega t}$, is the sine wave with which we are familiar and that has frequency f, where $f = \omega/2\pi$. The first term, $e^{\sigma t}$, represents the rate at which the signal increases or decreases. If σ is negative, the exponential term decreases with time and the signal gets smaller and smaller. If σ is positive, the signal gets larger and larger. If σ = 0, the exponential term equals 1, a constant, and the

Obtaining a Frequency Response

With the computer tools such as spreadsheets, it's easy to do the calculations and make a graph of frequency response. If you don't have a spreadsheet program, then use semi-log graph paper with the linear axis used for dB or phase and the logarithmic axis for frequency. An Excel spreadsheet set up to calculate and display frequency response is available in this book's downloadable supplemental information. You can modify it to meet your specific needs.

Follow these rules whether using a spreadsheet or graph paper:

- Measure input and output in the same units, such as volts, and use the same conventions, such as RMS or peak-to-peak.
- Measure phase shift from the input to the output. (The **Test Equipment and Measurements** chapter discusses how to make measurements of amplitude and phase.)
- Use 10 log (P_O/P_I) for power ratios and 20 log (V_O/V_I) for voltage or current.

To make measurements that are roughly equally spaced along the logarithmic frequency axis, follow the "1-2-5 rule." Dividing a range this way, for example 1-2-5-10-20-50-100-200-500 Hz, creates steps in approximately equal ratios that then appear equally spaced on a logarithmic axis.

signal amplitude stays the same.

Complex frequency is very useful in describing a circuit's stability. If the response to an input signal is at a frequency on the right-hand side of the s-plane for which $\sigma > 0$, the system is *unstable* and the output signal will get larger until it is limited by the circuit's power supply or some other mechanism. If the response is on the left-hand side of the s-plane, the system is *stable* and the response to the input signal will eventually die out. The larger the absolute value of σ, the faster the response changes. If the response is precisely on the *j*ω axis where $\sigma = 0$, the response will persist indefinitely.

In Figure 3.51 the equation for the simple RC-circuit's transfer function is shown at the left of the figure. It describes the circuit's behavior at real-world frequencies as well as imaginary frequencies whose values contain *j*. Because complex numbers are used for f, the transfer function describes the circuit's phase response, as well as amplitude. At one such frequency, $f = -j/2\pi RC$, the denominator of the transfer function is zero, and the gain is infinite! Infinite gain is a pretty amazing thing to achieve with a passive circuit — but because this can only happen at an imaginary frequency, it does not happen in the real world.

The practical effects of complex frequency can be experienced in a narrow CW crystal or LC filter. The poles of such a filter are just to the left of the *j*ω axis, so the input signal causes the filters to "ring", or output a damped sine wave along with the desired signal. Similarly, the complex frequency of an oscillator's output at power-up must have $\sigma > 0$ or the oscillation would never start! The output amplitude continues to grow until limiting takes place, reducing gain until $\sigma = 1$ for a steady output.

POLES AND ZEROES

Frequencies that cause the transfer function to become infinite are called *poles*. This is shown at the bottom right of Figure 3.51 in the graph of the circuit's amplitude response for imaginary frequencies shown on the horizontal axis. (The pole causes the graph to extend up "as a pole under a tent," thus the name.) Similarly, circuits can have *zeroes* which occur at imaginary frequencies that cause the transfer function to be zero, a less imaginative name, but quite descriptive.

A circuit can also have poles and zeroes at frequencies of zero and infinity. For example, the circuit in Figure 3.51 has a zero at infinity because the capacitor's reactance is zero at infinity and the transfer function is zero, as well. If the resistor and capacitor were exchanged, so that the capacitor was in series with the output, then at zero frequency (dc), the output would be zero because the capacitor's reactance was infinite, creating a zero.

Complex circuits can have multiple poles or multiple zeroes at the same frequency. Poles and zeroes can also occur at frequencies that are combinations of real and imaginary numbers. The poles and zeroes of a circuit form a pattern in the complex plane that corresponds to certain types of circuit behavior. (The relationships between the pole-zero pattern and circuit behavior is beyond the scope of this book, but are covered in textbooks on circuit theory.)

What is a Pole?

Poles cause a specific change in the circuit's amplitude and phase response for real-world frequencies, even though we can't experience imaginary frequencies directly. A pole is associated with a bend in a magnitude response plot that changes the slope of the response downward with increasing frequency by 6 dB per octave (20 dB per decade; an octave is a 2:1 frequency ratio, a decade is a 10:1 frequency ratio).

There are four ways to identify the existence and frequency of a pole as shown in Figure 3.51:

1) For a downward bend in the magnitude versus frequency plot, the pole is at the –3 dB frequency for a single pole. If the bend causes a change in slope of more than 6 dB/octave, there must be multiple poles at this frequency.

2) A 90° lagging change on a phase versus frequency plot, where the lag increases with frequency. The pole is at the point of 45° added lag on the S-shaped transition. Multiple poles will add their phase lags, as above.

3) On a circuit diagram, a single pole looks like a simple RC low-pass filter. The pole is at the –3 dB frequency ($f = 1/2\pi RC$ Hz). Any other circuit with the same response has a pole at the same frequency.

4) In an equation for the transfer function of a circuit, a pole is a theoretical value of frequency that would result in infinite gain. This is clearly impossible, but as the value of frequency will either be absolute zero, or will have an imaginary component, it is impossible to make an actual real-world signal at a pole frequency.

For example, comparing the amplitude responses at top and bottom of Figure 3.51 shows that the frequency of the pole is equal to the circuit's –3 dB cutoff frequency ($1/2\pi fC$) multiplied by *j*, which is also the frequency at which the circuit causes a –45° (lagging) phase shift from input to output.

What Is a Zero?

A zero is the complement of a pole. In math, it is a frequency at which the transfer function equation of a circuit is zero. This is not impossible in the real world (unlike the pole), so zeroes can be found at real-number frequencies as well as complex-number frequencies.

Each zero is associated with an *upward* bend of 6 dB per octave in a magnitude response. Similarly to a pole, the frequency of the zero is at the +3 dB point. Each zero is associated with a transition on a phase-versus-frequency plot that reduces the lag by 90°. The zero is at the 45° leading phase point. Multiple zeroes add their phase shifts just as poles do.

In a circuit, a zero creates gain that increases with frequency forever above the zero frequency. This requires active circuitry that would inevitably run out of gain at some frequency, which implies one or more poles up there. In real-world circuits, zeroes are usually not found by themselves, making the magnitude response go up, but rather paired with a pole of a different frequency, resulting in the magnitude response having a slope between two frequencies but flat above and below them.

Real-world circuit zeroes are only found accompanied by a greater or equal number of poles. Consider a classic RC high-pass filter, such as if the resistor and capacitor in Figure 3.51 were exchanged. The response of such a circuit increases at 6 dB per octave from 0 Hz (so there must be a zero at 0 Hz) and then levels off at 1/2πRC Hz. This leveling off is due to the presence of a pole adding its 6 dB-per-octave roll-off to cancel the 6 dB-per-octave roll-up of the zero. The transfer function for such as circuit would equal zero at zero frequency and infinity at the imaginary pole frequency.

FEEDBACK AND OSCILLATION

The *stability* of an amplifier refers to its ability to provide gain to a signal without tending to oscillate. For example, an amplifier just on the verge of oscillating is not generally considered to be "stable." If the output of an amplifier is fed back to the input, the feedback can affect the amplifier stability. If the amplified output is added to the input, the output of the sum will be larger. This larger output, in turn, is also fed back. As this process continues, the amplifier output will continue to rise until the amplifier cannot go any higher (clamps). Such *positive feedback* increases the amplifier gain, and is called *regeneration*. (The chapter on **Oscillators and Synthesizers** includes a discussion of positive feedback.)

Most practical amplifiers have some intrinsic and unavoidable feedback either as part of the circuit or in the amplifying device(s) itself. To improve the stability of an amplifier, *negative feedback* can be added to counteract any unwanted positive feedback. Negative feedback is often combined with a phase-shift *compensation* network to improve the amplifier stability.

Although negative feedback reduces amplifier or stage gain, the advantages of *stable* gain, freedom from unwanted oscillations and the reduction of distortion are often key design objectives and advantages of using negative feedback.

The design of feedback networks depends on the desired result. For amplifiers, which should not oscillate, the feedback network is customized to give the desired frequency response without loss of stability. For oscillators, the feedback network is designed to create a steady oscillation at the desired frequency.

SUMMING

In a linear system, nature does most of the work for us when it comes to adding signals; placing two signals together naturally causes them to add according to the principle of superposition. When processing signals, we would like to control the summing operation so the signals do not distort or combine in a nonlinear way. If two signals come from separate stages and they are connected together directly, the circuitry of the stages may interact, causing distortion of either or both signals.

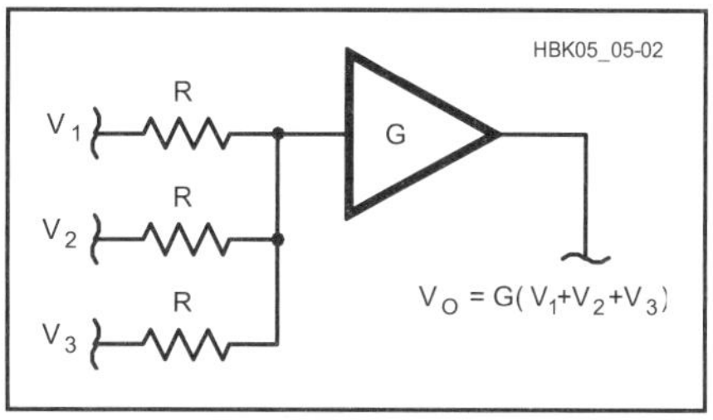

Figure 3.52 — Summing amplifier. The output voltage is equal to the sum of the input voltages times the amplifier gain, G. As long as the resistance values, R, are equal and the amplifier input impedance is much higher, the actual value of R does not affect the output signal.

Summing amplifiers generally use a resistor in series with each stage, so the resistors connect to the common input of the following stage. This provides some *isolation* between the output circuits of each stage. **Figure 3.52** illustrates the resistors connecting to a summing amplifier. Ideally, any time we wanted to combine signals (for example, combining an audio signal with a sub-audible tone in a 2 meter FM transmitter prior to modulating the RF signal) we could use a summing amplifier.

FILTERING

A *filter* is a common linear stage in radio equipment. Filters are characterized by their ability to selectively attenuate certain frequencies in the filter's *stop band*, while passing or amplifying other frequencies in the *passband*. If the filter's passband extends to or near dc, it is a *low-pass* filter, and if to infinity (or at least very high frequencies for the circuitry involved), it is a *high-pass* filter. Filters that pass a range of frequencies are *band-pass* filters. *All-pass* filters are designed to affect only the phase of a signal without changing the signal amplitude. The range of frequencies between a band-pass circuit's low-pass and high-pass regions is its *mid-band*.

Figure 3.50A is the amplitude response for a typical band-pass audio filter. It shows that the input signal is passed to the output with no loss (0 dB) between 200 Hz and 5 kHz. This is the filter's *mid-band response*. Above and below those frequencies the response of the filter begins to drop. By 20 Hz and 20 kHz, the amplitude response has been reduced to one-half of (–3 dB) the mid-band response. These points are called the circuit's *cutoff* or *corner* or *half-power frequencies*. The range between the cutoff frequencies is the filter's passband. Outside the filter's passband, the amplitude response drops to 1/200th (–23 dB) of mid-band response at 1 Hz and only 1/1000th (–30 dB) at 500 kHz. The steepness of the change in response with frequency is the filter's *roll-off* and it is usually specified in dB/octave (an octave is a doubling or halving of frequency) or dB/decade (a decade is a change to 10 times or 1/10th frequency).

Figure 3.50B represents the phase response of a different filter — the simple RC low-pass filter shown at the upper right. As frequency increases, the reactance of the capacitor becomes smaller, causing most of the input signal to appear across the fixed-value resistor instead. At low frequencies, the capacitor has little effect on phase shift. As the signal frequency rises, however, there is more and more phase shift until at the cutoff frequency, there is 45° of lagging phase shift, plotted as a negative number. Phase shift then gradually approaches 90°.

Practical analog (both passive and active) and digital filters are discussed in the chapter **Analog and Digital Filtering**. Filters at RF may also be created by using transmission lines as described in the **Transmission Lines** chapter. All practical amplifiers are in effect either low-pass filters or band-pass filters, because their magnitude response decreases as the frequency increases beyond their ability to amplify signals.

3.9.4 Nonlinear Operations

All signal processing doesn't have to be linear. Any time that we treat various signal levels differently, the operation is called *nonlinear*. This is not to say that all signals must be treated the same for a circuit to be linear. High-frequency signals are attenuated in a low-pass filter while low-frequency signals are not, yet the filter can be linear. The distinction is that the amount of attenuation at different frequencies is always the same, regardless of the amplitude of the signals passing through the filter.

What if we do not want to treat all voltage levels the same way? This is commonly desired in analog signal processing for clipping, rectification, compression, modulation and switching.

CLIPPING AND RECTIFICATION

Clipping is the process of limiting the range of signal voltages passing through a circuit (in other words, *clipping* those voltages outside the desired range from the signals). There are a number of reasons why we would like to do this. As shown in Figure 3.49, clipping is the process of limiting the positive and negative peaks of a signal. (Clipping is also called *clamping*.)

Clipping might be used to prevent a large audio signal from causing excessive deviation in an FM transmitter that would interfere with communications on adjacent channels. Clipping circuits are also used to protect sensitive inputs from excessive voltages. Clipping distorts the signal, changing it so that the original signal waveform is lost.

Another kind of clipping results in *rectification*. A *rectifier* circuit clips off all voltages of one polarity (positive or negative) and passes only voltages of the other polarity, thus changing ac to pulsating dc (see the **Power Sources** chapter). Another use of rectification is in a *peak detection* circuit that measures the peak value of a waveform. Only one polarity of the ac voltage needs to be measured and so a rectifier clips the unwanted polarity.

LIMITING

Another type of clipping occurs when an amplifier is intentionally operated with so much gain that the input signals result in an output that is clipped at the limits of its power supply voltages (or some other designated voltages). The amplifier is said to be driven into *limiting* and an amplifier designed for this behavior is called a *limiter*. Limiters are used in FM receivers to amplify the signal until all amplitude variations in the signal are removed and the only characteristic of the original signal that remains is the frequency.

LOGARITHMIC AMPLIFICATION

It is sometimes desirable to amplify a signal logarithmically, which means amplifying low levels more than high levels. This type of amplification is often called *signal compression*. Speech compression is sometimes used in audio amplifiers that feed modulators. The voice signal is compressed into a small range of amplitudes, allowing more voice energy to be transmitted without overmodulation (see the **Modulation** and the **Transmitting** chapters).

3.9.5 System Design Functions

Many kinds of electronic equipment are developed by combining basic analog signal processing circuits, often treating them as independent functional blocks. This section describes several topics associated with building systems from multiple blocks. Because analog circuits often interface with digital circuits or include digital elements in a hybrid circuit, some topics associated with digital systems are included. Many similar functions are implemented as part of Digital Signal Processing (DSP) systems and have similar behaviors and concerns. Although not all basic electronic functions are discussed here, the concepts associated with combining them can be applied generally.

Since our main concern is the effect that circuitry has on a signal, we often describe the circuit by its actions rather than by its specific components. A *black box* is a circuit that can be described entirely by the behavior of its interfaces with other blocks and circuitry. When circuits are combined in such as way as to perform sequential operations on a signal, the individual circuits are called *stages*.

The most general way of referring to an analog circuit is as a *network*. Two basic properties of analog networks are of principal concern: the effect that the network has on a signal and the interaction that the network has with the circuitry surrounding it. Interfaces between the network and the rest of the network are called *ports*.

Many analog circuits are analyzed as *two-port networks* with an input and an output port. The signal is fed into the input port, is modified inside the network and then exits from the output port. (See the chapter on **RF Techniques** for more information on two-port networks.)

TRANSFER FUNCTIONS

The specific way in which the analog circuit modifies the signal can be described mathematically as a transfer function. The mathematical operation that combines a signal with a transfer function is pictured symbolically in **Figure 3.53**. The transfer function, h(t) or h(f), describes the circuit's modification of the input signal in the time domain where all values are functions of time, such as a(t) or b(t), or in the frequency domain where all values are functions of frequency, such as a(f) or b(f). The mathematical operation by which h(t) operates on a(t) is called *convolution* and is represented as a dot, as in $a(t) \bullet h(t) = b(t)$. In the frequency domain, the transfer function multiplies the input, as in $a(f) \times h(f) = b(f)$.

While it is not necessary to understand transfer functions mathematically to work with analog circuits, it is useful to realize that they describe how a signal interacts with other signals in an electronic system. In general, the output signal of an analog system depends not only on the input signal at the same time, but also on past values of the input signal. This is a very important concept and is the basis of such essential functions as analog filtering.

CASCADING STAGES

If an analog circuit can be described with a transfer function, a combination of analog circuits can also be described similarly. This description of the combined circuits depends upon the relationship between the transfer functions of the parts and that of the combined circuits. In many cases this relationship allows us to predict the behavior of large and complex circuits from what we know about the parts of which they are made. This aids in the design and analysis of analog circuits.

When two analog circuits are cascaded (the output signal of one stage becomes the input signal to the next stage) their transfer functions are combined. The mechanism of the combination depends on the interaction between the stages. The ideal case is the functions of the stages are completely independent. In other words, when the action of a stage is unchanged, regardless of the characteristics of any stages connected to its input or output.

Just as the signal entering the first stage is modified by the action of the first transfer function, the ideal cascading of analog circuits results in changes produced only by the individual transfer functions. For any number of stages that are cascaded, the combination of their transfer functions results in a new transfer function. The signal that enters the circuit is changed by the composite transfer function to produce the signal that exits in the cascaded circuits.

While each stage in a series may use feedback within itself, feedback around more than one stage may create a function — and resultant performance — different from any of the included stages. Examples include

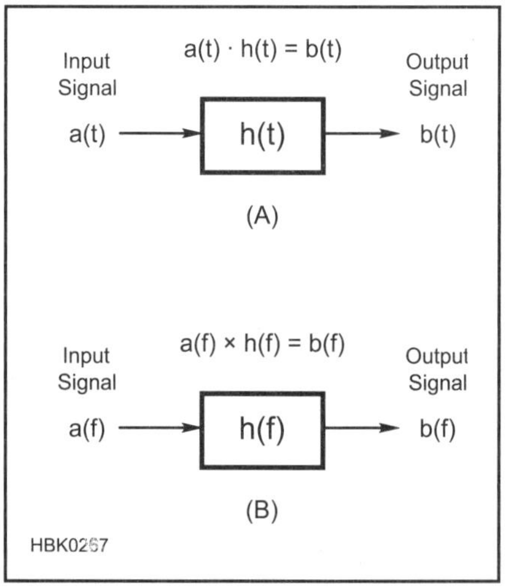

Figure 3.53 — Linear function blocks and transfer functions. The transfer function can be expressed in the time domain (A) or in the frequency domain (B). The transfer function describes how the input signal a(t) or a(f) is transformed into the output signal b(t) or b(f).

oscillation or negative feedback.

AMPLIFIER FREQUENCY RESPONSE

At higher frequencies a typical amplifier acts as a low-pass filter, decreasing amplification with increasing frequency. Signals within a range of frequencies are amplified consistently but outside that range the amplification changes. At high gains many amplifiers work properly only over a small range of frequencies. The combination of gain and frequency response is often expressed as a *gain-bandwidth product*. For many amplifiers, gain times bandwidth is approximately constant. As gain increases, bandwidth decreases, and vice versa.

Performance at lower frequencies depends on whether the amplifier is *dc- or ac-coupled*. Coupling refers to the transfer of signals between circuits. A dc-coupled amplifier amplifies signals at all frequencies down to dc. An ac-coupled amplifier acts as a high-pass filter, decreasing amplification as the frequency decreases toward dc. Ac-coupled circuits usually use capacitors to allow ac signals to flow between stages while blocking the dc bias voltages of the circuit.

INTERSTAGE LOADING AND IMPEDANCE MATCHING

Every two-port network can be further defined by its input and output impedance. The input impedance is the opposition to current, as a function of frequency, seen when looking into the input port of the network. Likewise, the output impedance is similarly defined when looking back into a network through its output port.

If the transfer function of a stage changes when it is cascaded with another stage, we say that the second stage has *loaded* the first stage. This often occurs when an appreciable amount of current passes from one stage to the next. Interstage loading is related to the relative output impedance of a stage and the input impedance of the stage that is cascaded after it.

In some applications, the goal is to transfer a maximum amount of power from the output of the stage to a load connected to the output. In this case, the output impedance of the stage is *matched* or transformed to that of the load (or vice versa). This allows the stage to operate at its optimum voltage and current levels. In an RF amplifier, the impedance at the input of the transmission line feeding an antenna is transformed by means of a matching network to produce the resistance the amplifier needs in order to efficiently produce RF power.

In contrast, it is the goal of most analog signal processing circuitry to modify a signal rather than to deliver large amounts of power. Thus, an impedance-matched condition may not be required. Instead, current between stages can be minimized by using mismatched impedances. Ideally, if the output impedance of a network is very low and the input impedance of the following stage is very high, very little current will pass between the stages, and interstage loading will be negligible.

NOISE

Generally we are only interested in specific man-made signals. Nature allows many signals to combine, however, so the desired signal becomes combined with many other unwanted signals, both man-made and naturally occurring. The broadest definition of noise is any signal that is not the one in which we are interested. One of the goals of signal processing is to separate desired signals from noise. (See the **RF Techniques** chapter for a more complete discussion on noise, including calculation and use of noise factor and noise figure.)

One form of noise that occurs naturally and must be dealt with in low-level processing circuits is called *thermal noise*, or *Johnson noise*. Thermal noise is produced by random motion of free electrons in conductors and semiconductors. This motion increases as temperature increases, hence the name. This kind of noise is present at all frequencies and is proportional to temperature. Naturally occurring noise can be reduced either by decreasing the circuit's bandwidth or by reducing the temperature in the system. Thermal noise voltage and current vary with the circuit impedance and follow Ohm's Law. Low-noise-amplifier-design techniques are based on these relationships.

Analog signal processing stages are characterized in part by the noise they add to a signal. A distinction is made between enhancing existing noise (such as amplifying it) and adding new noise. The noise added by analog signal processing is commonly quantified by the *noise factor, f*. Noise factor is the ratio of the total output noise power (thermal noise plus noise added by the stage) to the amplifier input noise power when the termination is at the standard temperature of 290 K (17 °C). When the noise factor is expressed in dB, we often call it *noise figure, NF*.

In a system of many cascaded signal processing stages, such as a communications receiver, each stage contributes to the total noise of the system. The noise factor of the first stage dominates the noise factor of the entire system because noise added at the first stage is then multiplied by each following stage. Noise added by later stages is not multiplied to the same degree and so is a smaller contribution to the overall noise at the output. Designers try to optimize system noise factor by using a first stage with a minimum possible noise factor and maximum possible gain. (Caution: A circuit that overloads is often as useless as one that generates too much noise.)

BUFFERING

It is often necessary to isolate the stages of an analog circuit. This isolation reduces the loading, coupling and feedback between stages. It is often necessary to connect circuits that operate at different impedance levels between stages. An intervening stage, a type of amplifier called a *buffer*, is often used for this purpose. If signal level is sufficient, an attenuation can also serve as a buffer at the expense of some signal loss.

Buffers can have high values of amplification but this is unusual. A buffer used for impedance transformation generally has a low or unity gain. In some circuits, notably power amplifiers, the desired goal is to deliver a maximum amount of power to the output device (such as a speaker or an antenna). Matching the amplifier output impedance to the output-device impedance provides maximum power transfer. A buffer amplifier may be just the circuit for this type of application. Such amplifier circuits must be carefully designed to avoid distortion. Combinations of buffer stages can also be effective at isolating the stages from each other and making impedance transformations, as well.

TRANSITION TIME

The transition between the binary 0 and binary 1 states of a digital signal or circuit does not occur instantly. There is a *transition time* between states. This transition time is a result of the time it takes to charge or discharge the stray capacitance in wires and other components because voltage cannot change instantaneously across a capacitor. Stray inductance in the wires also has an effect because the current through an inductor can't change instantaneously. The rate at which the digital circuit's output transistors can change state may also be a factor.

Distributed inductances and capacitances in wires or PC-board traces may cause rise and fall times to increase as the pulse moves away from the source. Ringing and reflections may occur due to transmission line effects as discussed in the **Transmission Lines** chapter.

The transition from a 0 to a 1 state is called the *rise time*, and is usually specified as the time for the pulse to rise from 10% of its final value to 90% of its final value. Similarly, the transition from a 1 to a 0 state is called the *fall time,* with a similar 10% to 90% definition. Note that these times need not be the same. **Figure 3.54A** shows an ideal signal, or *pulse*, with zero-time switching. Figure 3.54B shows

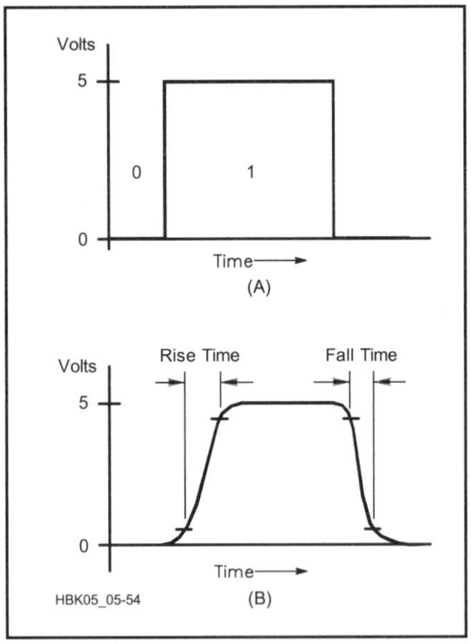

Figure 3.54 — (A) An ideal digital pulse and (B) a typical actual pulse, showing the gradual transition between states.

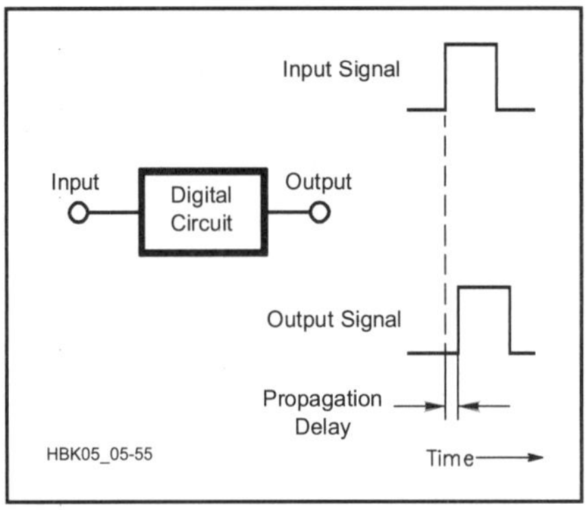

Figure 3.55 — Propagation delay in a digital circuit.

a typical pulse, as it changes between states in a smooth curve.

The faster the rise or fall time, the wider the bandwidth of signals associated with the transition. These signals can be radiated, causing noise and interfering signals in receivers or sensitive circuits. The general rule of thumb for the bandwidth of digital signals is:

$$\mathrm{BW(GHz)} = \frac{0.35}{\mathrm{RT(ns)}} \text{ and } \mathrm{RT(ns)} = \frac{0.35}{\mathrm{BW(GHz)}}$$

Rise and fall times for digital integrated circuits vary with the logic family used and the location in a circuit. Typical values of transition time are in the range of microseconds (4000-series CMOS with high-impedance loads) to sub-nanosecond range (modern TTL-derivatives and CMOS).

PROPAGATION DELAY

Rise and fall times only describe a relationship within a pulse. For a circuit, a pulse input into the circuit must propagate through the circuit; in other words it must pass through each component in the circuit until eventually it arrives at the circuit output. The time delay between providing an input to a circuit and seeing a response at the output is the *propagation delay* and is illustrated by **Figure 3.55**.

For modern switching logic, typical propagation delay values are in the 1 to 15 nanosecond range. (It is useful to remember that the propagation delay along a wire or printed-circuit-board trace is about 1.0 to 1.5 ns per inch.) Propagation delay is the result of cumulative transition times as well as transistor switching delays, reactive element charging times and the time for signals to travel through wires. In complex circuits, different propagation delays through different paths can cause problems when pulses must arrive somewhere at exactly the same time.

The effect of these delays on digital devices can be seen by looking at the speed of the digital pulses. Most digital devices and all PCs use *clock pulses*. If two pulses are supposed to arrive at a logic circuit at the same time, or very close to the same time, the path length for the two signals cannot be any different than two to three inches. This can be a very significant design problem for high-speed logic designs.

3.10 Electromagnetic Waves

Audio or *sonic* energy is the energy imparted by the mechanical movement of a medium, which can be air, metal, water or even the human body. Sound that humans can hear normally requires the movement of air between 20 Hz and 20 kHz, although the human ear loses its ability to detect the extremes of this range as we age. Some animals, such as elephants, can detect air vibrations well below 20 Hz, while others, such as dogs and cats, can detect air vibrations well above 20 kHz.

Electrical circuits do not directly produce air vibrations. Sound production requires a *transducer*, a device to transform one form of energy into another form of energy; in this case electrical energy into sonic energy. The speaker and the microphone are the most common audio transducers. There are numerous ultrasonic transducers for various applications.

Radio frequency energy exists at frequencies for which it is practical to generate and detect waves that exist independently of the movement of electrical charge, such as a radio signal. Like sonic energy, a transducer — an antenna — is required to convert the electrical energy in a circuit to electromagnetic waves. In a physical circuit, such as a wire, electromagnetic energy exists as both electromagnetic waves and the physical movement of electrical charge.

Electromagnetic waves have been generated and detected in many forms with frequencies from below 1 Hz to above 10^{12} GHz, including at the higher frequencies infrared, visible, and ultraviolet light, and a number of energy forms of greatest interest to physicists and astronomers. **Table 3.5** provides a brief glimpse at the total spectrum of electromagnetic energy. The *radio spectrum* is generally considered to begin around 3 kHz and end at infrared light.

Within the part of the electromagnetic energy spectrum of most interest to radio amateurs, frequencies have been classified into groups and given names. Table 3.5 provides a reference list of these classifications. To a significant degree, the frequencies within each group exhibit similar properties, both in circuits and as RF waves. For example, HF or high frequency waves, with frequencies from 3 to 30 MHz, all exhibit ionospheric refraction that permits regular long-range radio communications. This property also applies occasionally both to MF (medium frequency) and to VHF (very high frequency) waves, as well.

Despite the close relationship between electromagnetic energy and waves, it remains important to distinguish the two. To a circuit producing or amplifying a 15-kHz alternating current, the ultimate transformation and use of the electrical energy may make no difference to the circuit's operation. By choosing the right transducer, one can produce either a sonic wave or an electromagnetic wave — or both. Such is a common problem of video monitors and switching power supplies; forces created by the ac currents cause electronic parts both to vibrate audibly *and* to radiate electromagnetic energy.

Table 3.5

Key Regions of the Electromagnetic Energy Spectrum

Region Name	*Frequency Range*		
Radio frequencies*	3.0×10^{3} Hz	to	3.0×10^{11} Hz
Infrared	3.0×10^{11} Hz	to	4.3×10^{14} Hz
Visible light	4.3×10^{14} Hz	to	7.5×10^{14} Hz
Ultraviolet	7.5×10^{14} Hz	to	6.0×10^{16} Hz
X-rays	6.0×10^{16} Hz	to	3.0×10^{19} Hz
Gamma rays	3.0×10^{19} Hz	to	5.0×10^{20} Hz
Cosmic rays	5.0×10^{20} Hz	to	8.0×10^{21} Hz

Range Name	*Abbreviation*	*Frequency Range*
Very Low Frequency	VLF	3 kHz - 30 kHz
Low Frequency	LF	30 kHz - 300 kHz
Medium Frequency	MF	300 kHz - 3 MHz
High Frequency	HF	3 MHz - 30 MHz
Very High Frequency	VHF	30 MHz - 300 MHz
Ultra High Frequency	UHF	300 MHz - 3 GHz
Super High Frequency	SHF	3 GHz - 30 GHz
Extremely High Frequency	EHF	30 GHz - 300 GHz

*Note: The range of radio frequencies can also be written as 3 kHz to 300 GHz

3.10.1 Electric and Magnetic Fields

Electrical and magnetic energy are invisible — you can't detect them with any of your senses. All you can do is observe their effects such as when a resistor gets hot, a motor spins, or an electromagnet picks up iron or steel. The energy exists as a *field* — a region of space in which energy is stored and through which electrical and magnetic forces act. (For serious inquiries as to the nature of fields, see **en.wikipedia.org/wiki/Electric_field** and **en.wikipedia.org/wiki/Magnetic_field**.)

You are already quite familiar with fields in the form of gravity. You are being pulled down toward the Earth as you read this because you are in the Earth's *gravitational field*. Because your body has mass it interacts with the gravitational field in such a way that the Earth attracts you. (You have your own gravitational field, too, but many orders of magnitude smaller than that of the Earth.) Think of a bathroom scale as a "gravitational voltmeter" that instead of reading "volts," reads "pounds." The heavier something is, the stronger the Earth is attracting it. Weight is the same as force. (Metric scales provide readings in kilograms, a unit of mass. To do so, the scales assume a standard strength for gravity in order to convert weight [a force] to an equivalent mass in kilograms.)

This field makes you do work, such as when you climb stairs. Work has a precise definition when it comes to fields: *Work* equals force times distance moved in the direction of the field's force. For example, let's say you pick up a mass — a stone that weighs 1 pound — and lift it to a shelf 10 feet above where it previously lay. How much work did you do? You moved a weight of 1 pound a distance of 10 feet against the attraction of the field, so you have done 10 foot-pounds of work. (It doesn't count if you move the stone sideways instead of vertically.)

What did that work accomplish? You stored gravitational energy in the stone equal to the amount of work that you performed. This stored energy is called *potential energy*, whether gravitational, electrical or magnetic. You could store the same amount of gravitational energy by lifting a 10-pound stone 1 foot or by lifting a stone that weighs 1/10th of a pound 100 feet. If you drop the stone (or it falls off the shelf), the same amount of potential energy is converted back to *kinetic energy* as the stone moves toward the Earth in the gravitational field.

In electronics we are interested in two types of fields: *electric fields* and *magnetic fields*. Electric fields can be detected as voltage differences between two points. The electric field's analog to gravitational mass is electric charge. Every electric charge has its own electric field, just as every mass has its own gravitational field. The more charged a body is, the "heavier" it is in terms of an electric field. Just as a body with mass feels a force to move in a gravitational field, so does an electric charge in an electric field. Electrical energy is stored by moving electrical charges apart so that there is a voltage between them. If the field does not change with time, it is called an *electrostatic field*.

Magnetic energy is detected by its effects on moving electrical charges or current. Magnetic energy is stored through the motion of electric charge (current) creating a magnetic field. Magnetic fields that don't change with time, such as from a stationary permanent magnet, are called *magnetostatic fields*.

The potential energy is released by allowing the charges to move in the field. For example, electric energy is released when a current flows from a charged-up capacitor. Magnetic energy stored by current flowing in an inductor is released when the current is allowed to change, such as a relay's armature does when the coil is de-energized.

3.10.2 Electromagnetic Fields and Waves

An *electromagnetic field* is created when the potential energy stored in an electric field or magnetic field changes. The changing electric and magnetic fields create *electro-*

magnetic waves (what we call *radio waves*) that propagate through space carrying both electric and magnetic energy. The electric and magnetic fields in the wave vary with time in a sinusoidal pattern. The potential energy is shared between the electric and magnetic fields making up the electromagnetic field.

The *field strength* of an electromagnetic wave can be measured either by the electric field (volts/meter) or the magnetic field (amps/meter). Usually the wave's field strength is stated only in volts/meter since that is easier to measure than the magnetic field. If we multiply the electric and magnetic field strengths, we have power per unit area:

$$\frac{E}{m} \times \frac{H}{m} = \frac{watts}{m^2}$$

MAXWELL'S EQUATIONS

The basic theory of electromagnetic fields was established by James Maxwell in 1860-1864. The behavior of the fields are described by the four equations known today as Maxwell's equations. (This form of the equations was actually produced by Oliver Heaviside in his work prior to 1890.) A discussion of Maxwell's equations and their application to electromagnetic simulation is presented the **Computer-Aided Circuit Design** chapter. A more complete treatment is provided by Bob Zavrel, W7SX, in his book on antenna physics (see the References and Bibliography section of this chapter). A summary treatment of the equations in a pair of Hand-On Radio columns by Ward Silver, NØAX, is included in the downloadable supplemental information. These include an explanation of the vector calculus concepts of gradient, divergence, and curl, as well as illustrating how waves are created by moving electric charge.

3.10.3 Electromagnetic Wave Propagation

All electromagnetic energy has one thing in common: it travels, or *propagates,* at the speed of light, abbreviated *c*. This speed is approximately 300,000,000 (or 3×10^8) meters per second in a vacuum, termed *free space*.

In general, the speed at which electromagnetic waves travel or *propagate* depends on the permittivity and permeability of the medium through which they travel.

$$c = \frac{1}{\sqrt{\varepsilon_0 \mu_0}}$$

The speed of light is highest in the vacuum of free space and only slightly lower in air. In materials such as glass or plastic, however, velocity can be quite a bit lower. For example, in polyethylene (commonly used as a center insulator in coaxial cable), the *velocity of propagation* is about two-thirds (67%) of that in free space.

Electromagnetic waves have a wavelength uniquely associated with each possible frequency. (See **Figure 3.56**) The *wavelength* (λ) is the speed of propagation, c, divided by the frequency (f) in hertz.

$$f\,(\text{Hz}) = \frac{3.0 \times 10^8 \left(\frac{\text{m}}{\text{s}}\right)}{\lambda\,(\text{m})}$$

and

$$\lambda\,(\text{m}) = \frac{3.0 \times 10^8 \left(\frac{\text{m}}{\text{s}}\right)}{f\,(\text{Hz})}$$

Example: What is the frequency of an RF wave with wavelength of 80 meters?

$$f\,(\text{Hz}) = \frac{3.0 \times 10^8 \left(\frac{\text{m}}{\text{s}}\right)}{\lambda\,(\text{m})}$$

$$= \frac{3.0 \times 10^8 \left(\frac{\text{m}}{\text{s}}\right)}{80.0\ \text{m}}$$

$$= 3.75 \times 10^6\ \text{Hz}$$

This is 3.750 MHz or 3750 kHz, a frequency in the middle of the ham band known as "80 meters."

A similar equation is used to calculate the wavelength of a sound wave in air, substituting the speed of sound instead of the speed of light in the numerator. The speed of propagation of the mechanical movement of air that we call sound varies considerably with air temperature and altitude. The speed of sound at sea level is about 331 m/s at 0 ºC and 344 m/s at 20 ºC.

To calculate the frequency of an electromagnetic wave directly in kilohertz, change the speed constant to 300,000 (3×10^5) km/s.

$$f\,(\text{kHz}) = \frac{3.0 \times 10^5 \left(\frac{\text{km}}{\text{s}}\right)}{\lambda\,(\text{m})}$$

and

$$\lambda\,(\text{m}) = \frac{3.0 \times 10^5 \left(\frac{\text{km}}{\text{s}}\right)}{f\,(\text{kHz})}$$

For frequencies in megahertz, change the speed constant to 300 (3×10^2) Mm/s.

$$f\,(\text{MHz}) = \frac{300 \left(\frac{\text{Mm}}{\text{s}}\right)}{\lambda\,(\text{m})}$$

and

$$\lambda\,(\text{m}) = \frac{300 \left(\frac{\text{Mm}}{\text{s}}\right)}{f\,(\text{MHz})}$$

Stated as it is usually remembered and used, "wavelength in meters equals 300 divided by frequency in megahertz." Assuming the proper units for the speed of light constant simplify the equation.

$$\lambda\,(\text{in m}) = \frac{300}{f\,(\text{in MHz})}$$

$$\text{and } f\,(\text{in MHz}) = \frac{300}{\lambda\,(\text{in m})}$$

Example: What is the wavelength of an RF

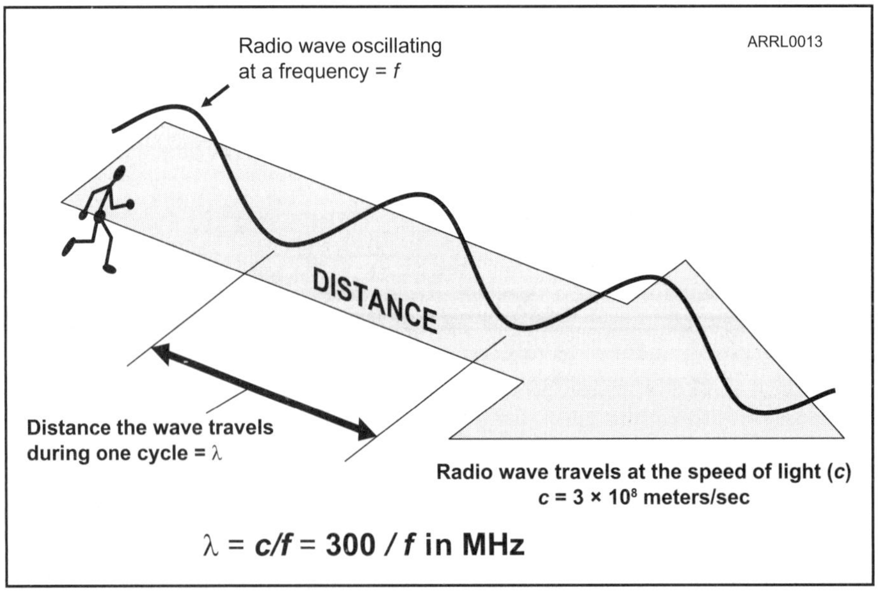

Figure 3.56 — As a radio wave travels, it oscillates at the frequency of the signal. The distance covered by the wave during the time it takes for one complete cycle is its wavelength.

wave whose frequency is 4.0 MHz?

$$\lambda(m) = \frac{300}{f(MHz)} = \frac{300}{4.0} = 75 \text{ m}$$

At higher frequencies, circuit elements with lengths that are a significant fraction of a wavelength can act like transducers. This property can be useful, but it can also cause problems for circuit operations. Therefore, wavelength calculations are of some importance in designing ac circuits for those frequencies.

3.10.4 Electromagnetic Wave Structure

The waves move through space independently of any component or conductor. The electric and magnetic fields of the wave are oriented at right angles to each other as shown by **Figure 3.57**. The direction of the right angle between the electric and magnetic fields determines the direction the wave travels, as illustrated by Figure 3.50. The term "lines of force" in the figure means the direction in which a force would be felt by an electron (from the electric field) or by a magnet (from the magnetic field).

An important note about electromagnetic waves: The electric and magnetic fields making up the wave are not just perpendicular electric and magnetic fields that simply happen to be in the same place at the same time! The fields are *coupled*; that is they are both aspects of the same entity — the electromagnetic wave. The fields cannot be separated although the energy in the wave can be detected as either electric or magnetic force. The electromagnetic wave is created as a single entity by the motion of electrons, such as in a transmitting antenna.

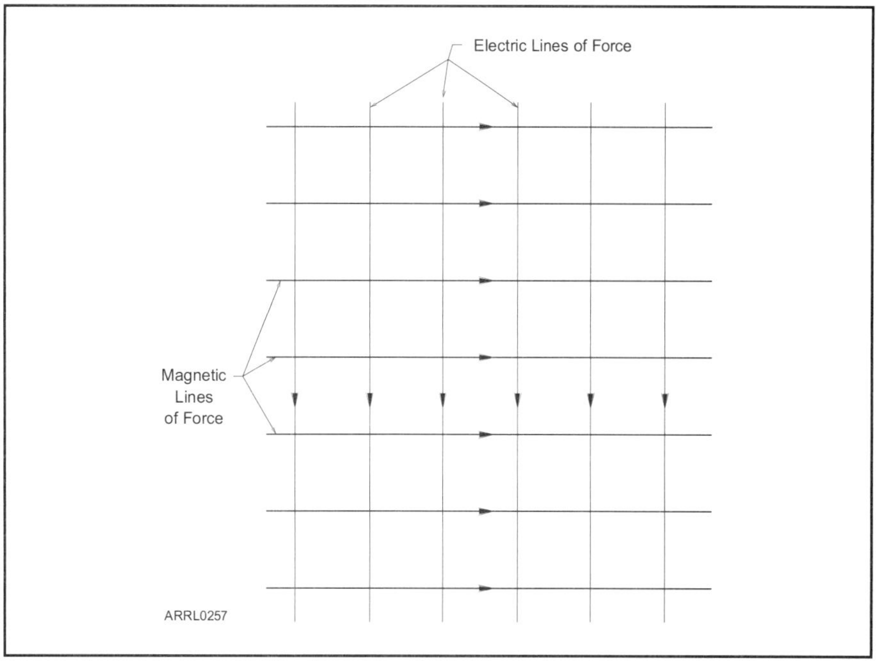

Figure 3.57 — Representation of electric and magnetic lines of force in an electromagnetic wavefront. Arrows indicate the instantaneous directions of the fields for a wavefront in a wave traveling toward you, out of the page. Reversing the direction of either of the fields would also reverse the direction of the wave.

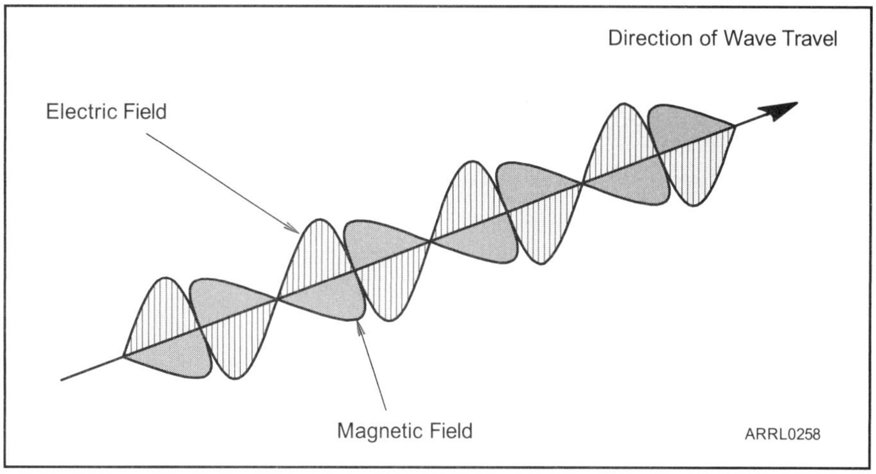

Figure 3.58 — Representation of the magnetic and electric field strengths of a vertically polarized electromagnetic wave. In the diagram, the electric field is oriented vertically and the magnetic field horizontally.

WAVEFRONTS

To an observer staying in one place, such as a fixed station's receiving antenna, the electric and magnetic fields of the wave appear to oscillate as the wave passes. That is, the fields create forces on electrons in the antenna that increase and decrease in the sine wave pattern. Some of the energy in the propagating wave is transferred to the electrons as the forces from the changing fields cause them to move. This creates a sine wave current in the antenna with a frequency determined by the rate at which the field strength changes in the passing wave.

If the observer is moving along with the wave at the same speed, however, the strength of the fields will not change. To that observer, the electric and magnetic field strengths are fixed, as in a photograph. This is a *wavefront* of the electromagnetic wave — a flat surface or plane moving through space on which the electric and magnetic fields have a constant value as illustrated in Figure 3.57.

Just as an ac voltage is made up of an infinite sequence of instantaneous voltages, each slightly larger or smaller than the next, an infinite number of wavefronts make up an electromagnetic wave, one behind another like a deck of cards. The direction of the wave is the direction in which the wavefronts move. The fields on each successive wavefront have a slightly different strength, so as they pass a fixed location the detected field strength changes as well. The result is that the fixed observer "sees" fields with strengths varying as a sine wave.

Figure 3.58 is a drawing of what would happen if we could suddenly freeze all of the wavefronts in the wave and take measurements of the electric and magnetic field strengths in each. In this example, the electric field is oriented vertically and the magnetic field horizontally. (Each of the vertical lines in the electric field can be thought of as representing an individual wavefront.) **Figure 3.59** illustrates the right-angle relationship of the *E* and *H* fields, and the direction of their motion.

All of the wavefronts are moving in the direction indicated — the whole set of them moves together at the same speed. As the wave — the set of wavefronts — moves past the receive antenna, the varying field strengths of the different wavefronts are perceived as a continuously changing wave. What we call a "wave" is really this entire group of wavefronts moving through space.

POLARIZATION

The orientation of the pair of fields in an electromagnetic wave can have any orientation with respect to the surface of the Earth, but the electric and magnetic fields will always be at right angles to each other. The orientation of the wave's electric field determines the *polarization* of the wave. If the electric field's lines of force are parallel to the surface of the Earth (meaning those of the magnetic field are perpendicular to the Earth), the wave is *horizontally polarized.* Conversely, if the magnetic field's lines of force are parallel to the surface of the Earth (and those of the electric field are perpendicular to the Earth), the wave is *vertically polarized.* Knowing the polarization of the wave allows the receiving antenna to be oriented so that the passing wave will exert the maximum force on the electrons in the antenna, maximizing received signal strength.

For the most part, the wave's polarization is determined by the type of transmitting antenna and its orientation. For example, a Yagi antenna with its elements parallel to the Earth's surface transmits a horizontally polarized wave. On the other hand, an amateur mobile whip antenna, mounted vertically on an automobile, radiates a vertically polarized wave. If a vertically polarized antenna is used to receive a horizontally polarized radio wave (or vice versa), received signal strength can be reduced by more than 20 dB as compared to using an antenna with the same polarization as the wave. This is called *cross-polarization.*

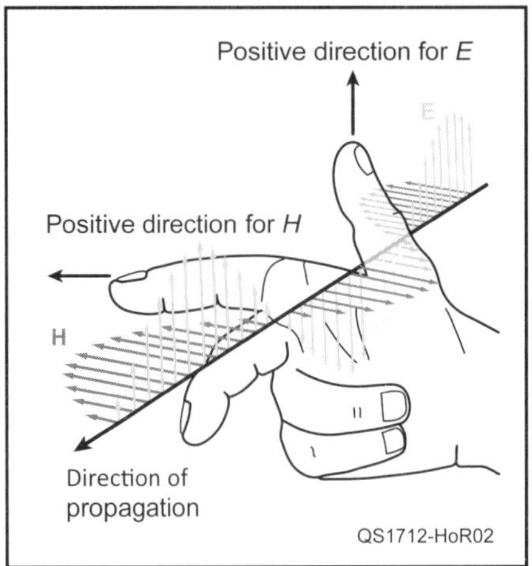

Figure 3.59 — The right-hand rule shows how to determine direction of propagation of an electromagnetic wave. Point your thumb in the positive direction for the *E* field, your Index finger in the positive direction for *H*, and your middle finger will point in the direction the wave is traveling.

It is also possible to generate electromagnetic waves in which the orientation of successive wavefronts rotates around the direction of travel — both the electric and magnetic fields. This is called *circular polarization.* Imagine the wave of Figure 3.51 being twisted so at one point the direction of the electric field is horizontal and a bit further along the wave it is vertical. As the twisted, circularly polarized wave passes the receiving antenna, the polarization of its fields will appear to rotate. The rate at which the polarization changes and the direction of the rotation — *right-handed* or *left-handed* — is determined by the construction of the transmitting antenna. Note that the electric and magnetic fields rotate together so the right-angle between them remains fixed. Polarization that does not rotate is called *linear polarization* or *plane polarization.* Horizontal and vertical polarization are examples of linear polarization.

To best receive a circularly polarized wave, the structure of the receiving antenna should match that of the transmitting antenna. It is particularly helpful to use circular polarization in satellite communication, where polarization tends to shift with the orientation of the satellite and the path of its signal through the atmosphere. Circular polarization is usable with linearly polarized antennas at one end of the signal's path. There will be some small loss in this case, however.

IMPEDANCE OF FREE SPACE

Maxwell's equations provide the relationships (direction and ratio) between the magnetic and electric fields associated with an electromagnetic wave. Far from an antenna or other distorting surfaces, the wave is treated as a *plane* wave in which the wavefronts are infinite, flat planes. In a plane wave, the ratio of the two fields' amplitudes remains constant and the two fields are always at right angles. (There are exceptions but they are not discussed here.)

Since the ratio of the two fields is constant in free space, that gives rise to the idea of an intrinsic impedance. If the impedance is zero or infinite, the magnetic and electric fields would have to be infinite or zero and there could be no electromagnetic radiation.

The impedance can be derived from the permittivity (ε_0) and permeability (μ_0) of free space:

$$\varepsilon_0 = \frac{\text{F(farads)}}{\text{meter}} \text{ and } \mu_0 = \frac{\text{H(henries)}}{\text{meter}}$$

Taking the ratio of the two, noting that farads have units of joules/volt^2 and henries have units of joules/ampere^2:

$$\sqrt{\frac{\mu_0}{\varepsilon_0}} = \sqrt{\frac{H}{F}} = \sqrt{\frac{J/I^2}{J/V^2}} = \sqrt{\frac{V^2}{I^2}} = \frac{V}{I} \approx 377\Omega$$

It is interesting to remember that the speed of light is:

$$c = \frac{1}{\sqrt{\varepsilon_0 \mu_0}}$$

This links the fundamental electrical and magnetic constants to both velocity of electromagnetic waves and an impedance describing how energy is distributed between the electric and magnetic fields.

3.11 References and Bibliography

BOOKS AND ARTICLES

Alexander and Sadiku, *Fundamentals of Electric Circuits* (McGraw-Hill)

Banzhaf, W., WB1ANE, *Understanding Basic Electronics*, 2nd ed (ARRL)

Horowitz and Hill, *The Art of Electronics* (Cambridge University Press)

Kaplan, S., *Wiley Electrical and Electronics Dictionary* (Wiley Press)

Millman and Grabel, *Microelectronics: Digital and Analog Circuits and Systems* (McGraw-Hill, 1988)

Orr, W., *Radio Handbook* (Newnes)

Rautio, J., AJ3K, "The Long Road to Maxwell's Equations," IEEE Spectrum, **spectrum.ieee.org/telecom/wireless/the-long-road-to-maxwells-equations**

Silver, W., NØAX, "Experiment #74 — Resonant Circuits," *QST*, Mar 2009, pp 72-73

Silver, W., NØAX, "Experiment #178 — Maxwell's Equations — Grad, Div, and Curl," *QST*, Nov 2017, pp 77-78.

Silver, W., NØAX, "Experiment #179 — Maxwell's Equations — The Wave Emerges," *QST*, Dec 2017, pp 59-60

Smith, GS, "Analysis of Hertz's Experimentum Crucis on Electromagnetic Waves," IEEE Antennas and Propagation Magazine, Oct 2016, pp. 96-108

Terman, F., *Radio Engineer's Handbook* (McGraw-Hill)

Zavrel, R., W7SX, *Antenna Physics: An Introduction*, ARRL, 2016.

WEBSITES

Giselowitz, M. "Did You Know? Someone Else Wrote Maxwell's Equations," **theinstitute.ieee.org/tech-history/technology-history/did-you-know-someone-else-wrote-maxwells-equations**.

Oliver Heaviside — **en.wikipedia.org/wiki/Oliver_Heaviside**

History of Maxwell's Equations — **en.wikipedia.org/wiki/History_of_Maxwell%27s_equations**

Rohde & Schwarz, "dB or not dB? Everything you ever wanted to know about decibels but were afraid to ask…," Application Note 1MA98, **www.rohde-schwarz.us/en/applications/db-or-not-db-application-note_56280-15534.html**

Contents

Chapter 4

Circuits and Components

This chapter begins by covering the various aspects of dealing with real components — resistors, capacitors, inductors, and transformers. All of these have special features and behaviors you must take into account, especially at RF. We then cover common semiconductors you'll encounter in radio and their important characteristics.

The discussion then proceeds to building block circuits, beginning with various types of amplifiers constructed with bipolar and field-effect transistors. Building-block circuits including op amps and miscellaneous analog ICs are also covered. Finally, a section on Heat Management discusses how to deal with heat in electronic devices.

Chapter 4 — Downloadable Supplemental Content

Articles

- "Hands-On Radio: The Common Emitter Amplifier" by Ward Silver, NØAX
- "Hands-On Radio: The Emitter-Follower Amplifier" by Ward Silver, NØAX
- "Hands-On Radio: The Common Base Amplifier" by Ward Silver, NØAX
- "Hands-On Radio: Field Effect Transistors" by Ward Silver, NØAX
- "Hands-On Radio: Basic Operational Amplifiers" by Ward Silver, NØAX
- "Hands-On Radio: Load Lines" by Ward Silver, NØAX
- Large Signal Transistor Operation

Tools and Data

- *LTSpice* Simulation Files
- Frequency Response Spreadsheet

4.1 Practical Resistors

4.1.1 Resistance of Wires

The problem of determining the resistance of a round wire of given diameter and length — or the converse, finding a suitable size and length of wire to provide a desired amount of resistance — can easily be solved with the help of the copper wire table given in the chapter on **Component Data and References**. This table gives the resistance, in ohms per 1000 ft, of each standard wire size. For example, suppose you need a resistance of 3.5 Ω, and some #28 AWG wire is on hand. The wire table shows that #28 AWG wire has a resistance of 63.31 Ω / 1000 ft. Since the desired resistance is 3.5 Ω, the required length of wire is:

$$\text{Length} = \frac{R_{DESIRED}}{\frac{R_{WIRE}}{1000\text{ ft}}} = \frac{3.5\,\Omega}{\frac{63.31\,\Omega}{1000\text{ ft}}}$$

$$= \frac{3.5\,\Omega \times 1000\text{ ft}}{63.31\,\Omega} = 53.6\text{ ft}$$

As another example, suppose that the resistance of wire in a radio's power cable must not exceed 0.05 Ω and that the length of wire required for making the connections totals 14 ft. Then:

$$\frac{R_{WIRE}}{1000\text{ ft}} < \frac{R_{MAXIMUM}}{\text{Length}} = \frac{0.05\,\Omega}{14.0\text{ ft}}$$

$$= 3.57 \times 10^{-3}\,\frac{\Omega}{\text{ft}} \times \frac{1000\text{ ft}}{1000\text{ ft}}$$

$$\frac{R_{WIRE}}{1000\text{ ft}} < \frac{3.57\,\Omega}{1000\text{ ft}}$$

Find the value of R_{WIRE} / 1000 ft that is less than the calculated value. The wire table shows that #15 AWG is the smallest size having a resistance less than this value. (The resistance of #15 AWG wire is given as 3.1810 Ω / 1000 ft.) Select any wire size larger than this for the connections in your circuit, to ensure that the total wire resistance will be less than 0.05 Ω.

When the wire in question is not made of copper, the resistance values in the wire table should be multiplied by the ratios shown in Table 2.1 to obtain the resulting resistance. If the wire in the first example were made from nickel instead of copper, the length required for 3.5 Ω would be:

$$\text{Length} = \frac{R_{DESIRED}}{\frac{R_{WIRE}}{1000\text{ ft}}}$$

$$= \frac{3.5\,\Omega}{\frac{66.17\,\Omega}{1000\text{ ft}} \times 5.1} = \frac{3.5\,\Omega \times 1000\text{ ft}}{66.17\,\Omega \times 5.1}$$

$$\text{Length} = \frac{3500\text{ ft}}{337.5} = 10.5\text{ ft}$$

4.1.2 Temperature Effects on Resistors

The resistance of a conductor changes with its temperature. The resistance of practically every metallic conductor increases with increasing temperature. Carbon, however, acts in the opposite way; its resistance decreases when its temperature rises. It is seldom necessary to consider temperature in making resistance calculations for amateur work. The temperature effect is important when it is necessary to maintain a constant resistance under all conditions, however. Special materials that have little or no change in resistance over a wide temperature range are used in that case.

4.1.3 Component Resistors

The size and construction of resistors having the same value of resistance in ohms may

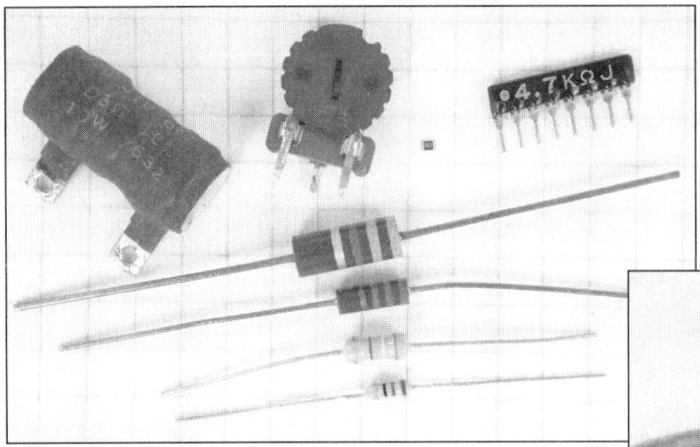

Figure 4.1 — Examples of various resistors. At the top left is a small 10-W wirewound resistor. A single in-line package (SIP) of resistors is at the top right. At the top center is a small PC-board-mount variable resistor. A tiny surface-mount (chip) resistor is also shown at the top. Below the variable resistor is a 1-W carbon composition resistor and then a ½-W composition unit. The dog-bone-shaped resistors at the bottom are ½-W and ¼-W film resistors. The ¼-inch-ruled graph paper background provides a size comparison. The inset photo shows the chip resistor with a penny for size comparison.

vary considerably based on how much power they are intended to dissipate, how much voltage is expected to be applied to them, and so forth (see **Figure 4.1**). See the **Component Data and References** chapter for information on resistor value marking conventions.

TYPES OF RESISTORS

Resistors are made in several different ways: carbon composition, metal oxide, carbon film, metal film, and wirewound. In some circuits, the resistor value may be critical. In this case, precision resistors are used. These are typically wirewound or carbon-film devices whose values are carefully controlled during manufacture. In addition, special material or construction techniques may be used to provide temperature compensation, so the value does not change (or changes in a precise manner) as the resistor temperature changes.

Carbon composition resistors are simply small cylinders of carbon mixed with various binding agents to produce any desired resistance. The most common sizes of "carbon comp" resistors are ½- and ¼-W resistors. They are moderately stable from 0 to 60 °C (their resistance increases above and below this temperature range). They can absorb short overloads better than film-type resistors, but they are relatively noisy, and have relatively wide tolerances. Because carbon composition resistors tend to be affected by humidity and other environmental factors and because they are difficult to manufacture in surface-mount packages, they have largely been replaced by film-type resistors.

Metal-oxide resistors are similar to carbon composition resistors in that the resistance is supplied by a cylinder of metal oxide. Metal-oxide resistors have replaced carbon composition resistors in higher power applications because they are more stable and can operate at higher temperatures.

Wirewound resistors are made from wire, which is cut to the proper length and wound on a coil form (usually ceramic). They are capable of handling high power; their values are very stable, and they are manufactured to close tolerances. The wound-wire construction creates inductance so these resistors are not suitable for ac circuits above a few kHz

Metal-film resistors are made by depositing a thin film of aluminum, tungsten, or other metal on an insulating substrate. Their resistances are controlled by careful adjustments of the width, length and depth of the film. As a result, they have very tight tolerances. They are used extensively in surface-mount technology. As might be expected, their power handling capability is somewhat limited. They also produce very little electrical noise.

Carbon-film resistors use a film of carbon mixed with other materials instead of metal. They are not quite as stable as other film resistors and have wider tolerances than metal-film resistors, but they are still as good as (or better than) carbon composition resistors.

Thin-film resistors are also available at high power ratings in a transistor-like TO-220 package. Because of their packaging, they can be mounted to heat sinks and are available with power ratings up to 50 W. These resistors also have low inductance for use in switch-mode circuits and high-frequency applications.

THERMAL CONSIDERATIONS FOR RESISTORS

Current through a resistance causes the conductor to become heated; the higher the resistance and the larger the current, the greater the amount of heat developed. Resistors intended for carrying large currents must be physically large so the heat can be radiated quickly to the surrounding air or some type of heat sinking material. If the resistor does not dissipate the heat quickly, it may get hot enough to melt or burn.

The amount of heat a resistor can safely dissipate depends on the material, surface area and design. Typical resistors used in amateur electronics (⅛ to 2-W resistors) dissipate heat primarily through the surface area of the case, with some heat also being carried away through the connecting leads. Wirewound resistors are usually used for higher power levels. Some have finned cases for better convection cooling and/or metal cases for better conductive cooling.

The major departure of resistors from ideal behavior at low-frequencies is their *temperature coefficient* (TC). (See the chapter on **RF Techniques** for a discussion of the behavior of resistors at high frequencies.) The resistivity of most materials changes with temperature, and typical TC values for resistor materials are given in **Table 4.1**. TC values are usually expressed in parts-per-million (PPM) for each degree (centigrade) change from some nominal temperature, usually room temperature (77 °F or 27 °C). A positive TC indicates an increase in resistance with

Component Tolerance

Resistors are manufactured with a specific *nominal* value of resistance. This is the value printed on the body of the resistor or marked with stripes of colored paint. The *actual* value of resistance varies from the nominal value because of random variations in the manufacturing process. The maximum allowable amount of variation is called the *tolerance* and it is expressed in percent. For example, a 1000 Ω resistor with a tolerance of 5% could have any value of resistance between 95% and 105% of 1000 Ω; 950 to 1050 Ω. In most circuits, this small variation doesn't have much effect, but it is important to be aware of tolerance and choose the correct value (10%, 5%, 1%, or even tighter tolerance values are available for *precision components*) of tolerance for the circuit to operate properly, no matter what the actual value of resistance. All components have this same nominal-to-actual value relationship.

Table 4.1
Temperature Coefficients for Various Resistor Compositions
1 PPM = 1 part per million = 0.0001%

Type	*TC (PPM/°C)*
Wire wound	±(30 - 50)
Metal Film	±(100 - 200)
Carbon Film	+350 to –800
Carbon composition	±800

Digital Electronics Tutorial

The chapter on digital basics found in previous editions has been converted to a supplemental item in this book's downloadable supplemental material. The number of excellent book and online references have reduced the need for a separate chapter on digital electronics in this book. A set of references on digital electronics, including current ARRL publications on the use of microcontrollers for Amateur Radio projects are listed here.

DIGITAL ELECTRONICS REFERENCES

Bignell and Donovan, *Digital Electronics* (Delmar Learning, 2006)
Holdsworth, B., *Digital Logic Design* (Newnes, 2002)
Klotz, L., Jr, WA5ZNU, *Ham Radio for Arduino and PICAXE* (ARRL, 20130
Lancaster and Berlin, *CMOS Cookbook* (Newnes, 1997)
Popiel, G., KW5GP, *Arduino for Ham Radio* (ARRL, 2014)
Popiel, G., KW5GP, *More Arduino Projects for Ham Radio* (ARRL, 2017)
Purdum, J., Kidder, D., *Arduino Projects for Amateur Radio* (McGraw Hill, 2013)
Tocci, Widmer and Moss, *Digital Systems: Principles and Applications* (Prentice Hall, 2006)
Tokheim, R., *Digital Electronics: Principles and Applications* (McGraw-Hill, 2008)
Logic simulation software: *Getting Started with Digital Works*, **www.spu.edu/cs/faculty/bbrown/circuits/howto.html**

MICROPROCESSORS AND MICROCONTROLLERS

Dumas, J., *Computer Architecture: Fundamentals and Principles of Computer Design* (CRC Press, 2005)
Gilmore, C., *Microprocessors: Principles and Applications* (McGraw-Hill, 1995)
Klotz, L., WA5ZNU (Ed.), *Ham Radio for Arduino and PICAXE* (ARRL, 2013)
Korneev and Kiselev, *Modern Microprocessors* (Charles River Press, 2004)
Spencer, M., WA8SME, ARRL's PIC Programming for Beginners (ARRL, 2010)
Tocci and Ambrosio, Microprocessors and Microcomputers: Hardware and Software (Prentice-Hall, 2002)

increasing temperature while a negative TC indicates a decreasing resistance. For example, if a 1000-Ω resistor with a TC of +300 PPM/°C is heated to 50 °C, the *change* in resistance is 300 × (50 – 27) = 6900 PPM, yielding a new resistance of

$$1000\left(1+\frac{6900}{1000000}\right)=1006.9\ \Omega$$

Carbon-film resistors are unique among the major resistor families because they alone have a negative temperature coefficient. They are often used to "offset" the thermal effects of the other components.

If the temperature increase is small (less than 30-40 °C), the resistance change with temperature is nondestructive — the resistor will return to normal when the temperature returns to its nominal value. Resistors that get too hot to touch, however, may be permanently damaged even if they appear normal. For this reason, be conservative when specifying power ratings for resistors. It's common to specify a resistor rated at 200% to 400% of the expected dissipation.

4.1.4 Voltage Dividers

According to Kirchoff's Voltage Law (KVL), the voltage drop across each resistor in a series circuit is directly proportional to the resistance. When connected in series, a resistor that has a value twice as large as another will have twice the voltage drop across it.

Resistors in series without any other connections form a *resistive voltage divider*. (Other types of components can form voltage dividers, too.) The voltage across any specific resistor in the divider, R_n, is equal to the voltage across the entire string of resistors multiplied by the ratio of R_n to the sum of all resistors in the string.

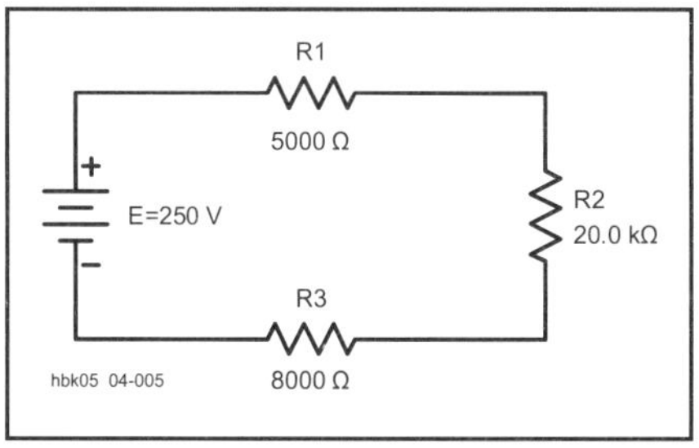

Figure 4.2 — An example of resistors in series.

For example, in the circuit of **Figure 4.2**, the voltage across the 5000 Ω resistor is:

$$E1=250\,\frac{5000}{5000+20000+8000}=37.9\ V$$

This is a more convenient method than calculating the current through the resistor and using Ohm's Law.

Voltage dividers can be used as a source of voltage. As long as the device connected to the output of the divider has a much higher resistance than the resistors in the divider, there will be little effect on the divider output voltage. For example, for a voltage divider with a voltage of E = 15 V and two resistors of R1 = 5 kΩ and R2 = 10 kΩ, the voltage across R2 will be 10 V measured on a high-impedance voltmeter because the measurement draws very little current from the divider. However, if the measuring device or load across R2 draws significant current, it will increase the amount of current drawn through the divider and change the output voltage.

The following equations show how to calculate the voltage produced by a voltage divider. Using the circuit in **Figure 4.3**, the *unloaded* output voltage (with R3 not connected) is:

$$V_{OUT}=V_{IN}\left(\frac{R2}{R1+R2}\right)$$

If R3 is connected, the *loaded* output voltage is:

$$V_{OUT}=V_{IN}\left(\frac{R2//R3}{R1+R2//R3}\right)$$

where // indicates "in parallel with."

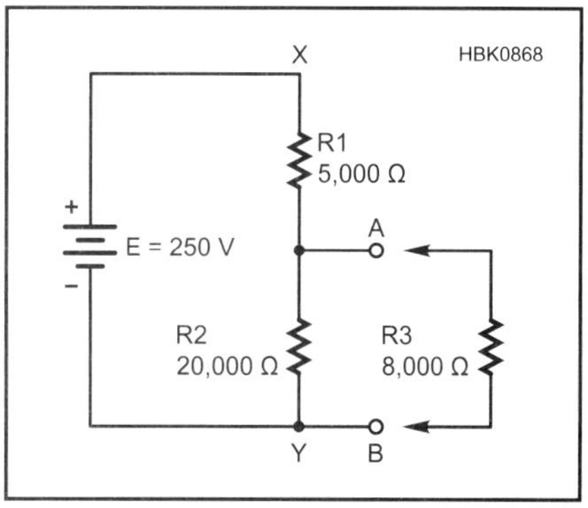

Figure 4.3 — A voltage divider showing both unloaded (R3 not connected) and loaded (R3 connected) conditions.

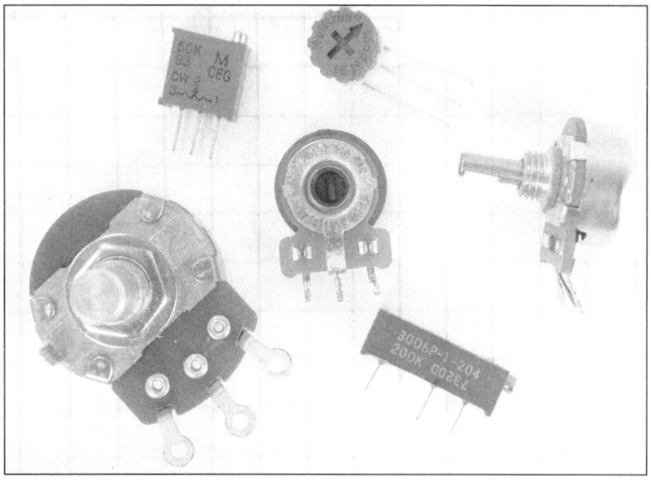

Figure 4.4 — This photo shows examples of different styles of potentiometers. The ¼-inch-ruled graph paper background provides a size comparison.

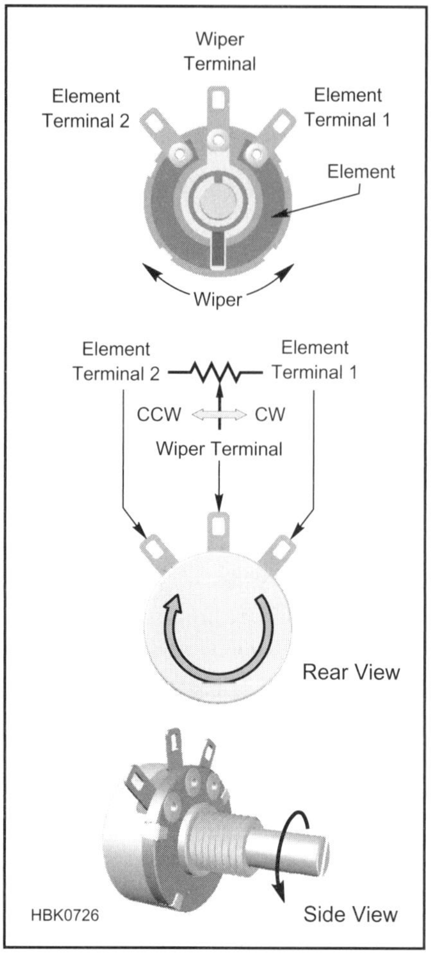

Figure 4.5 — Typical potentiometer construction and schematic symbol. Rotation on the shaft moves the wiper along the element, changing the resistance between the wiper terminal and the element terminals. Moving the wiper closer to an element terminal reduces the resistance between them.

A good rule of thumb to keep the loaded output voltage within about 10% of the unloaded voltage is for the load resistance to be at least 10 times higher than the output resistor of the divider. As the load resistance approaches the value of the output resistor, the additional current through the load causes additional voltage drop across the divider's input resistor.

Potentiometers (variable resistors described in the next section) are often used as adjustable voltage dividers and this is how they got their name. Potential is an older name for voltage and a "potential-meter" is a device that can "meter" or adjust potential, thus potentiometer.

4.1.5 Current Dividers

Resistors connected in parallel form a circuit called a *resistive current divider*. For any number of resistors connected in parallel (R1, R2, R3, ... R4), the current through one of the resistors, R_n, is equal to the sum of all resistor currents multiplied by the ratio of the equivalent of all parallel resistors *except* R_n to the sum of R_n and the equivalent value.

$$I_n = I_{TOT} (R_{EQ}/R_n + R_{EQ})$$

For example, in a circuit with three parallel resistors; R1, R2, and R3, the current through R2 is equal to:

$$I_2 = I \frac{R1 + R3}{R1 + R2 + R3}$$

where I is the total current through all the resistors. If I = 100 mA, R1 = 100 Ω, R2 = 50 Ω, and R3 = 200 Ω:

$$100\ \text{mA} \frac{100 + 200}{100 + 50 + 200} = 85.7\ \text{mA}$$

4.1.6 Potentiometers

Potentiometer (pronounced po-ten-tchee-AH-meh-tur) is a formal name for a variable resistor and the common name for these components is "pots." A typical potentiometer consists of a circular *element* of resistive material which can be a carbon compound similar to that used in carbon composition resistors or a conductive plastic. One contact is made to each end of the element. A variable-position *wiper* makes contact with the element at different positions. As the wiper moves along the material, more resistance is introduced between the wiper and one of the element's contacts. The wiper is turned by a shaft to move across the material.

For higher power applications, the element may be wire wound around a core, like a wirewound resistor. Like the wirewound resistor, this type of pot is not suitable for high-frequency applications due to inductance.

A potentiometer may be used to control current, voltage, or resistance in a circuit. **Figure 4.4** shows several different types of potentiometers. **Figure 4.5** shows the schematic symbol for a potentiometer and how changing the position of the shaft changes the resistance between its three terminals. The figure shows a *panel pot*, designed to be mounted on an equipment panel and adjusted by an operator. The small rectangular *trimmer* potentiometers in Figure 4.5 are adjusted with a screwdriver and have wire terminals.

Typical specifications for a potentiometer include element resistance, power dissipation, voltage and current ratings, number of turns (or degrees) the shaft can rotate, type and size of shaft, mounting arrangements, and resistance *taper*. Taper describes how the resistance of the element changes with position along it.

Pots with a *linear taper* have equal change in resistance with position along the element. That is, the change in resistance is the same for a given number of degrees of shaft rotation anywhere along different portions of the resistive material.

Some pots have *non-linear tapers*. A typical use for a nonlinear taper is as a volume control in an audio amplifier. Since the human ear has a logarithmic response to sound, a volume control must change the amplifier output much more near one end of the element than the other (for a given amount of rotation) so that the "perceived" change in volume is about the same for a similar change in the control's position. This is commonly called an *audio taper* or *log taper* as the change in resistance per degree of rotation attempts to match the response of the human ear. Tapers can be designed to match almost any desired control function for a given application. Linear and audio tapers are the most common tapers.

4.2 Practical Capacitors

4.2.1 Component Capacitors

The ideal capacitor does not conduct any current at dc, dissipates none of the energy stored in it, has the same value at all temperatures, and operates with any amount of voltage applied across it or ac current flowing through it. As actual components, they deviate considerably from that ideal and have imperfections that must be considered when selecting capacitors and designing circuits that use capacitors. (The characteristics of capacitors at high frequencies is discussed in the **RF Techniques** chapter.)

LEAKAGE RESISTANCE

If we use anything other than a vacuum for the insulating layer, even air, two imperfections are created. Because there are atoms between the plates, some electrons will be available to create a current between the plates when a dc voltage is applied. The magnitude of this *leakage current* will depend on the insulator quality, and the current is usually very small. Leakage current can be modeled by a resistance R_L in parallel with the capacitance (in an ideal capacitor, R_L is infinite). **Table 4.2** shows typical dc leakage resistances for different dielectric materials. Leakage also generally increases with increasing temperature.

Table 4.2

Typical Temperature Coefficients and Leakage Resistances for Various Capacitor Constructions

Type	*TC @ 20°C (PPM/°C)*	*DC Leakage Resistance (Ω)*
Ceramic Disc	±300(NP0)	> 10 M
	+150/–1500(GP)	> 10 M
Mica	–20 to +100	> 100,000 M
Polyester	±500	> 10 M
Tantalum Electrolytic	±1500	> 10 MΩ
Small Al Electrolytic(≈ 100 µF)	–20,000	500 k - 1 M
Large Al Electrolytic(≈ 10 mF)	–100,000	10 k
Vacuum (glass)	+100	≈ ∞
Vacuum (ceramic)	+50	≈ ∞

CAPACITOR LOSSES

When an ac current flows through the capacitor (even at low frequencies), capacitors dissipate some of the energy stored in the dielectric due to the electromagnetic properties of dielectric materials. This loss can be thought of as a resistance in series with the capacitor and it is often specified in the manufacturer's data for the capacitor as *effective (or equivalent) series resistance* (*ESR*) which is specified in ohms.

Loss can also be specified as the capacitor's *loss angle,* θ. (Some literature uses δ for loss angle.) Loss angle is the angle between X_C (the reactance of the capacitor without any loss) and the impedance of the capacitor (impedance is discussed later in this chapter) made up of the combination of ESR and X_C. Increasing loss increases loss angle. The loss angle is usually quite small, and is zero for an ideal capacitor.

Dissipation Factor (DF) or *loss tangent* is the ratio of loss resistance to reactance.

$$DF = \tan\theta = ESR / X_C$$

The loss angle of a given capacitor is relatively constant over frequency, meaning that ESR = (tan θ) / 2πfC goes down as frequency goes up. For this reason, ESR must be specified at a given frequency.

TOLERANCE AND TEMPERATURE COEFFICIENT

As with resistors, capacitor values vary in production, and most capacitors have a tolerance rating either printed on them or listed on a data sheet. Typical capacitor tolerances and the labeling of tolerance are described in the chapter on **Component Data and References**.

Because the materials that make up a capacitor exhibit mechanical changes with temperature, capacitance also varies with temperature. This change in capacitance with temperature is the capacitor's *temperature coefficient* or *tempco (TC)*. The lower a capacitor's TC, the less its value changes with temperature.

TC is important to consider when constructing a circuit that will carry high power levels, operate in an environment far from room temperature, or must operate consistently at different temperatures. Typical temperature coefficients for several capacitor types are given in Table 4.2. (Capacitor temperature coefficient behaviors are listed in the **Component Data and References** chapter.)

VOLTAGE RATINGS AND BREAKDOWN

When voltage is applied to the plates of a capacitor, force is exerted on the atoms and molecules of the dielectric by the electrostatic field between the plates. If the voltage is high enough, the atoms of the dielectric will ionize (one or more of the electrons will be pulled away from the atom), causing a large dc current to flow discharging the capacitor. This is *dielectric breakdown,* and it is generally destructive to the capacitor because it creates punctures or defects in solid dielectrics that provide permanent low-resistance current paths between the plates. (*Self-healing* dielectrics have the ability to seal off this type of damage.) With most gas dielectrics such as air, once the voltage is removed, the arc ceases and the capacitor is ready for use again.

The *breakdown voltage* of a dielectric depends on the chemical composition and thickness of the dielectric. Breakdown voltage is not directly proportional to the thickness; doubling the thickness does not quite double the breakdown voltage. A thick dielectric must be used to withstand high voltages. Since capacitance is inversely proportional to dielectric thickness (plate spacing) for a given plate area, a high-voltage capacitor must have more plate area than a low-voltage one of the same capacitance. High-voltage, high-capacitance capacitors are therefore physically large.

Dielectric strength is specified in terms of a *dielectric withstanding voltage* (DWV), given in volts per mil (0.001 inch) at a specified temperature. Taking into account the design temperature range of a capacitor and a safety margin, manufacturers specify *dc working voltage* (dcwv) to express the maximum safe limits of dc voltage across a capacitor to prevent dielectric breakdown.

For use with ac voltages, the peak value of ac voltage should not exceed the dc working voltage, unless otherwise specified in component ratings. In other words, the RMS value of sine-wave ac waveforms should be 0.707 times the dcwv value, or lower. With many types of capacitors, further derating is required as the operating frequency increases. An additional safety margin is good practice.

Dielectric breakdown in a gas or air dielectric capacitor occurs as a spark or arc between the plates. Spark voltages are generally given with the units *kilovolts per centimeter*. For air, the spark voltage or V_s may range from more than 120 kV/cm for gaps as narrow as 0.006 cm down to 28 kV/cm for gaps as wide as 10 cm. In addition, a large number of variables enter into the actual breakdown voltage in a real situation. Among the variables are the plate shape, the gap distance, the air pressure or density, the voltage, impurities in the air (or any other dielectric material) and the nature of the external circuit (with air, for instance, the humidity affects conduction on the surface of the capacitor plate).

Dielectric breakdown occurs at a lower voltage between pointed or sharp-edged surfaces than between rounded and polished surfaces. Consequently, the breakdown voltage between metal plates of any given spacing in air can be increased by buffing the edges of the plates. If the plates are damaged so they are no longer smooth, they may have to be polished or the capacitor replaced.

4.2.2 Capacitor Types and Uses

Quite a variety of capacitors are used in radio circuits, differing considerably in physical size, construction and capacitance. Some of the different types are shown in **Figure 4.6** and many other types and packages are available. (See the **Component Data and References** chapter for illustrations of capacitor types and labeling conventions.)

The dielectric determines many properties of the capacitor, although the construction of the plates strongly affects the capacitor's ac performance and some dc parameters. Various materials are used for different reasons such as working voltage and current, availability, cost, and desired capacitance range.

Fixed capacitors having a single, nonadjustable value of capacitance can also be made with metal plates and with air as the dielectric, but are usually constructed from strips of metal foil with a thin solid or liquid dielectric sandwiched between, so that a relatively large capacitance can be obtained in a small package. Solid dielectrics commonly used in fixed capacitors are plastic films, mica, paper and special ceramics. Two typical types of fixed capacitor construction are shown in **Figure 4.7**.

For capacitors with wire leads, there are two basic types of lead orientation; *axial* (shown in Figure 4.7A) in which the leads are aligned with the long axis of the capacitor body and *radial* (shown in Figure 4.7B) in which the leads are at right angles to the capacitor's length or width.

Vacuum — Both fixed and variable vacuum capacitors are available. They are rated by their maximum working voltages (3 to 60 kV) and currents. Losses are specified as negligible for most applications. The high working voltage and low losses make vacuum capacitors widely used in transmitting applications. Vacuum capacitors are also unaffected by humidity, moisture, contamination, or dust, unlike air-dielectric capacitors discussed next. This allows them to be used in environments for which air-dielectric capacitors would be unsuitable.

Air — Since K ≈ 1 for air, air-dielectric capacitors are large when compared to those of the same value using other dielectrics. Their capacitance is very stable over a wide temperature range, leakage losses are low, and therefore a high Q can be obtained. They also can withstand high voltages. Values range from a few tens to hundreds of pF.

For these reasons (and ease of construction) most variable capacitors in tuning circuits are *air-variable* capacitors made with one set of plates movable with respect to the other set to vary the area of overlap and thus the capacitance. A *transmitting-variable* capacitor has heavy plates far enough apart to withstand the high voltages and currents encountered in a transmitter. (Air variable capacitors with more closely-spaced plates are often referred to as *receiving-variables.*)

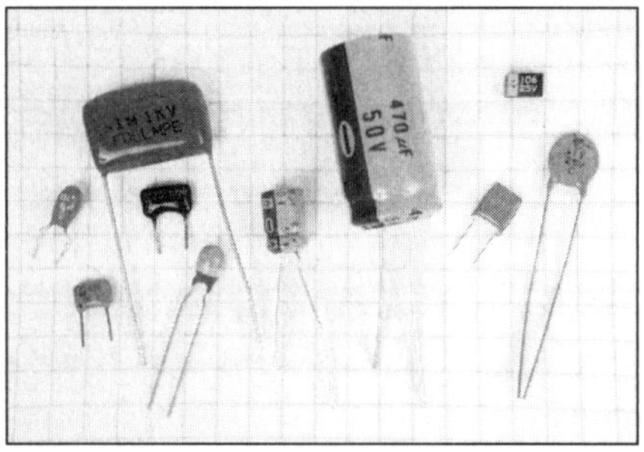

(A)

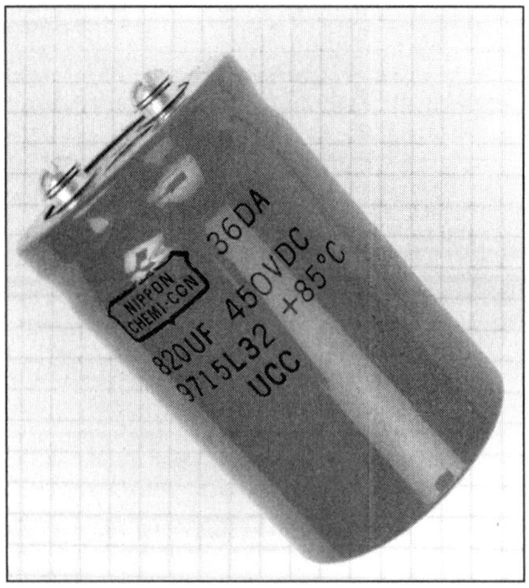

(B)

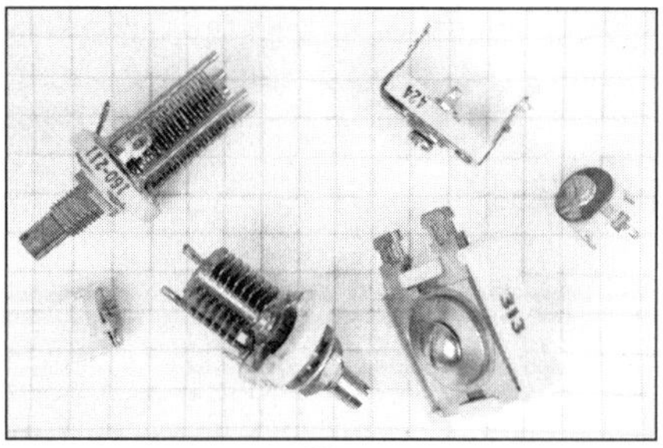

(C)

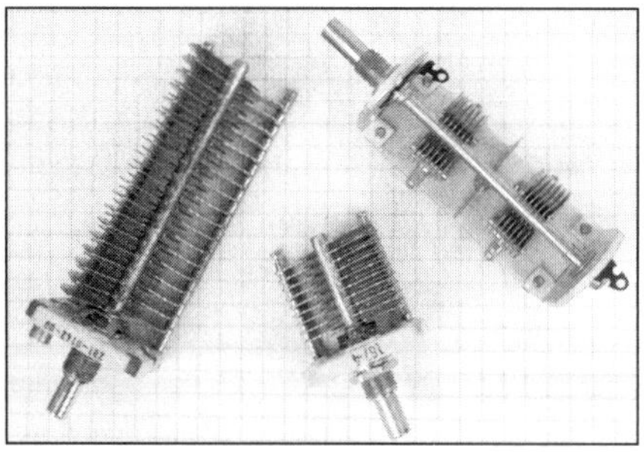

(D)

(E)

Figure 4.6 — Fixed-value capacitors are shown in parts A and B. Aluminum electrolytic capacitors are pictured near the center of photo A. The small tear-drop units to the left of center are tantalum electrolytic capacitors. The rectangular units are silvered-mica, polystyrene film and monolithic ceramic. At the right edge is a disc-ceramic capacitor and near the top right corner is a surface-mount capacitor. B shows a large "computer-grade" electrolytic. These have very low equivalent series resistance (ESR) and are often used as filter capacitors in switch-mode power supplies, and in series-strings for high-voltage supplies of RF power amplifiers. Parts C and D show a variety of variable capacitors, including air variable capacitors and mica compression units. Part E shows a vacuum variable capacitor such as is sometimes used in high-power amplifier circuits. The 1/4-inch-ruled graph paper backgrounds provide size comparisons.

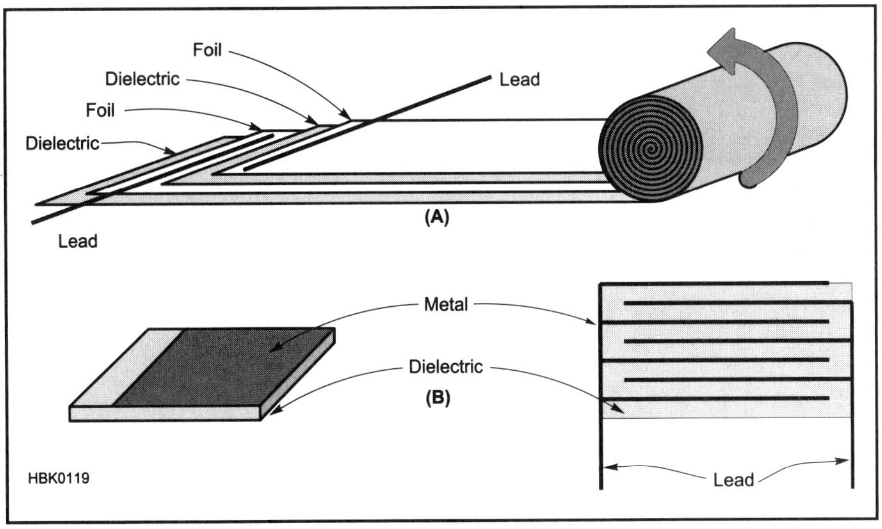

Figure 4.7 — Two common types of capacitor construction. A shows the roll method for film capacitors with axial leads. B shows the alternating layer method for ceramic capacitors. Axial leads are shown in A and radial leads in B.

Plastic film — Capacitors with plastic film (such as polystyrene, polyethylene, or Mylar) dielectrics are widely used in bypassing and coupling applications up to several megahertz. They have high leakage resistances (even at high temperatures) and low TCs. Values range from tens of pF to 1 µF. Plastic-film variable capacitors are also available.

Most film capacitors are not polarized; however, the body of the capacitor is usually marked with a color band at one end. The band indicates the terminal that is connected to the outermost plate of the capacitor. This terminal should be connected to the side of the circuit at the lower potential as a safety precaution.

Film capacitors are often made using roll construction as in Figure 4.7. This construction has relatively high inductance and the capacitor may not be suitable for RF applications.

Mica — The capacitance of mica capacitors is very stable with respect to time, temperature and electrical stress. Leakage and losses are very low and they are often used in transmitting equipment. Values range from 1 pF to 0.1 µF. High working voltages are possible, but they must be derated severely as operating frequency increases. Note that many WWII-era mica capacitors are still available on the used and surplus market. Given the age of these components (now approaching 80 years) either use newer components or test them before using them in a high-power or high-voltage circuit.

Silver-mica — These capacitors are made by depositing a thin layer of silver on the mica dielectric. This makes the value even more stable, but it presents the possibility of silver migration through the dielectric. The migration problem worsens with increased dc voltage, temperature and humidity. Avoid using silver-mica capacitors under such conditions. Silver-mica capacitors are often used in RF circuits requiring stable capacitor values, such as oscillators and filters.

Ceramic — Ceramic capacitors are available with values from 1 pF to 1 µF and with voltage ratings up to 1 kV. *Monolithic ceramic* capacitors are constructed from a stack of thin ceramic layers with a metal coating on one side. The layer is then compressed with alternating metal coatings connected together to form the capacitor's plates. The high dielectric constant makes these capacitors physically small for their capacitance, but their value is not as stable and their dielectric properties vary with temperature, applied voltage and operating frequency. They also exhibit piezoelectric behavior. Use them only in coupling and bypass roles. *Disc ceramic* capacitors are made similarly to monolithic ceramic capacitors but with a lower dielectric constant so they are larger and tend to have higher voltage ratings. Ceramic capacitors are useful into the VHF and UHF ranges.

Transmitting ceramic capacitors are made, like transmitting air-variables, with heavy plates and high-voltage ratings. They are relatively large (often called "doorknobs"), but very stable and have nearly as low losses as mica capacitors at HF.

Electrolytic — Electrolytic capacitors are constructed with plates made of aluminum-foil strips and a semi-liquid conducting chemical compound between them. They are sometimes called *aluminum electrolytics*. The actual dielectric is a very thin film of insulating material that forms on one set of plates through electrochemical action when a dc voltage is applied to the capacitor. The capacitance of an electrolytic capacitor is very large compared to capacitors having other dielectrics, because the dielectric film is so thin — much thinner than is practical with a solid dielectric. Electrolytic capacitors are available with values from approximately 1 µF to 1 F and with voltage ratings up to hundreds of volts.

Electrolytic capacitors are popular because they provide high capacitance values in small packages at a reasonable cost. Leakage resistance is comparatively low and they are polarized — there is a definite positive and negative plate, due to the chemical reaction that creates the dielectric. Internal inductance restricts aluminum-foil electrolytics to low-frequency applications such as power-supply filtering and bypassing in audio circuits. To maintain the dielectric film, electrolytic capacitors should not be used if the applied dc potential will be well below the capacitor working voltage.

Supercapacitors are a special type of electrolytic capacitor with very high capacitance (greater than 1 F) and a low working voltage (a few volts, typically). Supercapacitors have one electrode that is a porous material with an extremely high ratio of surface area to volume and is immersed in electrolyte fluid or gel. The porous electrode is contained in a metal can that forms the other electrode. The dielectric forms on the porous material's surface, similarly to foil-type electrolytics. "Supercaps" are used as short-term power sources and as filter capacitors for power connections with large, sudden, short-term current demands.

A cautionary note is warranted regarding electrolytic capacitors found in older equipment, both vacuum tube and solid-state. The chemical paste in electrolytics dries out when the component is heated and with age, causing high losses and reduced capacitance. The dielectric film also disappears when the capacitor is not used for long periods. It is possible to "reform" the dielectric by applying a low voltage to an old or unused capacitor and gradually increasing the voltage. However, old electrolytics rarely perform as well as new units. To avoid expensive failures and circuit damage, it is recommended that electrolytic capacitors in old equipment be replaced if they have not been in regular use for more than ten years.

Tantalum — Related to the electrolytic capacitor, *tantalum* capacitors substitute a *slug* of extremely porous tantalum (a rare-earth metallic element) for the aluminum-foil strips as one plate. As in the electrolytic capacitor, the dielectric is an oxide film that forms on the surface of the tantalum. The slug is immersed in a liquid compound contained in a metal can that serves as the other plate.

Tantalum capacitors are commonly used with values from 0.1 to several hundred µF and voltage ratings of less than 100 V. Tantalum capacitors are smaller, lighter and more stable, with less leakage and inductance than their aluminum-foil electrolytic counterparts but their cost is higher.

Paper — Paper capacitors are generally not used in new designs and are largely encountered in older equipment; capacitances from 500 pF to 50 µF are available. High working voltages are possible, but paper-dielectric capacitors have low leakage resistances and tolerances are no better than 10 to 20%. Paper capacitors are not available as new stock (except possible for specialty restoration applications) and should not be used in new equipment.

Trimming capacitors — Small-value variable capacitors are often referred to as *trimmers* because they are used for fine-tuning or frequency adjustments, called *trimming*. Trimmers have dielectrics of Teflon, air, or ceramic and generally have values of less than 100 pF. *Compression trimmers* have higher values of up to 1000 pF and are constructed with mica dielectrics.

Oil-filled — Oil-filled capacitors use special high-strength dielectric oils to achieve voltage ratings of several kV. Values of up to 100 µF are commonly used in high-voltage applications such as high-voltage power supplies and energy storage. (See the chapter on **Power Sources** for additional information about the use of oil-filled and electrolytic capacitors.)

4.3 Practical Inductors

4.3.1 Component Inductors

Various facets of radio circuits make use of inductors ranging from the tiny up to the massive. Small values of inductance, such as those inductors in **Figure 4.8A**, serve mostly in RF circuits. They may be self-supporting, air-core or air-wound inductors, or the winding may be supported by nonmagnetic strips or a form. Phenolic, certain plastics and ceramics are the most common *coil forms* for air-core inductors. These inductors range in value from a few hundred µH for medium- and high-frequency circuits down to tenths of a µH at VHF and UHF.

The most common inductor in small-signal RF circuits is the *encapsulated inductor*. These components look a lot like carbon-composition or film resistors and are often marked with colored paint stripes to indicate value. (The chapter **Component Data and References** contains information on inductor color codes and marking schemes.) These inductors have values from less than 1 µH to a few mH. They cannot handle much current without saturating or over-heating.

It is possible to make solenoid inductors variable by inserting a moveable *slug* in the center of the inductor. (Slug-tuned inductors normally have a ceramic, plastic, or phenolic insulating form between the conductive slug and the inductor winding.) If the slug material is magnetic, such as powdered iron, the inductance increases as the slug is moved into the center of the inductor. If the slug is brass or some other nonmagnetic material, inserting the slug will reduce the inductor's inductance.

An alternative to air-core inductors for RF work are *toroidal* inductors (or *toroids*) wound on powdered-iron or ferrite cores. The availability of many types and sizes of powdered-iron cores has made these inductors popular for low-power fixed-value service. The toroidal shape concentrates the inductor's field nearly completely inside the inductor, eliminating the need in many cases for other forms of shielding to limit the interaction of the inductor's magnetic field with the fields of other inductors. (Ferrite core materials are discussed here and in the chapter on **RF Techniques**.)

Figure 4.8B shows samples of inductors in the millihenry (mH) range. Among these inductors are multi-section RF chokes designed to block RF currents from passing beyond them to other parts of circuits. Low-frequency radio work may also use inductors in this range of values, sometimes wound with

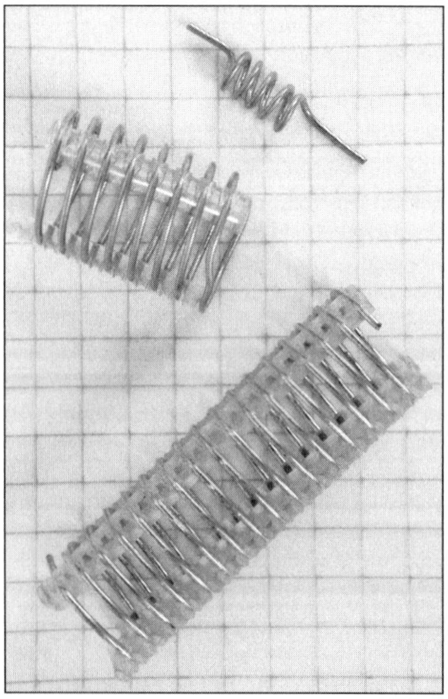

(A)

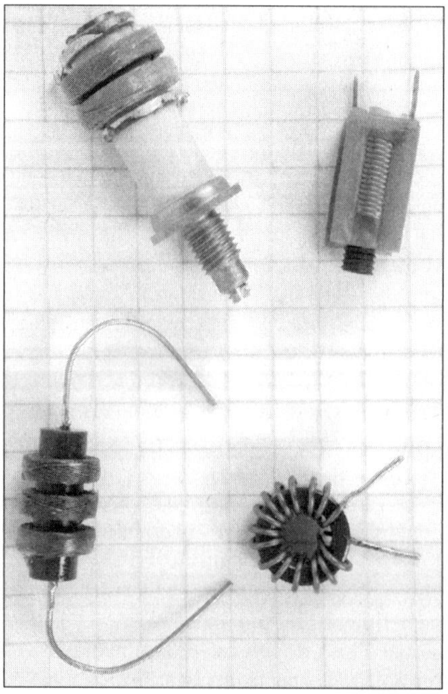

(B)

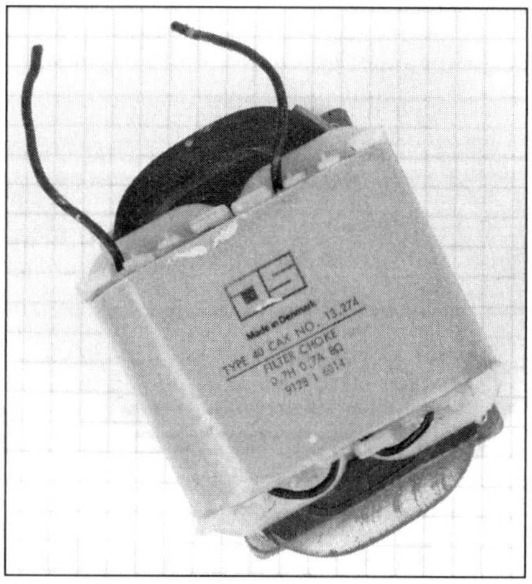

(C)

Figure 4.8 — Part A shows small-value air-wound inductors. Part B shows some inductors with values in the range of a few millihenrys and C shows a large inductor such as might be used in audio circuits or as power-supply chokes. The 1/4-inch-ruled graph paper background provides a size comparison.

litz wire. Litz wire is a special version of stranded wire, with each strand insulated from the others, and is used to minimize losses associated with skin effect.

For audio filters, toroidal inductors with values up to 100 mH are useful. Resembling powdered-iron-core RF toroids, these inductors are wound on ferrite or molybdenum-permalloy cores having much higher permeabilities.

Audio and power-supply inductors appear in Figure 4.8C. Lower values of these iron-core inductors, in the range of a few henrys, are useful as audio-frequency chokes. Larger values up to about 20 H may be found in power supplies, as choke filters, to suppress 120-Hz ripple. Although some of these inductors are open frame, most have iron covers to confine the powerful magnetic fields they produce.

Although builders and experimenters rarely construct their own capacitors, inductor fabrication for low- and high-power RF circuits is common. In fact, it is often necessary, since commercially available units may be unavailable or expensive. Even if available, they may consist of inductor stock to be trimmed to the required value. Core materials and wire for winding both solenoid and toroidal inductors are readily available. The following information includes fundamental formulas and design examples for calculating practical inductors, along with additional data on the theoretical limits in the use of some materials.

4.3.2 Air-Core Inductors

Many circuits require air-core inductors using just one layer of wire. The approximate inductance of a single-layer air-core inductor may be calculated from the simplified formula:

$$L\,(\mu H) = \frac{d^2\,n^2}{18d + 40\ell}$$

where

L = inductance in microhenrys,

d = inductor diameter in inches (from wire center to wire center),

ℓ = inductor length in inches, and

n = number of turns.

If dimensions are given in cm, the equation is:

$$L(\mu H) = \frac{d^2 n^2}{6.4\left(7.2d + 15.8\ell\right)}$$

The notation is illustrated in **Figure 4.9**. This formula is a close approximation for inductors having a length equal to or greater than 0.4d. (Note: Inductance varies as the square of the turns. If the number of turns is doubled, the inductance is quadrupled. This relationship is inherent in the equation, but is often overlooked. For example, to double the inductance, add additional turns equal to 1.4 times the original number of turns, or 40% more turns.)

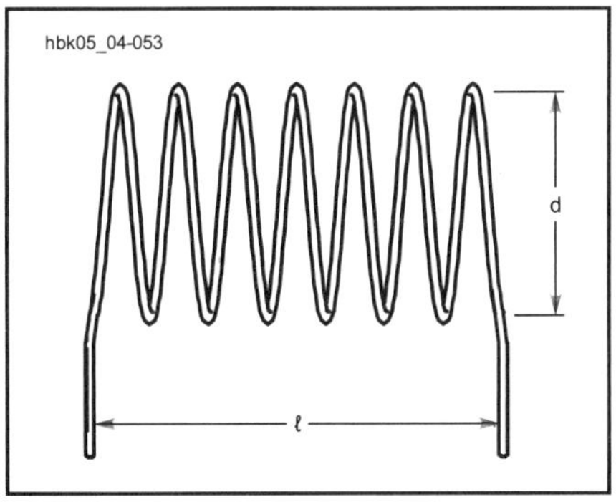

Figure 4.9 — Coil dimensions used in the inductance formula for air-core inductors.

Example: What is the inductance of an inductor if the inductor has 48 turns wound at 32 turns per inch and a diameter of ¾ inch? In this case, d = 0.75, ℓ = 48/32 = 1.5 and n = 48.

$$L\,(\mu H) = \frac{0.75^2 \times 48^2}{(18 \times 0.75) + (40 \times 1.5)}$$

$$= \frac{1300}{74} = 18\,\mu H$$

To calculate the number of turns of a single-layer inductor for a required value of inductance, the formula becomes:

$$n = \frac{\sqrt{L(18d + 40\ell)}}{d} \text{ (inches)}$$

$$n = \frac{\sqrt{L(7.2d + 15.8\ell)}}{d} \text{ (cm)}$$

Example: Suppose an inductance of 10.0 µH is required. The form on which the inductor is to be wound has a diameter of one inch and is long enough to accommodate an inductor of 1¼ inches. Then d = 1.00 inch, ℓ= 1.25 inches and L = 10.0. Substituting:

$$n = \frac{\sqrt{10.0\,[\,(18 \times 1.0) + (40 \times 1.25)}}{1}$$

$$= \sqrt{680} = 26.1 \text{ turns}$$

A 26-turn inductor would be close enough in practical work. Since the inductor will be 1.25 inches long, the number of turns per inch will be 26.1 / 1.25 = 20.9. Consulting the wire table in the **Component Data and References** chapter, we find that #17 AWG enameled wire (or anything smaller) can be used. The proper inductance is obtained by winding the required number of turns on the form and

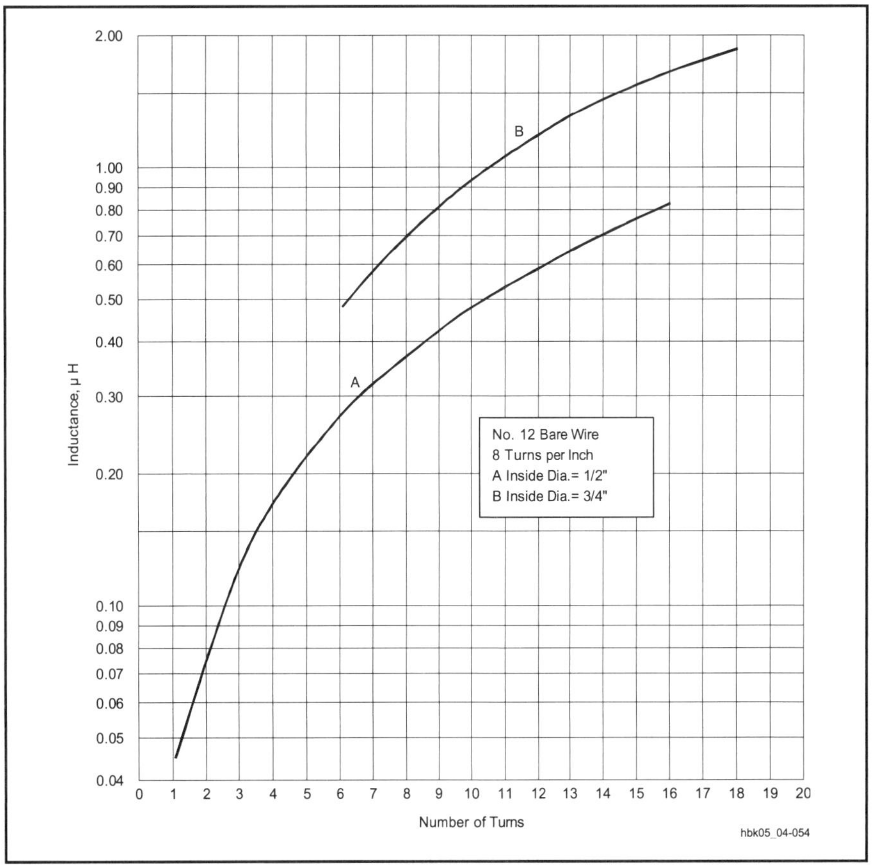

Figure 4.10 — Measured inductance of coils wound with #12 bare wire, eight turns to the inch. The values include half-inch leads.

then adjusting the spacing between the turns to make a uniformly spaced inductor 1.25 inches long.

Most inductance formulas lose accuracy when applied to small inductors (such as are used in VHF work and in low-pass filters built for reducing harmonic interference to televisions) because the conductor thickness is no longer negligible in comparison with the size of the inductor. **Figure 4.10** shows the measured inductance of VHF inductors and may be used as a basis for circuit design. Two curves are given; curve A is for inductors wound to an inside diameter of ½ inch; curve B is for inductors of ¾ -inch inside diameter. In both curves, the wire size is #12 AWG and the winding pitch is eight turns to the inch (⅛-inch turn spacing). The inductance values include leads ½-inch long.

Machine-wound inductors with the preset diameters and turns per inch are available from component distributors, under the trade names of B&W Miniductor and Airdux. Information on using such coil stock is provided in the **Component Data and References** chapter to simplify the process of designing high-quality inductors for most HF applications.

Forming a wire into a solenoid increases its inductance, but also introduces distributed capacitance. Since each turn is at a slightly different ac potential, each pair of turns effectively forms a capacitor in parallel with part of the inductor. (See the chapter on **RF Techniques** for information on the effects of these and other factors that affect the behavior of the "ideal" inductors discussed in this chapter.)

Moreover, the Q of air-core inductors is, in part, a function of the inductor shape, specifically its ratio of length to diameter. Q tends to be highest when these dimensions are nearly equal. With wire properly sized to the current carried by the inductor, and with high-caliber construction, air-core inductors can achieve Q above 200.

For a large collection of formulas useful in constructing air-core inductors of many configurations, see the "Circuit Elements" section in Terman's *Radio Engineers' Handbook* (listed in the References section).

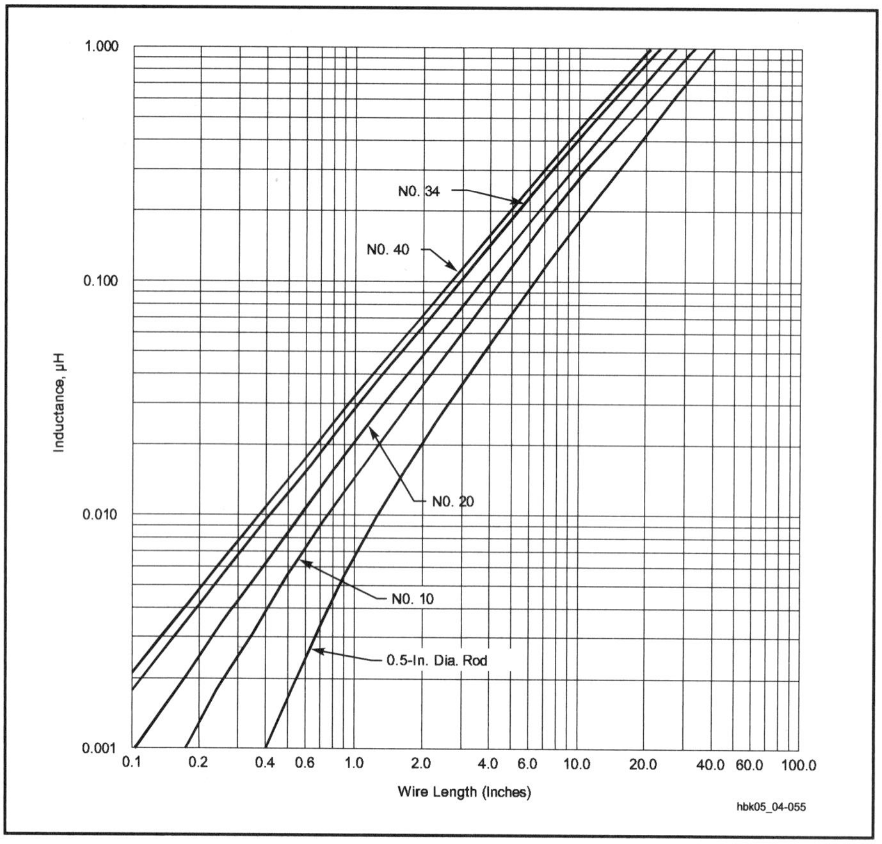

Figure 4.11 — Inductance of various conductor sizes as straight wires.

4.3.3 Straight-Wire Inductance

At low frequencies the inductance of a straight, round, nonmagnetic wire in free space is given by:

$$L = 0.00508\,b\left\{\left[\ln\left(\frac{2\,b}{a}\right)\right] - 0.75\right\}$$

where

L = inductance in µH,

a = wire radius in inches,

b = wire length in inches, and

ln = natural logarithm = 2.303 × common logarithm (base 10).

If the dimensions are expressed in millimeters instead of inches, the equation may still be used, except replace the 0.00508 value with 0.0002.

Skin effect reduces the inductance at VHF and above. As the frequency approaches infinity, the 0.75 constant within the brackets approaches unity. As a practical matter, skin effect will not reduce the inductance by more than a few percent.

Example: What is the inductance of a wire that is 0.1575 inch in diameter and 3.9370 inches long? For the calculations, a = 0.0787 inch (radius) and b = 3.9370 inch.

$$L = 0.00508\,b\left\{\left[\ln\left(\frac{2\,b}{a}\right)\right] - 0.75\right\}$$

$$= 0.00508\,(3.9370) \times \left\{\left[\ln\left(\frac{2 \times 3.9370}{0.0787}\right)\right] - 0.75\right\}$$

$$= 0.20 \times [\ln(100) - 0.75)]$$

$$= 0.20 \times (4.60 - 0.75)$$

$$= 0.20 \times 3.85 = 0.077\ \mu H$$

Figure 4.11 is a graph of the inductance for wires of various radii as a function of length.

A VHF or UHF tank circuit can be fabricated from a wire parallel to a ground plane, with one end grounded. A formula for the inductance of such an arrangement is given in **Figure 4.12**.

Example: What is the inductance of a wire 3.9370 inches long and 0.0787 inch in radius, suspended 1.5748 inch above a ground plane? (The inductance is measured between the free end and the ground plane, and the formula includes the inductance of the 1.5748-inch grounding link.) To demonstrate the use of the formula in Figure 4.12, begin by evaluating these quantities:

$$b + \sqrt{b^2 + a^2}$$

$$= 3.9370 + \sqrt{3.9370^2 + 0.0787^2}$$

$$= 3.9370 + 3.94 = 7.88$$

$$b + \sqrt{b^2 + 4\,(h^2)}$$

$$= 3.9370 + \sqrt{3.9370^2 + 4\,(1.5748^2)}$$

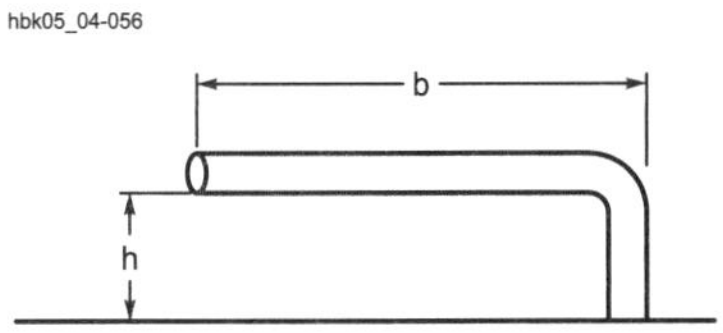

$$L = 0.0117b\left\{\mathrm{Log}_{10}\left[\frac{2h}{a}\left(\frac{b+\sqrt{b^2+a^2}}{b+\sqrt{b^2+4h^2}}\right)\right]\right\} + 0.00508\left(\sqrt{b^2+4h^2} - \sqrt{b^2+a^2} + \frac{b}{4} - 2h + a\right)$$

where

L = inductance in µH
a = wire radius in inches
b = wire length parallel to ground plane in inches
h = wire height above ground plane in inches

Figure 4.12 — Equation for determining the inductance of a wire parallel to a ground plane, with one end grounded. If the dimensions are in millimeters, the numerical coefficients become 0.0004605 for the first term and 0.0002 for the second term.

$$= 3.9370 + \sqrt{15.50 + 4\,(2.480)}$$

$$= 3.9370 + \sqrt{15.50 + 9.920}$$

$$= 3.9370 + 5.0418 = 8.9788$$

$$\frac{2\,h}{a} = \frac{2 \times 1.5748}{0.0787} = 40.0$$

$$\frac{b}{a} = \frac{3.9370}{4} = 0.098425$$

Substituting these values into the formula yields:

$$L = 0.0117 \times 3.9370\left\{\log_{10}\left[40.0 \times \left(\frac{7.88}{8.9788}\right)\right]\right\}$$

$$+ 0.00508 \times (5.0418 - 3.94 + 0.98425 - 3.1496 + 0.0787)$$

$$L = 0.0662\ \mu\mathrm{H}$$

Another conductor configuration that is frequently used is a flat strip over a ground plane. This arrangement has lower skin-effect loss at high frequencies than round wire because it has a higher surface-area to volume ratio. The inductance of such a strip can be found from the formula in **Figure 4.13**.

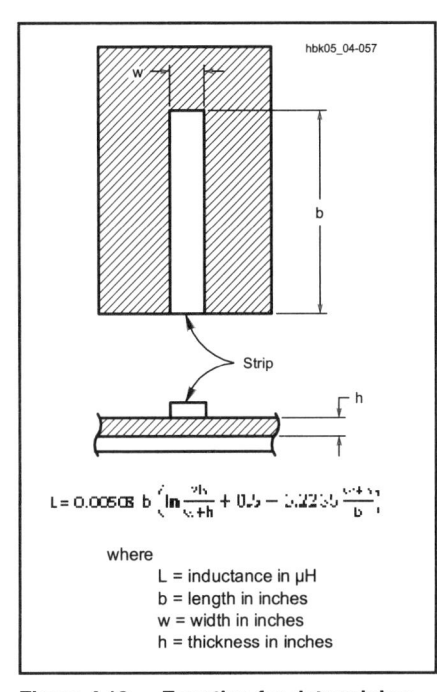

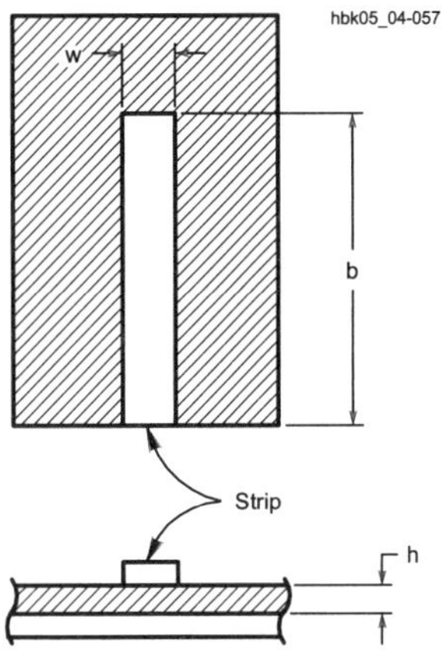

$$L = 0.00508\, b\left\{\ln\frac{2b}{w+h} + 0.5 - 0.2235\,\frac{w+h}{b}\right\}$$

where

L = inductance in µH
b = length in inches
w = width in inches
h = thickness in inches

Figure 4.13 — Equation for determining the inductance of a flat strip inductor.

4.3.4 Iron-Core Inductors

If the permeability of an iron core in an inductor is 800, then the inductance of any given air-wound inductor is increased 800 times by inserting the iron core. The inductance will be proportional to the magnetic flux through the inductor, other things being equal. The inductance of an iron-core inductor is highly dependent on the current flowing in the inductor, in contrast to an air-core inductor, where the inductance is independent of current because air does not saturate.

Iron-core inductors are used chiefly in power-supply equipment. They usually have direct current flowing through the winding, and any variation in inductance with current is usually undesirable. Inductance variations may be overcome by keeping the flux density below the saturation point of the iron. Opening the core so there is a small air gap will achieve this goal, as discussed in the earlier section on inductors. The reluctance or magnetic resistance introduced by such a gap is very large compared with that of the iron, even though the gap is only a small fraction of an inch. Therefore, the gap — rather than the iron — controls the flux density. Air gaps in iron cores reduce the inductance, but they hold the value practically constant regardless of the current magnitude.

When alternating current flows through an inductor wound on an iron core, a voltage is induced. Since iron is a conductor, eddy currents also flow in the core as discussed earlier. Eddy currents represent lost power because they flow through the resistance of the iron and generate heat. Losses caused by eddy currents can be reduced by laminating the core (cutting the core into thin strips). These strips or laminations are then insulated from each other by painting them with some insulating material such as varnish or shellac. Eddy current losses add to hysteresis losses, which are also significant in iron-core inductors.

Eddy-current and hysteresis losses in iron increase rapidly as the frequency of the alternating current increases. For this reason, ordinary iron cores can be used only at power-line and audio frequencies — up to approximately 15000 Hz. Even then, a very good grade of iron or steel is necessary for the core to perform well at the higher audio frequencies. Laminated iron cores become completely useless at radio frequencies because of eddy current and hysteresis losses.

4.3.5 Slug-Tuned Inductors

For RF work, the losses in iron cores can be reduced to a more useful level by grinding the iron into a powder and then mixing it with a binder of insulating material in such a way that the individual iron particles are insulated from each other. Using this approach, cores can be made that function satisfactorily even into the VHF range. Because a large part of the magnetic path is through a nonmagnetic material (the binder), the permeability of the powdered iron core is low compared with the values for solid iron cores used at power-line frequencies.

The slug is usually shaped in the form of a cylinder that fits inside the insulating form on which the inductor is wound. Despite the fact that the major portion of the magnetic path for the flux is in air, the slug is quite effective in increasing the inductor inductance. By pushing (or screwing) the slug in and out of the inductor, the inductance can be varied over a considerable range.

4.3.6 Powdered-Iron Toroidal Inductors

For fixed-value inductors intended for use at HF and VHF, the powdered-iron toroidal core has become the standard in low- and medium-power circuits. **Figure 4.14** shows the general outlines of a toroidal inductor on a magnetic core.

Manufacturers offer a wide variety of core materials, or *mixes*, to create conductor cores that will perform over a desired frequency range with a reasonable permeability. Permeabilities for powdered-iron cores fall in the range of 3 to 35 for various mixes. In addition, core sizes are available in the range of 0.125-inch outside diameter (OD) up to 1.06-inch OD, with larger sizes to 5-inch OD available in certain mixes. The range of sizes permits the builder to construct single-layer inductors for almost any value using wire sized to meet the circuit current demands.

The use of powdered iron in a binder reduces core losses usually associated with iron, while the permeability of the core permits a reduction in the wire length and associated resistance in forming an inductor of a given inductance. Therefore, powdered-iron-core toroidal inductors can achieve Q well above 100, often approaching or exceeding 200 within the frequency range specified for a given core. Moreover, these inductors are considered *self-shielding* since most of the magnetic flux is within the core, a fact that simplifies circuit design and construction.

Each powdered-iron core has an *inductance factor* or *index* A_L determined by the manufacturer. (See the **Component Data and References** chapter.) Amidon specifies A_L in μH per 100 turns-squared and other manufacturers specify A_L in μH or nH per turns-squared. Check the manufacturer's website or product information for the correct units for A_L and method of calculating the inductance or desired number of turns.

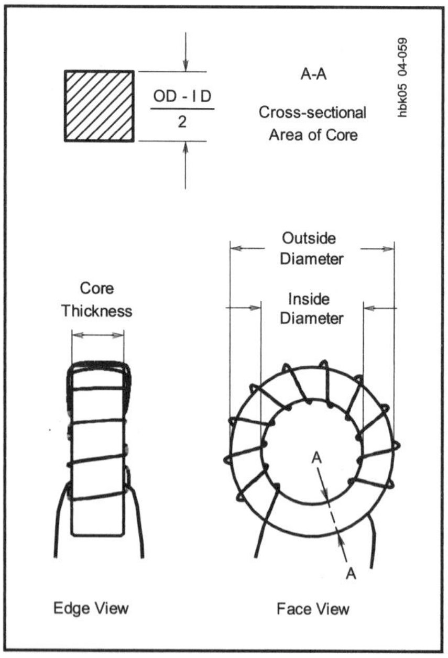

Figure 4.14 — A typical toroidal inductor wound on a powdered-iron or ferrite core. Some key physical dimensions are noted. Equally important are the core material, its permeability, its intended range of operating frequencies, and its A_L value. This is an 11-turn toroid.

$$L = \frac{A_L \times N^2}{10000} \text{ (Amidon) or}$$

$$L = A_L \times N^2 \text{ (Other manufacturers)}$$

where
L = the inductance in μH,
A_L = the inductance index (see text above)
N = the number of turns.

The builder must then ensure that the core is capable of holding the calculated number of turns of wire of the required wire size. See the **Component Data and References** chapter for more detailed data on the range of available cores.

Example: What is the inductance of a 60-turn inductor on a core with an A_L of 55 μH/100-turns²?

$$L = \frac{A_L \times N^2}{10000} = \frac{55 \times 60^2}{10000}$$

$$= \frac{198000}{10000} = 19.8 \ \mu H$$

Example: What is the inductance of a 20-turn inductor on a core with an A_L of 0.3 μH/turns²?

$$L = A_L \times N^2 = 0.3 \times 20^2$$
$$= 0.3 \times 400 = 120 \ \mu H$$

To calculate the number of turns needed for a particular inductance, use the formula:

$$N = 100\sqrt{\frac{L}{A_L}} \text{ (Amidon) or}$$

$$N = \sqrt{\frac{L}{A_L}} \text{ (Other manufacturers)}$$

Example: How many turns are needed for a 12.0-μH inductor if the A_L for the selected core is 49 μH/100-turns²?

$$N = 100\sqrt{\frac{L}{A_L}} = 100\sqrt{\frac{12.0}{49}}$$

$$= 100\sqrt{0.245} = 100 \times 0.495 = 49.5 \text{ turns}$$

Example: How many turns are needed for a 300-nH inductor if the A_L for the selected core is 12 nH/turns²?

$$N = \sqrt{\frac{L}{A_L}} = \sqrt{\frac{300}{12}} = \sqrt{25} = 5 \text{ turns}$$

Count turns by each pass of the wire through the center of the core. (*A straight wire through a toroidal core counts as a one-turn inductor.*) Fine adjustment of the inductance may be possible by spreading or compressing inductor turns.

If the value is critical, experiment by starting with an extra turn or two, then measure the inductance or test the circuit. Core characteristics may vary slightly from batch to batch and winding style has a small effect on inductance, as well.

The power-handling ability of toroidal cores depends on many variables, which include the cross-sectional area through the core, the core material, the numbers of turns in the inductor, the applied voltage and the operating frequency. Although powdered-iron cores can withstand dc flux densities up to 5000 gauss without saturating, ac flux densities from sine waves above certain limits can overheat cores. Manufacturers provide guideline limits for ac flux densities to avoid overheating. The limits range from 150 gauss at 1 MHz to 30 gauss at 28 MHz, although the curve is not linear. To calculate the maximum anticipated flux density for a particular inductor, use the formula:

$$B_{max} = \frac{E_{RMS} \times 10^8}{4.44 \times A_e \times N \times f}$$

where
B_{max} = the maximum flux density in gauss,
E_{RMS} = the voltage across the inductor,
A_e = the cross-sectional area of the core in square centimeters,
N = the number of turns in the inductor, and
f = the operating frequency in Hz.

Example: What is the maximum ac flux density for an inductor of 15 turns if the frequency is 7.0 MHz, the RMS voltage is 25 V and the cross-sectional area of the core is 0.133 cm²?

$$B_{max} = \frac{E_{RMS} \times 10^8}{4.44 \times A_e \times N \times f}$$

$$= \frac{25 \times 10^8}{4.44 \times 0.133 \times 15 \times 7.0 \times 10^6}$$

$$= \frac{25 \times 10^8}{62 \times 10^6} = 40 \text{ gauss}$$

Since the recommended limit for cores operated at 7 MHz is 57 gauss, this inductor is well within guidelines.

4.3.7 Ferrite Toroidal Inductors

Although nearly identical in general appearance to powdered-iron cores, ferrite cores differ in a number of important characteristics. Composed of nickel-zinc ferrites for lower permeability ranges and of manganese-zinc ferrites for higher permeabilities, these cores span a permeability range from 20 to above 10000. Nickel-zinc cores with permeabilities from 20 to 800 are useful in high-Q applications, but function more commonly in amateur applications as RF chokes. They are also useful in wide-band transformers, discussed in the chapter **RF Techniques**.

Ferrite cores are often unpainted, unlike powdered-iron toroids. Ferrite toroids and rods often have sharp edges, while powdered-iron toroids usually have rounded edges.

Because of their higher permeabilities, the A_L values for ferrite cores are higher than for powdered-iron cores. Amidon Corp. is the most common supplier of cores for amateurs (see the **Component Data and References** chapter) and specifies A_L in mH per 1000 turns-squared. Other manufacturers specify A_L in nH per turns-squared.

To calculate the inductance of a ferrite toroidal inductor when the number of turns and the core material are known:

$$L = \frac{A_L \times N^2}{1000000} \quad \text{(Amidon)}$$

where

L = the inductance in mH,

A_L = the inductance index in mH per 1000 turns-squared, and

N = the number of turns.

$$L = A_L \times N^2 \quad \text{(Other manufacturers)}$$

where

L = the inductance in nH,

A_L = the inductance index in nH per turns-squared, and

N = the number of turns.

Calculations are performed similarly to the examples given for powdered-iron cores in the previous section. The builder must then ensure that the core is capable of holding the calculated number of turns of wire of the required wire size.

For inductors carrying both dc and ac currents, the upper saturation limit for most ferrites is a flux density of 2000 gauss, with power calculations identical to those used for powdered- iron cores. More detailed information is available on specific cores and manufacturers in the **Component Data and References** chapter.

4.4 Transformers

When the ac source current flows through every turn of an inductor, the generation of a counter-voltage and the storage of energy during each half cycle is said to be by virtue of self-inductance. If another inductor — not connected to the source of the original current — is positioned so the magnetic field of the first inductor intercepts the turns of the second inductor, coupling the two inductors and creating mutual inductance as described earlier, a voltage will be induced and current will flow in the second inductor. A load such as a resistor may be connected across the second inductor to consume the energy transferred magnetically from the first inductor.

Figure 4.15 illustrates a pair of coupled inductors, showing an ac energy source connected to one, called the *primary inductor*, and a load connected to the other, called the *secondary inductor*. If the inductors are wound tightly on a magnetic core so that nearly all magnetic flux from the first inductor intersects with the turns of the second inductor, the pair is said to be *tightly coupled*. Inductors not sharing a common core and separated by a distance would be *loosely coupled*.

The signal source for the primary inductor may be household ac power lines, audio, or other waveforms at low frequencies, or RF currents. The load may be a device needing power, a speaker converting electrical energy into sonic energy, an antenna using RF energy for communications or a particular circuit set up to process a signal from a preceding circuit. The uses of magnetically coupled energy in electronics are innumerable.

Mutual inductance (M) between inductors is measured in henrys. Two inductors have a mutual inductance of 1 H under the following conditions: as the primary inductor current changes at a rate of 1 A/s, the voltage across the secondary inductor is 1 V. The level of mutual inductance varies with many factors: the size and shape of the inductors, their relative positions and distance from each other, and the permeability of the inductor core material and of the space between them.

If the self-inductance values of two inductors are known (self-inductance is used in this section to distinguish it from the mutual inductance), it is possible to derive the mutual inductance by way of a simple experiment schematically represented in **Figure 4.16**.

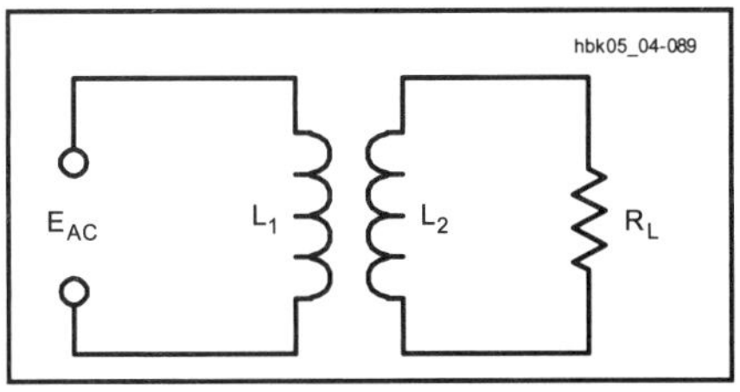

Figure 4.15 — A basic transformer: two inductors — one connected to an ac energy source, the other to a load — with coupled magnetic fields.

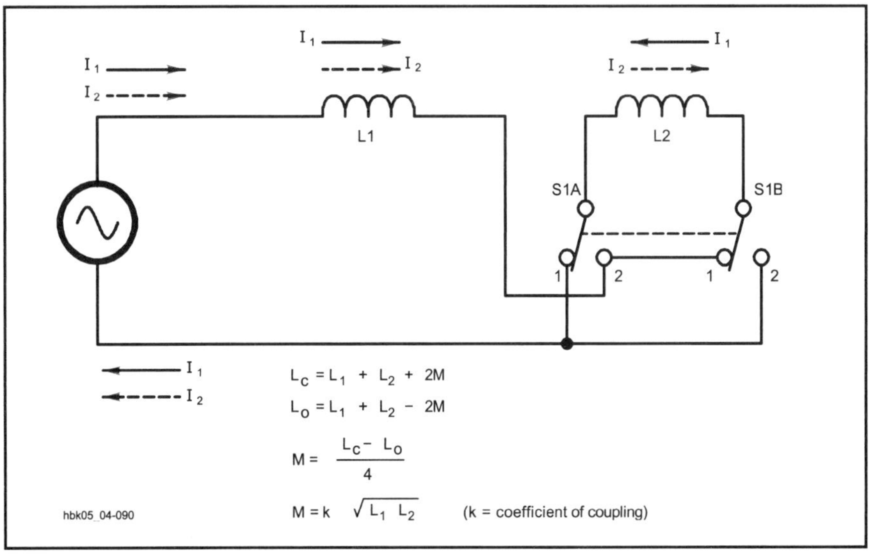

Figure 4.16 — An experimental setup for determining mutual inductance. Measure the inductance with the switch in each position and use the formula in the text to determine the mutual inductance.

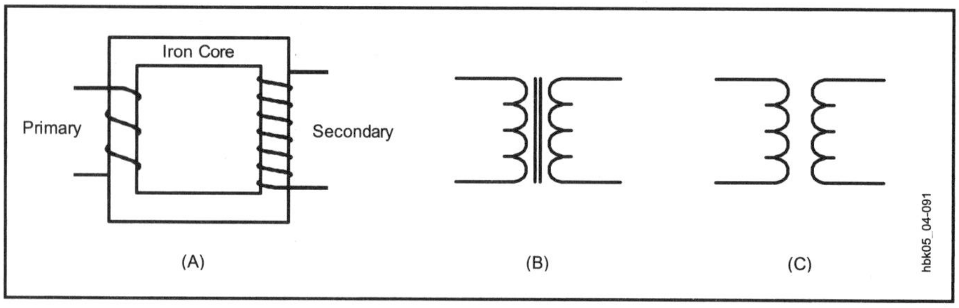

Figure 4.17 — A transformer. A is a pictorial diagram. Power is transferred from the primary coil to the secondary by means of the magnetic field. B is a schematic diagram of an iron-core transformer, and C is an air-core transformer.

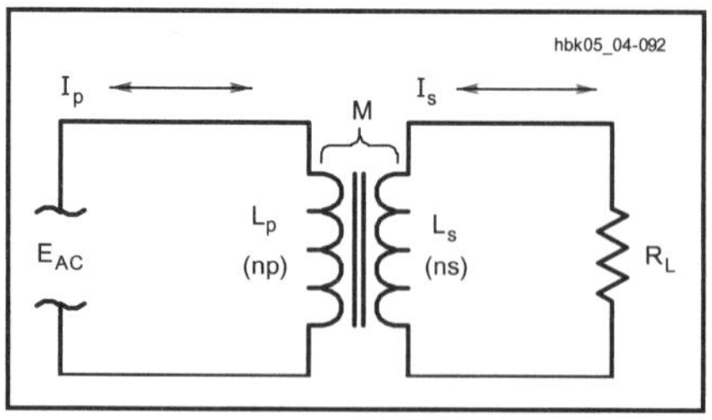

Figure 4.18 — The conditions for transformer action: two coils that exhibit mutual inductance, an ac power source, and a load. The magnetic field set up by the energy in the primary circuit transfers energy to the secondary for use by the load, resulting in a secondary voltage and current.

Without altering the physical setting or position of two inductors, measure the total coupled inductance, L_C, of the series-connected inductors with their windings complementing each other and again with their windings opposing each other. Since, for the two inductors, $L_C = L1 + L2 + 2M$, in the complementary case, and $L_O = L1 + L2 - 2M$ for the opposing case,

$$M = \frac{L_C - L_O}{4}$$

The ratio of magnetic flux set up by the secondary inductor to the flux set up by the primary inductor is a measure of the extent to which two inductors are coupled, compared to the maximum possible coupling between them. This ratio is the *coefficient of coupling* (k) and is always less than 1. If k were to equal 1, the two inductors would have the maximum possible mutual coupling. Thus:

$$M = k\sqrt{L1\,L2}$$

where

M = mutual inductance in henrys,

L1 and L2 = individual coupled inductors, each in henrys, and

k = the coefficient of coupling.

Using the experiment above, it is possible to solve for k with reasonable accuracy.

Any two inductors having mutual inductance comprise a *transformer* having a *primary winding* or inductor and a *secondary winding* or inductor. The word "winding" is generally dropped so that transformers are said to have "primaries" and "secondaries." **Figure 4.17** provides a pictorial representation of a typical iron-core transformer, along with the schematic symbols for both iron-core and air-core transformers. Conventionally, the term *transformer* is most commonly applied to coupled inductors having a magnetic core material, while coupled air-wound inductors are not called by that name. They are still transformers, however.

We normally think of transformers as ac devices, since mutual inductance only occurs when magnetic fields are changing. A transformer connected to a dc source will exhibit mutual inductance only at the instants of closing and opening the primary circuit, or on the rising and falling edges of dc pulses, because only then does the primary winding have a changing field. There are three principle uses of transformers: to physically isolate the primary circuit from the secondary circuit, to transform voltages and currents from one level to another, and to transform circuit impedances from one level to another. These functions are not mutually exclusive and have many variations.

4.4.1 Basic Transformer Principles

The primary and secondary windings of a transformer may be wound on a core of magnetic material. The permeability of the magnetic material increases the inductance of the windings so a relatively small number of turns may be used to induce a given voltage value with a small current. A closed core having a continuous magnetic path, such as that shown in Figure 4.17, also tends to ensure that practically all of the field set up by the current in the primary winding will intercept or "cut" the turns of the secondary winding.

For power transformers and impedance-matching transformers used at audio frequencies, cores made of soft iron strips or sheets called *laminations* are most common and generally very efficient. At higher frequencies, ferrite or powdered-iron cores are more frequently used. This section deals with basic transformer operation at audio and power frequencies. RF transformer operation is discussed in the chapter on **RF Techniques**.

The following principles presume a coefficient of coupling (k) of 1, that is, a perfect transformer. The value k = 1 indicates that all the turns of both windings link with all the magnetic flux lines, so that the voltage induced per turn is the same with both windings. This condition makes the induced voltage independent of the inductance of the primary and secondary inductors. Iron-core transformers for low frequencies closely approach this ideal condition. **Figure 4.18** illustrates the conditions for transformer action.

VOLTAGE RATIO

For a given varying magnetic field, the voltage induced in an inductor within the field is proportional to the number of turns in the inductor. When the two windings of a transformer are in the same field (which is the case when both are wound on the same closed core), it follows that the induced voltages will be proportional to the number of turns in each winding. In the primary, the induced voltage practically equals, and opposes, the applied voltage, as described earlier. Hence:

$$E_S = E_P\left(\frac{N_S}{N_P}\right)$$

where

E_S = secondary voltage,

E_P = primary applied voltage,

N_S = number of turns on secondary, and

N_P = number of turns on primary.

Example: A transformer has a primary with 400 turns and a secondary with 2800 turns, and a voltage of 120 V is applied to the primary. What voltage appears across the secondary winding?

$$E_S = 120\text{ V}\left(\frac{2800}{400}\right) = 120\text{ V} \times 7 = 840\text{ V}$$

(Notice that the number of turns is taken as a known value rather than a measured quantity, so they do not limit the significant figures in the calculation.) Also, if 840 V is applied to the 2800-turn winding (which then becomes the primary), the output voltage from the 400-turn winding will be 120 V.

Either winding of a transformer can be used as the primary, provided the winding has enough turns (enough inductance) to induce a voltage equal to the applied voltage without requiring an excessive current. The windings must also have insulation with a voltage rating sufficient for the voltages applied or created. Transformers are called *step-up* or *step-down* transformers depending on whether the secondary voltage is higher or lower than the primary voltage, respectively.

CURRENT OR AMPERE-TURNS RATIO

The current in the primary when no current is taken from the secondary is called the *magnetizing current* of the transformer. An ideal transformer, with no internal losses, would consume no power, since the current through the primary inductor would be 90° out of phase with the voltage. In any properly designed transformer, the power consumed by the transformer when the secondary is open (not delivering power) is only the amount necessary to overcome the losses in the iron core and in the resistance of the wire with which the primary is wound.

When power is transferred from the secondary winding to a load, the secondary current creates a magnetic field that opposes the field established by the primary current. For the induced voltage in the primary to equal the applied voltage, the original magnetizing field must be maintained. Therefore, enough additional current must flow in the primary to create a field exactly equal and opposite to the field set up by the secondary current, leaving the original magnetizing field.

In practical transformer calculations it may be assumed that the entire primary current is caused by the secondary load. This is justifiable because the magnetizing current should be very small in comparison with the primary load current at rated power output.

If the magnetic fields set up by the primary and secondary currents are to be equal, the number of ampere-turns must be equal in each winding. (See the previous discussion of magnetic fields and magnetic flux density.) Thus, primary current multiplied by the primary turns must equal the secondary current multiplied by the secondary turns.

$$I_P N_P = I_S N_S$$

and

$$I_P = I_S \left(\frac{N_S}{N_P} \right)$$

where

I_P = primary current,

I_S = secondary current,

N_P = number of turns in the primary winding, and

N_S = number of turns in the secondary winding.

Example: Suppose the secondary of the transformer in the previous example is delivering a current of 0.20 A to a load. What will be the primary current?

$$I_P = 0.20 \text{ A} \left(\frac{2800}{400} \right) = 0.20 \text{ A} \times 7 = 1.4 \text{ A}$$

Although the secondary voltage is higher than the primary voltage, the secondary current is lower than the primary current, and by the same ratio. The secondary current in an ideal transformer is 180° out of phase with the primary current, since the field in the secondary just offsets the field in the primary. The phase relationship between the currents in the windings holds true no matter what the phase difference between the current and the voltage of the secondary. In fact, the phase difference, if any, between voltage and current in the secondary winding will be *reflected* back to the primary as an identical phase difference.

POWER RATIO

A transformer cannot create power; it can only transfer it and change the voltage and current ratios. Hence, the power taken from the secondary cannot exceed that taken by the primary from the applied voltage source. There is always some power loss in the resistance of the windings and in the iron core, so in all practical cases the power taken from the source will exceed that taken from the secondary.

$$P_O = \eta \, P_I$$

where

P_O = power output from secondary,

P_I = power input to primary, and

η = efficiency.

The efficiency, η, is always less than 1 and is commonly expressed as a percentage: if η is 0.65, for instance, the efficiency is 65%.

Example: A transformer has an efficiency of 85.0% at its full-load output of 150 W. What is the power input to the primary at full secondary load?

$$P_I = \frac{P_O}{\eta} = \frac{150 \text{ W}}{0.850} = 176 \text{ W}$$

A transformer is usually designed to have the highest efficiency at the power output for which it is rated. The efficiency decreases with either lower or higher outputs. On the other hand, the losses in the transformer are relatively small at low output but increase as more power is taken. The amount of power that the transformer can handle is determined by its own losses, because these losses heat the wire and core. There is a limit to the temperature rise that can be tolerated, because too high a temperature can either melt the wire or cause the insulation to break down. A transformer can be operated at reduced output, even though the efficiency is low, because the actual loss will be low under such conditions. The full-load efficiency of small power transformers such as are used in radio receivers and transmitters usually lies between about 60 and 90%, depending on the size and design.

IMPEDANCE RATIO

In an ideal transformer — one without losses or leakage inductance (see Transformer Losses) — the primary power, $P_P = E_P I_P$, and secondary power, $P_S = E_S I_S$, are equal. The relationships between primary and secondary voltage and current are also known. Since impedance is the ratio of voltage to current, Z = E/I, the impedances represented in each winding are related as follows:

$$Z_P = Z_S \left(\frac{N_P}{N_S} \right)^2$$

where

Z_P = impedance at the primary terminals from the power source,

Z_S = impedance of load connected to secondary, and

N_P/N_S = turns ratio, primary to secondary.

The transformer is converting input power at one ratio of voltage to current (i.e. impedance) to output power at a different ratio of voltage to current (i.e. a different impedance).

A load of any given impedance connected to the transformer secondary will thus be transformed to a different value at the primary terminals. The impedance transformation is proportional to the square of the primary-to-secondary turns ratio. (Take care to use the primary-to-secondary turns ratio, since the secondary-to-primary ratio is more commonly used to determine the voltage transformation ratio.)

The term *looking into* is often used to mean the conditions observed from an external perspective at the terminals specified. For example, "impedance looking into" the transformer primary means the impedance measured externally to the transformer at the terminals of the primary winding.

Example: A transformer has a primary-to-secondary turns ratio of 0.6 (the primary has six-tenths as many turns as the secondary) and a load of 3000 Ω is connected to the secondary. What is the impedance looking into the primary of the transformer?

$$Z_P = 3000 \, \Omega \times (0.6)^2 = 3000 \, \Omega \times 0.36$$

$$Z_P = 1080 \, \Omega$$

By choosing the proper turns ratio, the impedance of a fixed load can be transformed to any desired value, within practical limits.

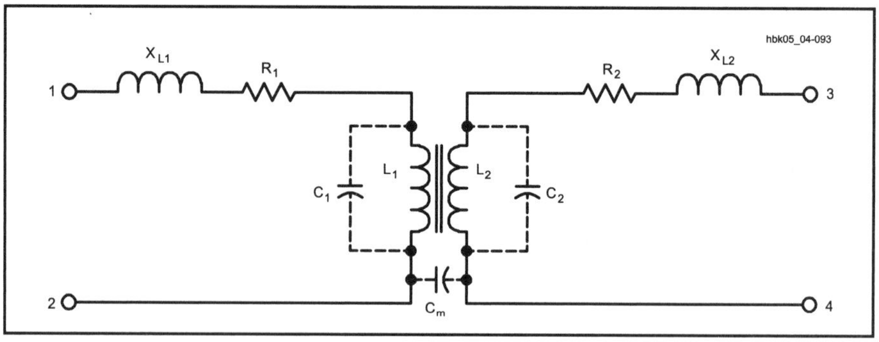

Figure 4.19 — A transformer as a network of resistances, inductances and capacitances. Only L1 and L2 contribute to the transfer of energy.

If transformer losses can be neglected, the transformed (reflected) impedance has the same phase angle as the actual load impedance. Thus, if the load is a pure resistance, the load presented by the primary to the power source will also be a pure resistance. If the load impedance is complex, that is, if the load current and voltage are out of phase with each other, then the primary voltage and current will have the same phase angle.

Many devices or circuits require a specific value of load resistance (or impedance) for optimum operation. The impedance of the actual load that is to dissipate the power may be quite different from the impedance of the source device or circuit, so an *impedance-matching transformer* is used to change the actual load into an impedance of the desired value. The turns ratio required is:

$$\frac{N_P}{N_S} = \sqrt{\frac{Z_P}{Z_S}}$$

where

N_P / N_S = required turns ratio, primary to secondary,

Z_P = primary impedance required, and

Z_S = impedance of load connected to secondary.

Example: A transistor audio amplifier requires a load of 150 Ω for optimum performance, and is to be connected to a loudspeaker having an impedance of 4.0 Ω. What primary-to-secondary turns ratio is required in the coupling transformer?

$$\frac{N_P}{N_S} = \sqrt{\frac{Z_P}{Z_S}} = \sqrt{\frac{150\,\Omega}{4.0\,\Omega}} = \sqrt{38} = 6.2$$

The primary therefore must have 6.2 times as many turns as the secondary.

These relationships may be used in practical circuits even though they are based on an ideal transformer. Aside from the normal design requirements of reasonably low internal losses and low leakage reactance, the only other requirement is that the primary has enough inductance to operate with low magnetizing current at the voltage applied to the primary.

The primary terminal impedance of an iron-core transformer is determined wholly by the load connected to the secondary and by the turns ratio. If the characteristics of the transformer have an appreciable effect on the impedance presented to the power source, the transformer is either poorly designed or is not suited to the voltage and frequency at which it is being used. Most transformers will operate quite well at voltages from slightly above to well below the design figure.

TRANSFORMER LOSSES

In practice, none of the formulas given so far provides truly exact results, although they afford reasonable approximations. Transformers in reality are not simply two coupled inductors, but a network of resistances and reactances, most of which appear in **Figure 4.19**. Since only the terminals numbered 1 through 4 are accessible to the user, transformer ratings and specifications take into account the additional losses created by these complexities.

In a practical transformer not all of the magnetic flux is common to both windings, although in well-designed transformers the amount of flux that cuts one winding and not the other is only a small percentage of the total flux. This *leakage flux* causes a voltage by self-induction in the winding creating the flux. The effect is the same as if a small *leakage inductance* existed independently of the main windings. Leakage inductance acts in exactly the same way as inductance inserted in series with the winding. It has, therefore, a certain reactance, depending on the amount of leakage inductance and the frequency. This reactance is called *leakage reactance* and is shown as X_{L1} and X_{L2} in Figure 4.19.

Current flowing through the leakage reactance causes a voltage drop. This voltage drop increases with increasing current (or frequency); hence, it increases as more power is taken from the secondary. The resistances of the transformer windings, R1 and R2, also cause voltage drops when there is current. Although these voltage drops are not in phase with those caused by leakage reactance, together they result in a lower secondary voltage under load than is indicated by the transformer turns ratio. Thus, in a practical transformer, the greater the secondary current, the smaller the secondary terminal voltage becomes.

At ac line frequencies (50 or 60 Hz), the voltage at the secondary, with a reasonably well-designed iron-core transformer, should not drop more than about 10% from open-circuit conditions to full load. The voltage drop may be considerably more than this in a transformer operating at audio frequencies, because the leakage reactance increases with frequency.

In addition to wire resistances and leakage reactances, certain unwanted or "stray" capacitances occur in transformers. The wire forming the separate turns of the windings acts as the plates of a small capacitor, creating a capacitance between turns and between the windings. This *distributed capacitance* appears in Figure 4.19 as C1, C2, and C_M. More-over, transformer windings can exhibit capacitance relative to nearby metal, for example, the chassis, the shield and even the core. When current flows through a winding, each turn has a slightly different voltage than its adjacent turns. This voltage causes a small current to flow in these *interwinding* and *winding-to-winding capacitances.*

Although stray capacitances are of little concern with power and audio transformers, they become important as the frequency increases. In transformers for RF use, the stray capacitance can resonate with either the leakage reactance or, at lower frequencies, with the winding reactances, L1 or L2, especially under very light or zero loads. In the frequency region around resonance, transformers no longer exhibit the properties formulated above or the impedance properties to be described below.

Iron-core transformers also experience losses within the core itself. *Hysteresis losses* include the energy required to overcome the retentivity of the core's magnetic material. Circulating currents through the core's resistance are *eddy currents*, which form part of the total core losses. These losses, which add to the required magnetizing current, are equivalent to adding a resistance in parallel with L1 in Figure 4.19.

CORE CONSTRUCTION

Audio and power transformers usually employ silicon steel as the core material. With permeabilities of 5000 or greater, these cores saturate at flux densities approaching 10^5 (Mx) per square inch of cross section. The cores consist of thin insulated laminations to

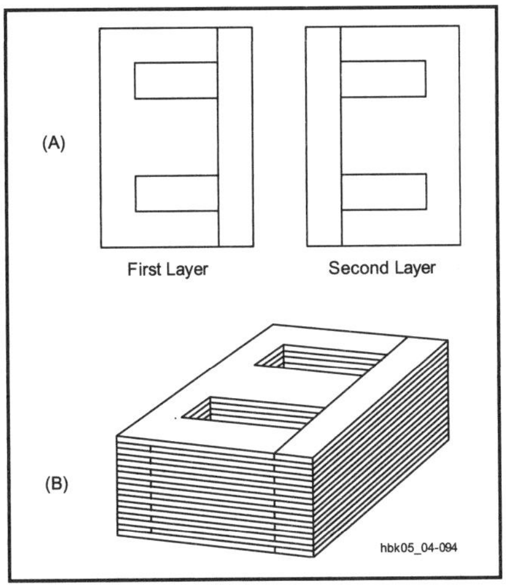

Figure 4.20 — A typical transformer iron core. The E and I pieces alternate direction in successive layers to improve the magnetic path while attenuating eddy currents in the core.

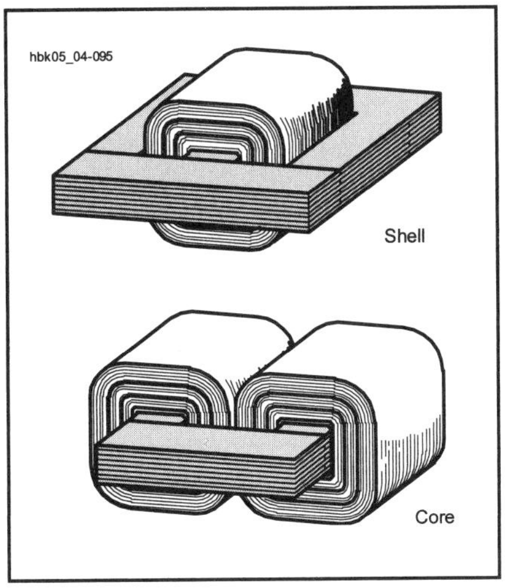

Figure 4.21 — Two common transformer constructions: shell and core.

break up potential eddy current paths.

Each core layer consists of an "E" and an "I" piece butted together, as represented in **Figure 4.20**. The butt point leaves a small gap. Each layer is reversed from the adjacent layers so that each gap is next to a continuous magnetic path so that the effect of the gaps is minimized. This is different from an air-gapped inductor in which the air gap is maintained for all layers of laminations.

Two core shapes are in common use, as shown in **Figure 4.21**. In the shell type, both windings are placed on the inner leg, while in the core type the primary and secondary windings may be placed on separate legs, if desired. This is sometimes done when it is necessary to minimize capacitance between

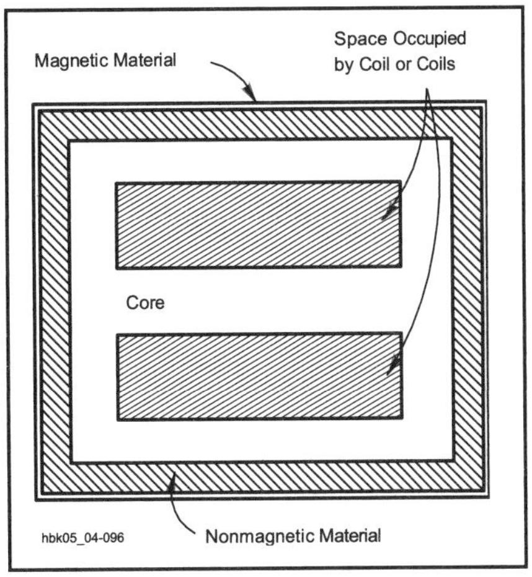

Figure 4.22 — A shielded transformer cross-section: the core plus an outer shield of magnetic material contain nearly all of the magnetic field.

the primary and secondary, or when one of the windings must operate at very high voltage.

The number of turns required in the primary for a given applied voltage is determined by the size, shape and type of core material used, as well as the frequency. The number of turns required is inversely proportional to the cross-sectional area of the core. As a rough indication, windings of small power transformers frequently have about six to eight turns per volt on a core of 1-square-inch cross section and have a magnetic path 10 or 12 inches in length. A longer path or smaller cross section requires more turns per volt, and vice versa.

In most transformers the windings are wound in layers, with a thin sheet of treated-paper insulation between each layer. Thicker insulation is used between adjacent windings and between the first winding and the core.

SHIELDING

Because magnetic lines of force are continuous loops, shielding requires a complete path for the lines of force of the leakage flux. The high-permeability of iron cores tends to concentrate the field, but additional shielding is often needed. As depicted in **Figure 4.22**, enclosing the transformer in a good magnetic material can restrict virtually all of the magnetic field in the outer case. The nonmagnetic material between the case and the core creates a region of high reluctance, attenuating the field before it reaches the case.

4.4.2 Autotransformers

The transformer principle can be used with only one winding instead of two, as shown in **Figure 4.23A**. The principles that relate voltage, current and impedance to the turns ratio also apply equally well. A one-winding trans-

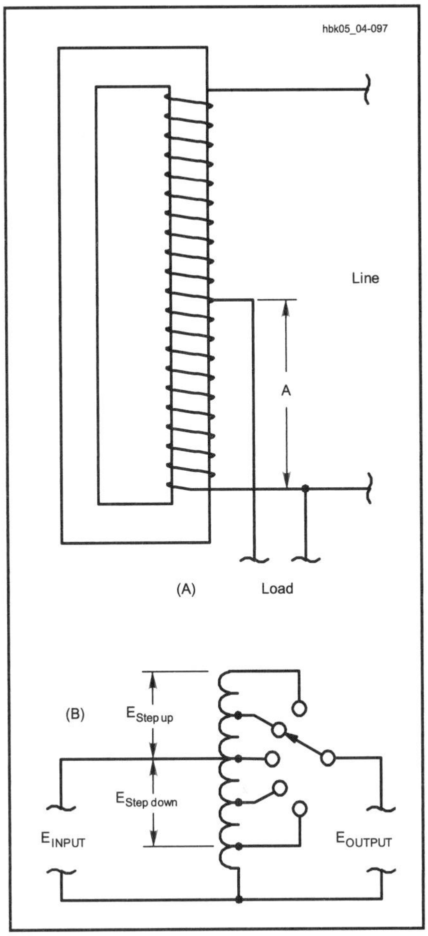

Figure 4.23 — The autotransformer is based on the transformer, but uses only one winding. The pictorial diagram at A shows the typical construction of an autotransformer. The schematic diagram at B demonstrates the use of an autotransformer to step up or step down ac voltage, usually to compensate for excessive or deficient line voltage.

former is called an *autotransformer*. The current in the common section (A) of the winding is the difference between the line (primary) and the load (secondary) currents, since these currents are out of phase. Hence, if the line and load currents are nearly equal, the common section of the winding may be wound with comparatively small wire. The line and load currents will be equal only when the primary (line) and secondary (load) voltages are not very different.

Autotransformers are used chiefly for boosting or reducing the power-line voltage by relatively small amounts. Figure 4.23B illustrates the principle schematically with a switched, stepped autotransformer. Continuously variable autotransformers are commercially available under a variety of trade names; Variac and Powerstat are typical examples.

Technically, tapped air-core inductors,

such as the one in the network in Figure 3.48 at the close of the discussion of resonant circuits in the chapter on **Radio Fundamentals**, are also autotransformers. The voltage from the tap to the bottom of the winding is less than the voltage across the entire winding. Likewise, the impedance of the tapped part of the winding is less than the impedance of the entire winding. Because in this case, leakage reactances are great and the coefficient of coupling is quite low, the relationships that are true in a perfect transformer grow quite unreliable in predicting the exact values. For this reason, tapped inductors are rarely referred to as transformers. The stepped-down situation in Figure 3.48 is better approximated — at or close to resonance — by the formula

$$R_P = \frac{R_L \, X_{COM}^2}{X_L}$$

where

R_P = tuned-circuit parallel-resonant impedance,

R_L = load resistance tapped across part of the winding,

X_{COM} = reactance of the portion of the winding common to both the resonant circuit and the load tap, and

X_L = reactance of the entire winding.

The result is approximate and applies only to circuits with a Q of 10 or greater.

4.5 Practical Semiconductors

There are several different kinds of components that can be used to build circuits for analog signal processing. Bipolar semiconductors, field-effect semiconductors and integrated circuits comprise a wide spectrum of active devices used in analog signal processing. (Vacuum tubes are discussed in the chapter on **RF Power Amplifiers**, their primary application in Amateur Radio.) Several different devices can perform the same function, each with its own advantages and disadvantages based on the physical characteristics of each type of device.

Understanding the specific characteristics of each device allows you to make educated decisions about which device would be best for a particular purpose when designing analog circuitry, or understanding why an existing circuit was designed in a particular way.

4.5.1 Device Characteristics

CHARACTERISTIC CURVES

Analog devices are described most completely with their *characteristic curves*. The characteristic curve is a plot of the interrelationships between two or three variables. The vertical (y) axis parameter is the output, or result of the device being operated with an input parameter on the horizontal (x) axis. Often the output is the result of two input values. The first input parameter is represented along the X-axis and the second input parameter by several curves, each for a different value.

Almost all devices of concern are nonlinear over a wide range of operating parameters. We are often interested in using a device only in the region that approximates a linear response. Characteristic curves are used to graphically describe a device's operation in both its linear and nonlinear regions.

Figure 4.24A shows the characteristic curve for a semiconductor diode with the Y-axis showing the forward current, I_F, flowing through the diode and the X-axis showing forward voltage, V_F, across the diode. This curve shows the relationship between current and voltage in the diode when it is conducting current. Characteristic curves showing voltage and current in two-terminal devices such as diodes are often called *I-V curves*. Characteristic curves may include all four quadrants of operation in which both axes include positive and negative values. It is also common for different scales to be used in the different quadrants, so inspect the legend for the curves carefully.

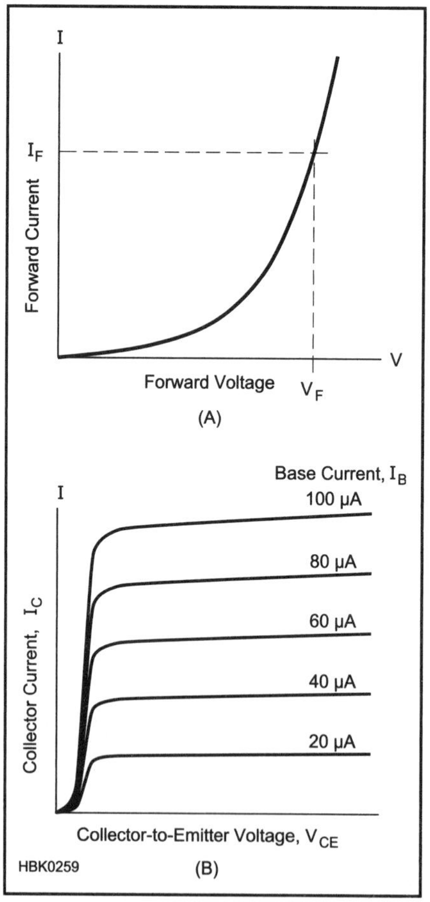

Figure 4.24 — Characteristic curves. A forward voltage vs forward current characteristic curve for a semiconductor diode is shown at (A). (B) shows a set of characteristic curves for a bipolar transistor in which the collector current vs collector-to-emitter voltage curve is plotted for five different values of base current.

The parameters plotted in a characteristic curve depend on how the device will be used so that the applicable design values can be obtained from the characteristic curve. The slope of the curve is often important because it relates changes in output to changes in input. To determine the slope of the curve, two closely-spaced points along that portion of the curve are selected, each defined by its location along the x and y axes. If the two points are defined by (x_1,y_1) and (x_2,y_2), the slope, m, of the curve (which can be a gain, a resistance or a conductance, for example) is calculated as:

$$m = \frac{\Delta y}{\Delta x} = \frac{y_1 - y_2}{x_1 - x_2}$$

It is important to pick points that are close together or the slope will not reflect the actual behavior of the device. A device whose characteristic curve is not a straight line will not have a linear response to inputs because the slope changes with the value of the input parameter.

For a device in which three parameters interact, such as a transistor, sets of characteristic curves can be drawn. Figure 4.24B shows a set of characteristic curves for a bipolar transistor where collector current, I_C, is shown on the y axis and collector-to-emitter voltage, V_{CE}, is shown on the x axis. Because the amount of collector current also depends on base current, I_B, the curve is repeated several times for different values of I_B. From this set of curves, an amplifier circuit using this transistor can be designed to have specific values of gain.

BIASING

The operation of an analog signal-processing device is greatly affected by which portion

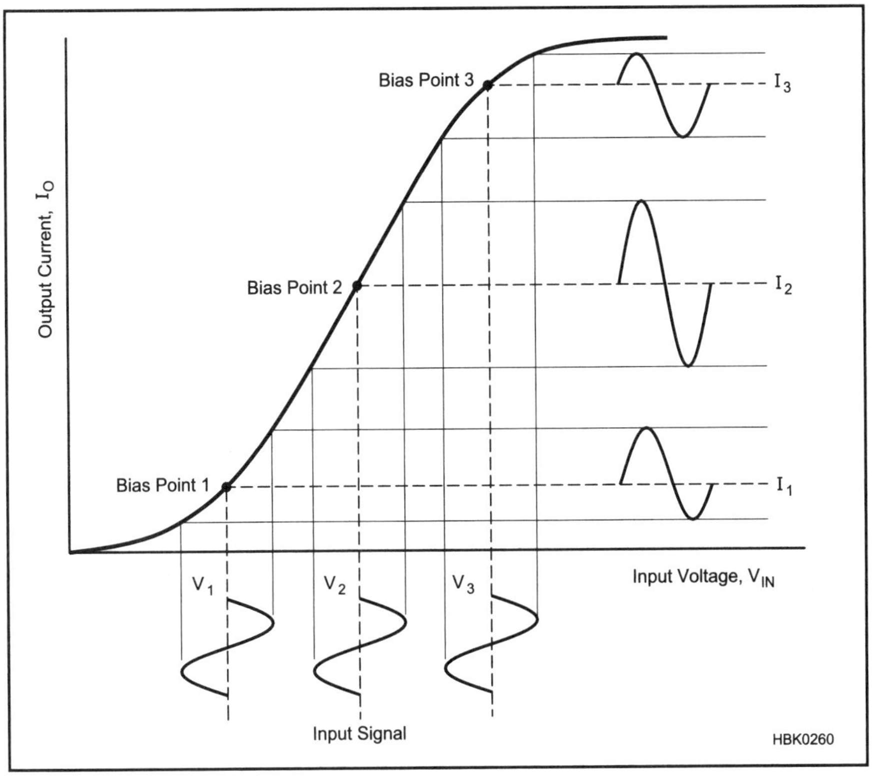

Figure 4.25 — Effect of biasing. An input signal may be reproduced linearly or nonlinearly depending on the choice of bias points.

of the characteristic curve is used to do the processing. The device's *bias point* is its set of operating parameters when no input signal is applied. The bias point is also known as the *quiescent point* or *Q-point*. By changing the bias point, the circuit designer can affect the relationship between the input and output signal. The bias point can also be considered as a dc offset of the input signal. Devices that perform analog signal processing require appropriate input signal biasing.

As an example, consider the characteristic curve shown in **Figure 4.25**. (The exact types of device and circuit are unimportant.) The characteristic curve shows the relationship between an input voltage and an output current. Increasing input voltage results in an increase in output current so that an input signal is reproduced at the output. The characteristic curve is linear in the middle, but is quite nonlinear in its upper and lower regions.

In the circuit described by the figure, bias points are established by adding one of the three voltages, V_1, V_2 or V_3 to the input signal. Bias voltage V_1 results in an output current of I_1 when no input signal is present. This is shown as Bias Point 1 on the characteristic curve. When an input signal is applied, the input voltage varies around V_1 and the output current varies around I_1 as shown. If the dc value of the output current is subtracted, a reproduction of the input signal is the result.

If Bias Point 2 is chosen, we can see that the input voltage is reproduced as a changing output current with the same shape. In this case, the device is operating linearly. If either Bias Point 1 or Bias Point 3 is chosen, however, the shape of the output signal is distorted because the characteristic curve of the device is nonlinear in this region. Either the increasing portion of the input signal results in more variation than the decreasing portion (Bias Point 1) or vice versa (Bias Point 3). Proper biasing is crucial to ensure that a device operates linearly.

MANUFACTURER'S DATA SHEETS

Manufacturer's data sheets list device characteristics, along with the specifics of the part type (polarity, semiconductor type), identity of the pins and leads (*pinouts*), and the typical use (such as small signal, RF, switching or power amplifier). The pin identification is important because, although common package pinouts are normally used, there are exceptions. Manufacturers may differ slightly in the values reported, but certain basic parameters are listed. Different batches of the same devices are rarely identical, so manufacturers specify the guaranteed limits for the parameters of their device. There are usually three values listed in the data sheet for each parameter: guaranteed minimum value, the guaranteed maximum value, and/or the typical value.

Another section of the data sheet lists ABSOLUTE MAXIMUM RATINGS, beyond which device damage may result. For example, the parameters listed in the ABSOLUTE MAXIMUM RATINGS section for a solid-state device are typically voltages, continuous currents, total device power dissipation (P_D) and operating- and storage-temperature ranges.

Rather than plotting the characteristic curves for each device, the manufacturer often selects key operating parameters that describe the device operation for the configurations and parameter ranges that are most commonly used. For example, a bipolar transistor data sheet might include an OPERATING PARAMETERS section. Parameters are listed in an OFF CHARACTERISTICS subsection and an ON CHARACTERISTICS subsection that describe the conduction properties of the device for dc voltages. The SMALL-SIGNAL CHARACTERISTICS section might contain a minimum Gain-Bandwidth Product (f_T or GBW), maximum output capacitance, maximum input capacitance, and the range of the transfer parameters applicable to a given device. Finally, the SWITCHING CHARACTERISTICS section might list absolute maximum ratings for Delay Time (t_d), Rise Time (t_r), Storage Time (t_s), and Fall Time (t_f). Other types of devices list characteristics important to operation of that specific device.

When selecting equivalent parts for replacement of specified devices, the data sheet provides the necessary information to tell if a given part will perform the functions of another. Lists of *cross-references* and *substitution guides* generally only specify devices that have nearly identical parameters. There are usually a large number of additional devices that can be chosen as replacements. Knowledge of the circuit requirements adds even more to the list of possible replacements. The device parameters should be compared individually to make sure that the replacement part meets or exceeds the parameter values of the original part required by the circuit. Be aware that in some applications a far superior part may fail as a replacement, however. A transistor with too much gain could easily oscillate if there were insufficient negative feedback to ensure stability.

4.5.2 Diodes

Although many types of semiconductor diodes are available, they share many common characteristics. The different types of diodes have been developed to optimize particular characteristics for one type of application. You will find many examples of diode applications throughout this book.

The diode symbol is shown in **Figure 4.26**. Forward current flows in the direction from anode to cathode, in the direction of the arrow. Reverse current flows from cathode to anode. (Current is considered to be conventional current as described in the **Electronic Funda-**

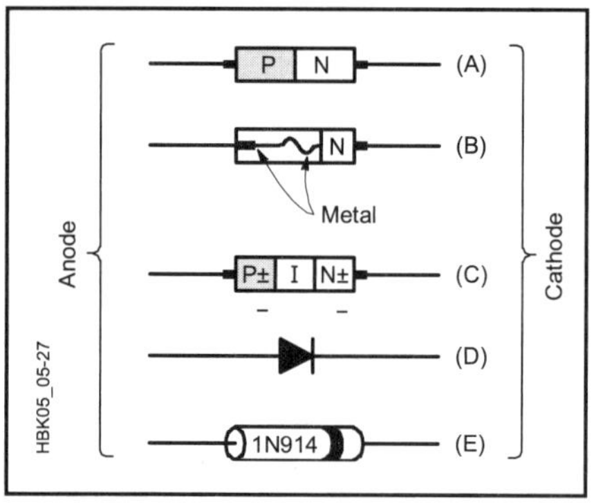

Figure 4.26 — Practical semiconductor diodes. All devices are aligned with anode on the left and cathode on the right. (A) Standard PN junction diode. (B) Point-contact or "cat's whisker" diode. (C) PIN diode formed with heavily doped P-type (P+), undoped (intrinsic) and heavily doped N-type (N+) semiconductor material. (D) Diode schematic symbol. (E) Diode package with marking stripe on the cathode end.

mentals chapter.) The anode of a semiconductor junction diode is made of P-type material and the cathode is made of N-type material, as indicated in Figure 4.26. Most diodes are marked with a band on the cathode end.

DIODE RATINGS

Five major characteristics distinguish standard junction diodes from one another: current handling capacity, maximum voltage rating, response speed, reverse leakage current and junction forward voltage. Each of these characteristics can be manipulated during manufacture to produce special purpose diodes.

Current Capacity

The ideal diode would have zero resistance in the forward direction and infinite resistance in the reverse direction. This is not the case for actual devices, which behave as shown in the plot of a diode response in **Figure 4.27A**. Note that the scales of the two graphs are drastically different. The inverse of the slope of the line (the change in voltage between two points on a straight portion of the line divided by the corresponding change in current) on the upper right is the resistance of the diode in the forward direction, R_F.

The range of voltages is small and the range of currents is large since the forward resistance is very small (in this example, about 2 Ω). Nevertheless, this resistance causes heat dissipation according to $P = I_F^2 \times R_F$.

In addition, there is a forward voltage, V_F, whenever the forward current is flowing. This also results in heat dissipation as $P = I \times V_F$. In power applications where the average forward current is high, heating from forward resistance and the forward voltage drop can be significant. Since forward current determines the amount of heat dissipation, the diode's power rating is stated as a *maximum average current*. Exceeding the current rating in a diode will cause excessive heating that leads to PN junction failure as described earlier.

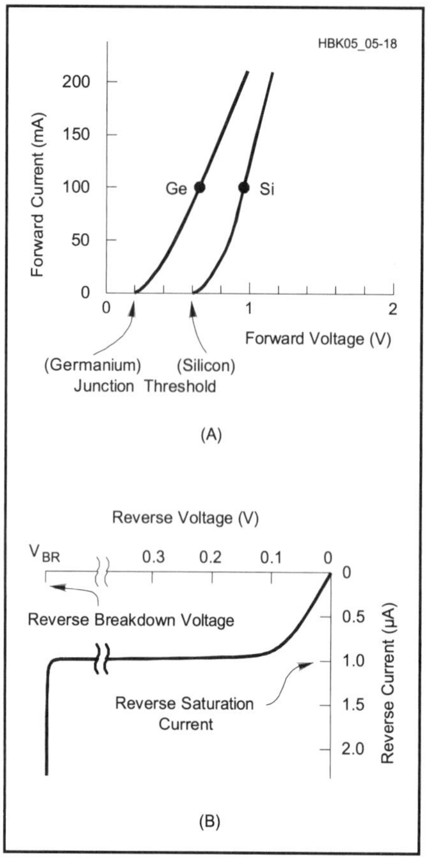

Figure 4.27 — Semiconductor diode (PN junction) characteristic curve. (A) Forward- biased (anode voltage higher than cathode) response for Germanium (Ge) and Silicon (Si) devices. Each curve breaks away from the X-axis at its junction threshold voltage. The slope of each curve is its forward resistance. (B) Reverse-biased response. Very small reverse current increases until it reaches the reverse saturation current (I_0). The reverse current increases suddenly and drastically when the reverse voltage reaches the reverse breakdown voltage, V_{BR}.

Peak Inverse Voltage (PIV)

In Figure 4.27B, the lower left portion of the curve illustrates a much higher resistance that increases from tens of kilohms to thousands of megohms as the reverse voltage gets larger, and then decreases to near zero (a nearly vertical line) very suddenly. This sudden change occurs because the diode enters *reverse breakdown* or when the reverse voltage becomes high enough to push current across the junction. The voltage at which this occurs is the *reverse breakdown voltage*. Unless the current is so large that the diode fails from overheating, breakdown is not destructive and the diode will again behave normally when the bias is removed. The maximum reverse voltage that the diode can withstand under normal use is the *peak inverse voltage* (*PIV*) rating. A related effect is *avalanche breakdown* in which the voltage across a device is greater than its ability to control or block current flow.

Response Speed

The speed of a diode's response to a change in voltage polarity limits the frequency of ac current that the diode can rectify. The diode response in Figure 4.27 shows how that diode will act at dc. As the frequency increases, the diode may not be able to turn current on and off as fast as the changing polarity of the signal.

Diode response speed mainly depends on *charge storage* in the depletion region. When forward current is flowing, electrons and holes fill the region near the junction to recombine. When the applied voltage reverses, these excess charges move away from the junction so that no recombination can take place. As reverse bias empties the depletion region of excess charge, it begins to act like a small capacitor formed by the regions containing majority carriers on either side of the junction and the depletion region acting as the dielectric. This *junction capacitance* is inversely proportional to the width of the depletion region and directly proportional to the cross-sectional surface area of the junction.

The effect of junction capacitance is to allow current to flow for a short period after the applied voltage changes from positive to negative. To halt current flow requires that the junction capacitance be charged. Charging this capacitance takes some time; a few μs for regular rectifier diodes and a few hundred nanoseconds for *fast-recovery* diodes. This is the diode's *charge-storage time*. The amount of time required for current flow to cease is the diode's *recovery time*.

Reverse Leakage Current

Because the depletion region is very thin, reverse bias causes a small amount of reverse leakage or reverse saturation current to flow from cathode to anode. This is typically 1 μA or less until reverse breakdown voltage is reached. Silicon diodes have lower reverse leakage currents than diodes made from other materials with higher carrier mobility, such as germanium.

The reverse saturation current I_s is not constant but is affected by temperature, with higher temperatures increasing the mobility of the majority carriers so that more of them cross the depletion region for a given amount of reverse bias. For silicon diodes (and transistors) near room temperature, I_s increases by a factor of 2 every 4.8 °C. This means that for every 4.8 °C rise in temperature, either the current doubles (if the voltage across it is constant), or if the current is held constant by other resistances in the circuit, the diode voltage will *decrease* by $V_T \times \ln 2 = 18$ mV. For germanium, the current doubles every 8 °C and for gallium-arsenide (GaAs), 3.7 °C. This dependence is highly reproducible and may actually be exploited to produce temperature-measuring circuits.

While the change resulting from a rise of several degrees may be tolerable in a circuit design, that from 20 or 30 degrees may not. Therefore it's a good idea with diodes, just as with other components, to specify power ratings conservatively (2 to 4 times margin) to prevent self-heating.

While component derating does reduce self-heating effects, circuits must be designed for the expected operating environment. For example, mobile radios may face temperatures from –20° to +140 °F (–29° to 60 °C).

Forward Voltage

The amount of voltage required to cause majority carriers to enter the depletion region and recombine, creating full current flow, is called a diode's *forward voltage*, V_F. It depends on the type of material used to create the junction and the amount of current. For silicon diodes at normal currents, $V_F = 0.7$ V, and for germanium diodes, $V_F = 0.3$ V. As you saw earlier, V_F also affects power dissipation in the diode.

POINT-CONTACT DIODES

One way to decrease charge storage time in the depletion region is to form a metal-semiconductor junction for which the depletion is very thin. This can be accomplished with a *point-contact diode*, where a thin piece of aluminum wire, often called a *whisker*, is placed in contact with one face of a piece of lightly doped N-type material. In fact, the original diodes used for detecting radio signals ("cat's whisker diodes") were made with a steel wire in contact with a crystal of impure lead (galena). Point-contact diodes have high response speed, but poor PIV and current-handling ratings. The 1N34 germanium point-contact diode is the best-known example of point-contact diode still in common use.

SCHOTTKY DIODES

An improvement to point-contact diodes, the *hot-carrier diode* is similar to a point-contact diode, but with more ideal characteristics attained by using more efficient metals, such as platinum and gold, that act to lower forward resistance and increase PIV. This type of contact is known as a *Schottky barrier*, and diodes made this way are called *Schottky diodes*. The junctions of Schottky diodes, being smaller, store less charge and as a result, have shorter switching times and junction capacitances than standard PN-junction diodes. Their forward voltage is also lower, typically 0.3 to 0.4 V. In most other respects they behave similarly to PN diodes.

PIN DIODES

The PIN diode, shown in Figure 4.24C is a *slow response* diode that is capable of passing RF and microwave signals when it is forward biased. This device is constructed with a layer of intrinsic (undoped) semiconductor placed between very highly doped P-type and N-type material (called P^+-type and N^+-type material to indicate the extra amount of doping), creating a *PIN junction*. These devices provide very effective switches for RF signals and are often used in transmit-receive switches in transceivers and amplifiers. The majority carriers in PIN diodes have longer than normal lifetimes before recombination, resulting in a slow switching process that causes them to act more like resistors than diodes at high radio frequencies. The amount of resistance can be controlled by the amount of forward bias applied to the PIN diode and this allows them to act as current-controlled attenuators. (For additional discussion of PIN diodes and projects in which they are used, see the chapters on **Transmitting**, **RF Power Amplifiers**, and **Test Equipment and Measurements**.)

VARACTOR DIODES

Junction capacitance can be used as a circuit element by controlling the reverse bias voltage across the junction, creating a small variable capacitor. Junction capacitances are small, on the order of pF. As the reverse bias voltage on a diode increases, the width of the depletion region increases, decreasing its capacitance. A *varactor* (also known by the trade name Varicap diode) is a diode with a junction specially formulated to have a relatively large range of capacitance values for a modest range of reverse bias voltages (**Figure 4.28**).

As the reverse bias applied to a diode changes, the width of the depletion layer, and therefore the capacitance, also changes. The diode junction capacitance (C_j) under a reverse bias of V volts is given by

$$C_j = \frac{C_{j0}}{\sqrt{V_{on} - V}}$$

where C_{j0} = measured capacitance with zero applied voltage.

Note that the quantity under the radical is a large *positive* quantity for reverse bias. As seen from the equation, for large reverse biases C_j is inversely proportional to the square root of the voltage.

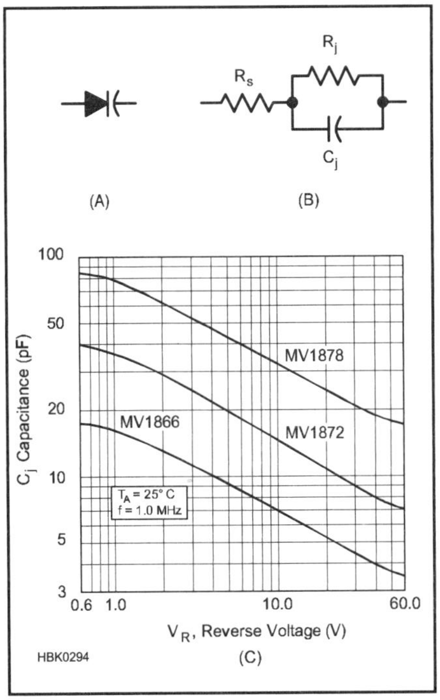

Figure 4.28 — Varactor diode. (A) Schematic symbol. (B) Equivalent circuit of the reverse biased varactor diode. R_S is the junction resistance, R_J is the leakage resistance and C_J is the junction capacitance, which is a function of the magnitude of the reverse bias voltage. (C) Plot of junction capacitance, C_J, as a function of reverse voltage, V_R, for three different varactor devices. Both axes are plotted on a logarithmic scale.

Although special forms of varactors are available from manufacturers, other types of diodes may be used as inexpensive varactor diodes, but the relationship between reverse voltage and capacitance is not always reliable.

When designing with varactor diodes, the reverse bias voltage must be absolutely free of noise since any variations in the bias voltage will cause changes in capacitance. For example, if the varactor is used to tune an oscillator, unwanted frequency shifts or instability will result if the reverse bias voltage is noisy. It is possible to frequency modulate a signal by adding the audio signal to the reverse bias on a varactor diode used in the carrier oscillator. (For examples of the use of varactors in oscillators and modulators, see the chapters on **Transmitting** and **Oscillators and Synthesizers**.)

ZENER DIODES

When the PIV of a reverse-biased diode is exceeded, the diode begins to conduct current as it does when it is forward biased. This current will not destroy the diode if it is limited to less than the device's maximum allowable value. By using heavy levels of doping during manufacture, a diode's PIV can be precisely controlled to be at a specific level, called the *Zener voltage*, creating a type of voltage reference. These diodes are called Zener diodes after their inventor, American physicist Clarence Zener.

When the Zener voltage is reached, the reverse voltage across the Zener diode remains constant even as the current through it changes. With an appropriate series current-limiting resistor, the Zener diode provides an accurate voltage reference (see **Figure 4.29**).

Zener diodes are rated by their reverse-breakdown voltage and their power-handling capacity, where $P = V_Z \times I_Z$. Since the same current must always pass though the resistor to drop the source voltage down to the reference voltage, with that current divided between the Zener diode and the load, this type of power source is very wasteful of current.

The Zener diode does make an excellent and efficient voltage reference in a larger voltage regulating circuit where the load current is provided from another device whose voltage is set by the reference. (See the **Power Sources** chapter for morc information about using Zener diodes as voltage regulators.) When operating in the breakdown region, Zener diodes can be modeled as a simple voltage source.

The primary sources of error in Zener-diode-derived voltages are the variation with load current and the variation due to heat. Temperature-compensated Zener diodes are available with temperature coefficients as low as 5 parts per million per °C. If this is unacceptable, voltage reference integrated circuits based on Zener diodes have been developed that include additional circuitry to counteract temperature effects.

A variation of Zener diodes, *transient voltage suppressor* (*TVS*) diodes are designed to dissipate the energy in short-duration, high-voltage transients that would otherwise damage equipment or circuits. TVS diodes have large junction cross-sections so that they can handle large currents without damage. These diodes are also known by the trade name TransZorbs. Since the polarity of the transient can be positive, negative, or both, transient protection circuits can be designed with two devices connected with opposite polarities.

RECTIFIERS

The most common application of a diode is to perform rectification; that is, permitting current flow in only one direction. Power rectification converts ac current into pulsating dc current. There are three basic forms of power rectification using semiconductor diodes: half wave (1 diode), full-wave center-tapped (2 diodes) and full-wave bridge (4 diodes). These applications are shown in

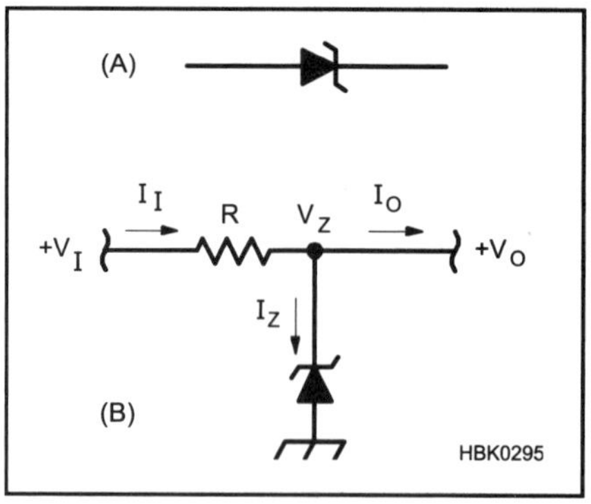

Figure 4.29 — Zener diode. (A) Schematic symbol. (B) Basic voltage regulating circuit. V_Z is the Zener reverse breakdown voltage. Above V_Z, the diode draws current until $V_I - I_IR = V_Z$. The circuit design should select R so that when the maximum current is drawn, $R < (V_I - V_Z) / I_O$. The diode should be capable of passing the same current when there is no output current drawn.

Figure 4.30A, **B** and **C** and are more fully described in the **Power Sources** chapter.

The most important diode parameters to consider for power rectification are the PIV and current ratings. The peak negative voltages that are blocked by the diode must be smaller in magnitude than the PIV and the peak current through the diode when it is forward biased must be less than the maximum average forward current.

Rectification is also used at much lower current levels in modulation and demodulation and other types of analog signal processing circuits. For these applications, the diode's response speed and junction forward voltage are the most important ratings.

4.5.3 Bipolar Junction Transistors (BJT)

The bipolar junction transistor is a *current-controlled device* with three basic terminals; *emitter*, *collector* and *base*. The current between the emitter and the collector is controlled by the current between the base and emitter. The convention when discussing transistor operation is that the three currents into the device are positive (I_c into the collector, I_b into the base and I_e into the emitter). Kirchhoff's Current Law applies to transistors just as it does to passive electrical networks: the total current entering the device must be zero. Thus, the relationship between the currents into a transistor can be generalized as

$$I_c + I_b + I_e = 0$$

which can be rearranged as necessary. For example, if we are interested in the emitter current,

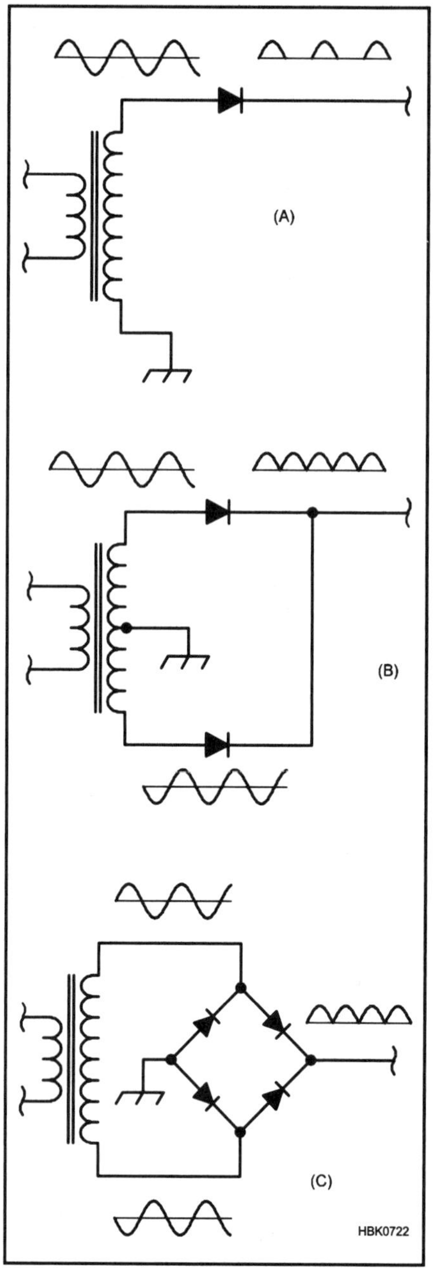

Figure 4.30 — Diode rectifier circuits. (A) Half wave rectifier circuit. Only when the ac voltage is positive does current pass through the diode. Current flows only during half of the cycle. (B) Full-wave center-tapped rectifier circuit. Center-tap on the transformer secondary is grounded and the two ends of the secondary are 180° out of phase. (C) Full-wave bridge rectifier circuit. In each half of the cycle two diodes conduct.

$$I_e = -(I_c + I_b)$$

The back-to-back diode model shown in Figure 2.36 is appropriate for visualization of transistor construction. In actual transistors, however, the relative sizes of the collector, base and emitter regions differ. A common transistor configuration that spans a distance of 3 mm between the collector and emitter contacts typically has a base region that is only 25 µm across.

The operation of the bipolar transistor is described graphically by characteristic curves as shown in **Figure 4.31**. These are similar to the I-V characteristic curves for the two-terminal devices described in the preceding sections. The parameters shown by the curves depend on the type of circuit in which they are measured, such as common emitter or common collector. The output characteristic shows a set of curves for either collector or emitter current versus collector-emitter voltage at various values of input current (either base or emitter). The input characteristic shows the voltage between the input and common terminals (such as base-emitter) versus the input current for different values of output voltage.

CURRENT GAIN

Two parameters describe the relationships between the three transistor currents at low frequencies:

$$\alpha = -\frac{\Delta I_C}{\Delta I_E} = 1$$

$$\beta = \frac{\Delta I_C}{\Delta I_B}$$

The relationship between α and β is defined as

$$\alpha = -\frac{\beta}{1+\beta}$$

Another designation for β is often used: h_{FE}, the *forward dc current gain*. (The "h" refers to "h parameters," a set of transfer parameters for describing a two-port network and described in more detail in the **RF Techniques** chapter.) The symbol, h_{fe}, in which the subscript is in lower case, is used for the forward current gain of ac signals.

OPERATING REGIONS

Current conduction between collector and emitter is described by *regions* of the transistor's characteristic curves in Figure 4.31. (References such as *common-emitter* or *common-base* refer to the configuration of the circuit in which the parameter is measured.) The transistor is in its *active* or *linear region* when the base-collector junction is reverse biased and the base-emitter junction is forward biased. The slope of the output current, I_O, versus the output voltage, V_O, is virtually flat, indicating that the output current is nearly independent of the output voltage. In this region, the output circuit of the transistor can be modeled as a constant-current source controlled by the input current. The slight slope that does exist is due to base-width modulation (known as the *Early effect*).

When both the junctions in the transistor are forward biased, the transistor is said to be in its *saturation region*. In this region, V_O is nearly zero and large changes in I_O occur for very small changes in V_O. Both junctions in the transistor are reverse-biased in the *cutoff region*. Under this condition, there is very little current in the output, only the nanoamperes or microamperes that result from the very small leakage across the input-to-output junction. Finally, if V_O is increased to very high values, avalanche breakdown begins as in a PN-junction diode and output current increases rapidly. This is the *breakdown region*, not shown in Figure 4.31.

These descriptions of junction conditions are the basis for the use of transistors. Various configurations of the transistor in circuitry make use of the properties of the junctions to serve different purposes in analog signal processing.

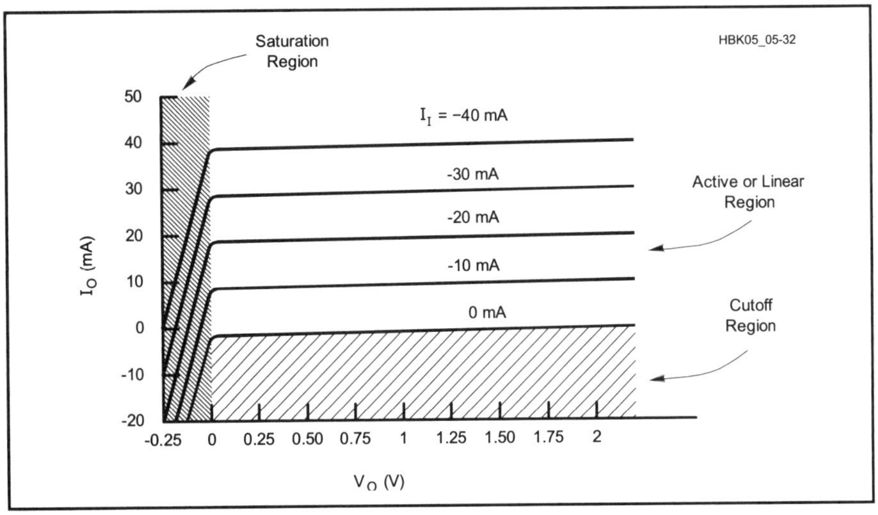

Figure 4.31 — Transistor response curve output characteristics. The X-axis is the output voltage, and the Y-axis is the output current. Different curves are plotted for various values of input current. The three regions of the transistor are its cutoff region, where no current flows in any terminal, its active region, where the output current is nearly independent of the output voltage and there is a linear relationship between the input current and the output current, and the saturation region, where the output current has large changes for small changes in output voltage.

OPERATING PARAMETERS

A typical general-purpose bipolar-transistor data sheet lists important device specifications. Parameters listed in the ABSOLUTE MAXIMUM RATINGS section are the three junction voltages (V_{CEO}, V_{CBO} and V_{EBO}), the continuous collector current (I_C), the total device power dissipation (P_D) and the operating and storage temperature range. Exceeding any of these parameters is likely to cause the transistor to be destroyed. (The "O" in the suffixes of the junction voltages indicates that the remaining terminal is not connected, or open.)

In the OPERATING PARAMETERS section, three guaranteed minimum junction breakdown voltages are listed $V_{(BR)CEO}$, $V_{(BR)CBO}$ and $V_{(BR)EBO}$. Exceeding these voltages is likely to cause the transistor to enter avalanche breakdown, but if current is limited, permanent damage may not result.

Under ON CHARACTERISTICS are the guaranteed minimum dc current gain (β or h_{FE}), guaranteed maximum collector-emitter saturation voltage, $V_{CE(SAT)}$, and the guaranteed maximum base-emitter on voltage, $V_{BE(ON)}$. Two guaranteed maximum collector cutoff currents, I_{CEO} and I_{CBO}, are listed under OFF CHARACTERISTICS.

The next section is SMALL-SIGNAL CHARACTERISTICS, where the guaranteed minimum current gain-bandwidth product, BW or f_T, the guaranteed maximum output capacitance, C_{obo}, the guaranteed maximum input capacitance, C_{ibo}, the guaranteed range of input impedance, h_{ie}, the small-signal current gain, h_{fe}, the guaranteed maximum voltage feedback ratio, h_{re} and output admittance, h_{oe} are listed.

Finally, the SWITCHING CHARACTERISTICS section lists absolute maximum ratings for delay time, t_d; rise time, t_r; storage time, t_s; and fall time, t_f.

4.5.4 Field-Effect Transistors (FET)

FET devices are controlled by the voltage level of the input rather than the input current, as in the bipolar transistor. FETs have three basic terminals, the *gate*, the *source* and the *drain*. They are analogous to bipolar transistor terminals: the gate to the base, the source to the emitter, and the drain to the collector. Symbols for the various forms of FET devices are pictured in **Figure 4.32**.

The FET gate has a very high impedance, so the input can be modeled as an open circuit. The voltage between gate and source, V_{GS}, controls the resistance of the drain-source channel, r_{DS}, and so the output of the FET is modeled as a current source, whose output current is controlled by the input voltage.

The action of the FET channel is so nearly ideal that, as long as the JFET gate does not become forward biased and inject current from the base into the channel, the drain and source currents are virtually identical. For JFETs the *gate leakage current,* I_G, is a function of V_{GS} and this is often expressed with an *input curve* (see **Figure 4.33**). The point at which there is a significant increase in I_G is called the *junction breakpoint voltage*. Because the gate of MOSFETs is insulated from the channel, gate leakage current is insignificant in these devices.

The dc channel resistance, r_{DS}, is specified in data sheets to be less than a maximum value when the device is biased on ($r_{DS(on)}$). When the gate voltage is maximum ($V_{GS} = 0$ for a JFET), $r_{DS(on)}$ is minimum. This describes the effectiveness of the device as an analog switch. Channel resistance is approximately the same for ac and dc signals until at high frequencies the capacitive reactances inherent in the FET structure become significant.

FETs also have strong similarities to vacuum tubes in that input voltage between the grid and cathode controls an output current between the plate and cathode. (See the chapter on **RF Power Amplifiers** for more information on vacuum tubes.)

FORWARD TRANSCONDUCTANCE

The change in FET drain current caused by a change in gate-to-source voltage is called *forward transconductance,* g_m.

$$g_m = \frac{\Delta I_{DS}}{\Delta V_{GS}}$$

or

$$\Delta I_{DS} = g_m \, \Delta V_{GS}$$

The input voltage, V_{GS}, is measured between the FET gate and source and drain current, I_{DS}, flows from drain to source. Analogous to a bipolar transistor's current gain, the units of transconductance are siemens (S) because it is the ratio of current to voltage. (Both g_m and g_{fs} are used interchangeably to indicate transconductance. Some sources specify g_{fs} as the *common-source forward transconductance*. This chapter uses g_m, the most common convention in the reference literature.)

OPERATING REGIONS

The most useful relationships for FETs are the output and transconductance response characteristic curves in **Figure 4.34**. (Refer-

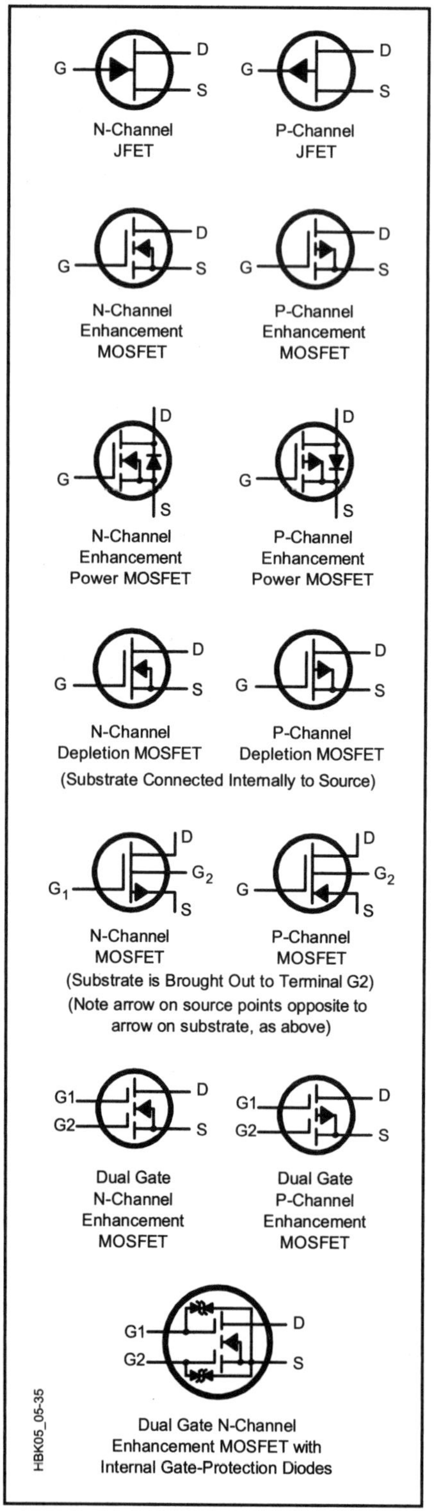

Figure 4.32 —FET schematic symbols.

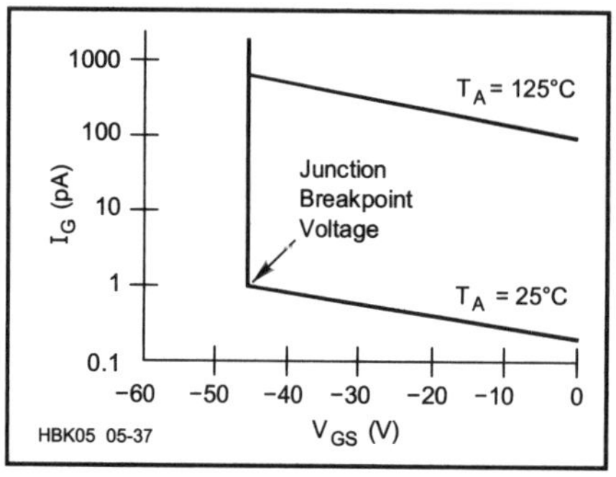

Figure 4.33 — JFET input leakage curves for common source amplifier configuration. Input voltage (V_{GS}) on the X-axis versus input current (I_G) on the Y-axis, with two curves plotted for different operating temperatures, 25 °C and 125 °C. Input current increases greatly when the gate voltage exceeds the junction breakpoint voltage.

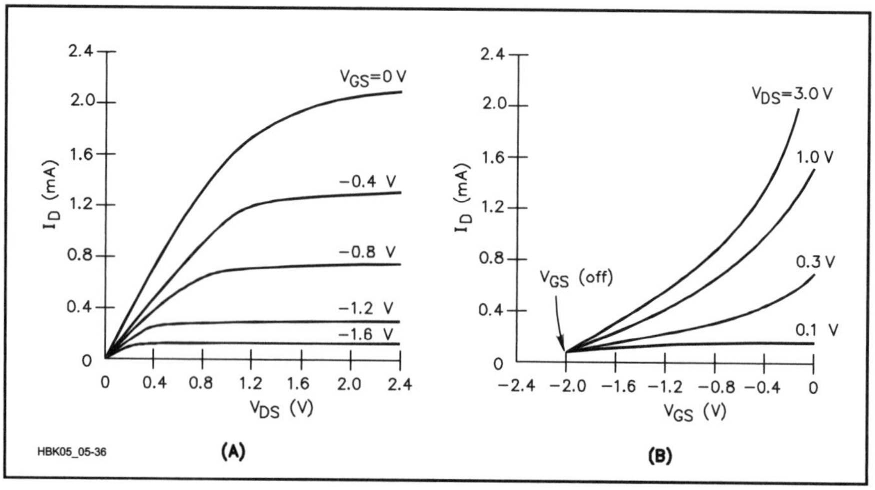

Figure 4.34 — JFET output and transconductance response curves for common source amplifier configuration. (A) Output voltage (V_{DS}) on the X-axis versus output current (I_D) on the Y-axis, with different curves plotted for various values of input voltage (V_{GS}). (B) Transconductance curve with the same three variables rearranged: V_{GS} on the X-axis, I_D on the Y-axis and curves plotted for different values of V_{DS}.

ences such as *common-source* or *common-gate* refer to the configuration of the circuit in which the parameter is measured.) Transconductance curves relate the drain current, I_D, to gate-to-source voltage, V_{GS}, at various drain-source voltages, V_{DS}. The FET's forward transconductance, g_m, is the slope of the lines in the forward transconductance curve. The same parameters are interrelated in a different way in the output characteristic, in which I_D is shown versus V_{DS} for different values of V_{GS}.

Like the bipolar transistor, FET operation can be characterized by regions. The *ohmic region* is shown at the left of the FET output characteristic curve in **Figure 4.35** where I_D is increasing nearly linearly with V_{DS} and the FET is acting like a resistance controlled by V_{GS}. As V_{DS} continues to increase, I_D saturates and becomes nearly constant. This is the FET's *saturation region* in which the channel of the FET can be modeled as a constant-current source. V_{DS} can become so large that V_{GS} no longer controls the conduction of the device and avalanche breakdown occurs as in bipolar transistors and PN-junction diodes. This is the *breakdown region*, shown in Figure 4.35 where the curves for I_D break sharply upward. If V_{GS} is less than V_P, so that transconductance is zero, the FET is in the *cutoff region*.

OPERATING PARAMETERS

A typical FET data sheet gives ABSOLUTE MAXIMUM RATINGS for V_{DS}, V_{DG}, V_{GS} and I_D, along with the usual device dissipation (P_D) and storage temperature range. Exceeding these limits usually results in destruction of the FET.

Under OPERATING PARAMTERS the OFF CHARACTERISTICS list the gate-source breakdown voltage, $V_{GS(BR)}$, the reverse gate current, I_{GSS} and the gate-source cutoff voltage, $V_{GS(OFF)}$. Exceeding $V_{GS(BR)}$ will not permanently damage the device if current is limited. The primary ON CHARACTERISTIC parameters are the channel resistance, r_{DS}, and the zero-gate-voltage drain current (I_{DSS}). An FET's dc channel resistance, r_{DS}, is specified in data sheets to be less than a maximum value when the device is biased on ($r_{DS(on)}$). For ac signals, $r_{ds(on)}$ is not necessarily the same as $r_{DS(on)}$, but it is not very different as long as the frequency is not so high that capacitive reactance in the FET becomes significant.

The SMALL SIGNAL CHARACTERISTICS include the forward transfer admittance, y_{fs}, the output admittance, y_{os}, the static drain-source on resistance, $r_{ds(on)}$ and various capacitances such as input capacitance, C_{iss}, reverse transfer capacitance, C_{rss}, the drain-substrate capacitance, $C_{d(sub)}$. FUNCTIONAL CHARACTERISTICS include the noise figure, NF, and the common source power gain, G_{ps}.

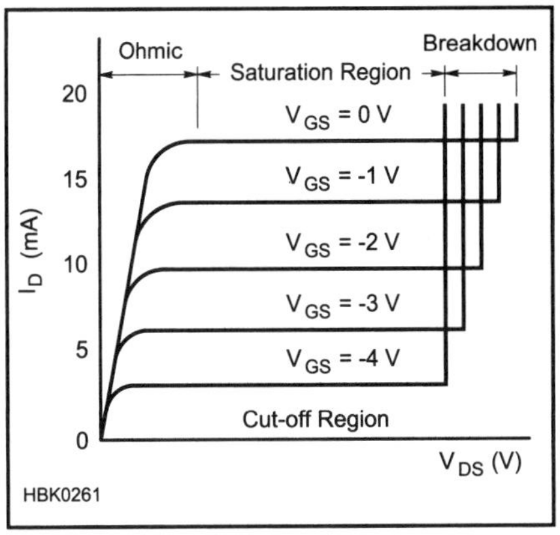

Figure 4.35 — JFET operating regions. At the left, I_D is increasing rapidly with V_{GS} and the JFET can be treated as resistance (R_{DS}) controlled by V_{GS}. In the saturation region, drain current, I_D, is relatively independent of V_{GS}. As V_{DS} increases further, avalanche breakdown begins and I_D increases rapidly.

MOSFETS

As described earlier, the MOSFET's gate is insulated from the channel by a thin layer of nonconductive oxide, doing away with any appreciable gate leakage current. Because of this isolation of the gate, MOSFETs do not need input and reverse transconductance curves. Their output curves (**Figure 4.36**) are similar to those of the JFET. The gate acts as a small capacitance between the gate and both the source and drain.

The output and transconductance curves in Figure 4.36A and 4.36B show that the depletion-mode N-channel MOSFET's transconductance is positive at $V_{GS} = 0$, like that of the N-channel JFET. Unlike the JFET, however, increasing V_{GS} does not forward-bias the gate-source junction and so the device can be operated with $V_{GS} > 0$.

In the enhancement-mode MOSFET, transconductance is zero at $V_{GS} = 0$. As V_{GS} is increased, the MOSFET enters the ohmic region. If V_{GS} increases further, the saturation region is reached and the MOSFET is said to be *fully-on*, with r_{DS} at its minimum value. The behavior of the enhancement-mode MOSFET is similar to that of the bipolar transistor in this regard.

The relatively flat regions in the MOSFET

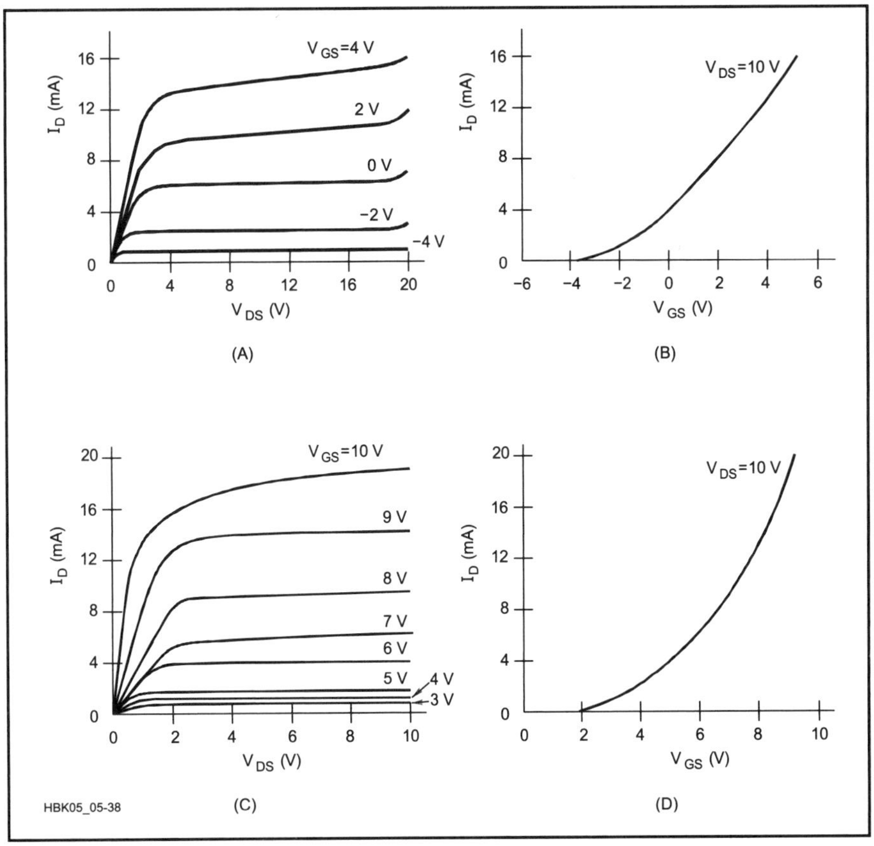

Figure 4.36 — MOSFET output [(A) and (C)] and transconductance [(B) and (D)] response curves. Plots (A) and (B) are for an N-channel depletion mode device. Note that V_{GS} varies from negative to positive values. Plots (C) and (D) are for an N-channel enhancement mode device. V_{GS} has only positive values.

output curves are often used to provide a constant current source. As is plotted in these curves, the drain current, I_D, changes very little as the drain-source voltage, V_{DS}, varies in this portion of the curve. Thus, for a fixed gate-source voltage, V_{GS}, the drain current can be considered to be constant over a wide range of drain-source voltages.

Multiple gate MOSFETs are also available. Due to the insulating layer, the two gates are isolated from each other and allow two signals to control the channel simultaneously with virtually no loading of one signal by the other. A common application of this type of device is an automatic gain control (AGC) amplifier. The signal is applied to one gate and a rectified, low-pass filtered form of the output (the AGC voltage) is fed back to the other gate. Another common application is as a mixer in which the two input signals are applied to the pair of gates.

MOSFET Gate Protection

The MOSFET is constructed with a very thin layer of SiO_2 for the gate insulator. This layer is extremely thin in order to improve the transconductance of the device but this makes it susceptible to damage from high voltage levels, such as *electrostatic discharge* (ESD) from static electricity. If enough charge accumulates on the gate terminal, it can *punch through* the gate insulator and destroy it. The insulation of the gate terminal is so good that virtually none of this potential is eased by leakage of the charge into the device. While this condition makes for nearly ideal input impedance (approaching infinity), it puts the device at risk of destruction from even such seemingly innocuous electrical sources as static electrical discharges from handling.

Some MOSFET devices contain an internal Zener diode with its cathode connected to the gate and its anode to the substrate. If the voltage at the gate rises to a damaging level the Zener diode junction conducts, bleeding excess charges off to the substrate. When voltages are within normal operating limits the Zener has little effect on the signal at the gate, although it may decrease the input impedance of the MOSFET.

This solution will not work for all MOSFETs. The Zener diode must always be reverse biased to be effective. In the enhancement-mode MOSFET, $V_{GS} > 0$ for all valid uses of the part, keeping the Zener reverse biased. In depletion mode devices however, V_{GS} can be both positive and negative; when negative, a gate-protection Zener diode would be forward biased and the MOSFET gate would not be driven properly. In some depletion mode MOSFETs, back-to-back Zener diodes are used to protect the gate.

MOSFET devices are at greatest risk of damage from static electricity when they are out of circuit. Even though an electrostatic discharge is capable of delivering little energy, it can generate thousands of volts and high peak currents. When storing MOSFETs, the leads should be placed into conductive foam. When working with MOSFETs, it is a good idea to minimize static by wearing a grounded wrist strap and working on a grounded workbench or mat. A humidifier may help to decrease the static electricity in the air. Before inserting a MOSFET into a circuit board it helps to first touch the device leads with your hand and then touch the circuit board. This serves to equalize the excess charge so that little excess charge flows when the device is inserted into the circuit board.

Power MOSFETs

Power MOSFETs are designed for use as switches, with extremely low values of $r_{DS(on)}$; values of 50 milliohms (mΩ) are common. The largest devices of this type can switch tens of amps of current with V_{DS} voltage ratings of hundreds of volts. The **Component Data and References** chapter includes a table of power FET ratings. The schematic symbol for power MOSFETs (see Figure 4.30) includes a *body diode* that allows the FET to conduct in the reverse direction, regardless of V_{GS}. This is useful in many high-power switching applications. Power MOSFETs used for RF amplifiers are discussed in more detail in the **RF Power Amplifiers** chapter.

While the maximum ratings for current and voltage are high, the devices cannot withstand both high drain current and high drain-to-source voltage at the same time because of the power dissipated; $P = V_{DS} \times I_D$. It is important to drive the gate of a power MOSFET such that the device is fully on or fully off so that either V_{DS} or I_D is at or close to zero. When switching, the device should spend as little time as possible in the linear region where both current and voltage are nonzero because their product (P) can be substantial. This is not a big problem if switching only takes place occasionally, but if the switching is repetitive (such as in a switching power supply) care should be taken to drive the gate properly and remove excess heat from the device.

Because the gate of a power MOSFET is capacitive (up to several hundred pF for large devices), charging and discharging the gate quickly results in short current peaks of more than 100 mA. Whatever circuit is used to drive the gate of a power MOSFET must be able to handle that current level, such as an integrated circuit designed for driving the capacitive load an FET gate presents.

The gate of a power MOSFET should not be left open or connected to a high-impedance circuit. Use a pull-down or pull-up resistor connected between the gate and the appropriate power supply to ensure that the gate is placed at the right voltage when not being driven by the gate drive circuit.

GaAsFETs

FETs made from gallium-arsenide (GaAs) material are used at UHF and microwave frequencies because they have gain at these frequencies and add little noise to the signal. The reason GaAsFETs have gain at these frequencies is the high mobility of the electrons in GaAs material. Because the electrons are more mobile than in silicon, they respond to the gate-source input signal more quickly and strongly than silicon FETs, providing gain at higher frequencies (f_T is directly proportional to electron mobility). The higher electron mobility also reduces thermally-generated noise generated in the FET, making the GaAsFET especially suitable for weak-signal preamps.

Because electron mobility is always higher than hole mobility, N-type material is used in GaAsFETs to maximize high-frequency gain. Since P-type material is not used to make a gate-channel junction, a metal Schottky junction is formed by depositing metal directly on the surface of the channel. This type of device is also called a *MESFET* (metal-semiconductor field-effect transistor).

4.5.5 Comparison of BJT and FET Devices

Analog signal processing deals with changing a signal to a desired form. The three primary types of devices — bipolar transistors, field-effect transistors and integrated circuits — perform similar functions, each with specific advantages and disadvantages. The vacuum tube, once the dominant signal processing component, is relegated to high-power amplifier and display applications and is found only in the **RF Power Amplifiers** chapter of this *Handbook*. *Cathode-ray tubes* (CRTs) are covered in a separate article in this book's downloadable supplemental material.

Bipolar transistors, when treated properly, can have virtually unlimited life spans. They are relatively small and, if they do not handle high currents, do not generate much heat. They make excellent high-frequency amplifiers. Compared to MOSFET devices they are less susceptible to damage from electrostatic discharge. Bipolar transistors and ICs, like all semiconductors, are susceptible to damage from power and lightning transients.

There are many performance advantages to FET devices, particularly MOSFETs. The extremely low gate currents allow the design of analog stages with nearly infinite input resistance. Signal distortion due to loading is minimized in this way. FETs are less expensive to fabricate in ICs and so are gradually replacing bipolar transistors in many IC applications.

RF amplifiers are now designed almost

exclusively using some variety of MOSFET in their final amplifiers. The transistors are often integrated into modules (a.k.a. "pallets") that include circuitry to protect the transistors from the high voltages generated by reflections under high SWR conditions. See the **RF Power Amplifier** chapter for more information on advances in RF amplifier technology.

An important consideration in the use of analog components is the future availability of parts. At an ever increasing rate, as new components are developed to replace older technology, the older components are discontinued by the manufacturers and become unavailable for future use. ASIC and PGA technology, discussed along with integrated circuits, brings the power of custom electronics to the radio, but can make it nearly impossible to repair by replacing an IC, even if the problem is known. If field repair and service at the component level are to be performed, it is important to use standard ICs wherever possible. Even so, when demand for a particular component drops, a manufacturer will discontinue its production. This happens on an ever-decreasing timeline.

A further consideration is the trend toward digital signal processing and software-defined radio systems. (See the chapter on **DSP and SDR Fundamentals**.) More and more analog functions are being performed by microprocessors and the analog signals converted to digital at higher and higher frequencies. It is now common practice to digitize the incoming RF signal directly at the antenna system interface.

There will always be a need for analog circuits, but the balance point between analog and digital is accelerating towards the latter. In future years, radio and test equipment will consist of a powerful, general-purpose digital signal processor, surrounded by the necessary analog circuitry to convert the signals to digital form and supply the processor with power.

4.5.6 Optical Semiconductors

In addition to electrical energy and heat energy, light energy also affects the behavior of semiconductor materials. If a device is made to allow photons of light to strike the surface of the semiconductor material, the energy absorbed by electrons disrupts the bonds between atoms, creating free electrons and holes. This increases the conductivity of the material (*photoconductivity*). The photon can also transfer enough energy to an electron to allow it to cross a PN junction's depletion region as current flow through the semiconductor (*photoelectricity*).

PHOTOCONDUCTORS

In commercial *photoconductors* (also called *photoresistors*) the resistance can change by as much as several kilohms for a light intensity change of 100 ft-candles. The most common material used in photoconductors is cadmium sulfide (CdS), with a resistance range of more than 2 MΩ in total darkness to less than 10 Ω in bright light. Other materials used in photoconductors respond best at specific colors. Lead sulfide (PbS) is most sensitive to infrared light and selenium (Se) works best in the blue end of the visible spectrum.

PHOTODIODES

A similar effect is used in some diodes and transistors so that their operation can be controlled by light instead of electrical current biasing. These devices, shown in **Figure 4.37**, are called *photodiodes* and *phototransistors*. The flow of minority carriers across the reverse biased PN junction is increased by light falling on the doped semiconductor material. In the dark, the junction acts the same as any reverse biased PN junction, with a very low current, I_{SC}, (on the order

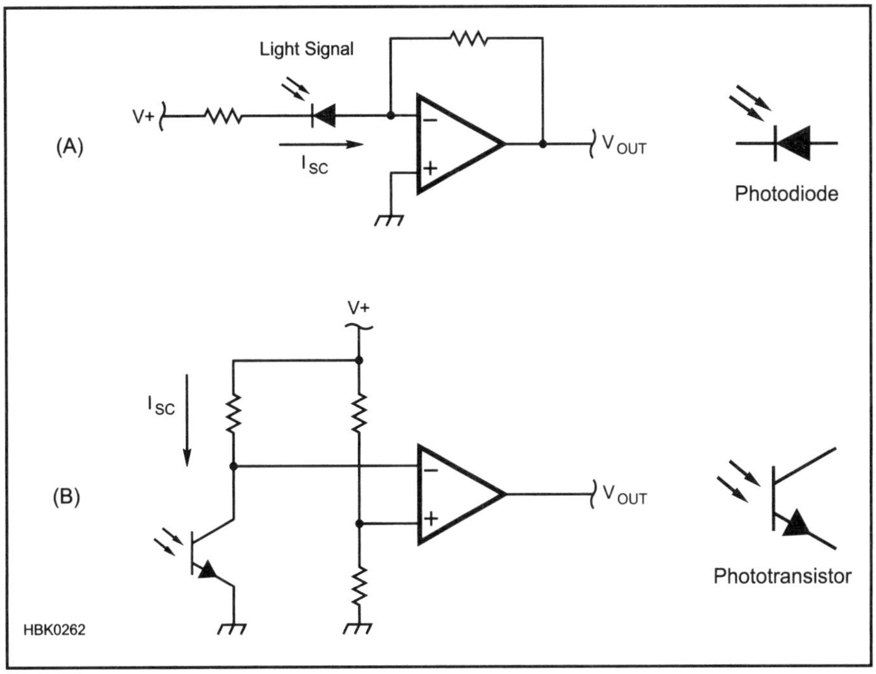

Figure 4.37 — The photodiode (A) is used to detect light. An amplifier circuit changes the variations in photodiode current to a change in output voltage. At (B), a photo-transistor conducts current when its base is illuminated. This causes the voltage at the collector to change causing the amplifier's output to switch between ON and OFF.

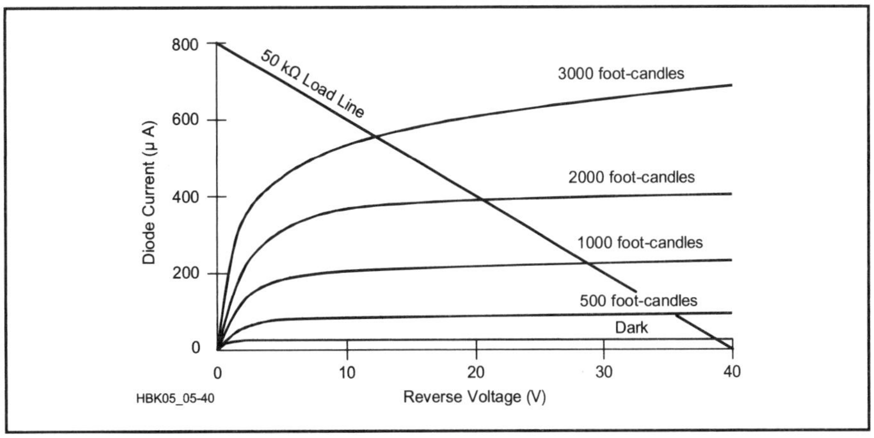

Figure 4.38 — Photodiode I-V curve. Reverse voltage is plotted on the X-axis and current through diode is plotted on the Y-axis. Various response lines are plotted for different illumination. Except for the zero illumination line, the response does not pass through the origin since there is current generated at the PN junction by the light energy. A load line is shown for a 50-kΩ resistor in series with the photodiode.

of 10 μA) that is nearly independent of reverse voltage. The presence of light not only increases the current but also provides a resistance-like relationship (reverse current increases as reverse voltage increases). See **Figure 4.38** for the characteristic response of a photodiode. Even with no reverse voltage applied, the presence of light causes a small reverse current, as indicated by the points at which the lines in Figure 4.38 intersect the left side of the graph.

Photoconductors and photodiodes are generally used to produce light-related analog signals that require further processing. For example, a photodiode is used to detect infrared light signals from remote control devices as in Figure 4.37A. The light falling on the reverse-biased photodiode causes a change in I_{SC} that is detected as a change in output voltage.

Light falling on the phototransistor acts as base current to control a larger current between the collector and emitter. Thus the phototransistor acts as an amplifier whose input signal is light and whose output is current. Phototransistors are more sensitive to light than the other devices. Phototransistors have lots of light-to-current gain, but photodiodes normally have less noise, so they make more sensitive detectors. The phototransistor in Figure 4.37B is being used as a detector. Light falling on the phototransistor causes collector current to flow, dropping the collector voltage below the voltage at the amplifier's + input and causing a change in V_{OUT}.

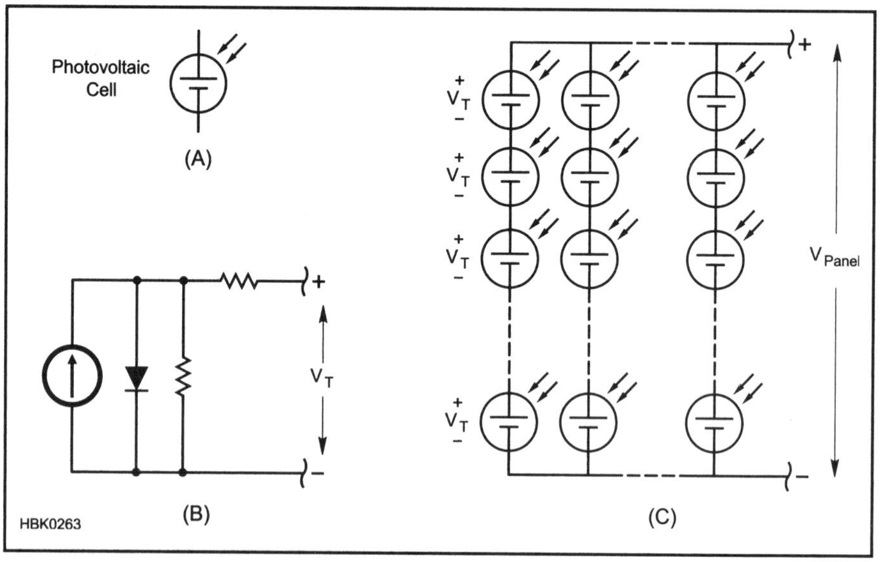

Figure 4.39 — A photovoltaic cell's symbol (A) is similar to a battery. Electrically, the cell can be modeled as the equivalent circuit at (B). Solar panels (C) consist of arrays of cells connected to supply power at a convenient voltage.

PHOTOVOLTAIC CELLS

When illuminated, the reverse-biased photodiode has a reverse current caused by excess minority carriers. As the reverse voltage is reduced, the potential barrier to the forward flow of majority carriers is also reduced. Since light energy leads to the generation of both majority and minority carriers, when the resistance to the flow of majority carriers is decreased these carriers form a forward current. The voltage at which the forward current equals the reverse current is called the *photovoltaic potential* of the junction. If the illuminated PN junction is not connected to a load, a voltage equal to the photovoltaic potential can be measured across it as the *terminal voltage,* V_T, or *open-circuit voltage,* V_{OC}.

Devices that use light from the sun to produce electricity in this way are called *photovoltaic (PV)* or *solar cells* or *solar batteries.* The symbol for a photovoltaic cell is shown in **Figure 4.39A**. The electrical equivalent circuit of the cell is shown in Figure 4.39B. The cell is basically a large, flat diode junction exposed to light. Metal electrodes on each side of the junction collect the current generated.

When illuminated, the cell acts like a current source, with some of the current flowing through a diode (made of the same material as the cell), a shunt resistance for leakage current and a series resistor that represents the resistance of the cell. Two quantities define the electrical characteristics of common silicon photovoltaic cells. These are an open-circuit voltage, V_{OC} of 0.5 to 0.6 V and the output *short-circuit current,* I_{SC} as above, that depends on the area of the cell exposed to light and the degree of illumination. A measure of the cell's effectiveness at converting light into current is the *conversion efficiency*. Typical silicon solar cells have a conversion efficiency of 10 to 15% although special cells with stacked junctions or using special light-absorbing materials have shown efficiencies as high as 40%.

Solar cells are primarily made from single-crystal slices of silicon, similar to diodes and transistors, but with a much greater area. *Polycrystalline silicon* and *thin-film* cells are less expensive, but have lower conversion efficiency. Technology is advancing rapidly in the field of photovoltaic energy and there are a number of different types of materials and fabrication techniques that have promise in surpassing the effectiveness of the single-junction silicon cells.

Solar cells are assembled into arrays called *solar panels*, shown in Figure 4.39C. Cells are connected in series so that the combined output voltage is a more useful voltage, such as 12 V. Several strings of cells are then connected in parallel to increase the available output current. Solar panels are available with output powers from a few watts to hundreds of watts. Note that unlike batteries, strings of solar cells can be connected directly in parallel because they act as sources of constant current instead of voltage. (More information on the use of solar panels for powering radio equipment can be found in the chapter on **Power Sources**.)

LIGHT EMITTING DIODES AND LASER DIODES

In the photodiode, energy from light falling on the semiconductor material is absorbed to create additional electron-hole pairs. When the electrons and holes recombine, the same amount of energy is given off. In normal diodes the energy from recombination of carriers is given off as heat. In certain forms of semiconductor material, the recombination energy is given off as light with a mechanism called *electroluminescence*. Unlike the incandescent light bulb, electroluminescence is a cold (non-thermal) light source that typically operates with low voltages and currents (such as 1.5 V and 10 mA). Devices made for this purpose are called *light emitting diodes (LEDs)*. They have the advantages of low power requirements, fast switching times (on the order of 10 ns) and narrow spectra (relatively pure color).

The LED emits light when it is forward biased and excess carriers are present. As the carriers recombine, light is produced with a color that depends on the properties of the semiconductor material used. Gallium-arsenide (GaAs) generates light in the infrared region, gallium-phosphide (GaP) gives off red light when doped with oxygen or green light when doped with nitrogen. Orange light is attained with a mixture of GaAs and GaP (GaAsP). Silicon-carbide (SiC) creates a blue LED.

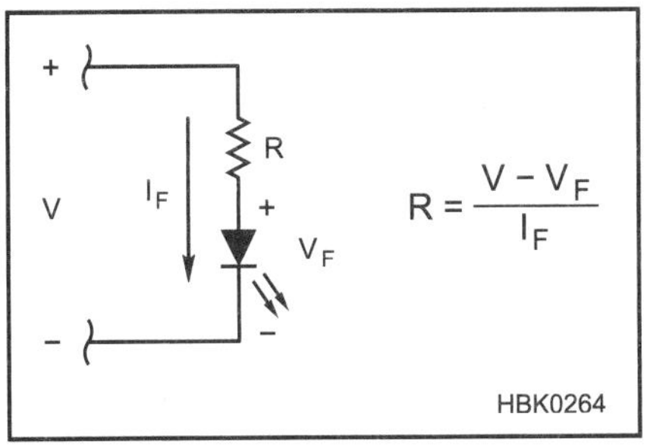

Figure 4.40 — A light-emitting diode (LED) emits light when conducting forward current. A series current-limiting resistor is used to set the current through the LED according to the equation.

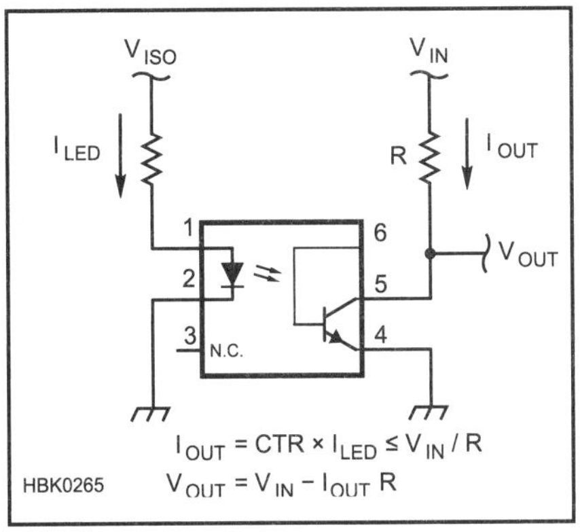

Figure 4.41 — The optoisolator consists of an LED (input) that illuminates the base of a phototransistor (output). The phototransistor then conducts current in the output circuit. CTR is the optoisolator's current transfer ratio.

White LEDs are made by coating the inside of the LED lens with a white-light emitting phosphor and illuminating the phosphor with light from a single-color LED. White LEDs are currently approaching the cost of cold-florescent (CFL) bulbs and will eventually displace CFL technology for lighting, just as CFL is replacing the incandescent bulb.

The LED, shown in **Figure 4.40**, is very simple to use. It is connected across a voltage source (V) with a series resistor (R) that limits the current to the desired level (I_F) for the amount of light to be generated.

$$R = \frac{V - V_F}{I_F}$$

where V_F is the forward voltage of the LED.

The cathode lead is connected to the lower potential, and is specially marked as shown in the manufacturer's data sheet. LEDs may be connected in series for additional light, with the same current flowing in all of the diodes. Diodes connected in parallel without current-limiting resistors for each diode are likely to share the current unequally, thus the series connection is preferred.

The laser diode operates by similar principles to the LED except that all of the light produced is *monochromatic* (of the same color and wavelength) and it is *coherent*, meaning that all of the light waves emitted by the device are in phase. Laser diodes generally require higher current than an LED and will not emit light until the *lasing current* level is reached. Because the light is monochromatic and coherent, laser diodes can be used for applications requiring precise illumination and modulation, such as high-speed data links, and in data storage media such as CD-ROM and DVD. LEDs are not used for high-speed or high-frequency analog modulation because of recovery time limitations, just as in regular rectifiers.

OPTOISOLATORS

An interesting combination of optoelectronic components proves very useful in many analog signal processing applications. An *optoisolator* consists of an LED optically coupled to a phototransistor, usually in an enclosed package (see **Figure 4.41**). The optoisolator, as its name suggests, isolates different circuits from each other. Typically, isolation resistance is on the order of 10^{11} Ω and isolation capacitance is less than 1 pF. Maximum voltage isolation varies from 1000 to 10,000 V ac. The most common optoisolators are available in 6-pin DIP packages.

Optoisolators are primarily used for voltage level shifting and signal isolation. Voltage level shifting allows signals (usually digital signals) to pass between circuits operating at greatly different voltages. The isolation has two purposes: to protect circuitry (and operators) from excessive voltages and to isolate noisy circuitry from noise-sensitive circuitry.

Optoisolators also cannot transfer signals with high power levels. The power rating of the LED in a 4N25 device is 120 mW. Optoisolators have a limited frequency response due to the high capacitance of the LED. A typical bandwidth for the 4N25 series is 300 kHz. Optoisolators with bandwidths of several MHz are available, but are somewhat expensive.

As an example of voltage level shifting, an optoisolator can be used to allow a low-voltage, solid-state electronic Morse code keyer to activate a vacuum-tube grid-block keying circuit that operates at a high negative voltage (typically about –100 V) but low current. No common ground is required between the two pieces of equipment.

Optoisolators can act as input protection for circuits that are exposed to high voltages or transients. For example, a short 1000-V transient that can destroy a semiconductor circuit will only saturate the LED in the optoisolator, preventing damage to the circuit. The worst that will happen is the LED in the optoisolator will be destroyed, but that is usually quite a bit less expensive than the circuit it is protecting.

Optoisolators are also useful for isolating different ground systems. The input and output signals are totally isolated from each other, even with respect to the references for each signal. A common application for optoisolators is when a computer is used to control radio equipment. The computer signal, and even its ground reference, typically contains considerable wide-band noise caused by the digital circuitry. The best way to keep this noise out of the radio is to isolate both the signal and its reference; this is easily done with an optoisolator.

The design of circuits with optoisolators is not greatly different from the design of circuits with LEDs and with transistors. On the input side, the LED is forward-biased and driven with a series current-limiting resistor whose value limits current to less than the maximum value for the device (for example, 60 mA is the maximum LED current for a 4N25). This is identical to designing with standalone LEDs.

On the output side, instead of current gain for a transistor, the optoisolator's *current transfer ratio* (*CTR*) is used. CTR is a ratio given in percent between the amount of current through the LED to the output transistor's maximum available collector current. For example, if an optoisolator's CTR = 25%, then an LED current of 20 mA results in the output transistor being able to conduct up to 20 × 0.25 = 5 mA of current in its collector circuit.

If the optoisolator is to be used for an analog signal, the input signal must be appropriately dc shifted so that the LED is always forward biased. A phototransistor with all three leads available for connection (as in Figure 4.41) is required. The base lead is used for biasing, allowing the optical signal to create variations above and below the transistor's operating point. The collector and emitter leads are used as they would be in any transistor amplifier circuit. (There are also linear optoisolators that include built-in linearizing circuitry.) The use of linear optoisolators is not common.

FIBER OPTICS

An interesting variation on the optoisolator is the *fiber-optic* connection. Like the optoisolator, the input signal is used to drive an LED or laser diode that produces modulated light (usually light pulses). The light is transmitted in a fiber optic cable, an extruded glass fiber that efficiently carries light over long distances and around fairly sharp bends. The signal is recovered by a photo detector (photoresistor, photodiode or phototransistor). Because the fiber optic cable is nonconductive, the transmitting and receiving systems are electrically isolated.

Fiber optic cables generally have far less loss than coaxial cable transmission lines. They do not leak RF energy, nor do they pick up electrical noise. Fiber optic cables are virtually immune to electromagnetic interference! Special forms of LEDs and phototransistors are available with the appropriate optical couplers for connecting to fiber optic cables. These devices are typically designed for higher frequency operation with gigahertz bandwidth.

4.5.7 Integrated Circuits (ICs)

If you look inside a transistor, the actual size of the semiconductor is quite small compared to the size of the packaging. For most semiconductors, the packaging takes considerably more space than the actual semiconductor device. Thus, an obvious way to reduce the physical size of circuitry is to combine more of the circuit inside a single package.

HYBRID INTEGRATED CIRCUITS

It is easy to imagine placing several small semiconductor chips in the same package. This is known as *hybrid circuitry*, a technology in which several semiconductor chips are placed in the same package and miniature wires are connected between them to make complete circuits.

Hybrid circuits miniaturize analog or analog/digital electronic circuits by eliminating much of the packaging and interconnections inherent in discrete electronics. The term *discrete* refers to the use of individual components to make a circuit, each in its own package. The individual components are attached together on a small circuit board or with bonding wires. Manufacturers often use hybrids when small size and specialized techniques are needed, but there is insufficient volume to justify the expense of a custom IC.

A current application for hybrid circuitry is UHF and microwave amplifiers — they are in wide use by the mobile phone industry. For example, the Motorola MW4IC915N Wideband Integrated Power Amplifier in **Figure 4.42** is a complete 15-W transmitting module. Its TO-272 package is only about 1 inch long by ⅜-inch wide. This particular device is designed for use between 750 and 1000 MHz and can be adapted for use on the amateur 902 MHz band. Other devices available as hybrid circuits include oscillators, signal processors, preamplifiers and so forth. Surplus hybrids can be hard to adapt to amateur use unless they are clearly identified with manufacturing identification such that a data sheet can be obtained.

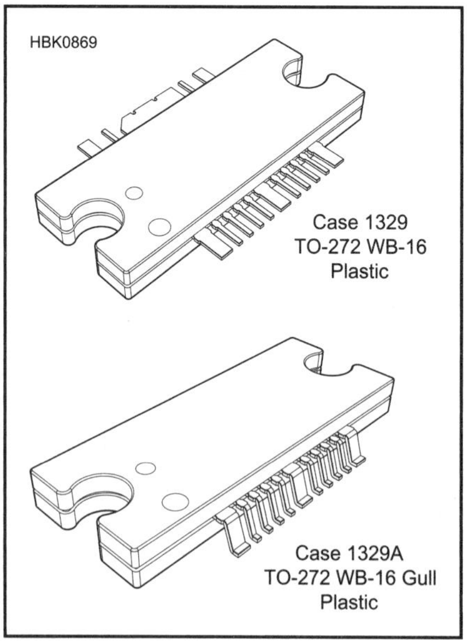

Figure 4.42 — The TO-272 is typical of packages used for hybrid IC RF amplifier modules at UHF and microwave frequencies.

MONOLITHIC INTEGRATED CIRCUITS

In order to build entire circuits on a single piece of semiconductor, it must be possible to fabricate resistors and capacitors, as well as transistors and diodes. Only then can the entire circuit be created on one piece of silicon called a *monolithic integrated circuit.* The following description is a relatively simplified view of monolithic IC structure and fabrication techniques. IC technology is advancing on many directions at a very rapid rate. Giving a comprehensive description of current ICs — even the limited number of types used in Amateur Radio — is well beyond the scope of this book. References on specific technologies are given at the end of each chapter for the interested reader to pursue.

An integrated circuit (IC) or "chip" is fabricated in layers. An example of a semiconductor circuit schematic and its implementation in an IC is pictured in **Figure 4.43**. The base layer of the circuit, the *substrate*, is made of P-type semiconductor material. Although less common, the polarity of the substrate can also be N-type material. Since the mobility of electrons is about three times higher than that of holes, bipolar transistors made with N-type collectors and FETs made with N-type channels are capable of higher speeds and power handling. Thus, P-type substrates are far more common. For devices with N-type substrates, all polarities in the ensuing discussion would be reversed.

Other substrates have been used, one of the most successful of which is the *silicon-on-sapphire* (SOS) construction that has been used to increase the bandwidth of integrated circuitry. Its relatively high manufacturing cost has impeded its use, however, except for the demanding military and aerospace applications. Many other types of substrates are employed in various special applications.

On top of the P-type substrate is a thin layer of N-type material in which the active and passive components are built. Impurities are diffused into this layer to form the appropriate component at each location. To prevent random diffusion of impurities into the N-layer, its upper surface must be protected. This is done by covering the N-layer with a layer of silicon dioxide (SiO_2). Wherever diffusion of impurities is desired, the SiO_2 is etched away. The precision of placing the components on the semiconductor material depends mainly on the fineness of the etching. The fourth layer of an IC is made of aluminum (copper is used in some high-speed digital ICs) and is used to make the interconnections between the components.

Different components are made in a single piece of semiconductor material by first diffusing a high concentration of acceptor impurities into the layer of N-type material. This process creates P-type semiconductor — often referred to as P^+-type semiconductor because of its high concentration of acceptor atoms — that isolates regions of N-type material. Each of these regions is then further processed to form single components.

A component is produced by the diffusion of a lesser concentration of acceptor atoms into the middle of each isolation region. This results in an N-type *isolation well* that contains P-type material, is surrounded on its sides by P^+-type material and has P-type material (substrate) below it. The cross sectional view in Figure 4.41B illustrates the various layers. Connections to the metal layer are often made by diffusing high concentrations of donor atoms into small regions of the N-type well and the P-type material in the well. The material in these small regions is N^+-type and facilitates electron flow between the metal contact and the semiconductor. In some configurations, it is necessary to connect the metal directly to the P-type material in the well.

Fabricating Resistors and Capacitors

An isolation well can be made into a resistor by making two contacts into the P-type semiconductor in the well. Resistance is inversely proportional to the cross-sectional area of the well. An alternate type of resistor that can be integrated in a semiconductor circuit is a *thin-film resistor*, where a metallic film is deposited on the SiO_2 layer, masked on its upper surface by more SiO_2 and then etched to make the desired geometry, thus adjusting the resistance.

There are two ways to form capacitors in a semiconductor. One is to make use of the PN junction between the N-type well and the

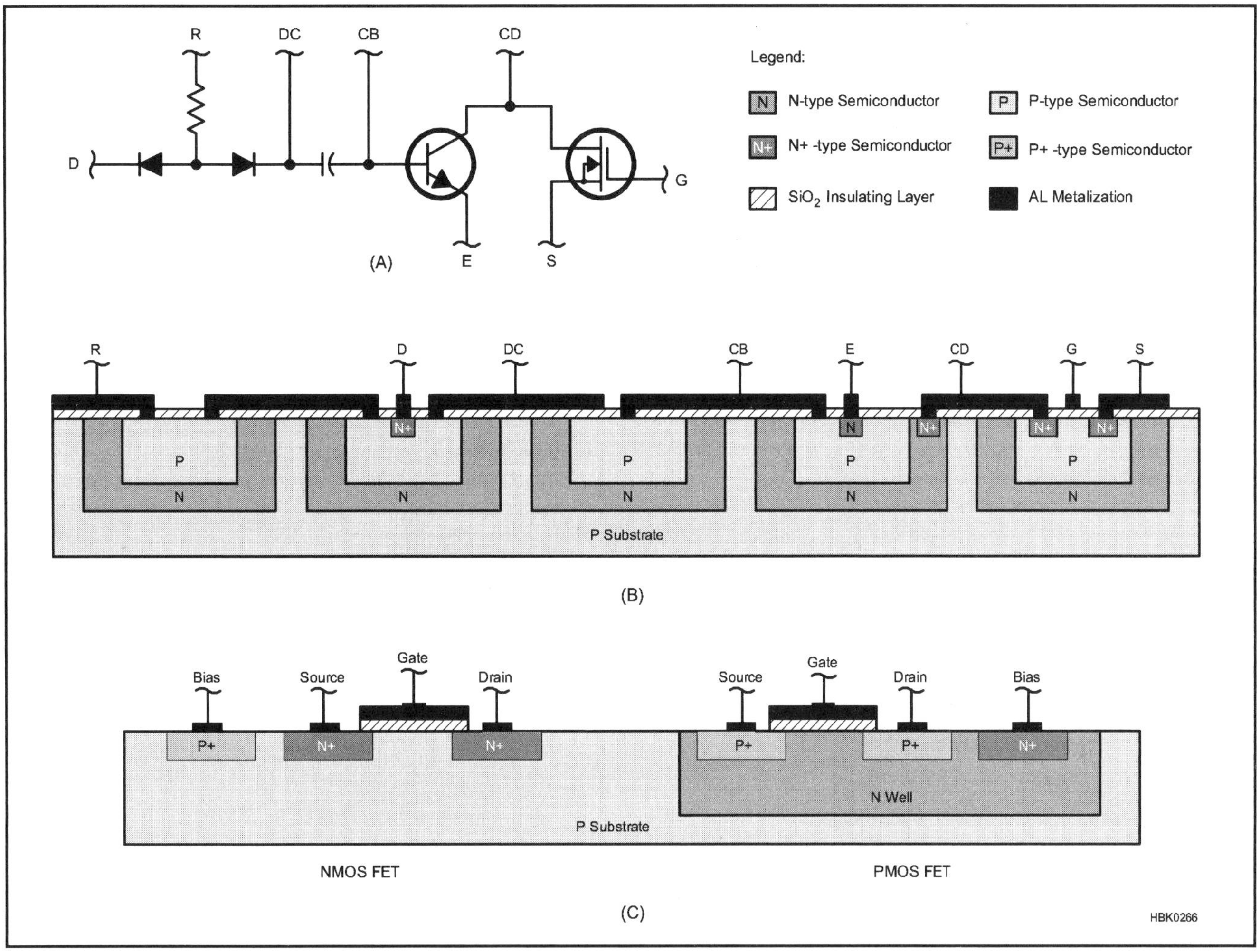

Figure 4.43 — Integrated circuit construction. (A) Circuit containing two diodes, a resistor, a capacitor, an NPN transistor and an N-channel MOSFET. Labeled leads are D for diode, R for resistor, DC for diode-capacitor, E for emitter, S for source, CD for collector-drain and G for gate. (B) Integrated circuit that is identical to circuit in (A). Same leads are labeled for comparison. Circuit is built on a P-type semiconductor substrate with N-type wells diffused into it. An insulating layer of SiO_2 is above the semiconductor and is etched away where aluminum metal contacts are made with the semiconductor. Most metal-to-semiconductor contacts are made with heavily doped N-type material (N^+-type semiconductor).

P-type material that fills it. Much like a varactor diode, when this junction is reverse biased a capacitance results. Since a bias voltage is required, this type of capacitor is polarized, like an electrolytic capacitor. Nonpolarized capacitors can also be formed in an integrated circuit by using thin film technology. In this case, a very high concentration of donor ions is diffused into the well, creating an N^+-type region. A thin metallic film is deposited over the SiO_2 layer covering the well and the capacitance is created between the metallic film and the well. The value of the capacitance is adjusted by varying the thickness of the SiO_2 layer and the cross-sectional size of the well. This type of thin film capacitor is also known as a metal oxide semiconductor (MOS) capacitor.

Unlike resistors and capacitors, it is very difficult to create inductors in integrated circuits. Generally, RF circuits that need inductance require external inductors to be connected to the IC. In some cases, particularly at lower frequencies, the behavior of an inductor can be mimicked by an amplifier circuit. In many cases the appropriate design of IC amplifiers can reduce or eliminate the need for external inductors. As the frequency of operation increases, however, the amount of inductance needed falls for an equivalent amount of reactance. This had led to several innovative techniques for creating small inductors using the metallization layers of the IC.

Fabricating Diodes and Transistors

The simplest form of diode is generated by connecting to an N^+-type connection point in the well for the cathode and to the P-type well material for the anode. Diodes are often converted from NPN transistor configurations. Integrated circuit diodes made this way can either short the collector to the base or leave the collector unconnected. The base contact is the anode and the emitter contact is the cathode.

Transistors are created in integrated circuitry in much the same way that they are fabricated in their discrete forms. The NPN transistor is the easiest to make since the wall of the well, made of N-type semiconductor, forms the collector, the P-type material in the well forms the base and a small region of N^+-type material formed in the center of the well becomes the emitter. A PNP transistor is made by diffusing donor ions into the P-type semiconductor in the well to make a pattern with P-type material in the center (emitter) surrounded by a ring of N-type material that connects all the way down to the well material (base), and this is surrounded by another ring of P-type material (collector). This configuration results in a large base width separating the emitter and collector, causing these devices to have much lower current gain than the NPN form. This is one reason why integrated circuitry is designed to use many more NPN transistors than PNP transistors.

FETs can also be fabricated in IC form as shown in Figure 4.43C. Due to its many functional advantages, the MOSFET is the most common form used for digital ICs. MOSFETs are made in a semiconductor chip much the same way as MOS capacitors, described earlier. In addition to the signal processing advantages offered by MOSFETs over other transistors, the MOSFET device can be fabricated in 5% of the physical space required for bipolar transistors. CMOS ICs can contain 20 times more circuitry than bipolar ICs with the same chip size, making the devices more powerful and less expensive than those based on bipolar technology. CMOS is the most popular form of integrated circuit.

The final configuration of the switching circuit is CMOS as described in a previous section of this chapter. CMOS gates require two FETs, one of each form (NMOS and PMOS as shown in the figure). NMOS requires fewer processing steps, and the individual FETs have lower on-resistance than PMOS. The fabrication of NMOS FETs is the same as for individual semiconductors; P+ wells form the source and drain in a P-type substrate. A metal gate electrode is formed on top of an insulating SiO_2 layer so that the channel forms in the P-type substrate between the source and drain. For the PMOS FET, the process is similar, but begins with an N-type well in the P-type substrate.

MOSFETs fabricated in this manner also have bias (B) terminals connected to the positive power supply to prevent destructive *latch-up*. This can occur in CMOS gates because the two MOSFETs form a *parasitic SCR*. If the SCR mode is triggered and both transistors conduct at the same time, large currents can flow through the FET and destroy the IC unless power is removed. Just as discrete MOSFETs are at risk of gate destruction, IC chips made with MOSFET devices have a similar risk. They should be treated with the same care to protect them from static electricity as discrete MOSFETs.

While CMOS is the most widely used technology, integrated circuits need not be made exclusively with MOSFETs or bipolar transistors. It is common to find IC chips designed with both technologies, taking advantage of the strengths of each.

4.6 Amplifiers

By far, the most common type of analog circuit is the amplifier. The basic component of most electronics — the transistor — is an amplifier in which a small input signal controls a larger signal. Most of modern electronics, both analog and digital, are based on the transistor amplifier or switch, regardless of whether the input signal is amplified at the output.

4.6.1 Amplifier Configurations

Amplifier configurations are described by the *common* part of the device. The word "common" is used to describe the connection of a lead directly to a reference that is used by both the input and output ports of the circuit. The most common reference is ground, but positive and negative power sources are also valid references.

The type of circuit reference used depends on the type of device (transistor [NPN or PNP] or FET [P-channel or N-channel]), which lead is chosen as common, and the range of signal levels. Once a common lead is chosen, the other two leads are used for signal input and output. Based on the biasing conditions, there is only one way to select these leads. Thus, there are three possible amplifier configurations for each type of three-lead device. (Vacuum tube amplifiers are discussed in the chapter on **RF Power Amplifiers**.)

DC power sources are usually constructed so that ac signals at the output terminals are bypassed to ground through a very low impedance. This allows the power source to be treated as an *ac ground*, even though it may be supplying dc voltages to the circuit. When a circuit is being analyzed for its ac behavior, ac grounds are usually treated as ground, since dc bias is ignored in the ac analysis. Thus, a transistor's collector can be considered the "common" part of the circuit, even though in actual operation, a dc voltage is applied to it.

Figure 4.44 shows the three basic types of bipolar transistor amplifiers: the common-base, common-emitter, and common-collector. The common terminal is shown connected to ground, although as mentioned earlier, a dc bias voltage may be present. Each type of amplifier is described in the following sections. Following the description of the amplifier, additional discussion of biasing transistors and their operation at high frequencies and for large signals is presented.

4.6.2 Transistor Amplifiers

Creating a useful transistor amplifier depends on using an appropriate model for the transistor itself, choosing the right configuration of the amplifier, using the design equations for that configuration and insuring that the amplifier operates properly at different temperatures. This section follows that sequence, first introducing simple transistor models and then extending that knowledge to the point of design guidelines for common circuits that use bipolar and FETs.

DEVICE MODELS AND CLASSES

Semiconductor circuit design is based on equivalent circuits that describe the physics of the devices. These circuits, made up of voltage and current sources and passive components such as resistors, capacitors and inductors, are called models. A complete model that describes a transistor exactly over a wide frequency range is a fairly complex circuit. As a result, simpler models are used in specific circumstances. For example, the *small-signal model* works well when the device is operated close to some nominal set of characteristics such that current and voltage interact fairly linearly. The *large-signal model* is used when the device is operated so that it enters its saturation or cut-off regions, for example.

Different frequency ranges also require different models. The *low-frequency models* used in this chapter can be used to develop circuits for dc, audio and very low RF applications. At higher frequencies, small capacitances and inductances that can be ignored at low frequencies begin to have significant effects on device behavior, such as gain or impedance. In addition, the physical structure of the device also becomes significant as gain begins to drop or phase shifts between input and output signals start to grow. In this region, *high-frequency models* are used.

Amplifiers are also grouped by their *operating class* that describes the way in which the input signal is amplified. There are several classes of analog amplifiers; A, B, AB, AB1, AB2 and C.

The analog class designators specify over how much of the input cycle the active device is conducting current. A class-A amplifier's active device conducts current for 100 percent of the input signal cycle, such as shown in Figure 4.25. A class-B amplifier conducts during one-half of the input cycle, class-AB, AB1, and AB2 some fraction between 50 and

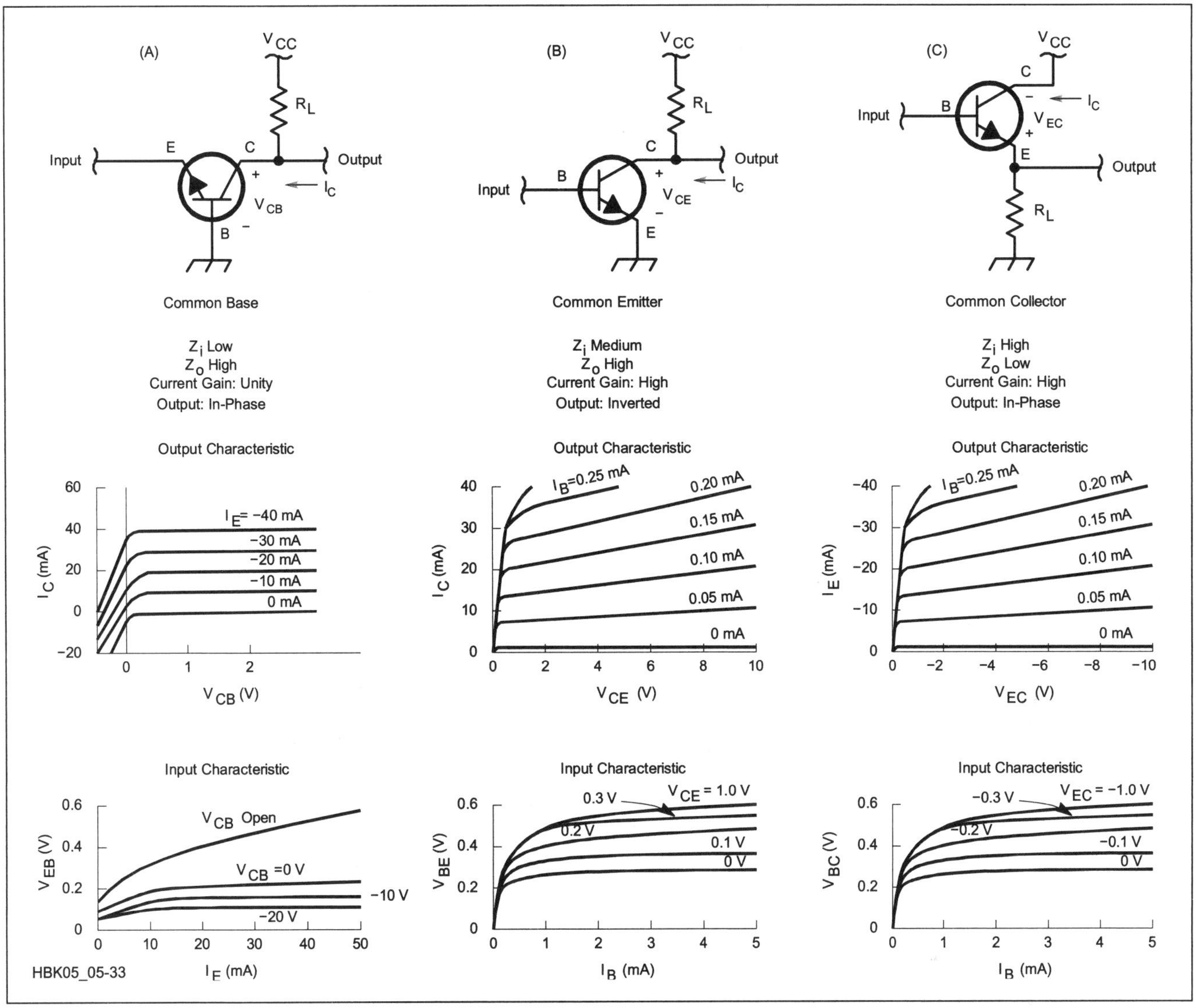

Figure 4.44 — The three configurations of bipolar transistor amplifiers. Each has a table of its relative impedance and current gain. The output characteristic curve is plotted for each, with the output voltage along the X-axis, the output current along the Y-axis and various curves plotted for different values of input current. The input characteristic curve is plotted for each configuration with input current along the X-axis, input voltage along the Y-axis and various curves plotted for different values of output voltage. (A) Common base configuration with input terminal at the emitter and output terminal at the collector. (B) Common emitter configuration with input terminal at the base and output terminal at the collector. (C) Common collector with input terminal at the base and output terminal at the emitter.

100 percent of the input cycle, and class-C for less than 50 percent of the input signal cycle.

Digital amplifiers, in which the active device is operated as a switch that is either fully-on or fully-off, similarly to switchmode power supplies, are also grouped by classes beginning with the letter D and beyond. Each different class uses a different method of converting the switch's output waveform to the desired RF waveform.

Amplifier classes, models and their use at high-frequencies are discussed in more detail in the chapter on **RF Techniques**. In addition, the use of models for circuit simulation is discussed at length in the **Computer-Aided Circuit Design** chapter.

4.6.3 Bipolar Transistor Amplifiers

In this discussion, we will focus on simple models for bipolar transistors (BJTs). This discussion is centered on NPN BJTs but applies equally well to PNP BJTs if the bias voltage and current polarities are reversed. This section assumes the small-signal, low-frequency models for the transistors.

SMALL-SIGNAL BJT MODEL

The transistor is usually considered as a *current-controlled* device in which the base current controls the collector current:

$$I_c = \beta I_b$$

where

I_c = collector current
I_b = base current
β = common-emitter current gain, beta.

(The term "common-emitter" refers to the type of transistor circuit described below in which the transistor operates with base current as its input and collector circuit as its output.) Current is positive if it flows *into* a device terminal.

The transistor can also be treated as a voltage-controlled device in which the transistor's emitter current, I_e, is controlled by the base-emitter voltage, V_{be}:

$$I_c = I_{es}\,[e^{(qV_{be}/kT)} - 1] \approx I_{es}e^{(qV_{be}/kT)}$$

where
- q = electronic charge
- k = Boltzmann's constant
- T = temperature in degrees Kelvin (K)
- I_{es} = emitter saturation current, typically 1×10^{-13} A.

The subscripts for voltages indicate the direction of positive voltage, so that V_{be} indicates positive is from the base to the emitter. It is simpler to design circuits using the current-controlled device, but accounting for the transistor's behavior with temperature requires an understanding of the voltage-controlled model.

Transistors are usually driven by both biasing and signal voltages. Both equations above for collector current apply to both transistor dc biasing and signal design. Both of these equations are approximations of the more complex behavior exhibited by actual transistors. The second equation applies to a simplification of the first *Ebers-Moll model* (see references). More sophisticated models for BJTs are described by Getreu (see references). Small-signal models treat only the signal components. We will consider bias later.

The next step is to use these basic equations to design circuits. We will begin with small-signal amplifier design and the limits of where the techniques can be applied. Later, we'll discuss large-signal amplifier design and the distortion that arises from operating the transistor in regions where the relationship between the input and output signals is nonlinear.

Common-Emitter Model

Figure 4.45 shows a BJT amplifier connected in the common-emitter configuration. (The emitter, shown connected to ground, is common to both the input circuit with the voltage source and the output circuit with the transistor's collector.) The performance of this circuit is adequately described by the simple equation $I_c = \beta I_b$. **Figure 4.46** shows the most common of all transistor small-signal models, a controlled current source with emitter resistance.

There are two variations of the model shown in the figure. Figure 4.46B shows the base as a direct connection to the junction of a current-controlled current source ($I_c = \beta I_b$) and a resistance, r_e, the *dynamic emitter resistance* representing the change in V_{be} with I_e. This resistance also changes with emitter current:

$$r_e = \frac{kT}{qI_c} \approx \frac{26}{I_e}$$

where I_e is the dc bias current in milliamperes.

The simplified approximation only applies at a typical ambient temperature of 300 K because r_e increases with temperature. In Figure 4.46A, the emitter resistance has been moved to the base connection, where it has the value $(\beta+1)r_e$. These models are electrically equivalent.

The transistor's output resistance (the Thevenin or Norton equivalent resistance between the collector and the grounded emitter) is infinite because of the current source. This is a good approximation for most silicon transistors at low frequencies (well below the transistor's gain-bandwidth product, F_T) and will be used for the design examples that follow.

As frequency increases, the capacitance inherent in BJT construction becomes significant and the *hybrid-pi model* shown in **Figure 4.47** is used, adding C_π in parallel with the input resistance. In this model the transfer parameter h_{ie} often represents the input impedance, shown here as a resistance at low frequencies.

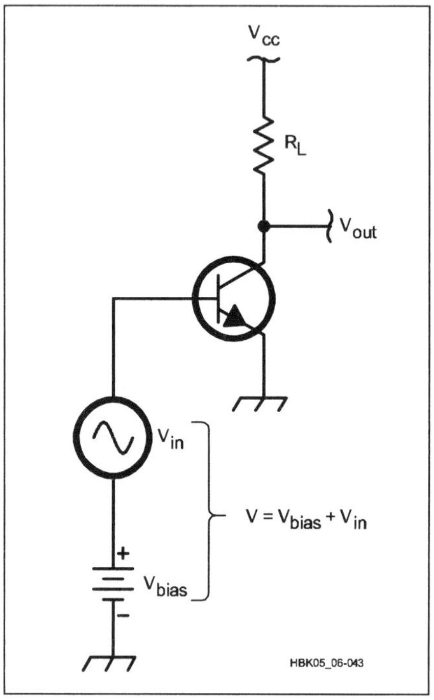

Figure 4.45 — Bipolar transistor with voltage bias and input signal.

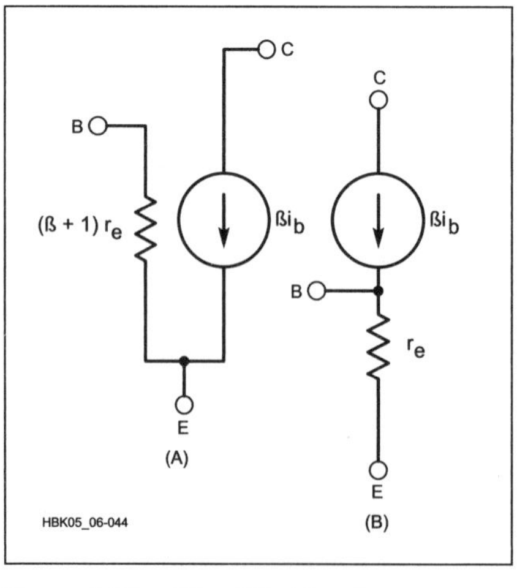

Figure 4.46 — Simplified low-frequency model for the bipolar transistor, a "beta generator with emitter resistance." r_e = 26 / I_e (mA dc).

THREE BASIC BJT AMPLIFIERS

Figure 4.48 shows a small-signal model applied to the three basic bipolar junction transistor (BJT) amplifier circuits: *common-emitter* (CE), *common-base* (CB) and *common-collector* (CC), more commonly known as the *emitter-follower* (EF). As defined earlier, the word "common" indicates that the referenced terminal is part of both the input and output circuits.

In these simple models, transistors in both the CE and CB configurations have infinite output resistance because the collector current source is in series with the output current. (The amplifier circuit's output impedance must include the effects of R_L.) The transistor connected in the EF configuration, on the other hand, has a finite output resistance because the current source is connected in parallel with the base circuit's equivalent resistance. Calculating the EF amplifier's output resistance requires including the input voltage source, V_s, and its impedance.

The three transistor amplifier configurations are shown as simple circuits in Figure 4.42. Each circuit includes the basic characteristics of the amplifier and characteristic curves for a typical transistor in each configuration. Two sets of characteristic curves are presented: one describing the input behavior and the other describing the output behavior in each amplifier configuration. The different transistor amplifier configurations have different gains, input and output imped-

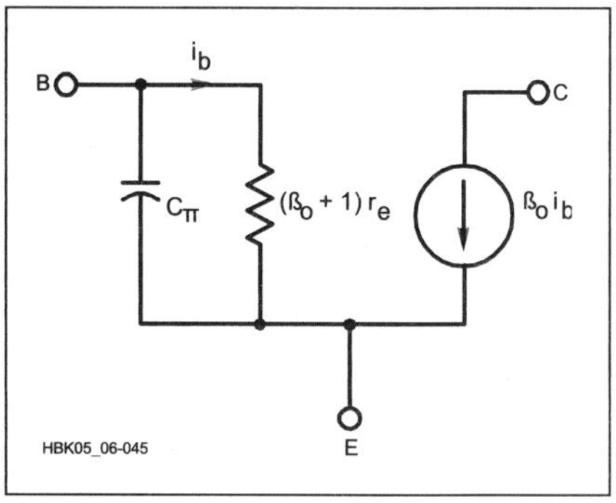

Figure 4.47 — The hybrid-pi model for the bipolar transistor.

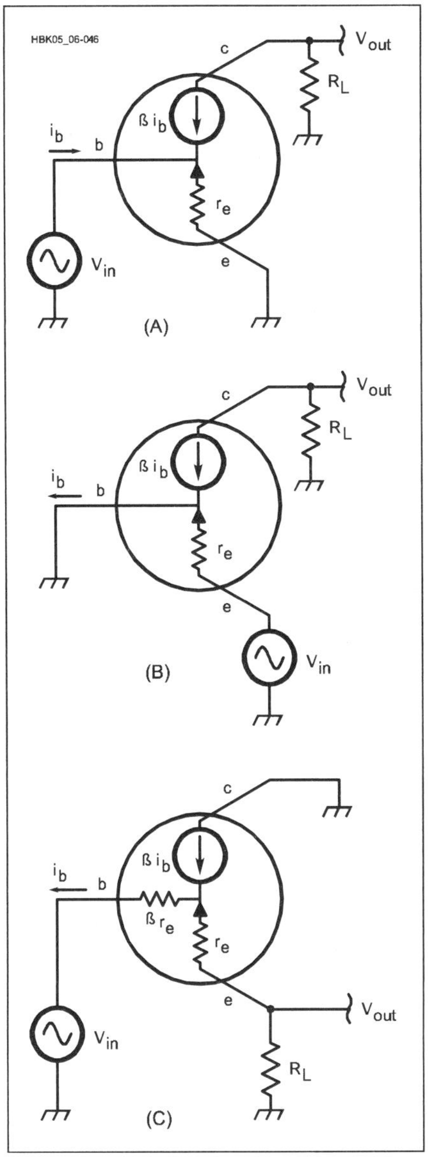

Figure 4.48 — Application of small-signal models for analysis of (A) the CE amplifier, (B) the CB and (C) the EF (CC) bipolar junction transistor amplifiers.

ances and phase relationships between the input and output signals.

Examining the performance needs of the amplifier (engineers refer to these as the circuit's *performance requirements*) determines which of the three circuits is appropriate. Then, once the amplifier configuration is chosen, the equations that describe the circuit's behavior are used to turn the performance requirements into actual circuit component values.

This text presents design information for the CE amplifier in some detail, then summarizes designs for the CC and CB amplifiers. Detailed design analysis for all three amplifiers is described in the texts listed in the reference section for this chapter. All of the analysis in the following sections assume the small-signal, low-frequency model and ignore the effects of the coupling capacitors. High-frequency considerations are discussed in the **RF Techniques** chapter and some advanced discussion of biasing and large signal behavior of BJT amplifiers is available in the downloadable supplemental content.

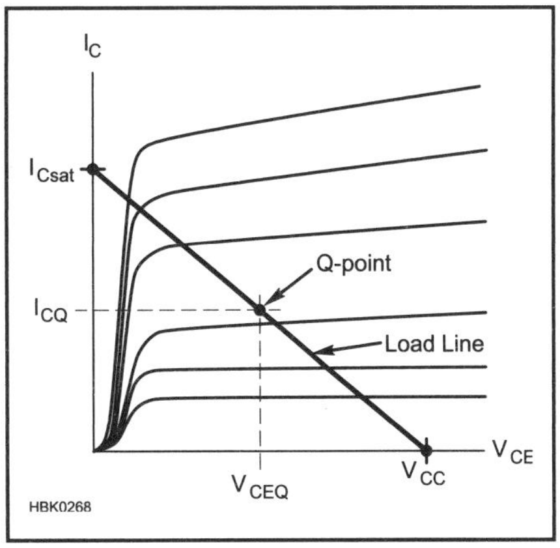

Figure 4.49 — A load line. A circuit's load line shows all of the possible operating points with the specific component values chosen. If there is no input signal, the operating point is the quiescent or Q-point.

LOAD LINES AND Q-POINT

The characteristic curves in Figure 4.44 show that the transistor can operate with an infinite number of combinations of current (collector, emitter and base) and voltage (collector-emitter, collector-base or emitter-collector). The particular combination at which the amplifier is operating is its *operating point*. The operating point is controlled by the selection of component values that make up the amplifier circuit so that it has the proper combination of gain, linearity and so forth. The result is that the operating point is restricted to a set of points that fall along a *load line*. The operating point with no input signal applied is the circuit's *quiescent point* or *Q-point*. As the input signal varies, the operating point moves along the load line, but returns to the Q-point when the input signal is removed.

Figure 4.49 shows the load line and Q-point for an amplifier drawn on a transistor's set of characteristic curves for the CE amplifier circuit. The two end-points of the load line correspond to transistor saturation (I_{Csat} on the I_C current axis) and cutoff (V_{CC} on the V_{CE} voltage axis).

When a transistor is in saturation, further increases in base current do not cause a further increase in collector current. In the CE amplifier, this means that V_{CE} is very close to zero and I_C is at a maximum. In the circuit of Figure 4.42B, imagine a short circuit across the collector-to-emitter so that all of V_{CC} appears across R_L. Increasing base current will not result in any additional collector current. At cutoff, base current is so small that V_{CE} is at a maximum because no collector current is flowing and further reductions in base current cause no additional increase in V_{CE}.

In this simple circuit, $V_{CE} = V_{CC} - I_C R_L$ and the relationship between I_C and V_{CE} is a straight line between saturation and cutoff. This is the circuit's *load line* and it has a slope of $R_L = (V_{CC} - V_{CE}) / I_C$. No matter what value of base current is flowing in the transistor, the resulting combination of I_C and V_{CE} will be somewhere on the load line.

With no input signal to this simple circuit, the transistor is at cutoff where $I_C = 0$ and $V_{CE} = V_{CC}$. As the input signal increases so that base current gets larger, the operating point begins to move along the load line to the left, so that I_C increases and the voltage drop across the load, $I_C R_L$, increases, reducing V_{CE}. Eventually, the input signal will cause enough base current to flow that saturation is reached, where $V_{CE} \approx 0$ (typically 0.1 to 0.3 V for silicon transistors) and $I_C \approx V_{CC} / R_L$. If R_L is made smaller, the load line will become steeper and if R_L increases, the load line's slope is reduced.

This simple circuit cannot reproduce negative input signals because the transistor is already in cutoff with no input signal. In addition, the shape and spacing of the characteristic curves show that the transistor responds nonlinearly when close to saturation and cutoff (the nonlinear regions) than it does in the middle of the curves (the linear or active region). Biasing is required so that the circuit does not operate in nonlinear regions, distorting the signal as shown in Figure 4.25.

If the circuit behaves differently for ac signals than for dc signals, a separate *ac load line* can be drawn as discussed below in the section "AC Performance" for the common-emitter amplifier. For example, in the preceding circuit, if R_L is replaced by a circuit that includes inductive or capacitive reactance, ac collector current will result in a different voltage drop across the circuit than will dc collector current. This causes the slope of the ac load line to be different than that of the dc load line.

The ac load line's slope will also vary with frequency, although it is generally treated as constant over the range of frequencies for which the circuit is designed to operate. The ac and dc load lines intersect at the circuit's Q-point because the circuit's ac and dc operation is the same if the ac input signal is zero.

COMMON-EMITTER AMPLIFIER

The *common-emitter amplifier* (*CE*) is the most common amplifier configuration of all

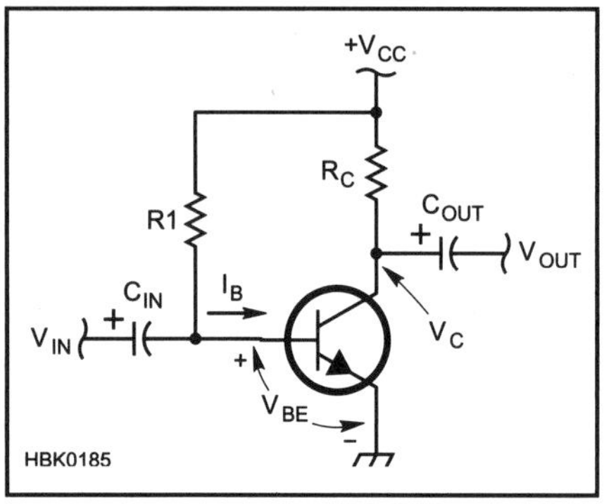

Figure 4.50 — Fixed-bias is the simplest common-emitter (CE) amplifier circuit.

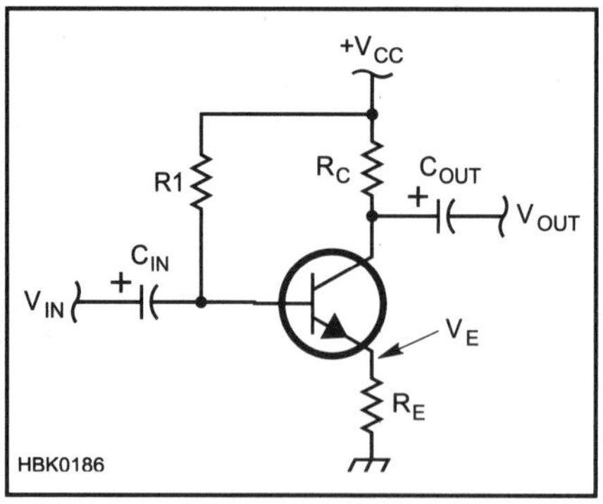

Figure 4.51 — Emitter degeneration. Adding R_E produces negative feedback to stabilize the bias point against changes due to temperature. As the bias current increases, the voltage drop across R_E also increases and causes a decrease in V_{BE}. This reduces bias current and stabilizes the operating point.

— found in analog and digital circuits, from dc through microwaves, made of discrete components and fabricated in ICs. If you understand the CE amplifier, you've made a good start in electronics.

The CE amplifier is used when modest voltage gain is required along with an *input impedance* (the load presented to the circuit supplying the signal to be amplified) of a few hundred to a few kΩ. The current gain of the CE amplifier is the transistor's current gain, β.

The simplest practical CE amplifier circuit is shown in **Figure 4.50**. This circuit includes both coupling and biasing components. The capacitors at the input (C_{IN}) and output (C_{OUT}) block the flow of dc current to the load or to the circuit driving the amplifier. This is an ac-coupled design. These capacitors also cause the gain at very low frequencies to be reduced — gain at dc is zero, for example, because dc input current is blocked by C_{IN}. Resistor R_1 provides a path for bias current to flow into the base, offsetting the collector current from zero and establishing the Q-point for the circuit.

As the input signal swings positive, more current flows into the transistor's base through C_{IN}, causing more current to flow from the collector to emitter. This causes more voltage drop across R_L and so the voltage at the collector also drops. The reverse is true when the input signal swings negative. Thus, the output from the CE amplifier is inverted from its input.

Kirchoff's Voltage Law is used to analyze the circuit. We'll start with the collector circuit and treat the power supply as a voltage source.

$$V_{cc} = I_c R_c + V_{ce}$$

We can determine the circuit's voltage gain, A_V, from the variation in output voltage caused by variations in input voltage. The output voltage from the circuit at the transistor collector is

$$V_c = V_{CC} - I_c R_c = V_{CC} - \beta I_B R_C$$

It is also necessary to determine how base current varies with input voltage. Using the transistor's equivalent circuit of Figure 4.46A,

$$I_B = \frac{V_B}{(\beta \mid 1)\, r_e}$$

so that

$$V_c = V_{CC} - V_B \frac{\beta}{\beta + 1} \times \frac{R_C}{r_e}$$

We can now determine the circuit's *voltage gain*, the variation in output voltage, ΔV_C, due to variations in input voltage, ΔV_B. Since V_{CC} is constant and β is much greater than 1 in our model:

$$A_V \approx -\frac{R_C}{r_e}$$

Because r_e is quite small (typically a few ohms, see the equation for r_e in the section on the Common-Emitter Model), A_V for this circuit can be quite high.

The circuit load line's end-points are $V_{CE} = V_{CC}$ and $I_C = V_{CC}/R_C$. The circuit's Q-point is determined by the collector resistor, R_C, and resistor R_1 that causes bias current to flow into the base. To determine the Q-point, again use KVL starting at the power source and assuming that $V_{BE} = 0.7$ V for a silicon transistor's PN junction when forward-biased.

$$V_{CC} - I_B R_1 = V_B = V_{BE} = 0.7 \text{ V}$$

so

$$I_B = \frac{V_{CC} - 0.7\text{V}}{R_1}$$

And the Q-point is therefore

$$V_{CEQ} = V_{CC} - \beta I_B R_C$$

and

$$I_{CQ} = \beta I_B$$

The actual V_{BE} of silicon transistors will vary from 0.6-0.75 V, depending on the level of base current, but 0.7 V is a good compromise value and widely used in small-signal, low-frequency design. Use 0.6 V for very low-power amplifiers and 0.75 V (or more) for high-current switch circuits.

This simple *fixed-bias* circuit is a good introduction to basic amplifiers, but is not entirely practical because the bias current will change due to the change of V_{BE} with temperature, leading to thermal instability. In addition, the high voltage gain can lead to instability due to positive feedback at high frequencies.

To stabilize the dc bias, **Figure 4.51** adds R_E, a technique called *emitter degeneration* because the extra emitter resistance creates negative feedback: as base current rises, so does V_E, the voltage drop across R_E. This reduces the base-emitter voltage and lowers base current. The benefit of emitter degeneration comes from stabilizing the circuit's dc behavior with temperature, but there is a reduction in gain because of the increased resistance in the emitter circuit. Ignoring the effect of R_L for the moment,

$$A_V \approx -\frac{R_C}{R_E}$$

In effect, the load resistor is now split between R_C and R_E, with part of the output voltage appearing across each because the changing current flows through both resistors. While somewhat lower than with the emitter connected directly to ground, voltage gain becomes easy to control because it is the ratio of two resistances.

Biasing the CE Amplifier

Figure 4.52 adds R_1 and R_2 from a voltage divider that controls bias current by fixing the base voltage at:

$$V_B = V_{CC} \frac{R_2}{R_1 + R_2}$$

Since

$$V_B = V_{BE} + (I_B + I_C) R_E$$
$$= 0.7 \text{ V} + (\beta + 1) I_B R_E$$

base current is

$$I_B = \frac{V_B - 0.7 \text{ V}}{(\beta + 1) R_E}$$

and Q-point collector current becomes for high values of β

$$I_{CQ} = \beta I_B \approx \frac{V_{CC} \frac{R_2}{R_1 + R_2} - 0.7}{R_E}$$

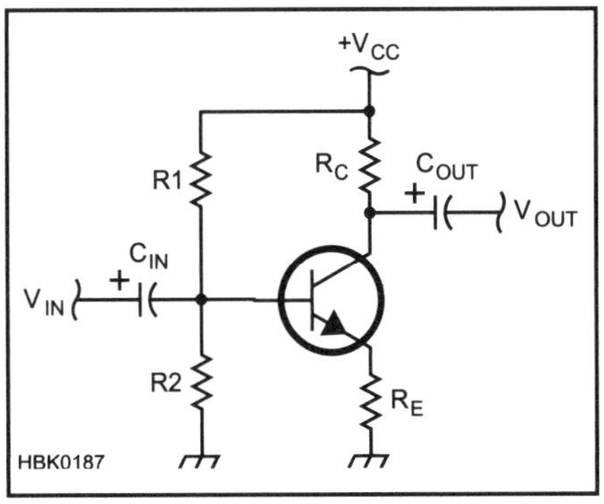

Figure 4.52 — Self-bias or self-emitter bias. R1 and R2 form a voltage divider to stabilize V_B and bias current. A good rule of thumb is for current flow through R1 and R2 to be 10 times the desired bias current. This stabilizes bias against changes in transistor parameters and component values.

This is referred to as *self-bias* or *self-emitter bias* in which the Q-point is much less sensitive to variations in temperature that affect β and V_{BE}.

A good rule-of-thumb for determining the sum of R_1 and R_2 is that the current flowing through the voltage divider, $V_{CC}/(R_1+R_2)$, should be at least 10 times the bias current, I_B. This keeps V_B relatively constant even with small changes in transistor parameters and temperature.

Q-point V_{CEQ} must now also account for the voltage drop across both R_C and R_E,

$$V_{CEQ} \approx V_{CC} - \beta I_B (R_C + R_E)$$

More sophisticated techniques for designing the bias networks of bipolar transistor circuits are described in reference texts listed at the end of this chapter.

Input and Output Impedance

With R_E in the circuit, the small changes in input current, I_B, when multiplied by the transistor's current gain, β, cause a large voltage change across R_E equal to $\beta I_B R_E$. This is the same voltage drop as if I_B was flowing through a resistance equal to βR_E. Thus, the effect of β on impedance at the base is to multiply the emitter resistance, R_E by β, as well. At the transistor's base,

$$Z_B \approx (\beta + 1) R_E$$

The input source doesn't just drive the base, of course, it also has to drive the combination of R1 and R2, the biasing resistors. From an ac point of view, both R1 and R2 can be considered as connected to ac ground and they can be treated as if they were connected in parallel. When R1//R2 are considered along with the transistor base impedance, Z_B, the impedance presented to the input signal source is:

$$Z_{IN} = R1 \,//\, R2 \,//\, (\beta + 1) R_E$$

where // designates "in parallel with."

For both versions of the CE amplifier, the collector output impedance is high enough that

$$Z_{OUT} \approx R_C$$

CE Amplifier Design Example

The general process depends on the circuit's primary performance requirements, including voltage gain, impedances, power consumption and so on. The most common situation in which a specific voltage gain is required and the circuit's Q-point has been selected based on the transistor to be used, and using the circuit of Figure 4.52, is as follows:

1) Start by determining the circuit's design constraints and assumptions: power supply $V_{CC} = 12$ V, transistor $\beta = 150$ and $V_{BE} = 0.7$ V. State the circuit's design requirements: $|A_V| = 5$, Q-point of $I_{CQ} = 4$ mA and $V_{CEQ} = 5$ V. (A $V_{CEQ} \approx ½\ V_{CC}$ allows a wide swing in output voltage with the least distortion.)

2) Determine the values of R_C and R_E: $R_C + R_E = (V_{CC} - V_{CEQ})/I_{CQ} = 1.75$ kΩ

3) $A_V = -5$, so $R_C = 5\ R_E$, thus $6R_E = 1.75$ kΩ and $R_E = 270$ Ω

4) Determine the base bias current, $I_B = I_{CQ}/\beta = 27$ μA. By the rule of thumb, current through R_1 and $R_2 = 10\ I_B = 270$ μA

5) Find the voltage across $R_2 = V_B = V_{BE} + I_C R_E = 0.7 + 4$ mA (0.27 kΩ) = 1.8 V. Thus, $R_2 = 1.8$ V / 270 μA = 6.7 kΩ

6) The voltage across $R_1 = V_{CC} - V_{R2} = 12 - 1.8 = 10.2$ V and $R_1 = 10.2$ V / 270 μA = 37.8 kΩ

Use the nearest standard values ($R_E = 270$ Ω, $R_1 = 39$ kΩ, $R_2 = 6.8$ kΩ) and circuit behavior will be close to predicted performance.

AC Performance

To achieve high gains for ac signals while maintaining dc bias stability, the *emitter-bypass capacitor*, C_E, is added in **Figure 4.53** to provide a low impedance path for ac signals around R_E. In addition, a more accurate formula for ac gain includes the effect of adding R_L through the dc blocking capacitor at the collector. In this circuit, the ac voltage gain is

$$A_V \approx -\frac{R_C \,//\, R_L}{r_e}$$

Because of the different signal paths for ac and dc signals, the ac performance of the circuit is different than its dc performance. This is illustrated in **Figure 4.54** by the intersecting load lines labeled "AC Load Line" and "DC Load Line." The load lines intersect at the Q-point because at that point dc performance is the same as ac performance if no ac signal is present.

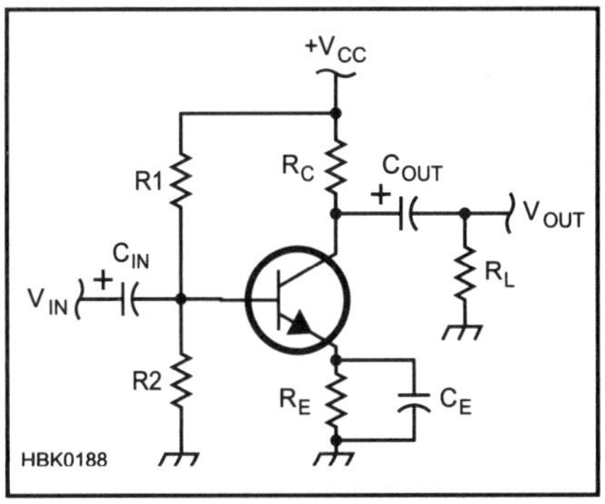

Figure 4.53 — Emitter bypass. Adding C_E allows ac currents to flow "around" R_E, returning ac gain to the value for the fixed-bias circuit while allowing R_E to stabilize the dc operating point.

The equation for ac voltage gain assumes that the reactances of C_{IN}, C_{OUT}, and C_E are small enough to be neglected (less than one-tenth that of the components to which they are connected at the frequency of interest). At low frequencies, where the capacitor reactances become increasingly large, voltage gain is reduced. Neglecting C_{IN} and C_{OUT}, the low-frequency 3 dB point of the amplifier, f_L, occurs where $X_{CE} = 0.414\ r_e$,

$$f_L = \frac{2.42}{2\pi r_e C_E}$$

This increases the emitter circuit impedance such that A_V is lowered to 0.707 of its mid-band value, lowering gain by 3 dB. (This ignores the effects of C_{IN} and C_{OUT}, which will also affect the low-frequency performance of the circuit.)

The ac input impedance of this version of the CE amplifier is lower because the effect of R_E on ac signals is removed by the bypass capacitor. This leaves only the internal emitter resistance, r_e, to be multiplied by the current gain,

$$Z_{IN} \approx R1 \,//\, R2 \,//\, \beta r_e$$

and

$$Z_{OUT} \approx R_C$$

again neglecting the reactance of the three capacitors.

The power gain, A_P, for the emitter-bypassed CE amplifier is the ratio of output

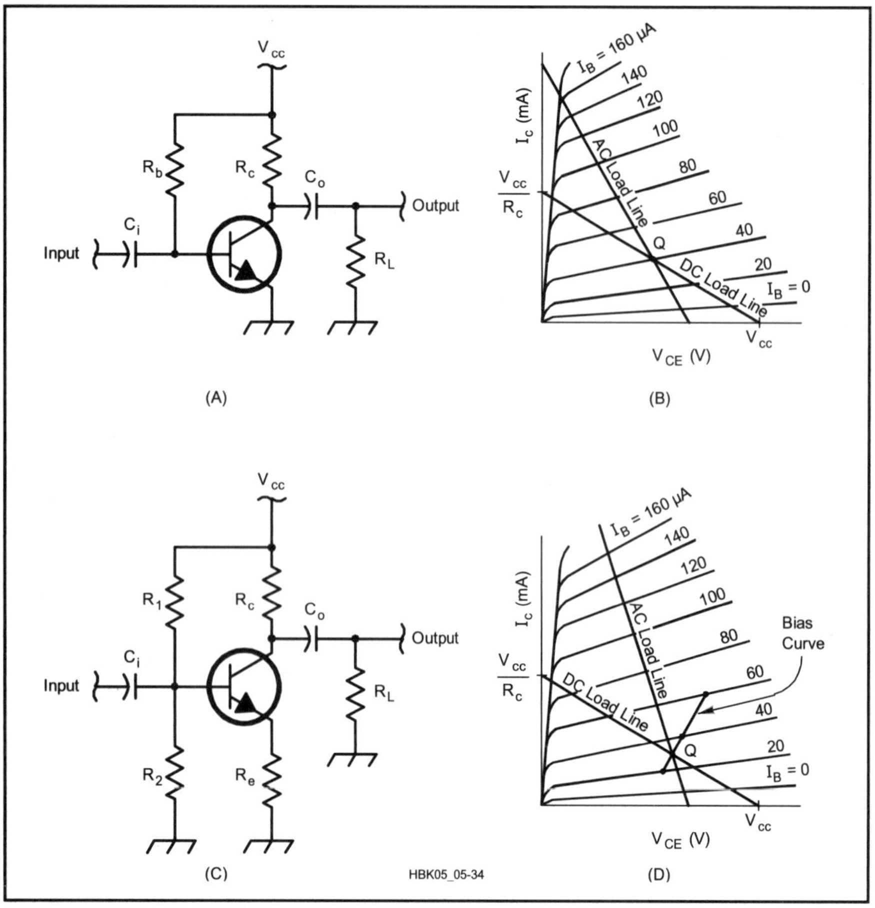

Figure 4.54 — Amplifier biasing and ac and dc load lines. (A) Fixed bias. Input signal is ac coupled through C_i. The output has a voltage that is equal to $V_{CC} - I_C \times R_C$. This signal is ac coupled to the load, R_L, through C_O. For dc signals, the entire output voltage is based on the value of R_C. For ac signals, the output voltage is based on the value of R_C in parallel with R_L. (B) Characteristic curve for the transistor amplifier pictured in (A). The slope of the dc load line is equal to $- 1 / R_C$. For ac signals, the slope of the ac load line is equal to $- 1 / (R_C // R_L)$. The quiescent-point, Q, is based on the base bias current with no input signal applied and the point where this characteristic line crosses the dc load line. The ac load line must also pass through point Q. (C) Self-bias. Similar to fixed bias circuit with the base bias resistor split into two: R1 connected to V_{CC} and R2 connected to ground. Also an emitter bias resistor, R_E, is included to compensate for changing device characteristics. (D) This is similar to the characteristic curve plotted in (B) but with an additional "bias curve" that shows how the base bias current varies as the device characteristics change with temperature. The operating point, Q, moves along this line and the load lines continue to intersect it as it changes. If C_E was added as in Figure 4.53, the slope of the ac load line would increase further.

power, V_O^2/Z_{OUT}, to input power, V_I^2/Z_{IN}. Since $V_O = V_I A_V$,

$$A_P = A_V^2 \frac{R1 // R2 // \beta r_e}{R_C}$$

COMMON-COLLECTOR (EMITTER-FOLLOWER) AMPLIFIER

The common-collector (CC) amplifier in **Figure 4.55** is also known as the *emitter-follower* (EF) because the emitter voltage "follows" the input voltage. In fact, the amplifier has no voltage gain (voltage gain ≈ 1), but is used as a buffer amplifier to isolate sensitive circuits such as oscillators or to drive low-impedance loads, such as coaxial cables. As in the CE amplifier, the current gain of the emitter-follower is the transistor's current gain, β. It has relatively high input impedance with low output impedance and good power gain.

The collector of the transistor is connected directly to the power supply without a resistor and the output signal is created by the voltage drop across the emitter resistor. There is no 180° phase shift as seen in the CE amplifier; the output voltage follows the input signal with 0° phase shift because increases in the input signal cause increases in emitter current and the voltage drop across the emitter resistor.

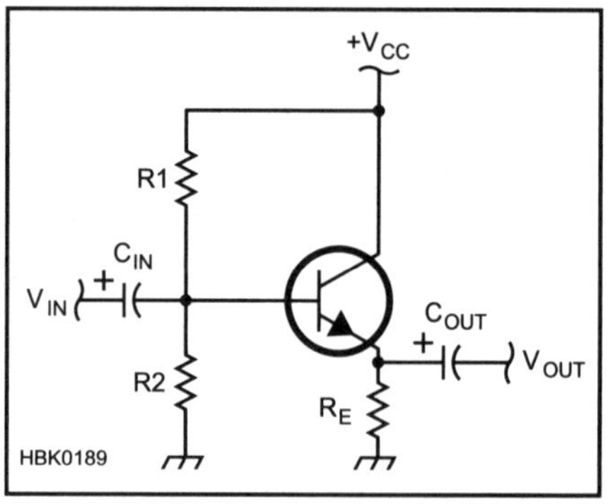

Figure 4.55 — Emitter follower (EF) amplifier. The voltage gain of the EF amplifier is unity. The amplifier has high input impedance and low output impedance, making it a good choice for use as a buffer amplifier.

The EF amplifier has high input impedance: following the same reasoning as for the CE amplifier with an unbypassed emitter resistor,

$$Z_{IN} = R1 // R2 // (\beta + 1) R_E$$

The impedance at the EF amplifier's output consists of the emitter resistance, R_E, in parallel with the series combination of the internal emitter resistance, r_e, the parallel combination of biasing resistors R1 and R2, and the internal impedance of the source providing the input signal. In this case, current gain acts to *reduce* the effect of the input circuit's impedance on output impedance:

$$Z_{OUT} = \left[\frac{R_S // R1 // R2}{(\beta + 1)} \right] // R_E$$

In practice, with transistor β of 100 or more, $Z_{OUT} \approx R_S/\beta$. However, if a very high impedance source is used, such as a crystal microphone element or photodetector, the effects of the biasing and emitter resistors must be considered.

Because the voltage gain of the EF amplifier is unity, the power gain is simply the ratio of input impedance to output impedance,

$$A_P \approx \frac{R1 // R2 // (\beta + 1) R_E}{R_E}$$

EF Amplifier Design Example

The following procedure is similar to the design procedure in the preceding section for the CE amplifier, except $A_V = 1$.

1) Start by determining the circuit's design constraints and assumptions: $V_{cc} = 12$ V (the power supply voltage), a transistor's β of 150 and $V_{BE} = 0.7$ V. State the circuit's design requirements: Q-point of $I_{CQ} = 5$ mA and $V_{CEQ} = 6$ V.

2) $R_E = (V_{CC} - V_{CEQ})/I_{CQ} = 1.2$ kΩ

3) Base current, $I_B = I_{CQ}/\beta = 33\ \mu A$

4) Current through R1 and R2 = 10 I_B = 330 µA (10 I_B rule of thumb as with the CE amplifier)

5) Voltage across R2 = $V_{BE} + I_C R_E$ = 0.7 + 5 mA (1.2 kΩ) = 6.7 V and R2 = 6.7 V / 330 µA = 20.3 kΩ (use the standard value 22 kΩ)

6) Voltage across R1 = V_{CC} – 6.7 V = 5.3 V

7) R1 = 5.3 V / 330 µA = 16.1 kΩ (use 16 kΩ)

8) $Z_{IN} = R1 // R2 // R_E(\beta + 1) \approx 8.5\ k\Omega$

COMMON-BASE AMPLIFIER

The common-base (CB) amplifier of **Figure 4.56** is used where low input impedance is needed, such as for a receiver preamp with a coaxial feed line as the input signal source. Complementary to the EF amplifier, the CB amplifier has unity current gain and high output impedance.

Figure 4.56A shows the CB circuit as it is usually drawn, without the bias circuit resistors connected and with the transistor symbol turned on its side from the usual orientation so that the emitter faces the input. In order to better understand the amplifier's function, Figure 4.56B reorients the circuit in a more familiar style. We can now clearly see that the input has just moved from the base circuit to the emitter circuit.

Placing the input in the emitter circuit allows it to cause changes in the base-emitter current as for the CE and EF amplifiers, except that for the CB amplifier a positive change in input amplitude reduces base current by lowering V_{BE} and raising V_C. As a result, the CB amplifier is noninverting, just like the EF, with output and input signals in-phase.

A practical circuit for the CB amplifier is shown in **Figure 4.57**. From a dc point of view (replace the capacitors with open circuits), all of the same resistors are there as in the CE amplifier. The input capacitor, C_{IN}, allows the dc emitter current to bypass the ac input signal source and C_B places the base at ac ground while allowing a dc voltage for biasing. (All voltages and currents are labeled to aid in understanding the different orientation of the circuit.)

The CB amplifier's current gain,

$$A_I = \frac{i_C}{i_E} = \frac{\beta}{\beta + 1}$$

is relatively independent of input and output impedance, providing excellent isolation between the input and output circuits. Output impedance does not affect input impedance, allowing the CB amplifier to maintain stable input impedance, even with a changing load.

Following reasoning similar to that for the CE and EF amplifiers for the effect of current gain on R_E, we find that input impedance for the CB amp is

$$Z_{IN} = R_E // (\beta + 1)\, r_e$$

With high-gain transistors having a β > 100, for typical values of r_e (about 1 kΩ) the input impedance is approximately R_E. If R_E is chosen to be 50 Ω, the result will be a good input impedance match to 50 Ω feed lines and signal sources.

The output impedance for the CB amplifier is approximately

$$Z_{OUT} = R_C // \frac{1}{h_{oe}} \approx R_C$$

where h_{oe} is the transistor's collector output admittance. The reciprocal of h_{oe} is in the range of 100 kΩ at low frequencies.

Voltage gain for the CB amplifier is

$$A_V \approx \frac{R_C // R_L}{r_e}$$

As a result, the usual function of the CB amplifier is to convert input current from a low-impedance source into output voltage at a higher impedance.

Power gain for the CB amplifier is approximately the ratio of output to input impedance,

$$A_P \approx \frac{R_C}{R_E // (\beta + 1)\, r_e}$$

CB Amplifier Design Example

Because of its usual function as a current-to-voltage converter, the design process for the CB amplifier begins with selecting R_E and A_V, assuming that R_L is known.

1) Start by determining the circuit's design constraints and assumptions: V_{cc} = 12 V (the power supply voltage), a transistor's β of 150 and V_{BE} = 0.7 V. State the circuit's design requirements: R_E = 50 Ω, R_L = 1 kΩ, I_{CQ} = 5 mA, V_{CEQ} = 6 V.

2) Base current, $I_B = I_{CQ}/\beta = 33\ \mu A$

3) Current through R1 and R2 = 10 I_B = 330 µA (10 × I_B rule of thumb as with the CE amplifier)

4) Voltage across R2 = $V_{BE} + I_C R_E$ = 0.7 + 5 mA (50 Ω) = 0.95 V and R2 = 0.95 V / 330 µA = 2.87 kΩ (use the standard value 2.7 kΩ)

5) Voltage across R1 = V_{CC} – 0.95 V = 11.05 V

6) R1 = 11.05 V / 330 µA = 33.5 kΩ (use 33 kΩ)

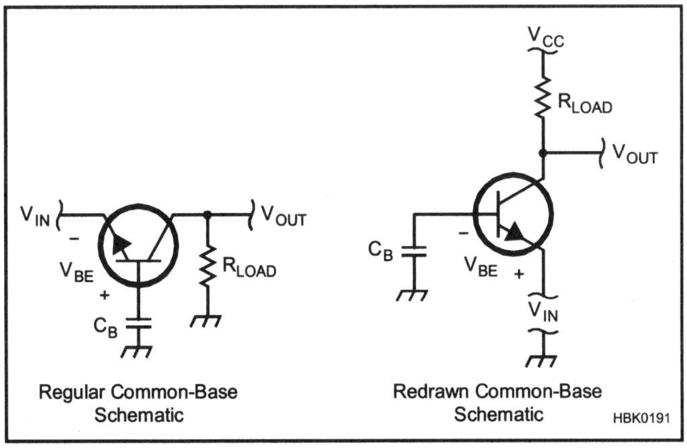

Figure 4.56 — The common-base (CB) amplifier is often drawn in an unfamiliar style (A), but is more easily understood when drawn similarly to the CE and EF amplifiers (B). The input signal to the CB amplifier is applied to the emitter instead of the base.

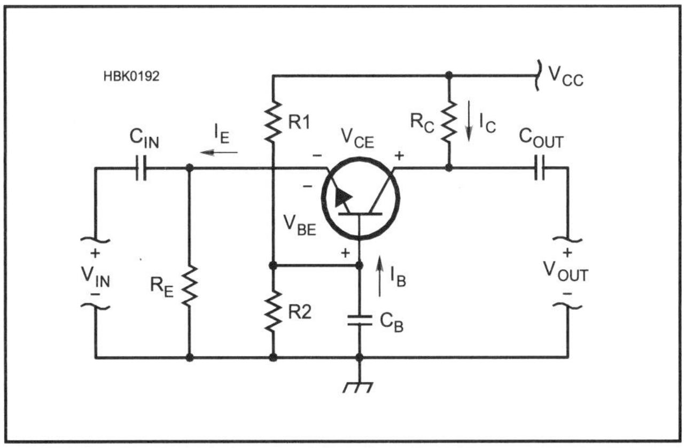

Figure 4.57 — A practical common-base (CB) amplifier. The current gain of the CB amplifier is unity. It has low input impedance and high output impedance, resulting in high voltage gain. The CB amplifier is used to amplify signals from low-impedance sources, such as coaxial cables.

7) $R_C = (V_{CC} - I_{CQ} R_E - V_{CEQ}) / I_{CQ} = (12 - 0.25 - 6) / 5 \text{ mA} = 1.15 \text{ k}\Omega$ (use 1.2 kΩ)

8) $A_V = (1.2 \text{ k}\Omega \,//\, 1 \text{ k}\Omega) / (26 \text{ mV} / I_E) = 105$

4.6.4 FET Amplifiers

The field-effect transistor (FET) is widely used in radio and RF applications. There are many types of FETs, with JFETs (junction FET) and MOSFETs (metal-oxide-semiconductor FET) being the most common types. In this section we will discuss JFETs, with the understanding that the use of MOSFETs is similar. (This discussion is based on N-channel JFETs, but the same discussion applies to P-channel devices if the bias voltages and currents are reversed.)

SMALL-SIGNAL FET MODEL

While bipolar transistors are most commonly viewed as current-controlled devices, the JFET, however, is purely a voltage-controlled device — at least at low frequencies. The input gate is treated as a reverse-biased diode junction with virtually no current flow. As with the bipolar transistor amplifier circuits, the circuits in this section are very basic and more thorough treatments of FET amplifier design can be found in the references at the end of the chapter.

The operation of an N-channel JFET for both biasing and signal amplification can be characterized by the following equation:

$$I_D = I_{DSS}\left(\frac{1 - V_{SG}}{V_P}\right)^2$$

where

I_{DSS} = drain saturation current
V_{GS} = the gate-source voltage
V_P = the pinch-off voltage.

I_{DSS} is the maximum current that will flow between the drain and source for a given value of drain-to-source voltage, V_{DS}. Note that the FET is a *square-law* device in which output current is proportional to the square of an input voltage. (The bipolar transistor's output current is an exponential function of input current.)

Also note that V_{GS} in this equation has the opposite sense of the bipolar transistor's V_{BE}. For this device, as V_{GS} increases (making the source more positive than the gate), drain current decreases until at V_P the channel is completely "pinched-off" and no drain current flows at all. This equation applies only if V_{GS} is between 0 and V_P. JFETs are seldom used with the gate-to-channel diode forward-biased ($V_{GS} < 0$).

None of the terms in this equation depend explicitly on temperature. Thus, the FET is relatively free of the thermal instability exhibited by the bipolar transistor. As temperature increases, the overall effect on the JFET is to

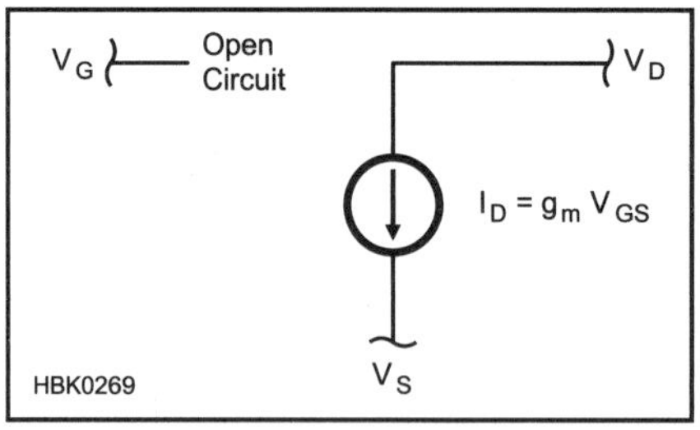

Figure 4.58 — Small-signal FET model. The FET can be modeled as a voltage-controlled current source in its saturation region. The gate is treated as an open-circuit due to the reverse-biased gate-channel junction.

reduce drain current and to stabilize the operation.

The small-signal model used for the JFET is shown in **Figure 4.58**. The drain-source channel is treated as a current source whose output is controlled by the gate-to-source voltage so that $I_D = g_m V_{GS}$. The high input impedance allows the input to be modeled as an open circuit (at low frequencies). This simplifies circuit modeling considerably as biasing of the FET gate can be done by a simple voltage divider without having to consider the effects of bias current flowing in the JFET itself.

The FET has characteristic curves as shown in Figure 4.34 that are similar to those of a bipolar transistor. The output characteristic curves are similar to those of the bipolar transistor, with the horizontal axis showing V_{DS} instead of V_{CE} and the vertical axis showing I_D instead of I_C. Load lines, both ac and dc, can be developed and drawn on the output characteristic curves in the same way as for bipolar transistors.

The set of characteristic curves in Figure 4.34 are called *transconductance response curves* and they show the relationship between input voltage (V_{GS}), output current (I_D) and output voltage (V_{DS}). The output characteristic curves show I_D and V_{DS} for different values of V_{GS} and are similar to the BJT output characteristic curve. The input characteristic curves show I_D versus V_{GS} for different values of V_{DS}.

MOSFETs act in much the same way as JFETs when used in an amplifier. They have a higher input impedance, due to the insulation between the gate and channel. The insulated gate also means that they can be operated with the polarity of V_{GS} such that a JFET's gate-channel junction would be forward biased, beyond V_P. Refer to the discussion of depletion- and enhancement-mode MOSFETs in the previous section on Practical Semiconductors.

THREE BASIC FET AMPLIFIERS

Just as for bipolar transistor amplifiers, there are three basic configurations of amplifiers using FETs; the *common-source* (CS) (corresponding to the common-emitter), *common-drain* (CD) or *source-follower* (corresponding to the emitter-follower) and the *common-gate* (CG) (corresponding to the common base). Simple circuits and design methods are presented here for each, assuming low-frequency operation and a simple, voltage-controlled current-source model for the FET. Discussion of the FET amplifier at high frequencies is available in the **RF Techniques** chapter and an advanced discussion of biasing FET amplifiers and their large-signal behavior is contained in this book's downloadable supplemental information.

COMMON-SOURCE AMPLIFIER

The basic circuit for a common-source FET amplifier is shown in **Figure 4.59**. In the ohmic region (see the previous discussion on FET characteristics), the FET can be treated as a variable resistance as shown in Figure 4.59A where V_{GS} effectively varies the resistance between drain and source. However, most FET amplifiers are designed to operate in the saturation region and the model of Figure 4.58 is used in the circuit of Figure 4.59B in which,

$$I_D = g_m V_{GS}$$

where g_m is the FET's forward transconductance.

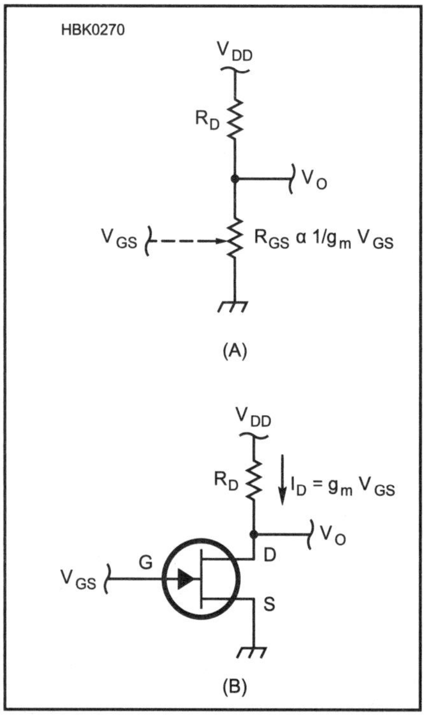

Figure 4.59 — In the ohmic region (A), the FET acts like a variable resistance, R_{DS}, with a value controlled by V_{GS}. The alpha symbol (α) means "is proportional to". In the saturation region (B), the drain-source channel of the FET can be treated like a current source with $I_D = g_m V_{GS}$.

If V_O is measured at the drain terminal (just as the common-emitter output voltage is measured at the collector), then

$$\Delta V_O = -g_m \Delta V_{GS} R_D$$

The minus sign results from the output voltage decreasing as drain current and the voltage drop across R_D increases, just as in the CE amplifier. Like the CE amplifier, the input and output voltages are thus 180° out of phase. Voltage gain of the CS amplifier in terms of transconductance and the drain resistance is:

$$A_V = -g_m R_D$$

As long as $V_{GS} < 0$, this simple CS amplifier's input impedance at low frequencies is that of a reverse-biased diode — nearly infinite with a very small leakage current. Output impedance of the CS amplifier is approximately R_D because the FET drain-to-source channel acts like a current source with very high impedance.

$$Z_{IN} = \infty \text{ and } Z_{OUT} \approx R_D$$

As with the BJT, biasing is required to create a Q-point for the amplifier that allows reproduction of ac signals. The practical circuit of Figure 4.59B is used to allow control of V_{GS} bias. A load line is drawn on the JFET output characteristic curves, just as for a bipolar transistor circuit. One end point of the load line is at $V_{DS} = V_{DD}$ and the other at $I_{DS} = V_{DD} / R_D$. The Q-point for the CS amplifier at I_{DQ} and V_{DSQ} is thus determined by the dc value of V_{GS}.

The practical JFET CS amplifier shown in **Figure 4.60** uses self-biasing in which the voltage developed across the source resistor, R_S, raises V_S above ground by $I_D R_S$ volts and $V_{GS} = -I_D R_S$ since there is no dc drop across R_G. This is also called *source degeneration.* The presence of R_S changes the equation of voltage gain to

$$A_V = -\frac{g_m R_D}{1 + g_m R_S} \approx -\frac{R_D}{R_S}$$

The value of R_S is obtained by substituting $V_{GS} = I_D R_S$ into the small-signal model's equation for I_D and solving for R_S as follows:

$$R_S = \frac{-V_P}{I_{DQ}} \left(1 - \sqrt{\frac{I_{DQ}}{I_{DSS}}} \right)$$

Once R_S is known, the equation for voltage gain can be used to find R_D.

The input impedance for the circuit of Figure 4.60 is essentially R_G. Since the gate of the JFET is often ac coupled to the input source through a dc blocking capacitor, C_{IN},

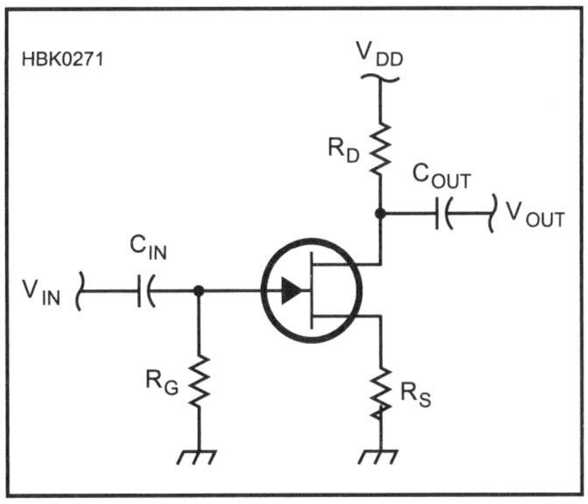

Figure 4.60 — Common-source (CS) amplifier with self-bias.

a value of 100 kΩ to 1 MΩ is often used for R_G to provide a path to ground for gate leakage current. If R_G is omitted in an ac-coupled JFET amplifier, a dc voltage can build up on the gate from leakage current or static electricity, affecting the channel conductivity.

$$Z_{IN} = R_G$$

Because of the high impedance of the drain-source channel in the saturation region, the output impedance of the circuit is:

$$Z_{OUT} \approx R_D$$

Designing the Common-Source Amplifier

The design of the CS amplifier begins with selection of a Q-point $I_{DQ} < I_{DSS}$. Because of variations in V_P and I_{DSS} from JFET to JFET, it may be necessary to select devices individually to obtain the desired performance.

1) Start by determining the circuit's design constraints and assumptions: V_{DD} = 12 V (the power supply voltage) and the JFET has an I_{DSS} of 35 mA and a V_P of –3.0V, typical of small-signal JFETs. State the circuit's design requirements: $|A_V|$ = 10 and I_{DQ} = 10 mA.

2) Use the equation above to find R_S = 139 Ω

3) Since $|A_V|$ = 10, R_D = 10 R_S = 1390 Ω. Use standard values for R_S = 150 Ω and R_D = 1.5 kΩ.

AC Performance

As with the CE bipolar transistor amplifier, a bypass capacitor can be used to increase ac gain while leaving dc bias conditions unchanged as shown in **Figure 4.61**. In the case of the CS amplifier, a *source bypass* capacitor is placed across R_S and the load, R_L, connected through a dc blocking capacitor. In this circuit voltage gain becomes:

$$A_V = -g_m (R_D // R_L)$$

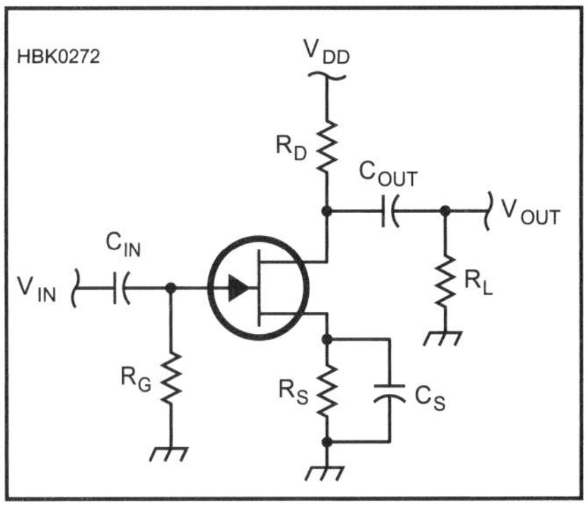

Figure 4.61 — Common-source amplifier with source bypass capacitor, C_S, to increase voltage gain without affecting the circuit's dc performance.

Assuming C_{IN} and C_{OUT} are large enough to ignore their effects, the low-frequency cutoff frequency of the amplifier, f_L, is approximately where X_{CS} = 0.707 (R_D // R_L),

$$f_L = \frac{1.414}{2\pi (R_D // R_L) C_S}$$

as this reduces A_V to 0.707 of its mid-band value, resulting in a 3 dB drop in output amplitude.

The low-frequency ac input and output impedances of the CS amplifier remain

$$Z_{IN} = R_G \text{ and } Z_{OUT} \approx R_D$$

COMMON-DRAIN (SOURCE-FOLLOWER) AMPLIFIER

The *common-drain* amplifier in **Figure 4.62** is also known as a *source-follower* (SF) because the voltage gain of the amplifier is unity, similar to the emitter follower (EF) bipolar transistor amplifier. The SF amplifier is used primarily as a buffer stage and to drive low-impedance loads.

At low frequencies, the input impedance of the SF amplifier remains nearly infinite.

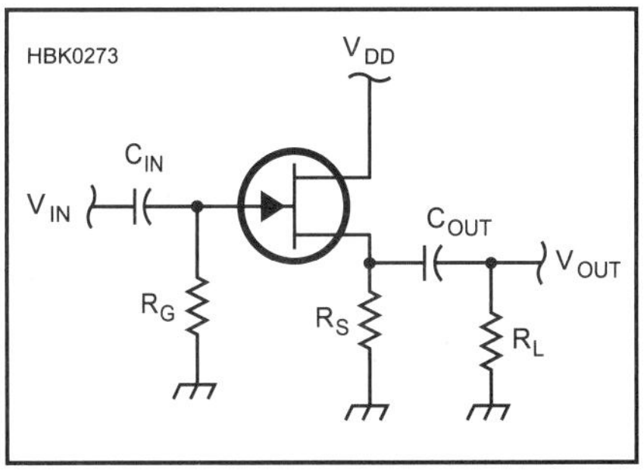

Figure 4.62 — Similar to the EF amplifier, the common-drain (CD) amplifier has a voltage gain of unity, but makes a good buffer with high input and low output impedances.

The SF amplifier's output impedance is the source resistance, R_S, in parallel with the impedance of the controlled current source, $1/g_m$.

$$Z_{OUT} = R_S \, // \, \frac{1}{g_m}$$

$$= \frac{R_S}{g_m R_S + 1} \approx \frac{1}{g_m} \text{ for } g_m R_S >> 1$$

Design of the SF amplifier follows essentially the same process as the CS amplifier, with $R_D = 0$.

THE COMMON-GATE AMPLIFIER

The *common-gate* amplifier in **Figure 4.63** has similar properties to the bipolar transistor common-base (CB) amplifier; unity current gain, high voltage gain, low input impedance and high output impedance. (Refer to the discussion of the CB amplifier regarding placement of the input and how the circuit schematic is drawn.) It is used as a voltage amplifier, particularly for low-impedance sources, such as coaxial cable inputs.

The CG amplifier's voltage gain is

$$A_V = g_m (R_D \, // \, R_L)$$

The output impedance of the CG amplifier is very high, we must take into account the output resistance of the controlled current source, r_o. This is analogous to the appearance of h_{oe} in the equation for output impedance of the bipolar transistor CG amplifier.

$$Z_O \approx r_o \, (g_m R_S + 1) \, // \, R_D$$

The CG amplifier input impedance is approximately

$$Z_I = R_S \, // \, \frac{1}{g_m}$$

Because the input impedance is quite low, the cascode circuit described later in the section on buffers is often used to present a higher-impedance input to the signal source.

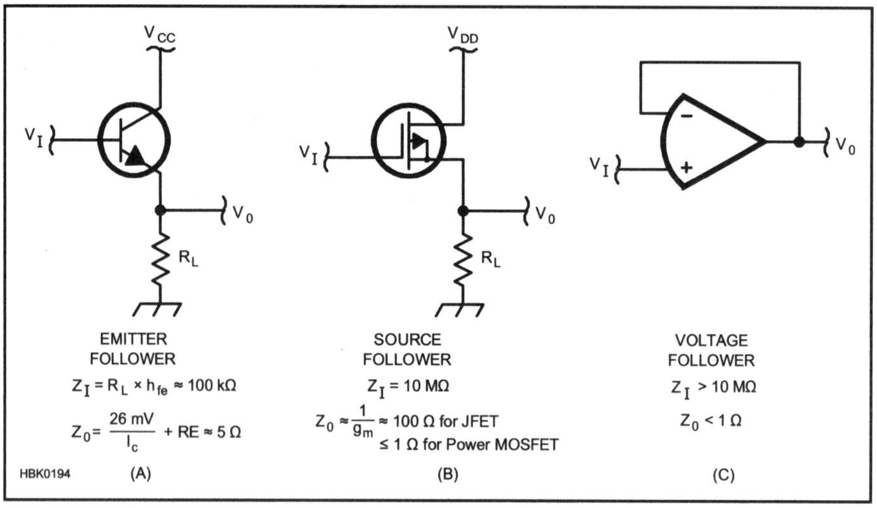

Figure 4.64 — Common buffer stages and some typical input (Z_I) and output (Z_O) impedances. (A) Emitter follower, made with an NPN bipolar transistor; (B) Source follower, made with an FET; and (C) Voltage follower, made with an operational amplifier. All of these buffers are terminated with a load resistance, R_L, and have an output voltage that is approximately equal to the input voltage (gain ≈ 1).

Occasionally, the value of R_S must be fixed in order to provide a specific value of input impedance. Solving the small-signal FET model equation for I_{DQ} results in the following equation:

$$I_{DQ} = \frac{V_P}{2 R_S^2 I_{DSS}} \left(V_P + \sqrt{V_P^2 - 4 R_S I_{DSS} V_P} \right) - \frac{V_P}{R_S}$$

Designing the Common-Gate Amplifier

Follow the procedure for designing a CS amplifier, except determine the value of R_D as shown in the equation above for voltage gain, A_V.

1) Start by determining the circuit's design constraints and assumptions: $V_{DD} = 12$ V (the power supply voltage) and the JFET has a g_m of 15 mA/V, an I_{DSS} of 60 mA and $V_P = -6$ V. State the circuit's design requirements: $A_V = 10$, $R_L = 1$ kΩ and $R_S = 50$ Ω.

2) Solve the A_V equation for R_D: $10 = 0.015 \times R_D // R_L$, so $R_D // R_L = 667$ Ω. $R_D = 667 \, R_L / (R_L - 667) = 2$ kΩ.

3) Use the equation above to find $I_{DQ} = 10$ mA. If I_{DQ} places the Q-point in the ohmic region, reduce A_V and repeat the calculations.

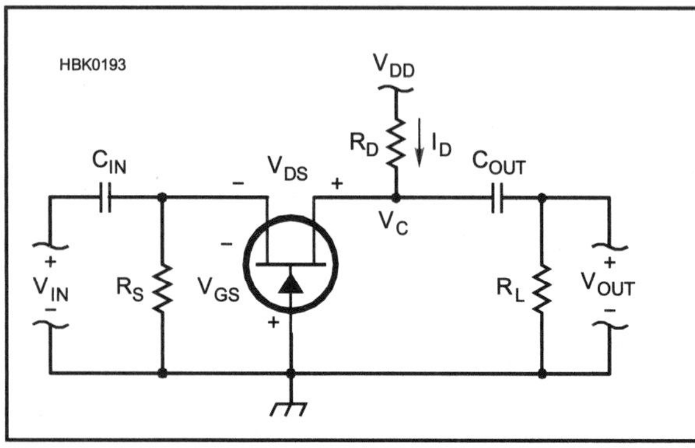

Figure 4.63 — FET common-gate (CG) amplifiers are often used as preamplifiers because of their high voltage gain and low input impedance. With the proper choice of transistor and quiescent-point current, the input impedance can match coaxial cable impedances directly.

4.6.5 Buffer Amplifiers

Figure 4.64 shows common forms of buffers with low-impedance outputs: the *emitter follower* using a bipolar transistor, the *source follower* using a field-effect transistor and the *voltage follower*, using an operational amplifier. (The operational amplifier is discussed later in this chapter.) These circuits are called "followers" because the output "follows" the input very closely with approximately the same voltage and little phase shift between the input and output signals.

4.6.6 Cascaded Buffers

THE DARLINGTON PAIR

Buffer stages that are made with single active devices can be more effective if cascaded. Two types of such buffers are in common use. The *Darlington pair* is a cascade of two transistors connected as emitter followers as shown in **Figure 4.65.** The current gain of the Darlington pair is the product of the current gains for the two transistors, $\beta_1 \times \beta_2$.

What makes the Darlington pair so useful is that its input impedance is equal to the load impedance times the current gain, effectively multiplying the load impedance;

$$Z_I = Z_{LOAD} \times \beta_1 \times \beta_2$$

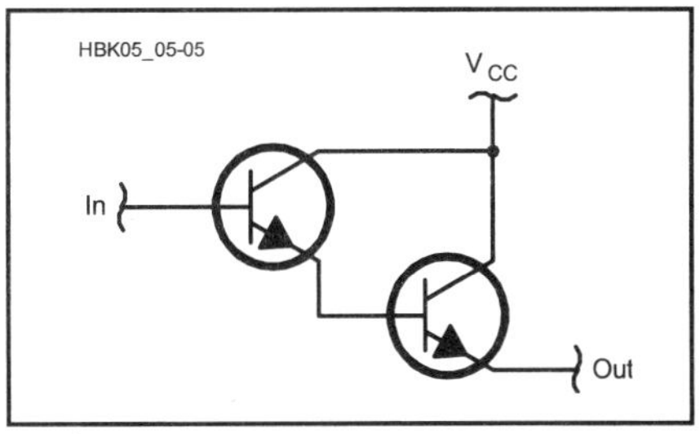

Figure 4.65 — Darlington pair made with two emitter followers. Input impedance, Z_I, is far higher than for a single transistor and output impedance, Z_O, is nearly the same as for a single transistor. DC biasing has been omitted for simplicity.

For example, if a typical bipolar transistor has β = 100 and Z_{LOAD} = 15 kΩ, a pair of these transistors in the Darlington-pair configuration would have:

$$Z_I = 15\ \text{k}\Omega \times 100 \times 100 = 150\ \text{M}\Omega$$

This impedance places almost no load on the circuit connected to the Darlington pair's input. The shunt capacitance at the input of real transistors can lower the actual impedance as the frequency increases.

Drawbacks of the Darlington pair include lower bandwidth and switching speed. The extremely high dc gain makes biasing very sensitive to temperature and component tolerances. For these reasons, the circuit is usually used as a switch and not as a linear amplifier.

CASCODE AMPLIFIERS

A common-emitter amplifier followed by a common-base amplifier is called a *cascode buffer*, shown in its simplest form in **Figure 4.66**. (Biasing and dc blocking components are omitted for simplicity — replace the transistors with the practical circuits described earlier.) Cascode stages using FETs follow a common-source amplifier with a common-gate configuration. The input impedance and current gain of the cascode amplifier are approximately the same as those of the first stage. The output impedance of the common-base or –gate stage is much higher than that of the common-emitter or common-source amplifier. The power gain of the cascode amplifier is the product of the input stage current gain and the output stage voltage gain.

As an example, a typical cascode buffer made with BJTs has moderate input impedance (Z_{IN} = 1 kΩ), high current gain (h_{fe} = 50), and high output impedance (Z_{OUT} = 1 MΩ). Cascode amplifiers have excellent input/output isolation (very low unwanted internal feedback), resulting in high gain with good stability. Because of its excellent isolation, the cascode amplifier has little effect on external tuning components. Cascode circuits are often used in tuned amplifier designs for these reasons.

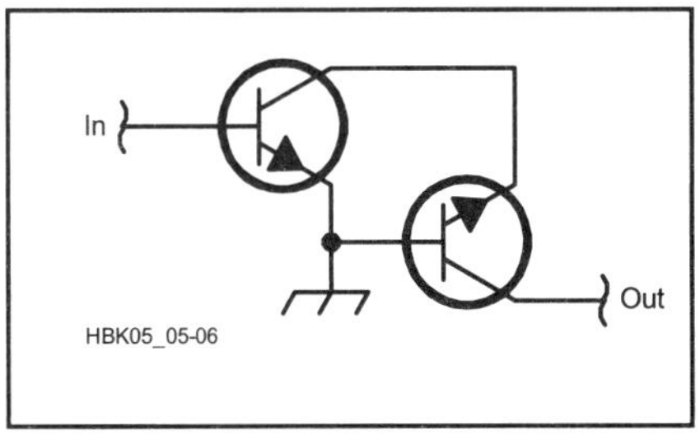

Figure 4.66 — Cascode buffer made with two NPN bipolar transistors has a medium input impedance and high output impedance. DC biasing has been omitted for simplicity.

4.6.7 Using the Transistor as a Switch

When designing amplifiers, the goal was to make the transistor's output a replica of its input, requiring that the transistor stay within its linear region, conducting some current at all times. A switch circuit has completely different properties — its output current is either zero or some maximum value. **Figure 4.67** shows both a bipolar and metal-oxide semiconductor field-effect transistor (or MOSFET) switch circuit. Unlike the linear amplifier circuits, there are no bias resistors in either circuit. When using the bipolar transistor as a switch, it should operate in saturation or in cutoff. Similarly, an FET switch should be either fully-on or fully-off. The figure shows the waveforms associated with both types of switch circuits.

This discussion is written with power control in mind, such as to drive a relay or motor or lamp. The concepts, however, are equally applicable to the much lower-power circuits that control logic-level signals. The switch should behave just the same — switch between on and off quickly and completely — whether large or small.

DESIGNING SWITCHING CIRCUITS

First, select a transistor that can handle the load current and dissipate whatever power is dissipated as heat. Second, be sure that the input signal source can supply an adequate input signal to drive the transistor to the required states, both on and off. Both of these conditions must be met to insure reliable driver operation.

To choose the proper transistor, the load current and supply voltage must both be known. Supply voltage may be steady, but sometimes varies widely. For example, a car's 12 V power bus may vary from 9 to 18 V, depending on battery condition. The transistor must withstand the maximum supply voltage, V_{MAX}, when off. The load resistance, $R_{L,}$ must also be known. The maximum steady-state current the switch must handle is:

MAX $\frac{\text{MAX}}{\ }$

If you are using a bipolar transistor, calculate how much base current is required to drive the transistor at this level of collector current. You'll need to inspect the transistor's data sheet because β decreases as collector current

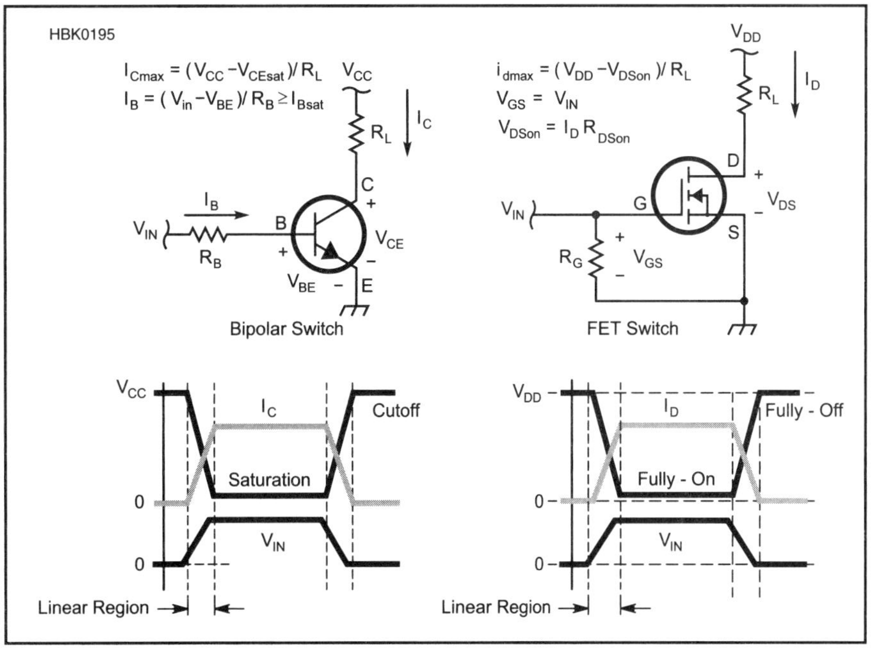

Figure 4.67 — A pair of transistor driver circuits using a bipolar transistor and a MOSFET. The input and output signals show the linear, cutoff and saturation regions.

increases, so use a value for β specified at a collector current at or above I_{MAX}.

$$I_B = \frac{I_{MAX}}{\beta}$$

Now inspect the transistor's data sheet values for V_{CEsat} and make sure that this value of I_B is sufficient to drive the transistor fully into saturation at a collector current of I_{MAX}. Increase I_B if necessary — this is I_{Bsat}. The transistor must be fully saturated to minimize heating when conducting load current.

Using the *minimum* value for the input voltage, calculate the value of R_B:

$$R_B = \frac{V_{IN(min)} - V_{BE}}{I_{Bsat}}$$

The minimum value of input voltage must be used to accommodate the *worst-case* combination of circuit voltages and currents.

Designing with a MOSFET is a little easier because the manufacturer usually specifies the value V_{GS} must have for the transistor to be fully on, $V_{GS(on)}$. The MOSFET's gate, being insulated from the conducting channel, acts like a small capacitor of a few hundred pF and draws very little dc current. R_G in Figure 4.67 is required if the input voltage source does not actively drive its output to zero volts when off, such as a switch connected to a positive voltage. The MOSFET won't turn off reliably if its gate is allowed to "float." R_G pulls the gate voltage to zero when the input is open-circuited.

Power dissipation is the next design hurdle. Even if the transistors are turned completely on, they will still dissipate some heat. Just as for a resistor, for a bipolar transistor switch the power dissipation is:

$$P_D = V_{CE} I_C = V_{CE(sat)}\ I_{MAX}$$

where $V_{CE(sat)}$ is the collector-to-emitter voltage when the transistor is saturated.

Power dissipation in a MOSFET switch is:

$$P_D = V_{DS} I_D = R_{DS(on)}\ I_{MAX}^2$$

$R_{DS(on)}$ is the resistance of the channel from drain to source when the MOSFET is on. MOSFETs are available with very low on-resistance, but still dissipate a fair amount of power when driving a heavy load. The transistor's data sheet will contain $R_{DS(on)}$ specification and the V_{GS} required for it to be reached.

Power dissipation is why a switching transistor needs to be kept out of its linear region. When turned completely off or on, either current through the transistor or voltage across it are low, also keeping the product of voltage and current (the power to be dissipated) low. As the waveform diagrams in Figure 4.67 show, while in the linear region, both voltage and current have significant values and so the transistor is generating heat when changing from off to on and vice versa. It's important to make the transition through the linear region quickly to keep the transistor cool.

The worst-case amount of power dissipated during each on-off transition is approximately

$$P_{transition} = \frac{1}{4} V_{MAX}\ I_{MAX}$$

assuming that the voltage and current increase and decrease linearly. If the circuit turns on and off at a rate of f, the total average power dissipation due to switching states is:

$$P_D = \frac{f}{2} V_{MAX}\ I_{MAX}$$

since there are two on-off transitions per switching cycle. This power must be added to the power dissipated when the switch is conducting current.

Once you have calculated the power the switch must dissipate, you must check to see whether the transistor can withstand it. The manufacturer of the transistor will specify a *free-air dissipation* that assumes no heat-sink and room temperature air circulating freely around the transistor. This rating should be at least 50% higher than your calculated power dissipation. If not, you must either use a larger transistor or provide some means of getting rid of the heat, such as heat sink. Methods of dissipating heat are discussed in this chapter's section on Heat Management.

INDUCTIVE AND CAPACITIVE LOADS

Voltage transients for inductive loads, such as solenoids or relays can easily reach dozens of times the power supply voltage when load current is suddenly interrupted. To protect the transistor, the voltage transient must be clamped or its energy dissipated. Where switching is frequent, a series-RC *snubber* circuit (see **Figure 4.68A**) is connected across the load to dissipate the transient's energy as heat. The most common method is to employ a "kickback" diode that is reverse-biased when the load is energized as shown in Figure 4.68B. When the load current is interrupted, the diode routes the energy back to the power supply, clamping the voltage at the power supply voltage plus the diode's forward voltage drop. (If the solenoid or relay is going to be used in an amateur station, add a small bypass capacitor (0.001 – 0.01 µF, value is not critical) across the diode to prevent it generating harmonics or mixing products from strong RF.)

Capacitive loads such as heavily filtered power inputs may temporarily act like short circuits when the load is energized or de-energized. The surge current is only limited by the internal resistance of the load capacitance. The transistor will have to handle the temporary overloads without being damaged or overheating. The usual solution is to select a transistor with an I_{MAX} rating greater to the surge current. Sometimes a small current-limiting resistor can be placed in series with the load to reduce the peak surge current at the expense of dissipating power continuously when the load is drawing current.

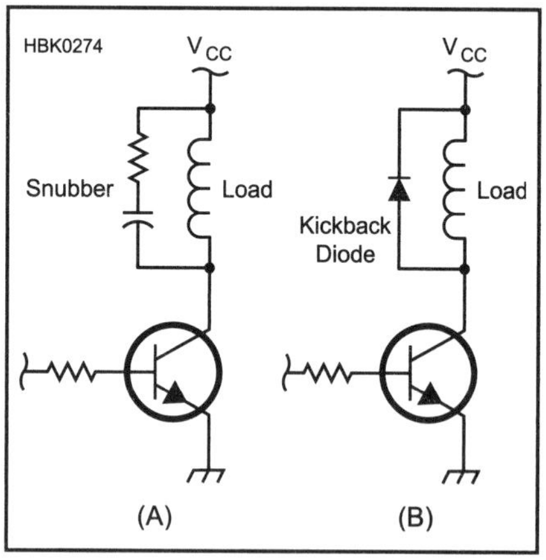

Figure 4.68 — The snubber RC circuit at (A) absorbs energy from transients with fast rise- and fall-times. At (B) a kickback diode protects the switching device when current is interrupted in the inductive load, causing a voltage transient, by conducting the energy back to the power source. See section on Analog-Digital Interfacing regarding bypassing kickback diodes.

HIGH-SIDE AND LOW-SIDE SWITCHING

The switching circuits shown in Figure 4.68 are *low-side switches*. This means the switch is connected between the load and ground. A *high-side switch* is connected between the power source and the load. The same concerns for power dissipation apply, but the methods of driving the switch change because of the voltage of the emitter or source of the switching device will be at or near the power supply voltage when the switch is on.

To drive an NPN bipolar transistor or an N-channel MOSFET in a high-side circuit requires the switch input signal to be at least $V_{BE(sat)}$ or $V_{GS(on)}$ *above* the voltage supplied to the load. If the load expects to see the full power supply voltage, the switch input signal will have to be *greater* than the power supply voltage. A small step-up or boost dc-to-dc converter is often used to supply the extra voltage needed for the driver circuit.

One alternate method of high-side switching is to use a PNP bipolar transistor as the switching transistor. A small input transistor turns the main PNP transistor on by controlling the larger transistor's base current. Similarly, a P-channel MOSFET could also be employed with a bipolar transistor or FET acting as its driver. P-type material generally does not have the same high conductivity as N-type material and so these devices dissipate somewhat more power than N-type devices under the same load conditions.

4.6.8 Choosing a Transistor

With all the choices for transistors — websites and catalogs can list hundreds — selecting a suitable transistor can be intimidating. Start by determining the maximum voltage (V_{CEO} or $V_{DS(MAX)}$), current (I_{MAX}) and power dissipation ($P_{D(MAX)}$) the transistor must handle. Determine what dc current gain, β, or transconductance, g_m, is required. Then determine the highest frequency at which full gain is required and multiply it by either the voltage or current gain to obtain f_T or h_{fe}. This will reduce the number of choices dramatically.

The chapter on **Component Data and References** has tables of parameters for popular transistors that tend to be the lowest-cost and most available parts, as well. You will find that a handful of part types satisfy the majority of your building needs. Only in very special applications will you need to choose a corresponding special part.

4.7 Operational Amplifiers

An *operational amplifier*, or *op amp*, is one of the most useful linear devices. While it is possible to build an op amp with discrete components, and early versions were, the symmetry of the circuit demanded for high performance requires a close match of many components. It is more effective, and much easier, to implement as an integrated circuit. (The term "operational" comes from the op amp's origin in analog computers where it was used to implement mathematical operations.)

The op amp's performance approaches that of an ideal analog circuit building block: an infinite input impedance (Z_i), a zero output impedance (Z_o) and an open loop voltage gain (A_v) of infinity. Obviously, practical op amps do not meet these specifications, but they do come closer than most other types of amplifiers. These attributes allow the circuit designer to implement many different functions with an op amp and only a few external components.

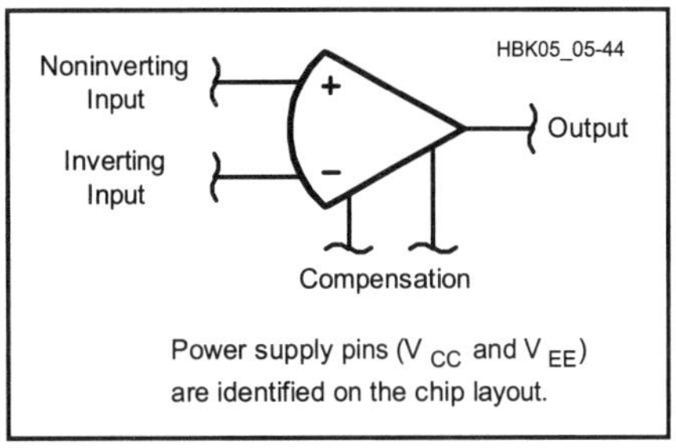

Figure 4.69 — Operational amplifier schematic symbol. The terminal marked with a + sign is the noninverting input. The terminal marked with a – sign is the inverting input. The output is to the right. On some op amps, external compensation is needed and leads are provided, pictured here below the device. Usually, the power supply leads are not shown on the op amp itself but are specified in the data sheet.

4.7.1 Characteristics of Practical Op-Amps

An op amp has three signal terminals (see **Figure 4.69**). There are two input terminals, the *noninverting input* marked with a + sign and the *inverting input* marked with a – sign. Voltages applied to the noninverting input cause the op amp output voltage to change with the same polarity.

The output of the amplifier is a single terminal with the output voltage referenced to the external circuit's reference voltage. Usually, that reference is ground, but the op amp's internal circuitry allows all voltages to *float*, that is, to be referenced to any arbitrary voltage between the op amp's power supply voltages. The reference can be negative, ground or positive. For example, an op amp powered from a single power supply voltage amplifies just as well if the circuit reference voltage is halfway between ground and the supply voltage.

GAIN-BANDWIDTH PRODUCT AND COMPENSATION

An ideal op amp would have infinite frequency response, but just as transistors have an f_T that marks their upper frequency limit, the op amp has a *gain-bandwidth product* (GBW or BW). GBW represents the maximum product of gain and frequency available to any signal or circuit: voltage gain × frequency = GBW. If an op-amp with a GBW of 10 MHz is connected as a ×50 voltage amplifier, the maximum frequency at which that gain could be guaranteed is GBW / gain = 10 MHz / 50 = 200 kHz. GBW is an important consideration in high-performance filters and signal processing circuits whose design equations require high-gain at the frequencies over which they operate.

Older operational amplifiers, such as the LM301, have an additional two connections for *compensation*. To keep the amplifier from oscillating at very high gains it is often necessary to place a capacitor across the compensation terminals. This also decreases the frequency response of the op amp but increases its stability by making sure that the output signal cannot have the right phase to create positive feedback at its inputs. Most modern op amps are internally compensated and do not have separate pins to add compensation capacitance. Additional compensation can be created by connecting a capacitor between the op amp output and the inverting input.

CMRR AND PSRR

One of the major advantages of using an op amp is its very high *common mode rejection ratio* (CMRR). *Common mode* signals are those that appear equally at all terminals. For example, if both conductors of an audio cable pick up a few tenths of a volt of 60 Hz signal from a nearby power transformer, that 60 Hz signal is a common-mode signal to whatever device the cable is connected. Since the op amp only responds to *differences* in voltage at its inputs, it can ignore or reject common mode signals. CMRR is a measure of how well the op amp rejects the common mode signal. High CMRR results from the symmetry between the circuit halves. CMRR is important when designing circuits that process low-level signals, such as microphone audio or the mV-level dc signals from sensors or thermocouples.

The rejection of power-supply imbalance is also an important op amp parameter. Shifts in power supply voltage and noise or ripple on the power supply voltages are coupled directly to the op amp's internal circuitry. The op amp's ability to ignore those disturbances is expressed by the *power supply rejection ratio* (PSRR). A high PSRR means that the op amp circuit will continue to perform well even if the power supply is imbalanced or noisy.

INPUT AND OUTPUT VOLTAGE LIMITS

The op amp is capable of accepting and amplifying signals at levels limited by the power supply voltages, also called *rails*. The difference in voltages between the two rails limits the range of signal voltages that can be processed. The voltages can be symmetrical positive and negative voltages (±12 V), a positive voltage and ground, ground and a negative voltage or any two different, stable voltages.

In most op amps the signal levels that can be handled are one or two diode forward voltage drops (0.7 V to 1.4 V) away from each rail. Thus, if an op amp has 15 V connected as its upper rail (usually denoted V^+) and ground connected as its lower rail (V^-), input signals can be amplified to be as high as 13.6 V and as low as 1.4 V in most amplifiers. Any values that would be amplified beyond those limits are clamped (output voltages that should be 1.4 V or less appear as 1.4 V and those that should be 13.6 V or more appear as 13.6 V). This clamping action was illustrated in Figure 3.49 in the **Radio Fundamentals** chapter.

"Rail-to-rail" op amps have been developed to handle signal levels within a few tens of mV of rails (for example, the MAX406, from Maxim Integrated Products processes signals to within 10 mV of the power supply voltages). Rail-to-rail op-amps are often used in battery-powered products to allow the circuits to operate from low battery voltages for as long as possible.

INPUT BIAS AND OFFSET

The inputs of an op amp, while very high impedance, still allow some input current to flow. This is the *input bias current* and it is in the range of nA in modern op amps. Slight asymmetries in the op amp's internal circuitry result in a slight offset in the op amp's out-put voltage, even with the input terminals shorted together. The amount of voltage difference between the op amp's inputs required to cause the output voltage to be exactly zero is the *input offset voltage*, generally a few mV or less. Some op amps, such as the LM741, have special terminals to which a potentiometer can be connected to *null* the offset by correcting the internal imbalance. Introduction of a small dc correction voltage to the non-inverting terminal is sometimes used to apply an offset voltage that counteracts the internal mismatch and centers the signal in the rail-to-rail range.

DC offset is an important consideration in op amps for two reasons. Actual op amps have a slight mismatch between the inverting and noninverting terminals that can become a substantial dc offset in the output, depending on the amplifier gain. The op amp output voltage must not be too close to the clamping limits or distortion will occur.

A TYPICAL OP AMP

As an example of typical values for these parameters, one of today's garden-variety op amps, the TL084, which contains both JFET and bipolar transistors, has a guaranteed minimum CMRR of 80 dB, an input bias current guaranteed to be below 200 pA (1 pA = 1 millionth of a µA) and a gain-bandwidth product of 3 MHz. Its input offset voltage is 3 mV. CMRR and PSRR are 86 dB, meaning that an unwanted signal or power supply imbalance of 1 V will only result in a 2.5 nV change at the op amp's output! All this for less than 50 cents even purchased in single quantities and there are four op-amps per package — that's a lot of performance.

4.7.2 Basic Op-Amp Circuits

If a signal is connected to the input terminals of an op amp without any other circuitry attached, it will be amplified at the device's *open-loop gain* (typically 200,000 for the TL084 at dc and low frequencies, or 106 dB). This will quickly saturate the output at the power supply rails. Such large gains are rarely used. In most applications, negative feedback is used to limit the circuit gain by providing a feedback path from the output terminal to the inverting input terminal. The resulting *closed-loop gain* of the circuit depends solely on the values of the passive components used to form the loop (usually resistors and, for frequency-selective circuits, capacitors). The higher the op-amp's open-loop gain, the closer the circuit's actual gain will approach that predicted from the component values. Note that the gain of the op amp itself has not changed — it is the configuration of the external components that determines the overall gain of the circuit. Some examples of different circuit configurations that manipulate the closed-loop gain follow.

INVERTING AND NONINVERTING AMPLIFIERS

The op amp is often used in either an *inverting* or a *noninverting* amplifier circuit as shown in **Figure 4.70**. (Inversion means that the output signal is inverted from the input signal about the circuit's voltage reference as described below.) The amount of amplification is determined by the two resistors: the feedback resistor, R_f, and the input resistor, R_i.

In the noninverting configuration shown in Figure 4.70A, the input signal is connected to the op-amp's noninverting input. The feedback resistor is connected between the output and the inverting input terminal. The inverting input terminal is connected to R_i, which is connected to ground (or the circuit reference voltage).

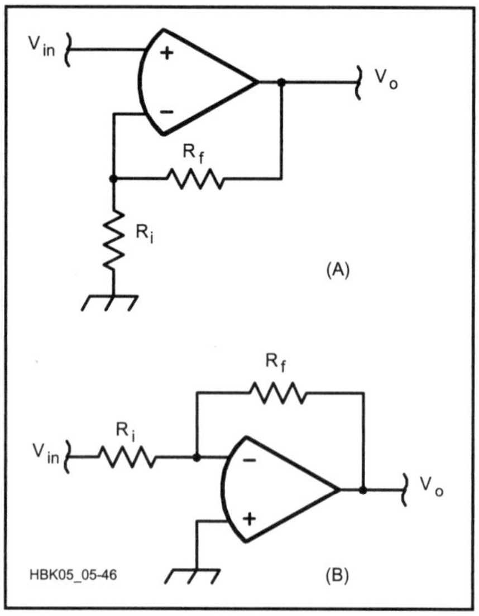

Figure 4.70 — Operational amplifier circuits. (A) Noninverting configuration. (B) Inverting configuration.

This circuit illustrates how op amp circuits use negative feedback, the high open-loop gain of the op amp itself, and the high input impedance of the op amp inputs to create a stable circuit with a fixed gain. The signal applied to the noninverting input causes the output voltage of the op-amp to change with the same polarity. That is, a positive input signal causes a positive change in the op amp's output voltage. This voltage causes current to flow in the voltage divider formed by R_f and R_i. Because the current into the inverting input is so low, the current through R_f is the same as R_i.

The voltage at the *summing junction*, the connection point for the two resistors and the inverting terminal, V_{INV}, is:

$$V_{INV} \quad V_O\left(\frac{\quad}{R_i \quad R_f}\right)$$

The op amp's output voltage will continue to rise until the *loop error signal*, the difference in voltage between the inverting and noninverting inputs, is close to zero. At this point, the voltage at the inverting terminal is approximately equal to the voltage at the noninverting terminal, V_{in}, so that $V_{INV} = V_{in}$. Substituting in equation for V_{INV}, the gain of this circuit is:

$$\frac{V_O}{V_{in}} = \left(1 + \frac{R_f}{R_i}\right)$$

where

V_o = the output voltage

V_{in} = the input voltage.

The higher the op amp's open-loop gain, the closer will be the voltages at the inverting and noninverting terminals when the circuit is balanced and the more closely the circuit's closed-loop gain will equal that in the equation. So the negative feedback creates an electronic balancing act with the op amp increasing its output voltage so that the input error signal is as small as possible.

In the inverting configuration of Figure 4.70B, the input signal (V_{in}) is connected through R_i to the inverting terminal. The feedback resistor is again connected between the inverting terminal and the output. The noninverting terminal is connected to ground (or the circuit reference voltage). In this configuration the feedback action results in the output voltage changing to whatever value is needed such that the current through R_i is balanced by an equal and opposite current through R_f. The gain of this circuit is:

$$\frac{V_O}{V_{in}} = -\frac{R_f}{R_{in}}$$

where V_{in} represents the voltage input to R_{in}.

For the remainder of this section, "ground" or "zero voltage" should be understood to be the circuit reference voltage. That voltage may not be "earth ground potential." For example, if a single positive supply of 12 V is used, 6 V may be used as the circuit reference voltage. The circuit reference voltage is a fixed dc voltage that can be considered to be an ac ground because of the reference source's extremely low ac impedance.

The negative sign in the voltage gain equation indicates that the signal is inverted. For ac signals, inversion represents a 180° phase shift. The gain of the noninverting configuration can vary from a minimum of 1 to the maximum of which the op amp is capable, as indicated by A_v for dc signals, or the gain-bandwidth product for ac signals. The gain of the inverting configuration can vary from a minimum of 0 (gains from 0 to 1 attenuate the signal while gains of 1 and higher amplify the signal) to the maximum of which the device is capable.

The inverting amplifier configuration results in a special condition at the op amp's inverting input called *virtual ground*. Because the op amp's high open-loop gain drives the two inputs to be very close together, if the noninverting input is at ground potential, the inverting input will be very close to ground as well and the op amp's output will change with the input signal to maintain the inverting input at ground. Measured with a voltmeter, the input appears to be grounded, but it is merely maintained at ground potential by the action of the op amp and the feedback loop. This point in the circuit may not be connected to any other ground connection or circuit point because the resulting additional current flow will upset the balance of the circuit.

The *voltage follower* or *unity-gain buffer* circuit of **Figure 4.71** is commonly used as a buffer stage. The voltage follower has the input connected directly to the noninverting terminal and the output connected directly to the inverting terminal. This configuration has unity gain because the circuit is balanced when the output and input voltages are the same (error voltage equals zero). It also provides the maximum possible input impedance and the minimum possible output impedance of which the device is capable.

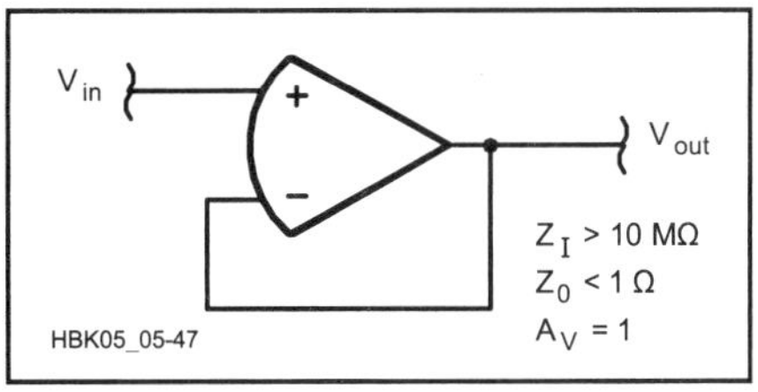

Figure 4.71 — Voltage follower. This operational amplifier circuit makes a nearly ideal buffer with a voltage gain of about one, and with extremely high input impedance and extremely low output impedance.

Differential and Difference Amplifier

A *differential amplifier* is a special application of an operational amplifier (see **Figure 4.72**). It amplifies the difference between two analog signals and is very useful to cancel noise under certain conditions. For instance, if an analog signal and a reference signal travel over the same cable they may pick up noise, and it is likely that both signals will have the same amount of noise. When the differential amplifier subtracts them, the signal will be unchanged but the noise will be completely removed, within the limits of the CMRR. The equation for differential amplifier operation is

$$V_O = \frac{R_f}{R_i}\left[\frac{1}{\frac{R_n}{R_g}+1}\left(\frac{R_i}{R_f}+1\right)V_n - V_i\right]$$

which, if the ratios R_i/R_f and R_n/R_g are equal, simplifies to:

$$V_O = \frac{R_f}{R_i}(V_n - V_I)$$

Note that the differential amplifier gain is identical to the inverting amplifier gain if the voltage applied to the noninverting terminal is equal to zero. If the voltage applied to the inverting terminal (V_i) is zero, the analysis is a little more complicated but it is possible to derive the noninverting amplifier gain from the differential amplifier gain by taking into account the influence of R_n and R_g. If all four resistors have the *same* value the *difference amplifier* is created and V_O is just the difference of the two voltages.

$$V_O = V_n - V_I$$

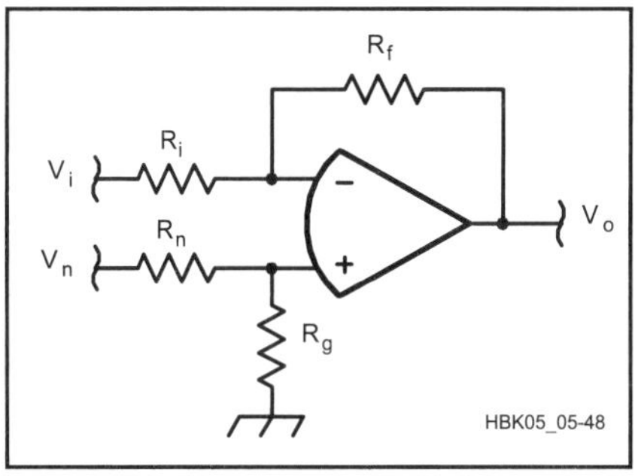

Figure 4.72 — Difference amplifier. This operational amplifier circuit amplifies the difference between the two input signals.

Instrumentation Amplifier

Just as the symmetry of the transistors making up an op amp leads to a device with high values of Z_i, A_v and CMRR and a low value of Z_o, a symmetric combination of op amps is used to further improve these parameters. This circuit, shown in **Figure 4.73** is called an *instrumentation amplifier*. It has three parts; each of the two inputs is connected to a noninverting buffer amplifier with a gain of 1 + R2/R1. The outputs of these buffer amplifiers are then connected to a differential amplifier with a gain of R4/R3. V2 is the circuit's inverting input and V1 the noninverting input.

The three amplifier modules are usually all part of the same integrated circuit. This means that they have essentially the same temperature and the internal transistors and resistors are very well matched. This causes the subtle gain and tracking errors caused by temperature differences and mismatched components between individual op amps to be cancelled out or dramatically reduced. In addition, the external resistors using the same designators (R2, R3, R4) are carefully matched as well, sometimes being part of a single integrated *resistor pack*. The result is a circuit with better performance than any single-amplifier circuit over a wider temperature range.

Summing Amplifier

The high input impedance of an op amp makes it ideal for use as a *summing amplifier*. In either the inverting or noninverting configuration, the single input signal can be replaced by multiple input signals that are connected together through series resistors, as shown in **Figure 4.74**. For the inverting summing amplifier, the gain of each input signal can be calculated individually using

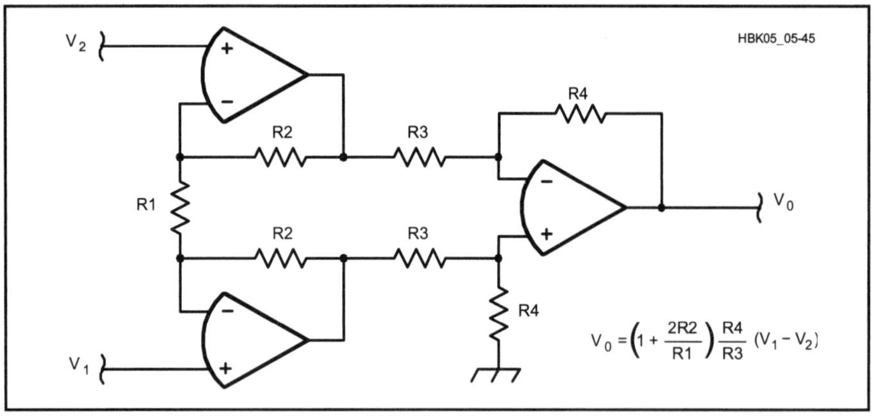

Figure 4.73 — Operational amplifiers arranged as an instrumentation amplifier. The balanced and cascaded series of op amps work together to perform differential amplification with good common-mode rejection and very high input impedance (no load resistor required) on both the inverting (V_1) and noninverting (V_2) inputs.

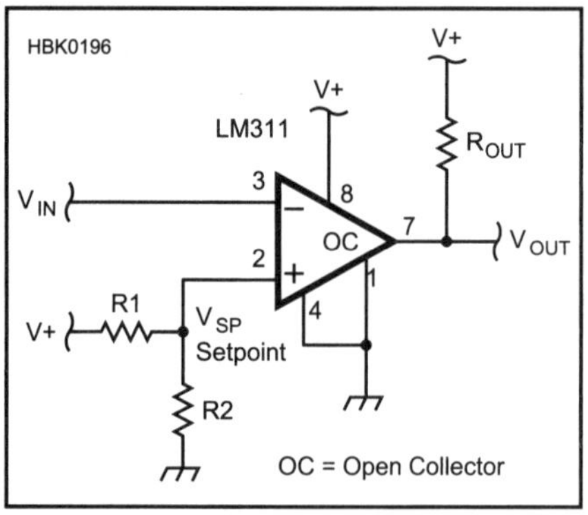

Figure 4.75 — A comparator circuit in which the output voltage is low when voltage at the inverting input is higher than the setpoint voltage at the noninverting input.

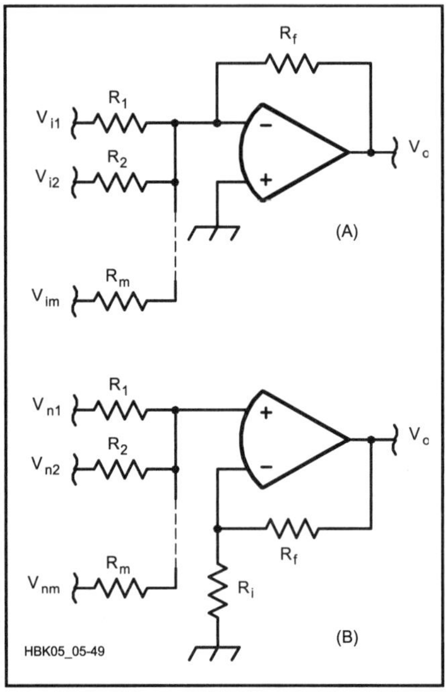

Figure 4.74 — Summing operational amplifier circuits. (A) Inverting configuration. (B) Noninverting configuration.

the equation for inverting amplifier gain and, because of the superposition property of linear circuits, the output is the sum of each input signal multiplied by its gain. In the noninverting configuration, the output is the gain times the weighted sum of the m different input signals:

$$V_n = V_{n1}\frac{R_{p1}}{R_1 + R_{p1}} + V_{n2}\frac{R_{p2}}{R_2 + R_{p2}} + \ldots$$

$$+V_{nm}\frac{R_{pm}}{R_m + R_{pm}}$$

where R_{pm} is the parallel resistance of all m resistors excluding R_m. For example, with three signals being summed, R_{p1} is the parallel combination of R_2 and R_3.

Comparators

A *voltage comparator* is another special form of op amp circuit, shown in **Figure 4.75**. It has two analog signals as its inputs and its output is either TRUE or FALSE depending on whether the noninverting or inverting signal voltage is higher, respectively. Thus, it "compares" the input voltages. TRUE generally corresponds to a positive output voltage and FALSE to a negative or zero voltage. The circuit in Figure 4.75 uses external resistors to generate a reference voltage, called the *setpoint*, to which the input signal is compared. A comparator can also compare two variable voltages.

A standard operational amplifier can be made to act as a comparator by connecting the two input voltages to the noninverting and inverting inputs with no input or feedback resistors. If the voltage of the noninverting input is higher than that of the inverting input, the output voltage will be driven to the positive clamping limit. If the inverting input is at a higher potential than the noninverting input, the output voltage will be driven to the negative clamping limit. If the comparator is comparing an unknown voltage to a known voltage, the known voltage is called the *setpoint* and the comparator output indicates whether the unknown voltage is above or below the setpoint.

An op amp that has been intended for use as a comparator, such as the LM311, is optimized to respond quickly to the input signals. In addition, comparators often have *open-collector outputs* that use an external *pull-up* resistor, R_{OUT}, connected to a positive power supply voltage. When the comparator output is TRUE, the output transistor is turned off and the pull-up resistor "pulls up" the output voltage to the positive power supply voltage. When the comparator output is FALSE, the transistor is driven into the saturation and the output voltage is the transistor's $V_{CE(sat)}$.

Hysteresis

Comparator circuits also use *hysteresis* to prevent "chatter" — the output of the comparator switching rapidly back and forth when the input voltage is at or close to the setpoint voltage. There may be noise on the input signal, as shown in **Figure 4.76A**, that causes the input voltage to cross the setpoint threshold repeatedly. The rapid switching of the output can be confusing to the circuits monitoring the comparator output.

Hysteresis is a form of positive feedback that "moves" the setpoint by a few mV in the direction *opposite* to that in which the input signal crossed the setpoint threshold. As shown in Figure 4.76B, the slight shift in the setpoint tends to hold the comparator output in the new state and prevents switching back to the old state. **Figure 4.77** shows how the output of the comparator is fed back to the positive input through resistor R3, adding or subtracting a small amount of current from the divider and shifting the setpoint. If V_{HYS} is the amount of hysteresis desired (the shift in the setpoint voltage):

$$V_{HYS} \approx (V_{OH})\ (R1\ //\ R2)\ /\ [R3 + (R1\ //\ R2)]$$

where V_{OH} is the high-level output voltage with the comparator's output is off. Solving for R3 if the other values are known:

$$R3 \approx [(V_{OH})(R1\ //\ R2)\ /\ V_{HYS}] - (R1\ //\ R2)$$

Some applications of a voltage comparator are a zero crossing detector, a signal squarer (which turns other cyclical wave forms into

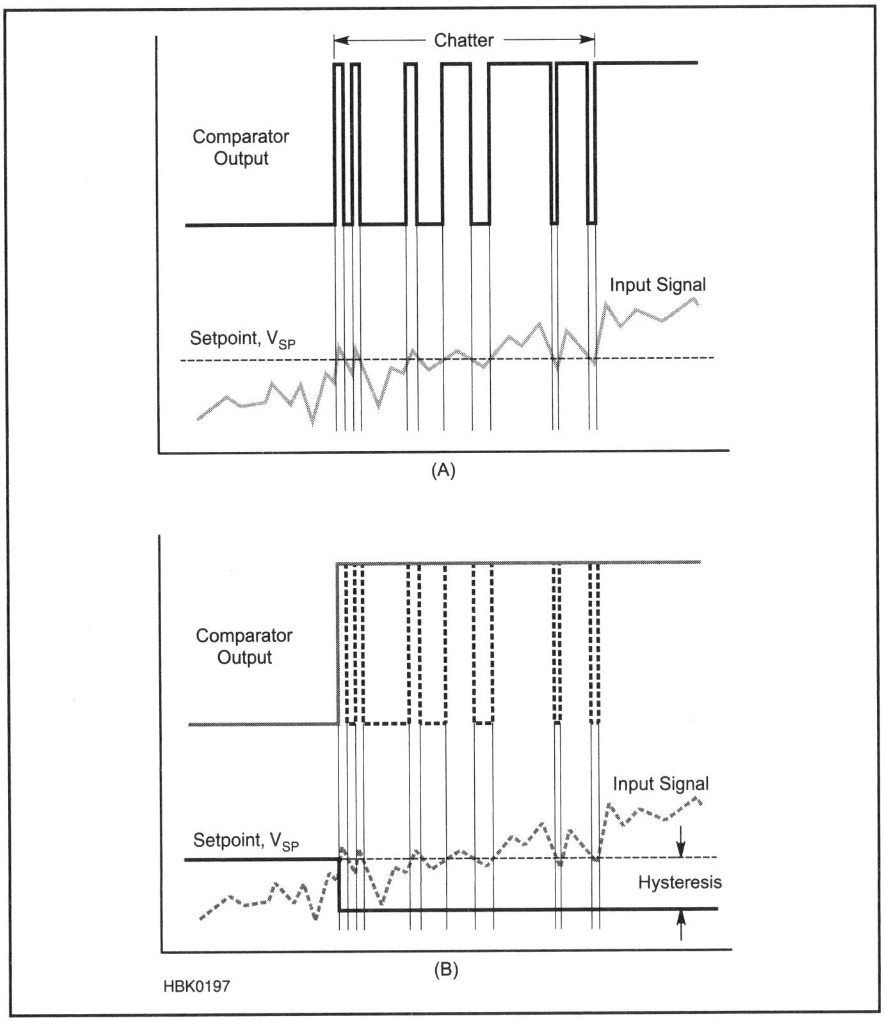

Figure 4.76 — Chatter (A) is caused by noise when the input signal is close to the setpoint. Chatter can also be caused by voltage shifts that occur when a heavy load is turned on and off. Hysteresis (B) shifts the setpoint a small amount by using positive feedback in which the output pulls the setpoint farther away from the input signal after switching.

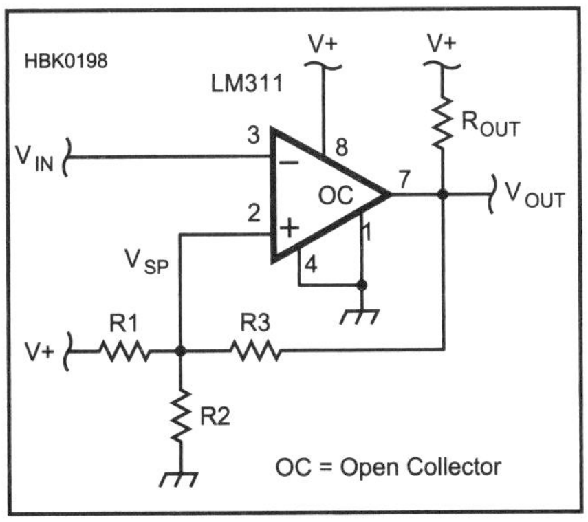

Figure 4.77 — Comparator circuit with hysteresis. R3 causes a shift in the comparator setpoint by allowing more current to flow through R1 when the comparator output is low.

square waves) and a peak detector. An amateur station application: Circuits that monitor the CI-V band data output voltage from ICOM HF radios use a series of comparators to sense the level of the voltage and indicate on which band the radio is operating.

FILTERS

One of the most important type of op amp circuits is the *active filter.* Two examples of op amp filter circuits are shown in **Figure 4.78.** The simple noninverting low-pass filter in Figure 4.78A has the same response as a passive single-pole RC low-pass filter, but unlike the passive filter, the op amp filter circuit has a very high input impedance and a very low output impedance so that the filter's frequency and voltage response are relatively unaffected by the circuits connected to the filter input and output. This circuit is a low-pass filter because

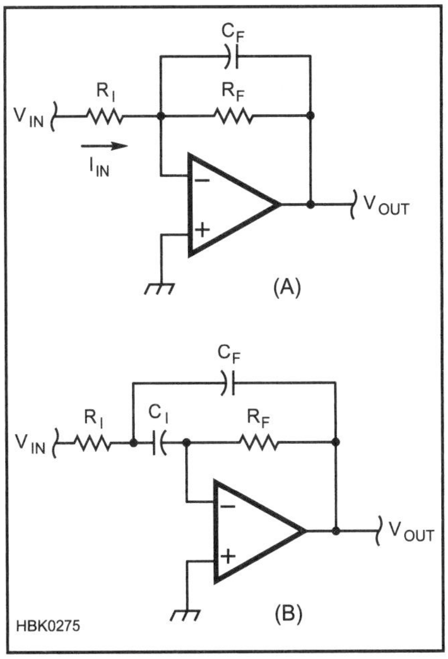

Figure 4.78 — Op amp active filters. The circuit at (A) has a low-pass response identical to an RC filter. The –3 dB frequency occurs when the reactance of C_F equals R_F. The band-pass filter at (B) is a multiple-feedback filter.

the reactance of the feedback capacitor decreases with frequency, requiring less output voltage to balance the voltages of the inverting and noninverting inputs.

The *multiple-feedback* circuit in Figure 4.78B results in a band-pass response while using only resistors and capacitors. This circuit is just one of many different types of active filters. Active filters are discussed in the **Analog and Digital Filtering** chapter.

RECTIFIERS AND PEAK DETECTORS

The high open-loop gain of the op amp can also be used to simulate the I-V characteristics of an ideal diode. A *precision rectifier* circuit is shown in **Figure 4.79** along with the I-V characteristics of a real (dashed lines) and ideal (solid line) diode. The high gain of the op amp compensates for the V_F forward voltage drop of the real diode in its feedback loop with an output voltage equal to the input voltage plus V_F. Remember that the op amp's output increases until its input voltages are balanced. When the input voltage is negative, which would reverse-bias the diode, the op amp's output can't balance the input because the diode blocks any current flow through the feedback loop. The resistor at the output holds the voltage at zero until the input voltage is positive once again. Precision half-wave and full-wave rectifier circuits are shown in **Figure 4.80** and their operation is described in

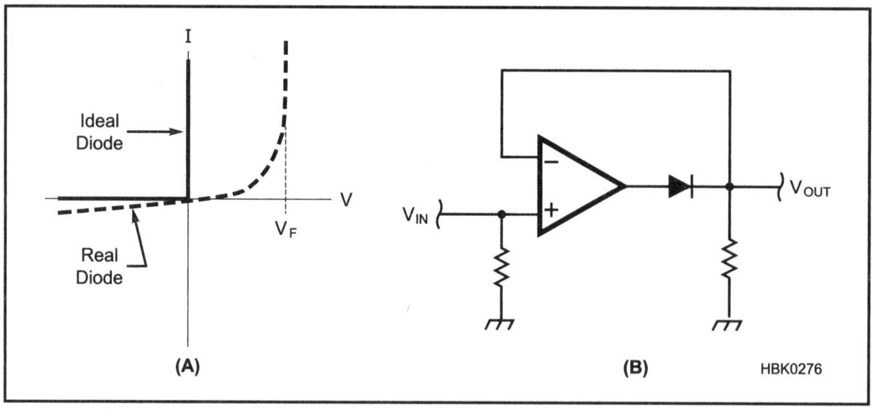

Figure 4.79 — Ideal and real diode I-V characteristics are shown at (A). The op amp precision rectifier circuit is shown at (B).

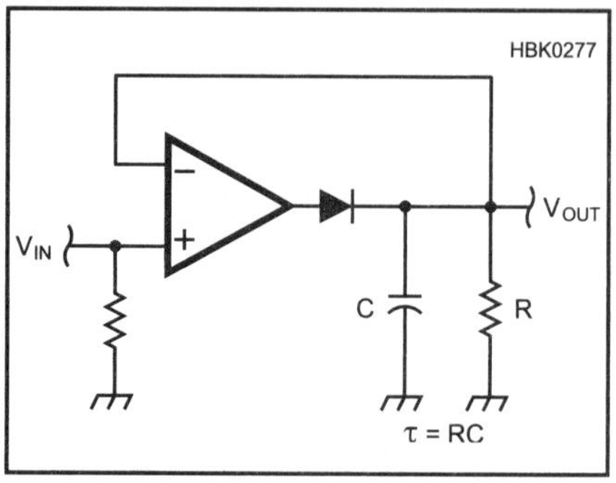

Figure 4.81 — Peak detector. Coupling a precision diode with a capacitor to store charge creates a peak detector. The capacitor will charge to the peak value of the input voltage. R discharges the capacitor with a time constant of τ = RC and can be omitted if it is desired for the out-

many reference texts.

One application of the precision rectifier circuit useful in radio is the *peak detector*, shown in **Figure 4.81**. A precision rectifier is used to charge the output capacitor which holds the peak voltage. The output resistor sets the time constant at which the capacitor discharges. The resistor can also be replaced by a transistor acting as a switch to reset the detector. This circuit is used in AGC loops, spectrum analyzers, and other instruments that measure the peak value of ac waveforms.

LOG AMPLIFIER

There are a number of applications in radio in which it is useful for the gain of an amplifier to be higher for small input signals than for large input signals. For example, an audio compressor circuit is used to reduce the variations in a speech signal's amplitude so that the average power output of an AM or SSB transmitter is increased. A *log amplifier* circuit whose gain for large signals is proportional to the logarithm of the input signal's amplitude is shown in **Figure 4.82**. The log amp circuit is used in compressors and limiter circuits.

At signal levels that are too small to cause significant current flow through the diodes, the gain is set as in a regular inverting amplifier, $A_V = -R_f / R_i$. As the signal level increases, however, more current flows through the diode according to the Fundamental Diode Equation (see the **Electronic Fundamentals** chapter). That means the op amp output voltage has to increase less (lower gain) to cause enough current to flow through R_i such that the input voltages balance. The larger the input voltage, the more the diode conducts and the lower the gain of the circuit. Since the diode's current is exponential in response to voltage, the gain of the circuit for large input signals is logarithmic.

Voltage-Current Converters

Another pair of useful op amp circuits convert voltage into current and current into voltage. These are frequently used to convert currents from sensors and detectors into voltages that are easier to measure. **Figure 4.83A** shows a voltage-to-current converter in which the output current is actually the current in the feedback loop. Because the op amp's high open-loop gain insures that its input voltages are equal, the current $I_{R1} = V_{IN} / R1$. Certainly, this could also be achieved with a resistor and

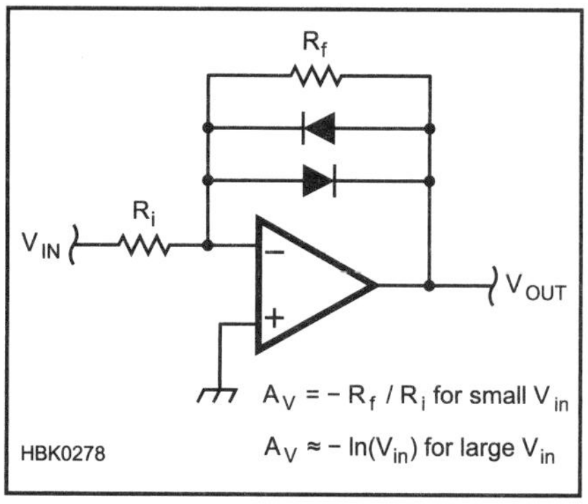

Figure 4.82 — Log amplifier. At low voltages, the gain of the circuit is $-R_f/R_i$, but as the diodes begin to conduct for higher-voltage signals, the gain changes to $-\ln(V_{in})$ in because of the diode's exponential current as described in the Fundamental Diode Equation.

Ohm's Law, but the op amp circuit's high input impedance means there is little interaction between the input voltage source and the output current.

Going the other way, Figure 4.83B is a

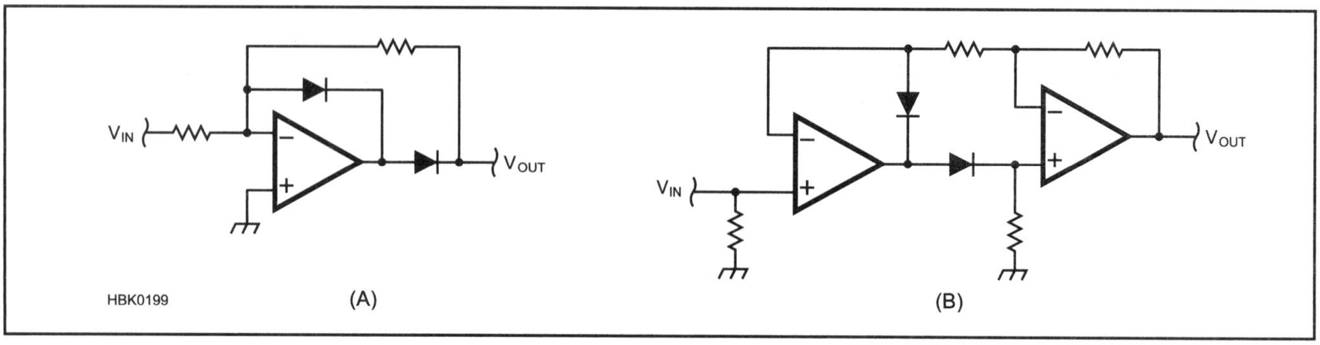

Figure 4.80 — Half-wave precision rectifier (A). The extra diode at the output of the op amp prevents the op amp from saturating on negative half-cycles and improves response time. The precision full-wave rectifier circuit at (B) reproduces both halves of the input waveform.

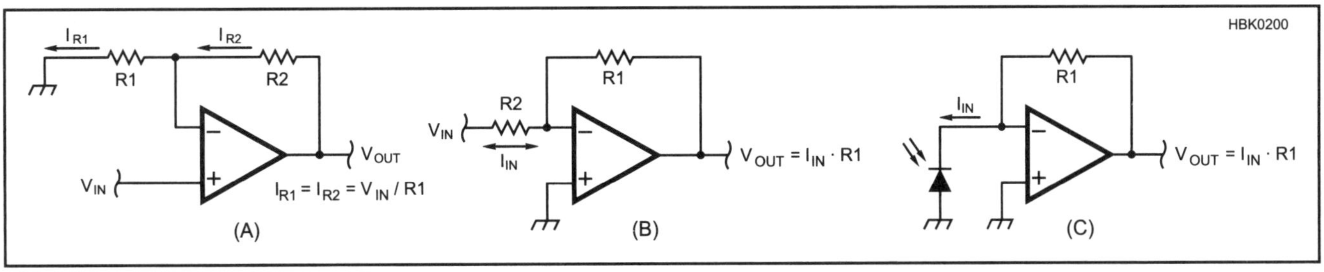

Figure 4.83 — Voltage-current converters. The current through R1 in (A) equals V_{in}/R1 because the op amp keeps both input terminals at approximately the same voltage. At (B), input current is balanced by the op amp, resulting in $V_{OUT} = I_{IN}R1$. Current through a photodiode (C) can be converted into a voltage in this way.

current-to-voltage converter. The op amp's output will change so that the current through the feedback resistor, R1, exactly equals the input current, keeping the inverting terminal at ground potential. The output voltage, V_O = I_{IN} R1. Again, this could be done with just a resistor, but the op amp provides isolation between the source of input current and the output voltage. Figure 4.83C shows an application of a current-to-voltage converter in which the small currents from a photodiode are turned into voltage. This circuit can be used as a detector for amplitude modulated light pulses or waveforms.

4.8 Miscellaneous Analog ICs

The three main advantages of designing a circuit into an IC are to take advantage of the matched characteristics of its components, to make highly complex circuitry more economical, and to miniaturize the circuit and reduce power consumption. As circuits standardize and become widely used, they are often converted from discrete components to integrated circuits. Along with the op amp described earlier, there are many such classes of linear ICs.

4.8.1 Transistor and Driver Arrays

The most basic form of linear integrated circuit and one of the first to be implemented is the component array. The most common of these are the resistor, diode and transistor arrays. Though capacitor arrays are also possible, they are used less often. Component arrays usually provide space saving but this is not the major advantage of these devices. They are the least densely packed of the integrated circuits because each device requires a separate off-chip connection. While it may be possible to place over a million transistors on a single semiconductor chip, individual access to these would require a total of three million pins and this is beyond the limits of practicability. More commonly, resistor and diode arrays contain from five to 16 individual devices and transistor arrays contain from three to six individual transistors. The advantage of these arrays is the very close matching of component values within the array. In a circuit that needs matched components, the component array is often a good method of obtaining this feature. The components within an array can be internally combined for special functions, such as termination resistors, diode bridges and Darlington pair transistors. A nearly infinite number of possibilities exists for these combinations of components and many of these are available in arrays.

Driver arrays, such as the ULN2000-series devices shown in **Figure 4.84** are very useful in creating an interface between low-power circuits such as microprocessors and higher-power loads and indicators. Each driver consists of a Darlington pair switching circuit as described earlier in this chapter. There are different versions with different types and arrangements of resistors and diodes.

Many manufacturers offer driver arrays. They are available with built-in kickback diodes to allow them to drive inductive loads, such as relays, and are heavy enough to source or sink current levels up to 1 A. (All of the drivers in the array cannot operate at full load at the same time, however. Read the data sheet carefully to determine what limitations on current and power dissipation may exist.)

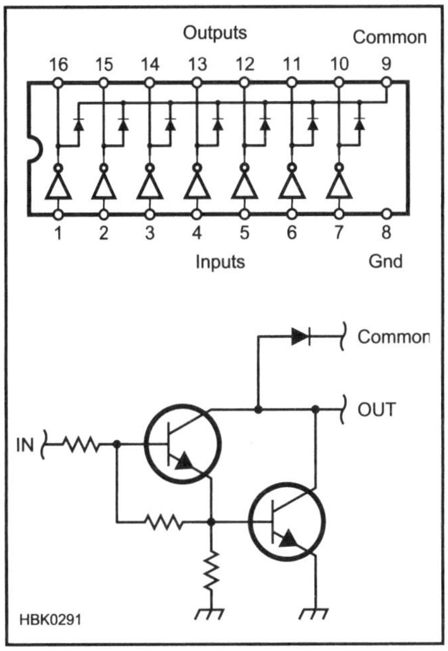

Figure 4.84 — Typical ULN2000-series driver array configuration and internal circuit. The use of driver array ICs is very popular as an interface between microprocessor or other low-power digital circuits and loads such as relays, solenoids or lamps.

4.8.2 Voltage Regulators and References

One of the most popular linear ICs is the voltage regulator. There are two basic types, the three-terminal regulator and the regulator controller. Examples of both are described in the **Power Sources** chapter.

The three-terminal regulator (input, ground, output) is a single package designed to perform all of the voltage regulation functions. The output voltage can be fixed, as in the 7800-series of regulators, or variable, as in the LM317 regulator. It contains a voltage reference, comparator circuits, current and temperature sensing protective circuits, and the main pass element. These ICs are usually contained in the same packages as power transistors and the same techniques of thermal management are used to remove excess heat.

Regulator controllers, such as the popular 723 device, contain all of the control and voltage reference circuitry, but require external components for the main pass element, current sensing, and to configure some of their control functions.

Voltage references such as the Linear Technology LT1635 are special semiconductor diodes that have a precisely controlled I-V characteristic. A buffer amplifier isolates the sensitive diode and provides a low output impedance for the voltage signal. Voltage references are used as part of power regulators and by analog-digital converter circuits.

4.8.3 Timers (Multivibrators)

A *multivibrator* is a circuit that oscillates between two states, usually with a square wave or pulse train output. The frequency of oscillation is accurately controlled with the addition of appropriate values of external resistance and capacitance. The most common multivibrator in use today is the 555 timer IC (NE555 by Signetics [now Philips] or LM555 by National Semiconductor). This very simple eight-pin device has a frequency range from less than one hertz to several hundred kilohertz. Such a device can also be used in *monostable* operation, where an input pulse generates an output pulse of a different duration, or in *a stable* or *free-running* operation, where the device oscillates continuously. Other applications of a multivibrator include a frequency divider, a delay line, a pulse width modulator and a pulse position modulator. (These can be found in the IC's data sheet or in the reference listed at the end of this chapter.)

Figure 4.85 shows the basic components of a 555. Connected between power input (V_{cc}) and ground, the three resistors labeled "R" at the top left of the figure form a *voltage divider* that divides V_{CC} into two equal steps—one at ⅔ V_{CC} and one at ⅓ V_{CC}. These serve as reference voltages for the rest of the circuit.

Connected to the reference voltages are blocks labeled *trigger comparator* and *threshold comparator*. (Comparators were discussed in a preceding section.) The trigger comparator in the 555 is wired so that its output is high whenever the trigger input is *less* than ⅓ V_{CC} and vice versa. Similarly, the threshold comparator output is high whenever the threshold input is *greater* than ⅔ V_{CC}.

These two outputs control a digital *flip-flop* circuit with an output, *Q*, that changes to high or low when the state of its *set* and *reset* input changes. The Q output stays high or low (it *latches* or *toggles*) until the opposite input changes. When the set input changes from low to high, Q goes low. When reset changes from low to high, Q goes high. The flip-flop ignores any other changes. An inverter makes the 555 output high when Q is low and vice versa — this makes the timer circuit easier to interface with external circuits.

The transistor connected to Q acts as a switch. When Q is high, the transistor is on and acts as a closed switch connected to ground. When Q is low, the transistor is off and the switch is open. These simple building blocks — voltage divider, comparator, flip-flop and switch — build a surprising number of useful circuits.

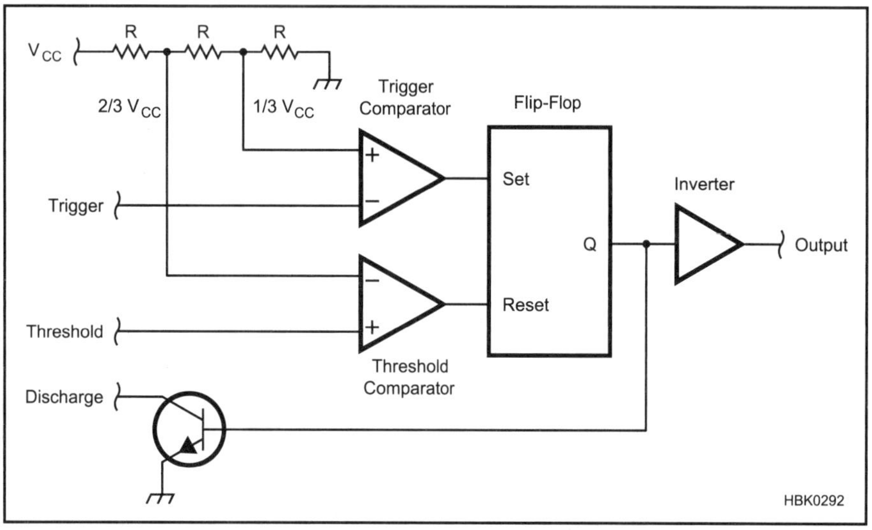

Figure 4.85 — Internal NE555 timer components. This simple array of components combines to make one of the most popular analog ICs. The 555 timer IC uses ratios of internal resistors to generate a precise voltage reference for generating time intervals based on charging and discharging a capacitor.

THE MONOSTABLE OR "ONE-SHOT" TIMER

The simplest 555 circuit is the monostable circuit. This configuration will output one fixed-length pulse when triggered by an input pulse. **Figure 4.86** shows the connections for this circuit.

Starting with capacitor C discharged, the flip-flop output, Q, is high, which keeps the discharge transistor turned on and the voltage on C below ⅔ V_{CC}. The circuit is in its stable state, waiting for a trigger pulse.

When the voltage at the trigger input drops below ⅓ V_{CC}, the trigger comparator output changes from low to high, which causes Q to toggle to the low state. This turns off the transistor (opens the switch) and allows C to begin charging toward V_{CC}.

When C reaches ⅔ V_{CC}, this causes the threshold comparator to switch its output from low to high and that resets the flip-flop. Q returns high, turning on the transistor and discharging C. The circuit has returned to its stable state. The output pulse length for the monostable configuration is:

$$T = 1.1 R C_1$$

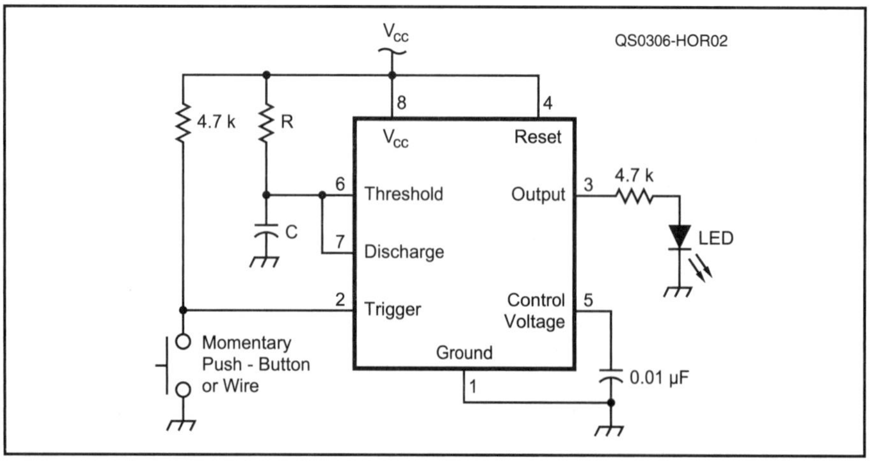

Figure 4.86 — Monostable timer. The timing capacitor is discharged until a trigger pulse initiates the charging process and turns the output on. When the capacitor has charged to 2/3 V_{CC}, the output is turned off, the capacitor is discharged and the timer awaits the next trigger pulse.

Notice that the timing is independent of the absolute value of V_{CC} — the output pulse width is the same with a 5 V supply as it is with a 15 V supply. This is because the 555 design is based on ratios and not absolute voltage levels.

THE ASTABLE MULTIVIBRATOR

The complement to the monostable circuit is the astable circuit in **Figure 4.87**. Pins 2, 6 and 7 are configured differently and timing resistor is now split into two resistors, R1 and R2.

Start from the same state as the monostable circuit, with C completely discharged. The monostable circuit requires a trigger pulse to initiate the timing cycle. In the astable circuit, the trigger input is connected directly to the capacitor, so if the capacitor is discharged, then the trigger comparator output must be high. Q is low, turning off the discharge transistor, which allows C to immediately begin charging.

C charges toward V_{CC}, but now through the combination of R1 and R2. As the capacitor voltage passes 2/3 V_{CC}, the threshold comparator output changes from low to high, resetting Q to high. This turns on the discharge transistor and the capacitor starts to discharge through R2. When the capacitor is discharged below ⅓ V_{CC}, the trigger comparator changes from high to low and the cycle begins again, automatically. This happens over and over, causing a train of pulses at the output while C charges and discharges between ⅓ and ⅔ V_{CC} as seen in the figure.

The total time it takes for one complete cycle is the charge time, T_c, plus the discharge time, T_d:

$$T = T_c + T_d = 0.693(R_1 + R_2)C + 0.693 R_2C = 0.693\,(R_1 + 2R_2)C$$

and the output frequency is:

$$f = \frac{1}{T} = \frac{1.443}{(R_1 + 2\,R_2)\,C}$$

When using the 555 in an application in or around radios, it is important to block any RF signals from the IC power supply or timing control inputs. Any unwanted signal present on these inputs, especially the Control Voltage input, will upset the timer's operation and cause it to operate improperly. The usual practice is to use a 0.01 µF bypass capacitor (shown on pin 5 in both Figure 4.86 and 4.87) to bypass ac signals such as noise or RF to ground. Abrupt changes in V_{CC} will also cause changes in timing and these may be prevented by connecting filter capacitors at the V_{CC} input to ground.

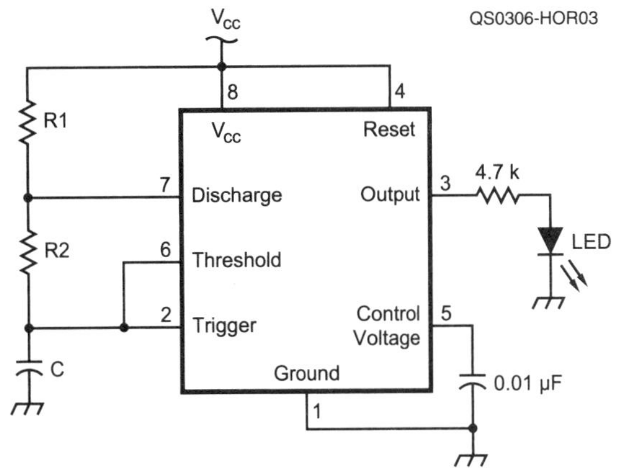

Figure 4.87 — Astable timer. If the capacitor discharge process initiates the next charge cycle, the timer will output a pulse train continuously.

4.8.4 Analog Switches and Multiplexers

Arrays of analog switches, such as the Maxim MAX312-series, allow routing of audio through lower frequency RF signals without mechanical switches. There are several types of switch arrays. Independent switches have isolated inputs and outputs and are turned on and off independently. Both SPST and SPDT configurations are available. Multiple switches can be wired with common control signals to implement multiple-pole configurations.

Use of analog switches at RF through microwave frequencies requires devices specifically designed for those frequencies. The Analog Devices ADG901 is a switch usable to 2.5 GHz. It absorbs the signal when off, acting as a terminating load. The ADG902 instead reflects the signal as an open circuit when off. Arrays of three switches called "tee-switches" are used when very high isolation between the input and output is required.

Multiplexers or "muxes" are arrays of SPST switches configured to act as a multi-position switch that connects one of four to sixteen input signals to a single output. Demultiplexers ("demuxes") have a single input and multiple outputs. Multiplexer ICs are available as single N-to-1 switches (the MAX4617 is an 8-to-1 mux) or as groups of N-to-1 switches (the MAX4618 is a dual 4-to-1 mux).

Crosspoint switch arrays are arranged so that any of four to sixteen signal inputs can be connected to any of four to sixteen output signal lines. The Analog Devices AD8108 is an 8-by-8 crosspoint switch with eight inputs and eight outputs. These arrays are used when it is necessary to switch multiple signal sources among multiple signal receivers. They are most commonly used in telecommunications.

All analog switches use FET technology as the switching element. To switch ac signals, most analog switches require both positive and negative voltage power supplies. An alternative is to use a single power supply voltage and ground, but bias all inputs and output at one-half the power supply voltage. This requires dc blocking capacitors in all signal paths, both input and output, and loading resistors may be required at the device outputs. The blocking capacitors can also introduce low-frequency roll-off.

The impedance of the switching element varies from a few ohms to more than 100 ohms. Check the switch data sheet to determine the limits for how much power and current the switches can handle. Switch arrays, because of the physical size of the array, can have significant coupling or *crosstalk* between signal paths. Use caution when using analog switches for high-frequency signals as coupling generally increases with frequency and may compromise the isolation required for high selectivity in receivers and other RF signal processing equipment.

4.8.5 Audio Output Amplifiers

While it is possible to use op amps as low power audio output drivers for headphones, they generally have output impedances that are too high for most audio transducers such as speakers and headphones. The LM380 series of audio driver ICs has been used in radio circuits for many years and a simple schematic for a speaker driver is shown in **Figure 4.88**.

The popularity of personal music players

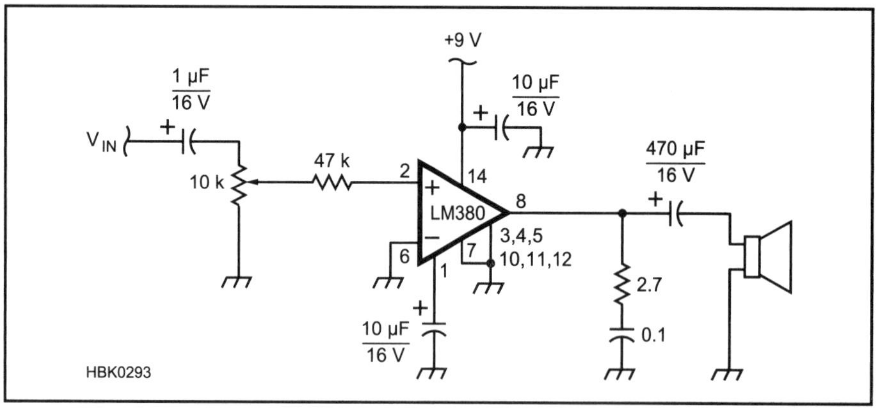

Figure 4.88 — Speaker driver. The LM380-series of audio output drivers are well-suited for low-power audio outputs, such as for headphones and small speakers. When using IC audio output drivers, be sure to refer to the manufacturer's data sheet for layout and power supply guidelines.

has resulted in the creation of many new and inexpensive audio driver ICs, such as the National Semiconductor LM4800- and LM4900-series. Drivers that operate from voltages as low as 1.5 V for battery-powered devices and up to 18 V for use in vehicles are now available.

When choosing an audio driver IC for communications audio, the most important parameters to evaluate are its power requirements and power output capabilities. An overloaded or underpowered driver will result in distortion. Driver ICs intended for music players have frequency responses well in excess of the 3000 Hz required for communications. This can lead to annoying and fatiguing hiss unless steps are taken to reduce the circuit's frequency response.

Audio power amplifiers should also be carefully decoupled from the power supply and the manufacturer may recommend specific circuit layouts to prevent oscillation or feedback. Check the device's data sheet for this information.

4.8.6 Temperature Sensors

Active temperature sensors use the temperature-dependent properties of semiconductor devices to create voltages that correspond to absolute temperature in degrees Fahrenheit (LM34) or degrees Celsius (LM35). These sensors (of which many others are available than the two examples given here) are available in small plastic packages, both leaded and surface-mount, that respond quickly to temperature changes. They are available with 1% and better accuracy, requiring only a source of voltage at very low current and ground. Complete application information is available in the manufacturer data sheets. Thermistors, a type of passive temperature sensor, are discussed in the Thermal Management section of this chapter. Temperature sensors are used in radio mostly in cooling and temperature control circuits.

4.9 Analog-Digital Interfacing

Quite often, logic circuits must either drive or be driven from non-logic sources. A very common requirement is sensing the presence or absence of a high (as compared to +5 V) voltage or perhaps turning on or off a 120 V ac device or moving the motor in an antenna rotator. A similar problem occurs when two different units in the shack must be interfaced because induced ac voltages or ground loops can cause problems with the desired signals.

A slow speed but safe way to interface such circuits is to use a relay. This provides absolute isolation between the logic circuits and the load. **Figure 4.89A** shows the correct way to provide this connection. The relay coil is selected to draw less than the available current from the driving logic circuit.

The diode is called a *kickback* or *flyback diode* that clamps the *back EMF* switching transient generated when current through the coil is interrupted. Voltage at the switching transistor from the transient can reach several hundred volts and damage or destroy the transistor. Use a 1N4148 for small relays or a 1N4001 for larger coils which generate higher surge currents.

The use of a kickback diode can increase the turn-off time of the relay. If the turn-off time is an important part of the design, a Zener diode in series with the kickback diode can be used. The Zener voltage should be approximately twice the supply voltage (a 1N5252 is a 24V Zener). This will still result in some turn-off delay. Experimentation may be necessary to find the best trade-off between Zener voltage and turn-off time for critical circuits.

Tranzorbs and MOVs can also be used. MOVs may change clamping voltages after extended use. A thorough discussion of relay drive protection can be found in STMicroelectronics Application Note AN-319, "Relay Drive Protection" which is available online from several sources.

For applications in which the relay is connected to circuits where strong RF might be present, such as antenna switches, rotator control cables, or tuning circuits, add a 0.01 to 0.001 µF ceramic capacitor (rated at 50 V or more) in parallel with the coil to prevent the diode(s) or clamping devices from generating mixing products or harmonics.

It is often not possible to find a relay that meets the load requirements *and* has a coil that can be driven directly from the logic output. Figure 4.89B shows two methods of using transistors to allow the use of higher power relays with logic gates.

Electro-optical couplers such as optoisolators and solid state relays can also be used for this circuit interfacing. Figure 4.89C uses an optoisolator to interface two sets of logic circuits that must be kept electrically isolated, and Figure 4.89D uses a solid state relay to control an ac line supply to a high current load. Note that this example uses a solid state relay with internal current limiting on the input side; the LED input has an impedance of approximately 300 Ω. Some devices may need a series resistor to set the LED current; always consult the device data sheet to avoid exceeding device limits of the relay or the processor's I/O pin.

For safely using signals with voltages higher than logic levels as inputs, the same simple resistor and Zener diode circuit similar to that shown in Figure 4.29 can be used to clamp the input voltage to an acceptable level. Care must be used to choose a resistor value that will not load the input signal unacceptably.

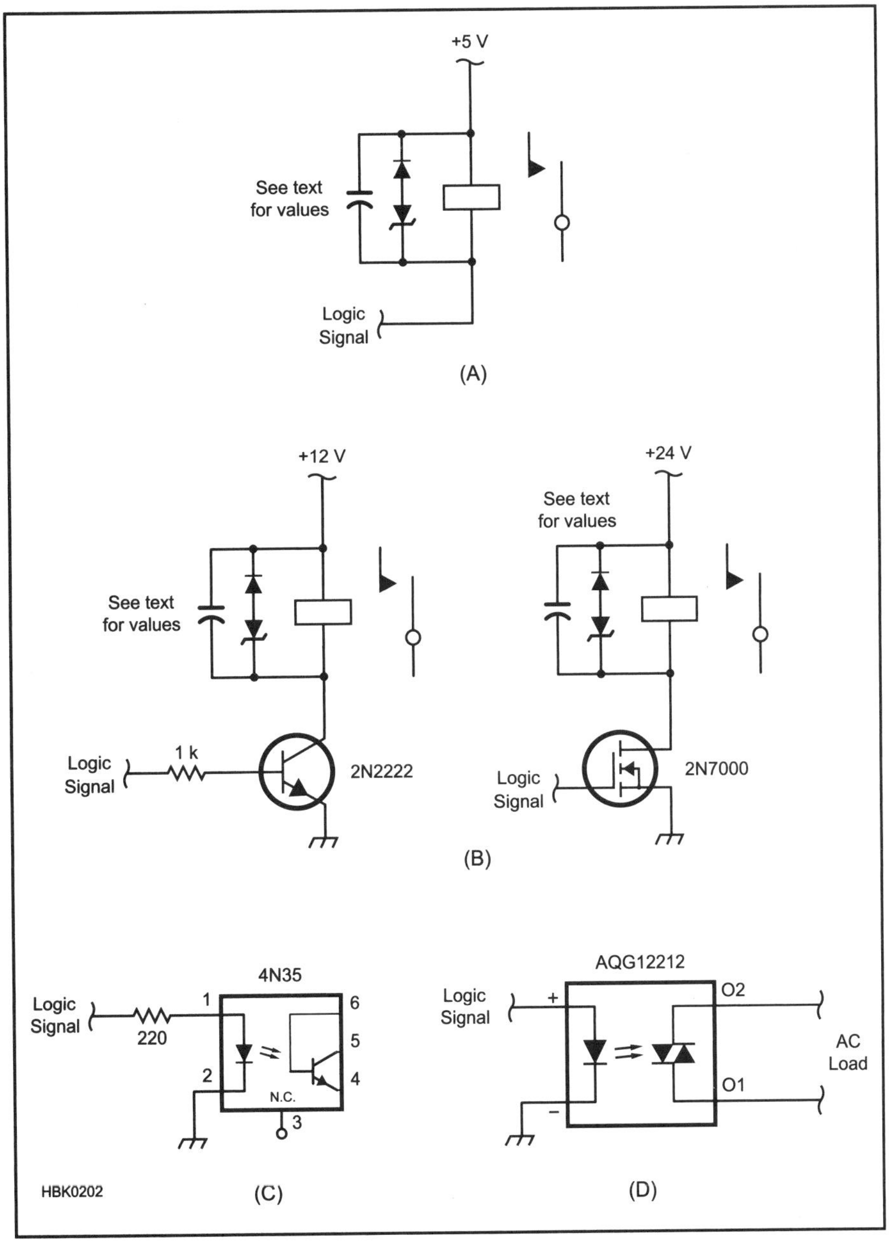

Figure 4.89 — Interface circuits for logic driving real-world loads. (A) driving a relay from a logic output; (B) using a bipolar transistor or MOSFET to boost current capacity; (C) using an optoisolator for electrical isolation; (D) using a solid-state relay for switching ac loads.

4.10 Analog Device and Circuits Glossary

AC ground — A circuit connection point that presents a very low impedance to ac signals.

Active — A device that requires power to operate.

Active region — The region in the characteristic curve of an analog device in which it is capable of processing the signal linearly.

Amplification — The process by which amplitude of a signal is increased. Gain is the amount by which the signal is amplified.

Analog signal — A signal that can have any amplitude (voltage or current) value and exists at any point in time.

Anode — The element of an analog device that accepts electrons or toward which electrons flow.

Attenuation — The process of reducing the amplitude of a signal.

Avalanche breakdown — Current flow through a semiconductor device in response to an applied voltage beyond the device's ability to control or block current flow.

Base — The terminal of a bipolar transistor in which control current flows.

Beta (β) — The dc current gain of a bipolar transistor, also designated h_{FE}.

Biasing — The addition of a dc voltage or current to a signal at the input of an analog device, changing or controlling the position of the device's operating point on the characteristic curve.

Bipolar transistor — An analog device made by sandwiching a layer of doped semiconductor between two layers of the opposite type: PNP or NPN.

Black box — Circuit or equipment that is analyzed only with regards to its external behavior.

Bode plot — Graphs showing amplitude response in dB and phase response in degrees versus frequency on a logarithmic scale.

Buffer — An analog stage that prevents loading of one analog stage by another.

Carrier — (1) Free electrons and holes in semiconductor material. (2) An unmodulated component of a modulated signal.

Cascade — Placing one analog stage after another to combine their effects on the signal.

Cathode — The element of an analog device that emits electrons or from which electrons are emitted or repelled.

Characteristic curve — A plot of the relative responses of two or three analog-device parameters, usually of an output with respect to an input. (Also called *I-V* or *V-I curve.*)

Class (amplifier) — For analog amplifiers (Class A, B, AB, C), a categorization of the fraction of the input signal cycle during which the amplifying device is active. For digital or switching amplifiers (Class D and above), a categorization of the method by which the signal is amplified.

Clipping — A nonlinearity in amplification in which the signal's amplitude can no longer be increased, usually resulting in distortion of the waveform. (Also called *clamping* or *limiting.*)

Closed-loop gain — Amplifier gain with an external feedback circuit connected.

Collector — The terminal of a bipolar transistor from which electrons are removed.

Common — A terminal shared by more than one port of a circuit or network.

Common mode — Signals that appear equally on all terminals of a signal port.

Comparator — A circuit, usually an amplifier, whose output indicates the relative amplitude of two input signals.

Compensation — The process of counteracting the effects of signals that are inadvertently fed back from the output to the input of an analog system. Compensation increases stability and prevents oscillation.

Compression — Reducing the dynamic range of a signal in order to increase the average power of the signal or prevent excessive signal levels.

Conversion efficiency — The amount of light energy converted to electrical energy by a photoelectric device, expressed in percent.

Coupling (ac or dc) — The type of connection between two circuits. DC coupling allows dc current to flow through the connection. AC coupling blocks dc current while allowing ac current to flow.

Cutoff frequency — Frequency at which a circuit's amplitude response is reduced to one-half its mid-band value (also called *half-power* or *corner* frequency).

Cutoff (region) — The region in the characteristic curve of an analog device in which there is no current through the device. Also called the OFF region.

Degeneration (emitter or source) — Negative feedback from the voltage drop across an emitter or source resistor in order to stabilize a circuit's bias and operating point.

Depletion mode — An FET with a channel that conducts current with zero gate-to-source voltage and whose conductivity is progressively reduced as reverse bias is applied.

Depletion region — The narrow region at a PN junction in which majority carriers have been removed. (Also called *space-charge* or *transition* region.)

Diode — A two-element semiconductor with a cathode and an anode that conducts current in only one direction.

Drain — The connection at one end of a field-effect-transistor channel from which electrons are removed.

Dynamic range — The range of signal levels over which a circuit operates properly. Usually refers to the range over which signals are processed linearly.

Emitter — The terminal of a bipolar transistor into which electrons are injected.

Enhancement mode — An FET with a channel that does not conduct with zero gate-to-source voltage and whose conductivity is progressively increased as forward bias is applied.

Feedback — Routing a portion of an output signal back to the input of a circuit. Positive feedback causes the input signal to be reinforced. Negative feedback results in partial cancellation of the input signal.

Field-effect transistor (FET) — An analog device with a semiconductor channel whose width can be modified by an electric field. (Also called *unipolar transistor.*)

Forward bias — Voltage applied across a PN junction in the direction to cause current flow.

Forward voltage — The voltage required to cause forward current to flow through a PN junction.

Free electron — An electron in a semiconductor crystal lattice that is not bound to any atom.

Frequency response — A description of a circuit's gain (or other behavior) with frequency.

Gain — see ***Amplification***.

Gain-bandwidth product — The relationship between amplification and frequency that defines the limits of the ability of a device to act as a linear amplifier. In many amplifiers, gain times bandwidth is approximately constant.

Gate — The control electrode of a field-effect transistor.

High-side — A switch or controlling device connecting between a power source and load.

Hole — A positively charged carrier that results when an electron is removed from an atom in a semiconductor crystal structure.

Hysteresis — In a comparator circuit, the practice of using positive feedback to shift the input setpoint in such a way as to minimize output changes when the input signal(s) are near the setpoint.

Integrated circuit (IC) — A semiconductor device in which many components, such as diodes, bipolar transistors, field-effect transistors, resistors and capacitors are fabricated to make an entire circuit.

Isolation — Eliminating or reducing electrical contact between one portion of a circuit and another or between pieces of equipment.

Junction FET (JFET) — A field-effect transistor whose gate electrode forms a PN junction with the channel.

Linearity — Processing and combining of analog signals independently of amplitude.

Load line — A line drawn through a family of characteristic curves that shows the operating points of an analog device for a given load or circuit component values.

Loading — The condition that occurs when the output behavior of a circuit is affected by the connection of another circuit to that output.

Low-side — A switch or controlling device connected between a load and ground.

Metal-oxide semiconductor (MOSFET) — A field-effect transistor whose gate is insulated from the channel by an oxide layer. (Also called *insulated gate FET* or *IGFET*)

Multivibrator — A circuit that oscillates between two states.

NMOS — N-channel MOSFET.

N-type impurity — A doping atom with an excess of valence electrons that is added to semiconductor material to act as a source of free electrons.

Network — General name for any type of circuit.

Noise — Any unwanted signal, usually random in nature.

Open-loop gain — Gain of an amplifier with no feedback connection.

Operating point — Values of a set of circuit parameters that specify a device's operation at a particular time.

Operational amplifier (op amp) — An integrated circuit amplifier with high open-loop gain, high input impedance, and low output impedance.

Optoisolator — A device in which current in a light-emitting diode controls the operation of a phototransistor without a direct electrical connection between them.

Oscillator — A circuit whose output varies continuously and repeatedly, usually at a single frequency.

P-type impurity — A doping atom with a shortage of valence electrons that is added to semiconductor material to create an excess of holes.

Passive — A device that does not require power to operate.

Peak inverse voltage (PIV) — The highest voltage that can be tolerated by a reverse biased PN junction before current is conducted. (See also ***avalanche breakdown***.)

Photoconductivity — Phenomenon in which light affects the conductivity of semiconductor material.

Photoelectricity — Phenomenon in which light causes current to flow in semiconductor material.

PMOS — P-channel MOSFET.

PN junction — The structure that forms when P-type semiconductor material is placed in contact with N-type semiconductor material.

Pole — Frequency at which a circuit's transfer function becomes infinite.

Port — A pair of terminals through which a signal is applied to or output from a circuit.

Quiescent (Q-) point — Circuit or device's operating point with no input signal applied. (Also called *bias point.*)

Pinch-off — The condition in an FET in which the channel conductivity has been reduced to zero.

Rail — Power supply voltage(s) for a circuit.

Range — The total span of analog values that can be processed by an analog-to-digital conversion.

Recombination — The process by which free electrons and holes are combined to produce current flow across a PN junction.

Recovery time — The amount of time required for carriers to be removed from a PN junction device's depletion region, halting current flow.

Rectify — Convert ac to pulsating dc.

Resolution — Smallest change in an analog value that can be represented in a conversion between analog and digital quantities. (Also called *step size.*)

Reverse bias — Voltage applied across a PN junction in the direction that does not cause current flow.

Reverse breakdown — The condition in which reverse bias across a PN junction exceeds the ability of the depletion region to block current flow. (See also ***avalanche breakdown.***)

Roll-off — Change in a circuit's amplitude response per octave or decade of frequency.

Safe operating area (SOA) — The region of a device's characteristic curve in which it can operate without damage.

Saturation (region) — The region in the characteristic curve of an analog device in which the output signal can no longer be increased by the input signal. See ***Clipping***.

Schottky barrier — A metal-to-semiconductor junction at which a depletion region is formed, similarly to a PN junction.

Semiconductor — (1) An element such as silicon with bulk conductivity between that of an insulator and a metal. (2) An electronic device whose function is created by a structure of chemically-modified semiconductor materials.

Signal-to-noise ratio (SNR) — The ratio of the strength of the desired signal to that of the unwanted signal (noise), usually expressed in dB.

Slew rate — The maximum rate at which a device can change the amplitude of its output.

Small-signal — Conditions under which the variations in circuit parameters due to the input signal are small compared to the quiescent operating point and the device is operating in its active region.

Source — The connection at one end of the channel of a field-effect transistor into which electrons are injected.

Stage — One of a series of sequential signal processing circuits or devices.

Substrate — Base layer of material on which the structure of a semiconductor device is constructed.

Superposition — Process in which two or more signals are added together linearly.

Total harmonic distortion (THD) — A measure of how much noise and distortion are introduced by a signal processing function.

Thermal runaway — The condition in which increasing device temperature increases device current in a positive feedback cycle.

Transconductance — Ratio of output current to input voltage, with units of Siemens (S).

Transfer characteristics — A set of parameters that describe how a circuit or network behaves at and between its signal interfaces.

Transfer function — A mathematical expression of how a circuit modifies an input signal.

Unipolar transistor — see ***Field-effect transistor (FET)***.

Virtual ground — Point in a circuit maintained at ground potential by the circuit without it actually being connected to ground.

Zener diode — A heavily-doped PN-junction diode with a controlled reverse breakdown voltage, used as a voltage reference or regulator.

Zero — Frequency at which a circuit's transfer function becomes zero.

4.11 Heat Management

While not strictly an electrical fundamental, managing the heat generated by electronic circuits is important in nearly all types of radio equipment. Thus, the topic is included in this chapter. Information on the devices and circuits discussed in this section may be found in other chapters.

Any actual energized circuit consumes electric power because any such circuit contains components that convert electricity into other forms of energy. This dissipated power appears in many forms. For example, a loudspeaker converts electrical energy into sound, the motion of air molecules. An antenna (or a light bulb) converts electricity into electromagnetic radiation. Charging a battery converts electrical energy into chemical energy (which is then converted back to electrical energy upon discharge). But the most common transformation by far is the conversion, through some form of resistance, of electricity into heat.

Sometimes the power lost to heat serves a useful purpose — toasters and hair dryers come to mind. But most of the time, this heat represents a power loss that is to be minimized wherever possible or at least taken into account. Since all real circuits contain resistance, even those circuits (such as a loudspeaker) whose primary purpose is to convert electricity to some *other* form of energy also convert some part of their input power to heat. Often, such losses are negligible, but sometimes they are not.

If unintended heat generation becomes significant, the involved components will get warm. Problems arise when the temperature increase affects circuit operation by either

- causing the component to fail, by explosion, melting, or other catastrophic event, or, more subtly,
- causing a slight change in the properties of the component, such as through a temperature coefficient (TC).

In the first case, we can design conservatively, ensuring that components are rated to safely handle two, three or more times the maximum power we expect them to dissipate. In the second case, we can specify components with low TCs, or we can design the circuit to minimize the effect of any one component. Occasionally we even exploit temperature effects (for example, using a resistor, capacitor or diode as a temperature sensor). Let's look more closely at the two main categories of thermal effects.

Not surprisingly, heat dissipation (more correctly, the efficient removal of generated heat) becomes important in medium- to high-power circuits: power supplies, transmitting circuits and so on. While these are not the only examples where elevated temperatures and related failures are of concern, the techniques we will discuss here are applicable to all circuits.

4.11.1 Thermal Resistance

The transfer of heat energy, and thus the change in temperature, between two ends of a block of material is governed by the following heat flow equation and illustrated in **Figure 4.90**):

$$P = \frac{kA}{L}\Delta T = \frac{\Delta T}{\theta}$$

where

P = power (in the form of heat) conducted between the two points

k = *thermal conductivity*, measured in W/(m °C), of the material between the two points, which may be steel, silicon, copper, PC board material and so on

L = length of the block

A = area of the block, and

ΔT = *difference* in temperature between the two points.

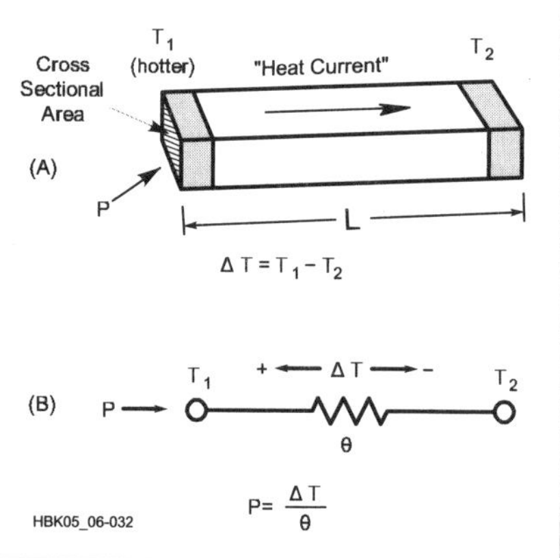

Figure 4.90 — Physical and "circuit" models for the heat-flow equation.

Table 4.3
Thermal Conductivities of Various Materials
Gases at 0 °C, Others at 25 °C; from *Physics*, by Halliday and Resnick, 3rd Ed.

Material	*k in units of W/m°C*
Aluminum	200
Brass	110
Copper	390
Lead	35
Silver	410
Steel	46
Silicon	150
Air	0.024
Glass	0.8

Thermal conductivities of various common materials at room temperature are given in **Table 4.3**.

The heat flow equation has the same form as the variation of Ohm's Law relating current flow to the ratio of a difference in potential to resistance; I = E/R. In this case, what's flowing is heat (P), the difference in potential is a temperature difference (ΔT), and what's resisting the flow of heat is the *thermal resistance*;

$$\theta = \frac{L}{kA}$$

with units of °C/W. (The units of resistance are equivalent to V/A.) The analogy is so apt that the same principles and methods apply to heat flow problems as circuit problems. The following correspondences hold:

- Thermal conductivity W/(m °C) ↔ Electrical conductivity (S/m).
- Thermal resistance (°C/W) ↔ Electrical resistance (Ω).
- Thermal current (heat flow) (W) ↔ Electrical current (A).
- Thermal potential (T) ↔ Electrical potential (V).
- Heat source ↔ Power source.

For example, calculate the temperature of a 2-inch (0.05 m) long piece of #12 copper wire at the end that is being heated by a 25 W (input power) soldering iron, and whose other end is clamped to a large metal vise (assumed to be an infinite heat sink), if the ambient temperature is 25 °C (77 °F).

First, calculate the thermal resistance of the copper wire (diameter of #12 wire is 2.052 mm, cross-sectional area is 3.31×10^{-6} m^2)

$$\theta = \frac{L}{k\,A} = \frac{(0.05\ \text{m})}{(390\ \text{W}/(\text{m}\ °\text{C})) \times (3.31 \times 10^{-6}\ \text{m}^2)}$$

$$= 38.7\ °\text{C/W}$$

Then, rearranging the heat flow equation above yields (after assuming the heat energy actually transferred to the wire is around 10 W)

$$\Delta T = P\,\theta = (10\ \text{W}) \times (38.7\ °\text{C/W}) = 387\ °\text{C}$$

So the wire temperature at the hot end is 25 C + ΔT = 412 °C (or 774 °F). If this sounds a little high, remember that this is for the steady state condition, where you've been holding the iron to the wire for a long time.

From this example, you can see that things can get very hot even with application of moderate power levels. For this reason, circuits that generate sufficient heat to alter, not necessarily damage, the components must employ some method of cooling, either active or passive. Passive methods include heat sinks or careful component layout for good ventilation. Active methods include forced air (fans) or some sort of liquid cooling (in some high-power transmitters).

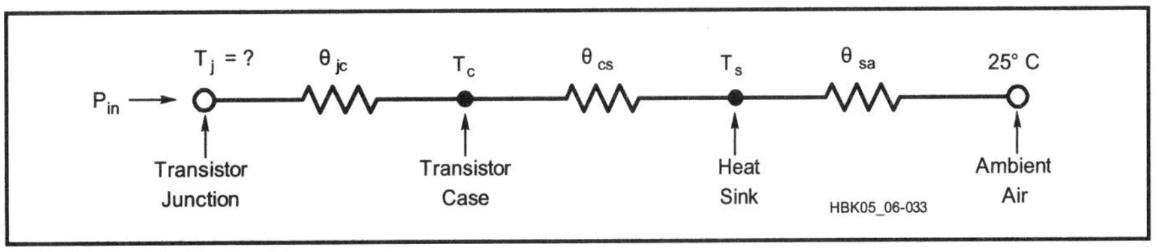

Figure 4.91 — Resistive model of thermal conduction in a power transistor and associated heat sink. See text for calculations.

4.11.2 Heat Sink Selection and Use

The purpose of a heat sink is to provide a high-power component with a large surface area through which to dissipate heat. To use the models above, it provides a low thermal-resistance path to a cooler temperature, thus allowing the hot component to conduct a large "thermal current" away from itself.

Power supplies probably represent one of the most common high-power circuits amateurs are likely to encounter. Everyone has certainly noticed that power supplies get warm or even hot if not ventilated properly. Performing the thermal design for a properly cooled power supply is a very well-defined process and is a good illustration of heat-flow concepts.

This material was originally prepared by ARRL Technical Advisor Dick Jansson, KD1K, during the design of a 28-V, 10-A power supply. (**Power Sources** chapter has more information on power supply design.) An outline of the design procedure shows the logic applied:

1. Determine the expected power dissipation (P_{in}).
2. Identify the requirements for the dissipating elements (maximum component temperature).
3. Estimate heat-sink requirements.
4. Rework the electronic device (if necessary) to meet the thermal requirements.
5. Select the heat exchanger (from heat sink data sheets).

The first step is to estimate the filtered, unregulated supply voltage under full load. Since the transformer secondary output is 32 V ac (RMS) and feeds a full-wave bridge rectifier, let's estimate 40 V as the filtered dc output at a 10-A load.

The next step is to determine our critical components and estimate their power dissipations. In a regulated power supply, the pass transistors are responsible for nearly all the power lost to heat. Under full load, and allowing for some small voltage drops in the power-transistor emitter circuitry, the output of the series pass transistors is about 29 V for a delivered 28 V under a 10-A load. With an unregulated input voltage of 40 V, the total energy heat dissipated in the pass transistors is (40 V – 29 V) × 10 A = 110 W. The heat sink for this power supply must be able to handle that amount of dissipation and still keep the transistor junctions below the specified safe operating temperature limits. It is a good rule of thumb to select a transistor that has a maximum power dissipation of twice the desired output power.

Now, consider the ratings of the pass transistors to be used. This supply calls for 2N3055s as pass transistors. The data sheet shows that a 2N3055 is rated for 15-A service and 115-W dissipation. But the design uses *four* in parallel. Why? Here we must look past the big, bold type at the top of the data sheet to such subtle characteristics as the junction-to-case thermal resistance, θ_{jc}, and the maximum allowable junction temperature, T_j.

The 2N3055 data sheet shows θ_{jc} = 1.52 °C/W, and a maximum allowable case (and junction) temperature of 220 °C. While it seems that one 2N3055 could barely, on paper at least, handle the electrical requirements — at what temperature would it operate?

To answer that, we must model the entire "thermal circuit" of operation, starting with the transistor junction on one end and ending at some point with the ambient air. A reasonable model is shown in **Figure 4.91**. The ambient air is considered here as an infinite heat sink; that is, its temperature is assumed to be a constant 25 °C (77 °F). θ_{jc} is the thermal resistance from the transistor junction to its case. θ_{cs} is the resistance of the mounting interface between the transistor case and the heat sink. θ_{sa} is the thermal resistance between the heat sink and the ambient air. In this "circuit," the generation of heat (the "thermal current source") occurs in the transistor at P_{in}.

Proper mounting of most TO-3 package power transistors such as the 2N3055 requires that they have an electrical insulator between the transistor case and the heat sink. However, this electrical insulator must at the same time exhibit a low thermal resistance. To achieve a quality mounting, use thin polyimid or mica formed washers and a suitable thermal compound to exclude air from the interstitial space. "Thermal greases" are commonly available for this function. Any silicone grease may be used, but filled silicone oils made specifically for this purpose are better.

Using such techniques, a conservatively high value for θ_{cs} is 0.50 °C/W. Lower values are possible, but the techniques needed to achieve them are expensive and not generally available to the average amateur. Further-

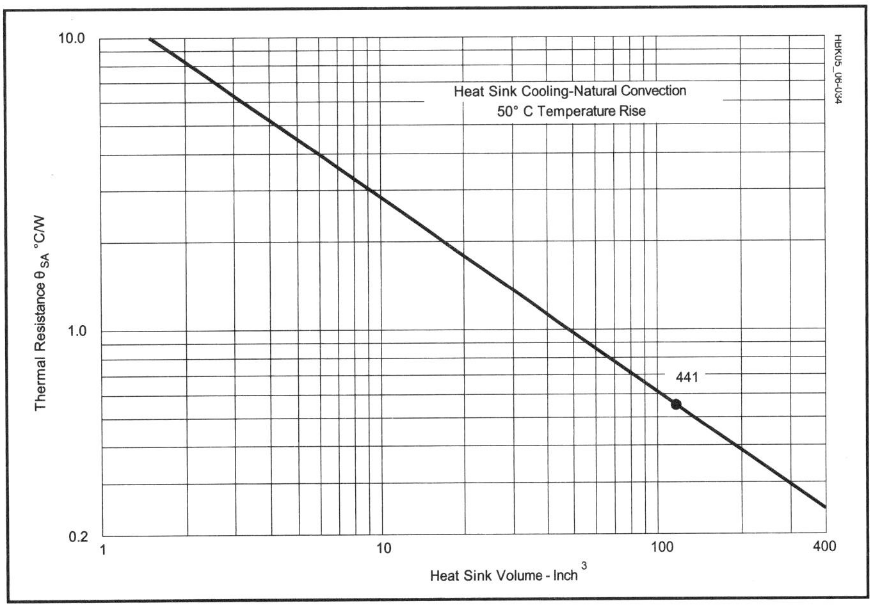

Figure 4.92 — Thermal resistance vs heat-sink volume for natural convection cooling and 50 °C temperature rise. The graph is based on engineering data from Wakefield Thermal Solutions, Inc.

more, this value of θ_{cs} is already much lower than θ_{jc}, which cannot be lowered without going to a somewhat more exotic pass transistor.

Finally, we need an estimate of θ_{sa}. **Figure 4.92** shows the relationship of heat-sink volume to thermal resistance for natural-convection cooling. This relationship presumes the use of suitably spaced fins (0.35 inch or greater) and provides a "rough order-of-magnitude" value for sizing a heat sink. For a first calculation, let's assume a heat sink of roughly 6 × 4 × 2 inch (48 cubic inches). From Figure 4.92, this yields a θ_{sa} of about 1 °C/W.

Returning to Figure 4.91, we can now calculate the approximate temperature increase of a single 2N3055:

$$\delta T = P\,\theta_{total}$$

$$= 110\text{ W} \times (1.52\text{ °C/W} + 0.5\text{ °C/W} + 1.0\text{ °C/W})$$

$$= 332\text{ °C}$$

Given the ambient temperature of 25 °C, this puts the junction temperature T_j of the 2N3055 at 25 + 332 = 357 °C! This is clearly too high, so let's work backward from the air end and calculate just how many transistors we need to handle the heat.

First, putting more 2N3055s in parallel means that we will have the thermal model illustrated in **Figure 4.93**, with several identical θ_{jc} and θ_{cs} in parallel, all funneled through the same θ_{as} (we have one heat sink).

Keeping in mind the physical size of the project, we could comfortably fit a heat sink of approximately 120 cubic inches (6 × 5 × 4 inches), well within the range of commercially available heat sinks. Furthermore, this application can use a heat sink where only "wire access" to the transistor connections is required. This allows the selection of a more efficient design. In contrast, RF designs require the transistor mounting surface to be completely exposed so that the PC board can be mounted close to the transistors to minimize parasitics. Looking at Figure 4.92, we see that a 120-cubic-inch heat sink yields a θ_{sa} of 0.55 °C/W. This means that the temperature of the heat sink when dissipating 110 W will be 25 °C + (110 W × 0.55 °C/W) = 85.5 °C.

Industrial experience has shown that silicon transistors suffer substantial failure when junctions are operated at highly elevated temperatures. Most commercial and military specifications will usually not permit design junction temperatures to exceed 125 °C. To arrive at a safe figure for our maximum allowed T_j, we must consider the intended use of the power supply. If we are using it in a 100% duty-cycle transmitting application such as RTTY or FM, the circuit will be dissipating 110 W continuously. For a lighter duty-cycle load such as CW or SSB, the "key-down" temperature can be slightly higher as long as the average is less than 125 °C. In this intermittent type of service, a good conservative figure to use is T_j = 150 °C.

Given this scenario, the temperature rise across each transistor can be 150 – 85.5 = 64.5 °C. Now, referencing Figure 2.4.93, remembering the total θ for each 2N3055 is 1.52 + 0.5 = 2.02 °C/W, we can calculate the maximum power each 2N3055 can safely dissipate:

$$P = \frac{\delta T}{\theta} = \frac{64.5\text{ °C}}{2.02\text{ °C / W}} = 31.9\text{ W}$$

Thus, for 110 W full load, we need four 2N3055s to meet the thermal requirements of the design. Now comes the big question: What is the "right" heat sink to use? We have already established its requirements: it must be capable of dissipating 110 W, and have a θ_{sa} of 0.55 °C/W (see above).

A quick consultation with several manufacturer's catalogs reveals that Wakefield Thermal Solutions, Inc. model nos. 441 and 435 heat sinks meet the needs of this application. A Thermalloy model no. 6441 is suitable as well. Data published in the catalogs of these manufacturers show that in natural-convection service, the expected temperature rise for 100 W dissipation would be just under 60 °C, an almost perfect fit for this application. Moreover, the No. 441 heat sink can easily mount four TO-3-style 2N3055 transistors as shown in **Figure 4.94**. Remember: heat sinks should be mounted with the fins and transistor mounting area vertical to promote convection cooling.

The design procedure just described is applicable to any circuit where heat buildup is a potential problem. By using the thermal-resistance model, we can easily calculate

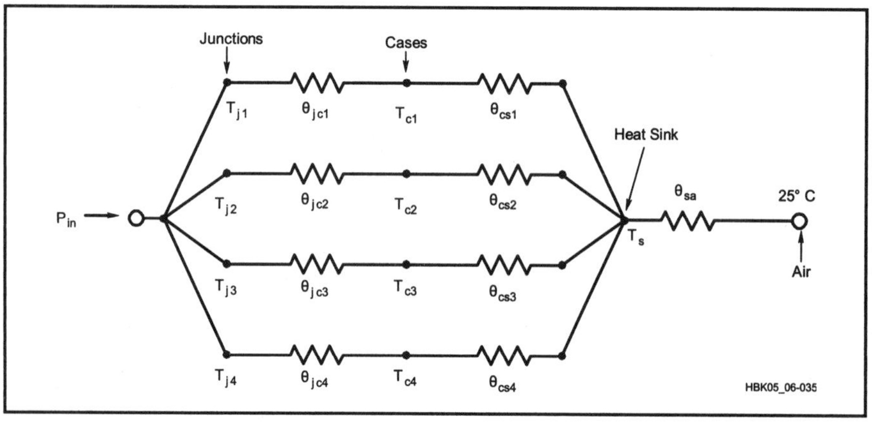

Figure 4.93 — Thermal model for multiple power transistors mounted on a common heat sink.

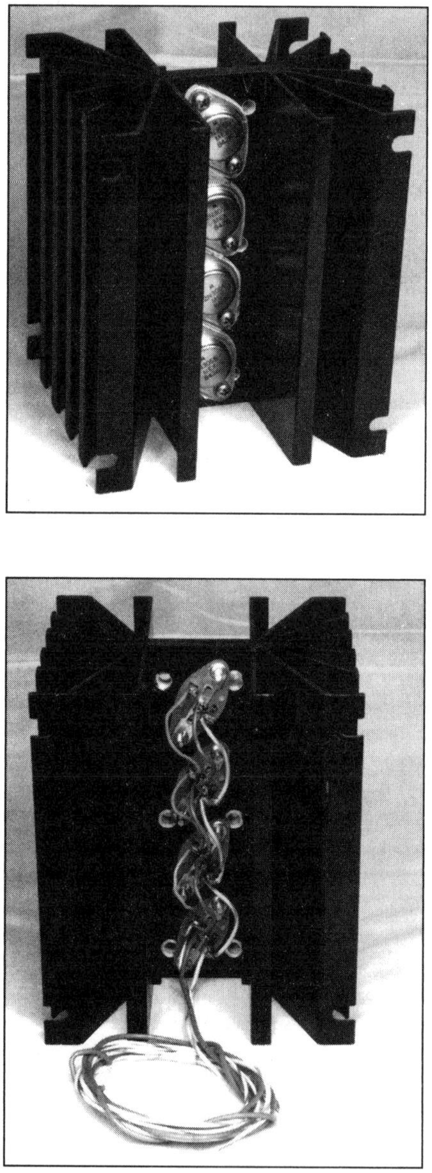

Figure 4.94 — A Wakefield 441 heat sink with four 2N3055 transistors mounted.

whether or not an external means of cooling is necessary, and if so, how to choose it. Aside from heat sinks, forced air cooling (fans) is another common method. In commercial transceivers, heat sinks with forced-air cooling are common.

4.11.3 Semiconductor Temperature Effects

The number of excess holes and electrons in semiconductor material is increased as the temperature of a semiconductor increases. Since the conductivity of a semiconductor is related to the number of excess carriers, this also increases with temperature. With respect to resistance, semiconductors have a negative temperature coefficient. The resistance of silicon *decreases* by about 8% per °C and by about 6% per °C for germanium. Semiconductor temperature properties are the opposite of most metals, which *increase* their resistance by about 0.4% per °C. These opposing temperature characteristics permit the design of circuits with opposite temperature coefficients that cancel each other out, making a temperature insensitive circuit.

Semiconductor devices can experience an effect called *thermal runaway* as the current causes an increase in temperature. (This is primarily an issue with bipolar transistors.) The increased temperature decreases resistance and may lead to a further increase in current (depending on the circuit) that leads to an additional temperature increase. This sequence of events can continue until the semiconductor destroys itself, so circuit design must include measures that compensate for the effects of temperature.

Semiconductor Failure Caused by Heat

There are several common failure modes for semiconductors that are related to heat. The semiconductor material is connected to the outside world through metallic *bonding leads*. The point at which the lead and the semiconductor are connected is a common place for the semiconductor device to fail. As the device heats up and cools down, the materials expand and contract. The rate of expansion and contraction of semiconductor material is different from that of metal. Over many cycles of heating and cooling the bond between the semiconductor and the metal can break. Some experts have suggested that the lifetime of semiconductor equipment can be extended by leaving the devices powered on all the time, but this requires removal of the heat generated during normal operation.

A common failure mode of semiconductors is caused by the heat generated during semiconductor use. If the temperatures of the PN junctions remain at high enough levels for long enough periods of time, the impurities resume their diffusion across the PN junctions. When enough of the impurity atoms cross the depletion region, majority carrier recombination stops functioning properly and the semiconductor device fails permanently.

Excessive temperature can also cause failure anywhere in the semiconductor from heat generation within any current-carrying conductor, such as an FET channel or the bonding leads. Integrated circuits with more than one output may have power dissipation limits that depend on how many of the outputs are active at one time. The high temperature can cause localized melting or cracking of the semiconductor material, causing a permanent failure.

Another heat-driven failure mode, usually not fatal to the semiconductor, is excessive leakage current or a shift in operating point that causes the circuit to operate improperly. This is a particular problem in complex integrated circuits — analog and digital — dissipating significant amounts of heat under normal operating conditions. Computer microprocessors are a good example, often requiring their own cooling systems. Once the device cools, normal operation is usually restored.

To reduce the risk of thermal failures, the designer must comply with the limits stated in the manufacturer's data sheet, devising an adequate heat removal system. (Thermal issues are discussed in the **Electrical Fundamentals** chapter.)

4.11.4 Safe Operating Area (SOA)

Devices intended for use in circuits handling high currents or voltages are specified to have a *safe operating area* (*SOA*). This refers to the area drawn on the device's characteristic curve containing combinations of voltage and current that the device can be expected to control without damage under specific conditions. The SOA combines a number of limits — voltage, current, power, temperature and various breakdown mechanisms — in order to simplify the design of protective circuitry. The SOA is also specified to apply to specific durations of use — steady-state, long pulses, short pulses and so forth. The device may have separate SOAs for resistive and inductive loads.

You may also encounter two specialized types of SOA for turning the device on and off. *Reverse bias safe operating area* (*RBSOA*) applies when the device is turning off. *Forward bias safe operating* area (*FBSOA*) applies when turning the device on. These SOAs are used because the high rate-of-change of current and voltage places additional stresses on the semiconductor.

4.11.5 Semiconductor Derating

Maximum ratings for power transistors are usually based on a case temperature of 25 °C. These ratings will decrease with increasing operating temperature. Manufacturer's data sheets usually specify a *derating* figure or curve that indicates how the maximum ratings change per degree rise in temperature. If such information is not available (or even if it is!), it is a good rule of thumb to select a power transistor with a maximum power dissipation of at least twice the desired output power.

RECTIFIERS

Diodes are physically quite small, and they operate at high current densities. As a result their heat-handling capabilities are somewhat limited. Normally, this is not a problem in high-voltage, low-current supplies in which rectifiers in axial-lead DO-type packages are used. (See the **Component Data and References** chapter for information on device packages.) The use of high-current (2 A or greater) rectifiers at or near their maximum ratings, however, requires some form of heat sinking. The average power dissipated by a rectifier is

$$P = I_{AVG} \times V_F$$

where

I_{AVG} is the average current, and
V_F is the forward voltage drop.

Average current must account for the conduction duty cycle and the forward voltage drop must be determined at the average current level.

Rectifiers intended for such high-current applications are available in a variety of packages suitable for mounting to flat surfaces. Frequently, mounting the rectifier on the main chassis (directly, or with thin mica insulating washers) will suffice. If the diode is insulated from the chassis, thin layers of thermal compound or thermal insulating washers should be used to ensure good heat conduction. Large, high-current rectifiers often require special heat sinks to maintain a safe operating temperature. Forced-air cooling is sometimes used as a further aid.

4.11.6 RF Heating

RF current often causes component heating problems where the same level of dc current may not. An example is the tank circuit of an RF oscillator. If several small capacitors are connected in parallel to achieve a desired capacitance, skin effect will be reduced and the total surface area available for heat dissipation will be increased, thus significantly reducing the RF heating effects as compared to a single large capacitor. This technique can be applied to any similar situation; the general idea is to divide the heating among as many components as possible.

4.11.7 Forced-Air and Water Cooling

In Amateur Radio today, forced-air cooling is most commonly found in vacuum-tube circuits or in power supplies built in small enclosures, such as those in solid-state transceivers or computers. Fans or blowers are commonly specified in cubic feet per minute (CFM). While the nomenclature and specifications differ from those used for heat sinks, the idea remains the same: to offer a low thermal resistance between the inside of the enclosure and the (ambient) exterior.

For forced air cooling, we basically use the "one resistor" thermal model of Figure 4.90. The important quantity to be determined is heat generation, P_{in}. For a power supply, this can be easily estimated as the difference between the input power, measured at the transformer primary, and the output power at full load. For variable-voltage supplies, the worst-case output condition is minimum voltage with maximum current. A discussion of forced-air cooling for vacuum tube equipment appears in the **RF Power Amplifiers** chapter.

Dust build-up is a common problem for forced-air cooling systems, even with powerful blowers and fans. If air intake grills and vents are not kept clean and free of lint and debris, air flow can be significantly reduced, leading to excessive equipment temperature and premature failure. Cleaning of air passageways should be included in regular equipment maintenance for good performance and maximum equipment life.

Water cooling systems are much less common in amateur equipment, used primarily for high duty cycle operating, such as RTTY, and at frequencies where the efficiency of the amplifier is relatively low, such as UHF and microwaves. In these situations, water cooling is used because water can absorb and transfer more than 3000 times as much heat as the same volume of air!

The main disadvantage of water cooling is that it requires pumps, hoses, and reservoirs whereas a fan or blower is all that is required for forced-air cooling. For high-voltage circuits, using water cooling also requires special insulation techniques and materials to allow water to circulate in close contact with the heat source while remaining electrically isolated.

Nevertheless, the technique can be effective. The increased availability of inexpensive materials designed for home sprinkler and other low-pressure water distribution systems make water-cooling less difficult to implement. It is recommended that the interested reader review articles and projects in the amateur literature to observe the successful implementation of water cooling systems.

4.11.8 Heat Pipe Cooling

A heat pipe is a device containing a *working fluid* in a reservoir where heat is absorbed and a channel to a second reservoir where heat is dissipated. Heat pipes work by *evaporative cooling*. The heat-absorbing reservoir is placed in thermal contact with the heat source which transfers heat to the working fluid, usually a liquid substance with a boiling point just above room temperature. The working fluid vaporizes and the resulting vapor pressure pushes the hot vapor through the channel to the cooling reservoir.

In the cooling reservoir, the working fluid gives up its heat of vaporization, returning to the fluid state. The cooled fluid then flows back through the channel to the heat-absorbing reservoir where the process is repeated.

Heat pipes require no fans or pumps — movement of the working fluid is driven entirely from the temperature difference between the two reservoirs. The higher the temperature difference between the absorbing and dissipating reservoirs, the more effective the heat pump becomes, up to the limit of the dissipating reservoir to dissipate heat.

The principle application for heat pipes is for space operations. Heat pipe applications in terrestrial applications are limited due to the gravity gradient sensitivity of heat pipes. At present, the only amateur equipment making use of heat pipes are computers and certain amplifier modules. Nevertheless, as more general-purpose products become available, this technique will become more common.

4.11.9 Thermoelectric Cooling

Thermoelectric cooling makes use of the *Peltier effect* to create heat flow across the junction of two different types of materials. This process is related to the *thermoelectric effect* by which thermocouples generate voltages based on the temperature of a similar junction. A *thermoelectric cooler* or *TEC* (also known as a *Peltier cooler*) requires only a source of dc power to cause one side of the device to cool and the other side to warm. TECs are available with different sizes and power ratings for different applications.

TECs are not available with sufficient heat transfer capabilities that they can be used in high-power applications, such as RF amplifiers. However, they can be useful in lowering the temperature of sensitive receiver circuits, such as preamplifiers used at UHF and microwave frequencies, or imaging devices, such as charge-coupled devices (CCDs). Satellites use TECs as *radiative coolers* that dissipate heat directly as thermal or infrared radiation. TECs are also found in some computing equipment where they are used to remove heat from microprocessors and other large integrated circuits.

4.11.10 Temperature Compensation

Aside from catastrophic failure, temperature changes may also adversely affect circuits if the temperature coefficient (TC) of one or more components is too large. If the resultant change is not too critical, adequate temperature stability can often be achieved simply by using higher-precision components with low TCs (such as NP0/C0G capacitors or metal-film resistors). For applications where this is impractical or impossible (such as many solid-state circuits), we can minimize temperature sensitivity by *compensation* or *matching* — using temperature coefficients to our advantage.

Compensation is accomplished in one of two ways. If we wish to keep a certain circuit quantity constant, we can interconnect pairs of components that have equal but opposite TCs. For example, a resistor with a negative TC can be placed in series with a positive TC resistor to keep the total resistance constant. Conversely, if the important point is to keep the *difference* between two quantities constant, we can use components with the *same* TC so that the pair "tracks." That is, they both change by the same amount with temperature.

An example of this is a Zener reference circuit. Since a diode is strongly affected by operating temperature, circuits that use diodes or transistors to generate stable reference voltages must use some form of temperature compensation. Since, for a constant current, a reverse-biased PN junction has a negative voltage TC while a forward-biased junction has a positive voltage TC, a good way to temperature-compensate a Zener reference diode is to place one or more forward-biased diodes in series with it.

4.11.11 Thermistors

Thermistors can be used to control temperature and improve circuit behavior or protect against excessive temperatures, hot or cold. Circuit temperature variations can affect gain, distortion or control functions like receiver AGC or transmitter ALC. Thermistors can be used in circuits that compensate for temperature changes.

A *thermistor* is a small bit of intrinsic (no N or P doping) metal-oxide semiconductor compound material between two wire leads. As temperature increases, the number of liberated hole/electron pairs increases exponentially, causing the resistance to decrease exponentially. You can see this in the resistance equation:

$$R(T) = R(T0)e^{-\beta(1/T0-1/T)}$$

where T is some temperature in Kelvins and T0 is a reference temperature, usually 298 K (25°C), at which the manufacturer specifies R(T0).

The constant β is experimentally determined by measuring resistance at various temperatures and finding the value of β that best agrees with the measurements. A simple way to get an approximate value of β is to make two measurements, one at room temperature, say 25 °C (298 K) and one at 100 °C (373 K) in boiling water. Suppose the resistances are 10 kΩ and 938 Ω.

$$\beta = \frac{\ln\left(\frac{R(T)}{R(T0)}\right)}{\frac{1}{T} - \frac{1}{T0}} = \frac{\ln\left(\frac{938}{1000}\right)}{\frac{1}{373} - \frac{1}{298}} = 3507$$

With the behavior of the thermistor known — either by equation or calibration table — its change in resistance can be used to create an electronic circuit whose behavior is controlled by temperature in a known fashion. Such a circuit can be used for controlling temperature or detecting specific temperatures.

See "Termistors in Homebrew Projects" by Bill Sabin, WØIYH, and "Thermistor Based Temperature Controller" by Bill Sabin, WØIYH in this book's downloadable supplemental information for practical projects using thermistors.

References and Bibliography

BOOKS

Alexander and Sadiku, *Fundamentals of Electric Circuits* (McGraw-Hill)

ARRL Lab Staff, "Lab Notes — Capacitor Basics," *QST*, Jan 1997, pp 85-86

Banzhaf, W., WB1ANE, *Understanding Basic Electronics*, 2nd ed (ARRL)

B. Bergeron, NU1N, "Under the Hood II: Resistors," *QST,* Nov 1993, pp 41-44

B. Bergeron, NU1N, "Under the Hood III: Capacitors," *QST,* Jan 1994, pp 45-48

B. Bergeron, NU1N, "Under the Hood IV: Inductors," *QST,* Mar 1994, pp 37-40

B. Bergeron, NU1N, "Under the Hood: Lamps, Indicators, and Displays," *QST,* Sep 1994, pp 34-37

Ebers, J., and Moll, J., "Large-Signal Behavior of Junction Transistors," *Proceedings of the IRE*, 42, Dec 1954, pp 1761-1772

Getreu, I., *Modeling the Bipolar Transistor* (Elsevier, New York, 1979). Also available from Tektronix, Inc, Beaverton, Oregon, in paperback form. Must be ordered as Part Number 062-2841-00.

Grover, F., Inductance Calculations (Dover Publications)

Glover, T., *Pocket Ref* (Sequoia Publishing)

Hayward, W., *Introduction to Radio Frequency Design* (ARRL, 2004)

Hayward, Campbell and Larkin, *Experimental Methods in RF Design* (ARRL, 2009)

Horowitz and Hill, *The Art of Electronics* (Cambridge University Press)

Jung, W. *IC Op Amp Cookbook* (Prentice-Hall, 1986)

Kaiser, C., *The Resistor Handbook* (Saddleman Press, 1998)

Kaiser, C., *The Capacitor Handbook* (Saddleman Press, 1995)

Kaiser, C., *The Inductor Handbook* (Saddleman Press, 1996)

Kaiser, C., *The Diode Handbook* (Saddleman Press, 1999)

Kaiser, C., *The Transistor Handbook* (Saddleman Press, 1999)

Kaplan, S., *Wiley Electrical and Electronics Dictionary* (Wiley Press)

McClanahan, J., W4JBM, "Understanding and Testing Capacitor ESR," *QST*, Sep 2003, pp 30-32

Millman and Grabel, *Microelectronics: Digital and Analog Circuits and Systems* (McGraw-Hill, 1988)

Mims, F., *Timer, Op Amp & Optoelectronic Circuits & Projects* (Master Publishing, 2004)

Orr, W., *Radio Handbook* (Newnes)

W. Silver, NØAX, "Experiment #24 — Heat Management," *QST*, Jan 2005, pp 64-65

W. Silver, NØAX, "Experiment #33 — The Transformer," *QST*, Oct 2005, pp 62-63

W. Silver, NØAX, "Experiment #62 — About Resistors," *QST*, Mar 2008, pp 66-67

W. Silver, NØAX, "Experiment #63 — About Capacitors," *QST*, Apr 2008, pp 70-71

W. Silver, NØAX, "Experiment #132 — Resistor Networks," *QST*, Jan 2014, pp 63-64

J. Smith, K8ZOA, "Carbon Composition, Carbon Film and Metal Oxide Film Resistors," *QEX*, Mar/Apr 2008, pp 46-57

Terman, F., *Radio Engineer's Handbook* (McGraw-Hill)

WEBSITES

Hyperphysics Op-Amp Circuit Tutorials, **hyperphysics.phy-astr.gsu.edu/Hbase/Electronic/opampvar.html#c2**

Rohde & Schwarz, "dB or not dB? Everything you ever wanted to know about decibels but were afraid to ask…," Application Note 1MA98, **www.rohde-schwarz.us/en/applications/db-or-not-db-application-note_56280-15534.html**

Safe-Operating Area for Power Semiconductors (ON Semiconductor AN-875-D), **www.onsemi.com**

"Selecting the Right CMOS Analog Switch", Maxim Semiconductor Application Note 638, **www.maxim-ic.com**

Notes

Notes

Notes

Notes

Notes

Notes